EXPERIMENTAL CELL RESEARCH

SUPPLEMENT 5 · 1958

EXPERIMENTAL CELL RESEARCH

SUPPLEMENT 5 · 1958

Published under the auspices of the International Society for Cell Biology

THE SUBMICROSCOPIC ORGANIZATION AND FUNCTION OF NERVE CELLS

Proceedings of the Symposium held March 15–22, 1957
by The Venezuelan Institute of Neurology and Brain Research, Caracas, Venezuela

ACADEMIC PRESS INC., PUBLISHERS, NEW YORK, 1958

ORGANIZER OF THE SYMPOSIUM: Professor Humberto Fernández-Morán
EDITORS: Professor Humberto Fernández-Morán and Dr. R. Brown
EDITORIAL SECRETARY: Mrs. Vera Reio

PRINTED IN SWEDEN

Almqvist & Wiksells

BOKTRYCKERI AKTIEBOLAG

UPPSALA 1958

The pictures on the preceding page show the Venzuelan Institute of Neurology and Brain Research, Caracas, Venezuela (*top*), and the participants in the Symposium (*bottom*).

TABLE OF CONTENTS

THE RECEPTORS

LIST OF CONTRIBUTORS

THE NERVE FIBERS

Experimental Cell Research, Suppl. **5**, *3–17 (1958)*

COMPARISON OF THE STRUCTURE, AS REVEALED WITH THE ELECTRON MICROSCOPE, AND THE PHYSIOLOGY OF THE UNMEDULLATED FIBERS IN THE SKIN NERVES AND IN THE OLFACTORY NERVES

H. S. GASSER

Rockefeller Institute for Medical Research, New York, N.Y., U.S.A.

MORPHOLOGY reaches the acme of its usefulness when it is brought into relationship with the function of the structures. My own experience may give some illustration of this. For a number of years I have been interested in the physiology of unmedullated nerve fibers, particularly those carrying afferent signals. At the outset they were visualizable only by the black dots and lines revealed through the silver stain; then through extension of resolving power beyond that of the wavelength of light the basis of the black dots was caused to take on form. Electron microscopy brought into conjunction with oscillography is making it possible to bring out of the obscurity that has so long surrounded them, the nature of the minute nerve fibers so extensively employed in reporting to the brain the state of the periphery of the body.

PHYSIOLOGY

It is disciplinary to look back at the blissful ignorance that permits a beginner to gain erroneous impressions from new findings in a hitherto unexplored field. When the gain in amplifiers became high enough a late elevation appeared in the action potential. Pending the time when the fibers producing it would be identified as unmedullated fibers they were called C fibers. Exploration soon showed C fibers to be present in both visceral and somatic nerves. Examination of the properties of C fibers in the presence of large numbers of medullated fibers was such a formidable task, that the properties were worked out in visceral nerves. That these fibers were not a prototype for all C fibers was long unsuspected. Then a discrepancy was found in the configuration of the excitability cycle of the C fibers of the saphenous nerve of the cat. After another long interval occasioned by the war the reason for the discrepancy was explored.

In the saphenous nerve, sensory for the skin, unmedullated fibers arising from cells in the dorsal root ganglia outnumber the medullated fibers between three and four times. Skin nerves provide the most favorable place for their study. When a technique was worked out C fibers in skin nerves were found to possess striking differences from the sympathetic C fibers of visceral nerves (e.g. hypogastric). A natural question was whether the differential properties

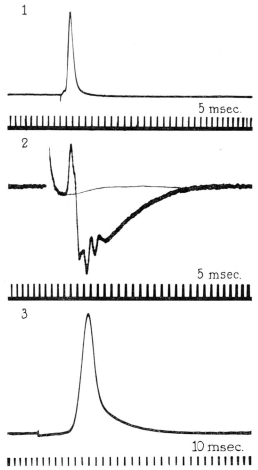

Fig. 1.—Action potentials of unmyelinated fibers. *1*, Those arising from cells of sympathic ganglia. Hypogastric nerve of the cat. *2*, Those arising from cells of dorsal root ganglia. Saphenous nerve of the cat. Through the base line the course of the after-potentials of the myelinated fibers is depicted. A negative after-potential is followed by a positive after-potential, the later course of which has been drawn in. *3*, Olfactory nerve, pike.

were correlated with afferent function. The fibers in the olfactory nerve have long been known to be unmedullated. Examination of the olfactory nerve of the pike gave a definite answer. All unmedullated fibers with afferent function are not alike.

A convenient criterion for differentiating the characteristics of nerve fibers is the size and configuration of the after-potentials. Fibers so differentiated are shown in Fig. 1. The usual configuration is a negative after-potential (accompanied by supernormality) followed by a positive after-potential (accompanied by subnormality). An early positive after-potential is more closely related to the spike than to the negative after-potential. During a tetanus it grows deeper to form the first positive component of the after-potential. The negative after-potential is continued by the second positive potential. In all the fibers shown the positivities shown can be homologized. What is unique about the dorsal root C fibers is the enormous size of the early positive overshooting. Whatever negative after-potential there may be present is completely obscured. Unlike the other fibers there is no super-normality. Absolute refractoriness ends after 2 msec.; and recovery of excitability passes through a long period of subnormality synchronous with the duration of the positivity. As between the C fibers with afferent function, for back reference from the histology, attention must be called to the spike: the simplicity of the olfactory spike, and the number of secondary elevations in the action potential of the dorsal root C fibers.

With this brief synopsis of the action potentials as an introduction, we can now turn to the structure of the fibers producing them. To keep within the scope of the title attention will be given only to the fibers with afferent function.

STRUCTURE

Nerve fibers are branches of nerve cells with sheaths on them. Nerve cells of afferent fibers, whether they arise from the neural crest or from head placodes, send a dendritic branch to the periphery and an axonal branch to the central nervous system. When the branches are from the dorsal root ganglion cells, the peripheral branch surrounded by its sheath is called a nerve fiber, and the central branch surrounded by its sheath is called a root fiber. The fibers of the olfactory nerves, strictly speaking, are root fibers.

Skin nerves

The sheath enveloping the cell processes to form a fiber is the Schwann sheath. Each adult medullated fiber has a sheath of its own. Not so the un-medullated fibers. Their sheaths, as originally described by Nageotte, are a syncytial system of tubes which divide and reunite. Through the branches the fibers weave their way. That the syncytial nature of the sheath is of interest to physiologists I shall now try to show. Fig. 2 presents a picture of a model, made to scale, showing the axes of the sheaths through which 54

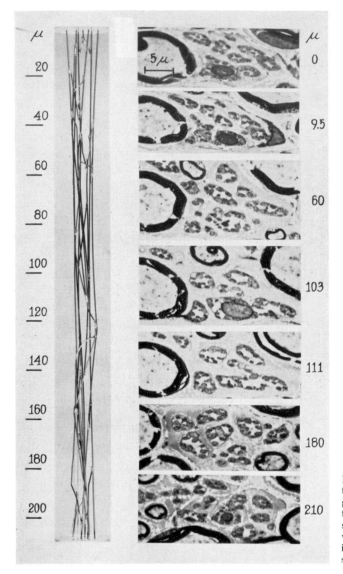

Fig. 2.—Model of the axes of the Schwann sheaths about a group of unmyelinated fibers, together with samples of the sections from which the model was made. Numbers on the side indicate the position in the sheath.

Fig. 3.—*a*, *b*, *c*, pictures of fibers in a cat skin nerve, at the same magnification. In the field are some delta fibers, grouped with which the unmyelinated fibers regularly appear. One of them is passing a Schwann nucleus in a mid-internode where the fiber is constricted. In *b* and *c* arrows point to longer mesaxons to axons away from the surface. *d*, shows the infoldings of the Schwann membrane to envelop two axons. (Courtesy of D. Fawcett.)

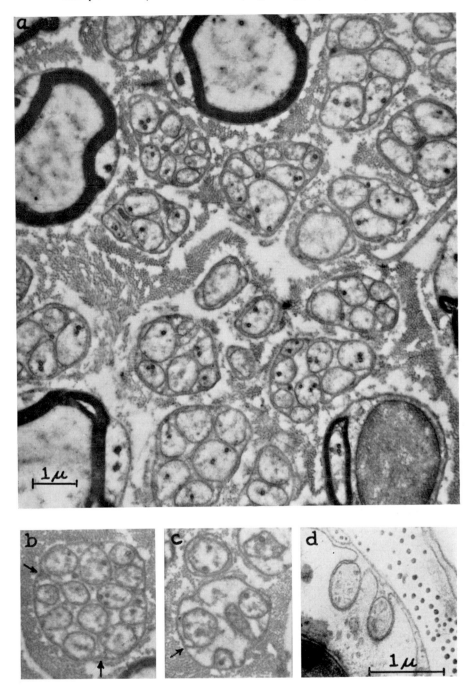

fibers pass in a distance of 210 micra. An idea of the sizes of the sheaths can be obtained from the accompanying reproductions of some of the sections from which the model was made. Owing to the thickness of the sections only the disposition of the fibers is visible. In places a fiber may appear singly in a sheath for a short distance as it passes on its way to the larger tubes containing a number of fibers. In the latter the fibers are disposed in juxtaposition to the Schwann membrane. As the Schwann nuclei come into view, they are axially located in the larger tubes.

The primary reason for making the model was to obtain evidence on the probability of suprathreshold interaction between the fibers. To interact the fibers must remain in parallel. Measurements of the lengths of the branches showed that they are short with respect to the wavelengths of the stimulating second phase of interaction of the action potential. This finding, taken with other evidence, makes the probability of the existence of suprathreshold interaction extremely low. Also, the sheathing arrangement shows how impossible it would be to dissect out a single fiber.

More about the fibers can be learned from higher magnifications of thinner sections. From analyses of such sections, two major features of physiological interest appear. The first is the variation in the size of the fibers (Fig. 3 *a*). In an adequate sampling, the diameters were found to range from 0.3 to 1.35 μ. From the size distribution and certain constants, the action potential, as recorded, could be faithfully reproduced from histological data. Thus, there is a satisfactory accounting for the compound nature of the action potential.

The other feature is connected with details of the sheath structure. The fibers are never free in the Schwann cytoplasm. They are always attached to the Schwann membrane. A sector of the circumference may be at the surface, or the fiber may be well inside the sheath and connected to it with a pedicle (Fig. 3 *b* and *c*). All gradations between the two exist. At first sight these attachments were given a name and admired as an excellent protective device for structures so delicate. Protective they certainly must be; but there was still something obviously unexplained. Its specialized shape is no disguise for the fact that the sheath is cellular. It contains nuclei and cytoplasmic organelles. There should also be a high content of potassium ions; and a high content of potassium ions in the external medium does not fit what is known about the mechanism of nerve conduction. I shall not follow the way out of this difficulty. In the end Dr. Don Fawcett, studying something else obtained a preparation of surpassing clearness, and he has kindly allowed me to make use of it (Fig. 3 *d*).

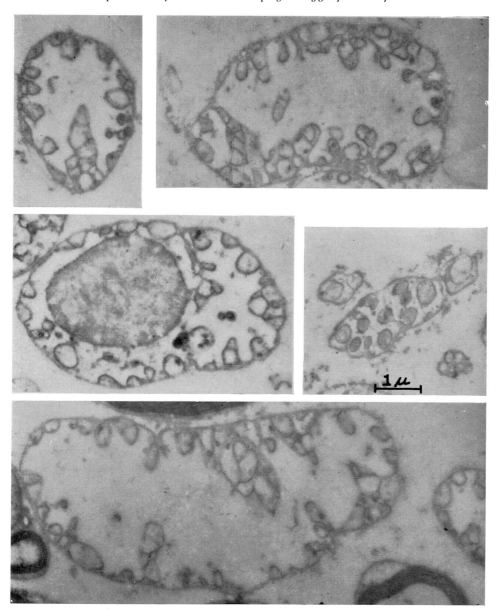

Fig. 4.—Samples of Schwann sheaths, with their content of unmyelinated fibers, in dorsal root of the cat.

At the outside of the sheath two osmiophilic lines are visible. The inner one marks the Schwann membrane. The axon lies in an infolding of this membrane. Where it lies against the membrane two osmiophilic lines again appear, of which the inner one outlines the plasma membrane of the axon. In the places where the infoldings of the Schwann membrane come together the mesaxon is formed. It can have various lengths. What is now quite obvious is that it is the outside of the Schwann membrane that is turned toward the axon membrane. The axon is not in direct contact with the Schwann cytoplasm.

While concern about the potassium content of the external medium is rendered not existent, many new problems are raised both for the physiologist and the cytologist. As the topology of the two kinds of C fibers is the same, the key to their difference is not at hand. One still has to postulate differences in the axons themselves. Physiologists interested in the movement of ions during conduction would like to know the width of the space between the axon and the Schwann membrane. Technical considerations make it a hard figure to come by. My best guess is that it is of the order of 100 Å. The permeability of the Schwann sheath, itself, becomes of interest. It is conceivably measurable experimentally at the surface of the sheath; but for the part about the axon a correction would have to be made for whatever contribution the basement membrane might make. Permeability of the Schwann sheath cannot safely be left as a problem of the C fibers alone. Geren has shown that at the first stage of myelin formation the picture is exactly the same as that for an adult C fiber. One only has to imagine the mesaxon of Fig. 3 c coiled about the axon to get the composition of the myelin layers. Myelinated and unmyelinated fibers now stand in closer relation. With present interest focused on the node there is a crying need for detailed knowledge of the anatomy of the node.

Dorsal roots

When the unmedullated fibers are followed to the root side of the ganglion a striking change in their appearance is found to take place. The fibers become much smaller (Fig. 4, same magnification as in Fig. 3), something that does not happen for the medullated fibers. Some of the sheaths are much larger than they are on the peripheral side of the ganglion, and there is more space in the cytoplasm unoccupied by fibers. The fibers are attached to the sheath in bunches as well as singly, with the largest aggregates in the largest sheaths in places where there is indication that the sheath is near a

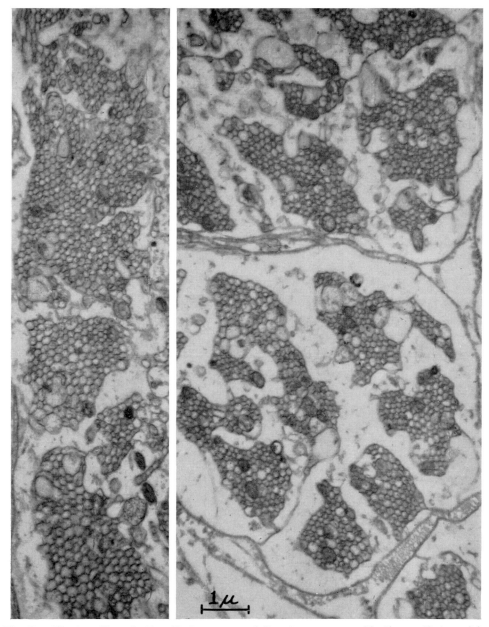

Fig. 5.—Olfactory fibers in the olfactory nerve of the pig, same magnification as that used in Figs. 3 and 4. Just visible on the left side of the left sample is the Schwann membrane of a large sheath, selected to show the extent of aggregation of the fibers; the sheath is larger then the whole figure. The larger sample on the right was selected because, owing to a vagary of the fixation, the nature of the attachment of the fibers is visible. A single mesaxon branches to include more than one group of fibers; and from a single group the way can be traced to more than one mesaxon.

division point. Before the fibers were first seen conduction in the root was known to be slower than it is in the nerve. The action potential is still compound. All the elevations in the nerve action potential are identifiable in the root action potential with velocities at about 0.6 of what they are in the nerve. When the root fibers could be surveyed, their range of sizes was found to be similarly scaled down.

Olfactory nerves

The root pictures serve as an introduction to the olfactory fibers, themselves morphologically roots. All the tendencies which we had just seen are carried forward into an exaggerated form. The fibers are extremely small (Fig. 5) with the reduction of size in comparison with the dendrite of the bipolar cells greater than holds in the dorsal root ganglia. The Schwann sheaths are larger, the mesaxon is more complex, and large numbers of fibers are held by a single mesaxon. In size the fibers are homogeneous as would be expected from the action potential. Their leading velocity of conduction is the slowest for any nerve in the body.

When the fibers were first seen the problem immediately presented was whether there could be a bipolar cell for each one of them. In an attempt to get an answer by tracing them to the bipolar cells much was learned about their sheath formation. At the outset it may be said that the evidence is all in favor of a one to one correspondence between cells and axons. It consists of comparative counts of dendrites and axons, and the tracing of the axon to the extent which will now appear.

Following the course of a structure with the electron microscope has its difficulties. According to what was already known from the Golgi stain, it was realized that in electronmicroscopic dimensions the axons would cross the basement membrane at enormous distances from an orthogonal projection of the bipolar cell. There was no hope of being able to follow any one axon. Such small bits of things are seen with the electron microscope that it became necessary to be able to recognize the structures in the olfactory mucous membrane by their internal morphology. But when this was done there were still residual difficulties.

Up to the basement membrane the sheathing of the bipolar cells is by the sustentacular cells. There are reasons for postulating that sheath cells have functions beyond supplying mechanical support for nerve fibers; and that view gains added evidence in the case of the sustentacular cells. In Fig. 6a, which shows a dendrite with its adjacent sustentacular cells, it can be seen that the latter have a much richer content of organelles than the former. In

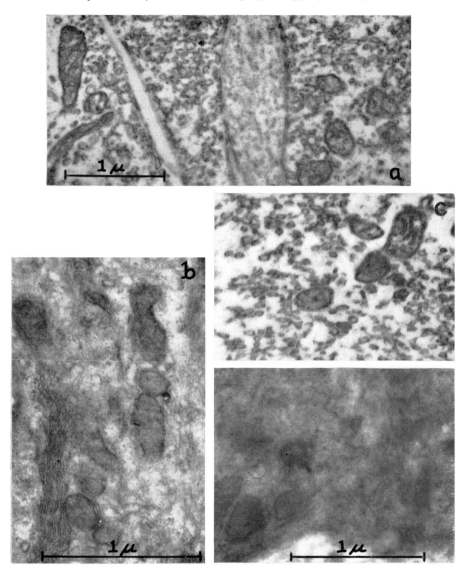

Fig. 6.—Cytoplasm in parts of the sustentacular cells of the olfactory mucous membrane (sections by G. Palade). *a*, parts of sustentacular cells adjacent to a dendrite from a bipolar cell, cat; *b*, cytoplasm in the centrally directed portion of the cell, cat; *c*, comparison of the cytoplasmic content of the outer and inner portions of the sustentacular cell. Sections from a single preparation (rat). Upper section, near a dendrite head. Lower section, at basement membrane; the clearer space at the bottom belongs to the submucosa.

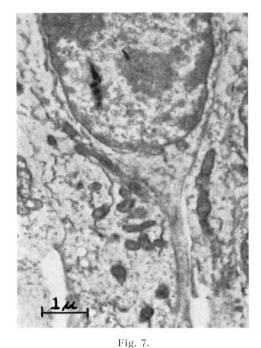

Fig. 7.

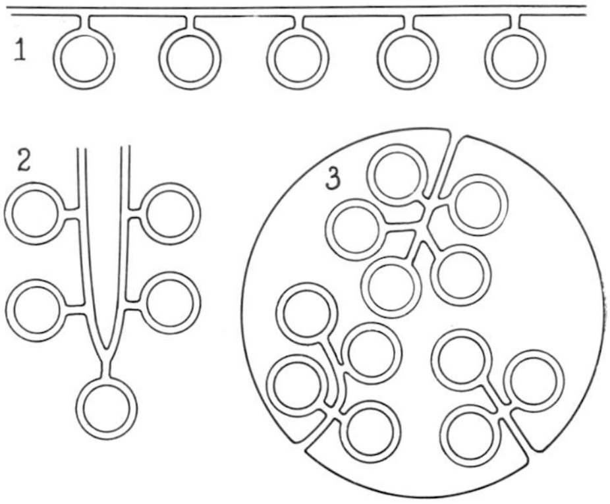

Fig. 9.

Fig. 9.—Diagram to illustrate how a small bundle might be formed. (See text.)

Fig. 7.—Axon leaving a bipolar cell, rat. Adjoining the cell body and axon are cell borders of sustentacular cells (section by G. Palade).

this region the sustentacular cells contain few, if any, fine particles. But on the central side of the nucleus a striking change takes place (Fig. 6 b, c). Fine particles become so numerous that, except in very thin sections at high magnification, the cytoplasm has a solid black appearance (Fig. 10). In part c of Fig. 6 there are shown at equal magnification two areas cut from the same preparation. The upper one was selected from a region near the dendrite heads, and the lower one at the abutment upon the basement membrane. In the basal region the fine particles have become so dense that only with close scrutiny is it possible to see the organelles.

Among the sections showing the axon leaving a bipolar cell only one followed the diameter of the axon for any distance (Fig. 7). When the axons become enveloped in the blackness of the sustentacular cells they are lost to view; and tracing them is made doubly difficult by the fact that the tissue in the basal region of the olfactory mucous membrane is so fragile that no method of fixation was found that would prevent fragmentation of the preparation (Fig. 10). Finally, however, Dr. Palade succeeded in obtaining some sections which showed the manner in which the axons leave the sustentacular cells. Thus, as far as the tracing of the axons is concerned, the case for con-

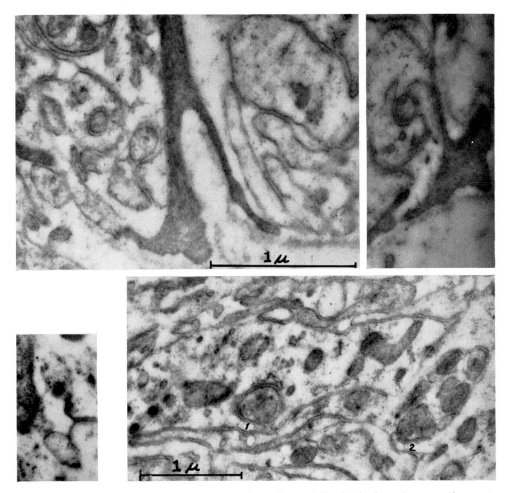

Fig. 8.—Emergence of axons from sustentacular cells, and the beginning of aggregation, cat. The upper print would be continuous if a strip representing 0.64 μ had not been removed between the left and right portions. Black areas, parts of sustentacular cells abutting upon the basement membrane. Along side are the basal cells in which can be seen profiles of pouches invaginated from the basal cell membrane with loops surrounding axons. In the upper left corner there is part of a small bundle. Print at lower left shows an axon pushing back the border of a basal cell in order to acquire a sheath. Lower right, interior of a basal cell. In profile, the two walls of the infolded pouches are clearly resolved. At *1*, there is a loop about an axon; at *2*, there is a small bundle.

tinuity of the axons with the bipolar cells rests upon observations of their entrance into and exit from the sustentacular cells.

When the axons leave the sustentacular cells they push back the membranes of the basal cells (Fig. 8, upper right and lower left); and the latter

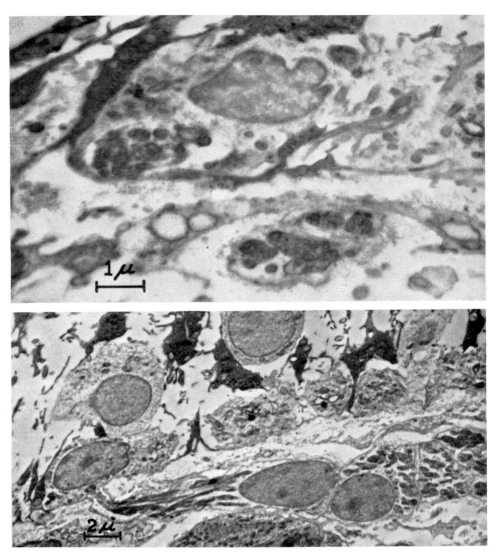

Fig. 10.—Delivery of the olfactory fibers to the nerve by the basal cells of the olfactory mucous membrane (cat). In both prints the base of the olfactory mucous membrane lies irregularly at the equator of the print. *Top:* Basal cell with nucleus and adjoined by black areas, the central portions of sustentacular cells. In the basal cell is a bundle of olfactory fibers ready for delivery. In the submucosa are two bundles already delivered by other cells. *Bottom:* A row of basal cells with the easily fragmentable region above them. In the latter the black areas are the central ends of sustentacular cells. On the left side the membrane of the basal cell (with nucleus) is seen to be continuous with the membrane of a Schwann sheath. A bundle of fibers is being delivered to the Schwann sheath. The similarity of the Schwann nuclei to the basal cell nucleus is to be noted. On the right, the sheath joins other sheaths of similar origin and the larger complex has turned into a vertical direction.

form sheaths about them in a manner resembling the infoldings of the Schwann membrane about an axon in a segmental nerve. The infoldings of the basal cell membranes, which in sections are always seen in profile, must actually be flattened pouches; and they extend far into the interior of the cells carrying the axons with them. In sections the latter are seen enclosed in loops evaginated from one of the walls of a pouch (Fig. 8). Next the axons are collected into small bundles in some such manner as is indicated diagrammatically in Fig. 9. By bringing together the ends of a row of axons, 1, stage 2 would be reached. Then, by a withdrawal of the inner surface, a proximation of the axons, and a bending of the outer surface an arrangement would be produced as conceived in stage 3. Here, the group is considered to have been joined by two other groups, of similar origin, to create a small bundle such as appears in Fig. 8.

After the formation of the small bundles successive aggregations of the axons take place. Even before the axons leave the basal cells a number of small bundles have come together (Fig. 10). The membranes of the Schwann tubes are directly continuous with those of the basal cells (Fig. 10); and through the orifices in the cells the collection of fibers is delivered from the cells to the tubes. Schwann tube now fuses with Schwann tube until the state is reached which was seen at the outset (Fig. 5).

Fundamentally the sheath system of the olfactory fibers is like that of other unmedullated fibers. It is only more complex in its elaboration. Indeed, through variations from a simple common starting point the sheaths of all vertebrate nerve fibers appear to be derived.

SUMMARY

The morphology of unmedullated nerve fibers with afferent function is described following an outline of their electrophysiological properties. Emphasis is placed on the role of the fiber sizes, the distribution of sizes, the configuration of the after-potentials, and the significance of the nature of the fiber sheaths. In common the sheaths are formed by infoldings of the Schwann membrane. They vary in elaboration. The latter is traced from simple enclosures of individual fibers in skin nerves, through the modification occurring in dorsal roots, to the highly branched suspensions in olfactory nerves which cause the fibers to be held in bundles.

X-RAY DIFFRACTION STUDIES OF THE MYELIN SHEATH IN PERIPHERAL AND CENTRAL NERVE FIBRES

J. B. FINEAN

Department of Medical Biochemistry and Pharmacology, University of Birmingham, England,
and Department of Nerve Ultrastructure, Instituto Venezolano de Neurología,
Caracas, Venezuela

A GENERAL picture of the spatial arrangement of lipid, protein, and water components in the concentrically wrapped layers of the myelin sheath of peripheral nerve has been suggested on the basis of polarised light data [16] and of X-ray diffraction studies of both normal and modified nerve specimens [1, 2, 4–12, 17, 18]. It has also been pointed out that the diffraction data obtained from central nerve fibres, and in particular from optic nerve, indicate considerable structural differences in the myelin of central origin [5, 10]. The evidence on which these structural suggestions for fresh nerve myelin are based has been presented in detail in previous publications, and I think it would be more profitable on this occasion to consider some X-ray diffraction studies which are of significance in relation to the examination of myelin structure in the electron microscope. The structural modifications introduced by fixation, dehydration, and embedding have been studied by X-ray diffraction methods, and the observations are of value in relating the electron microscope picture of myelin to our concept of the arrangement of structural components in fresh nerve myelin.

THE MOLECULAR ARCHITECTURE OF FRESH NERVE MYELIN

Our present ideas on the structure of the peripheral nerve myelin are summarised in Fig. 1. We consider the fundamental unit in peripheral nerve myelin to include two lipoprotein layers, each consisting of a bimolecular leaflet of lipid sandwiched between monolayers of protein. The two layers are distinguished by a difference factor, the nature of which is not yet established but whose origin is clearly indicated in the method of myelin formation from the Schwann cell membrane. Geren [13] concluded from an electron microscope study of developing nerve fibres in chick embryo that there was an infolding of the Schwann cell membrane and a rolling onto the axon in double layers. If the Schwann cell membrane should feature a bimolecular leaflet of lipid sandwiched between monolayers of protein then this would lead to an alternation of bimolecular leaflets of lipid and double layers of protein in the multilayered structure. The difference factor distinguishing alternate layers can be accounted for in terms of an asymmetry of the Schwann cell membrane. It may arise, for example, from the presence of certain groups on one surface of the membrane which are not present on the other. We think that this difference is more likely to involve the protein

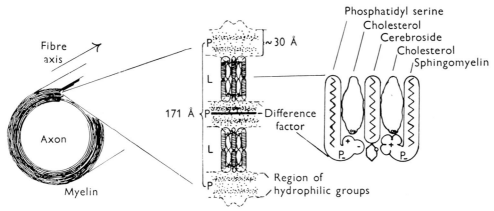

Fig. 1.—Diagram summarising structural features suggested for peripheral nerve myelin from polarised light and X-ray diffraction data.

layer than the lipid layer, and have therefore chosen to locate the difference factor provisionally in one of the protein layers. It should, however, be pointed out that the X-ray diffraction data simply requires a very similar distribution of scattering power in the two layers constituting the fundamental unit, and as the scattering powers of many biologically important organic materials do not differ very greatly the possibility of having protein at one membrane surface and another component such as mucopolysaccharide at the other is not excluded. The composition of the lipid layer has been considered previously, and the only detail so far emphasised is the possibility of a specific phospholipid-cholesterol complex. The unit featured in Fig. 1, which includes two phospholipid-cholesterol complexes and a cerebroside molecule, is simply a chemical unit which accounts for more than 90 per cent of the lipids in myelin. The possibility of defining a structural unit within the plane of the lipid layers has been considered and will probably be discussed after the presentation of electron microscope data and detailed chemical data in later papers. It will be noted that the interaction between lipid and protein is suggested to be an ionic one. This means that the hydrophilic groups of the structure will be confined to a well-defined layer which spans the lipoprotein interfaces on either side of the protein layer. We consider the water component to be confined to this region in fresh nerve myelin, and our studies [11] of the effects of variation of the ionic strength of the immersion medium on this structure indicate that the water is largely "organised" in relation to these hydrophilic groups.

DIFFRACTION CHANGES DURING NORMAL DEHYDRATION

When freshly dissected nerve specimens are examined with the direction of the X-ray beam perpendicular to the fibre axis of the nerve trunk, the diffraction patterns feature a rather diffuse wide angle reflection with meridional intensification at about 4.7 Å, and a number of sharp equatorial reflections at low angles [18]. The wide angle reflection is probably derived largely from the separation of hydrocarbon chains in the lipid layer, and most of the low angle reflections are related to the radial organisation of the lipoprotein layers. In this presentation we are concerned mainly with the low angle reflections. In the diffraction patterns reproduced here, a slit collimating system has been used to define the X-ray beam, and the precise equatorial nature of the reflections is therefore obscured. The low angle reflections from fresh nerve material can all be interpreted in terms of a single fundamental radial repeating unit of 160 to 190 Å which consists of two parts having very similar distributions of X-ray scattering power. The magnitude of the difference between these two parts can be judged from the intensities of the odd order reflections in the low angle diffraction patterns. The difference is appreciable and almost identical for amphibian and mammalian peripheral nerve myelin but appears to be negligible for the freshly-dissected optic nerve (Fig. 2). In the case of peripheral nerve, the effect of the difference factor can be removed by freezing and thawing the preparation (Fig. 3). Such treatment also results in an appreciable increase in the dimension of the radial unit [2].

When myelin is air-dried there is an extensive breakdown of structure. In the case of peripheral nerve a separation of a lipoprotein and several lipid phases has been demonstrated. In the diffraction pattern reproduced in Fig. 4, the residual lipoprotein phase is represented by the reflections at 154 Å and 77 Å; two phospholipid polymorphs are mainly responsible for the 61 Å and 47 Å reflections, though cerebroside may also contribute; and there is also a faint reflection at 34.5 Å which we associate with a cholesterol phase [1, 2]. A detailed study of the process of drying has been made, first using a photographic recording [1] and more recently applying a Geiger

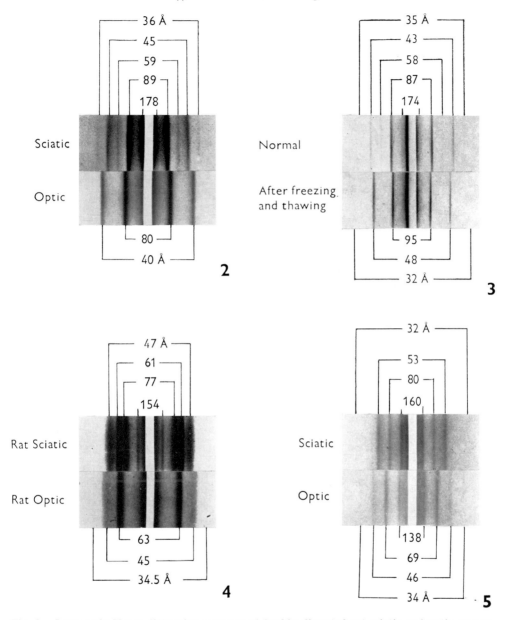

Fig. 2.—Low angle X-ray diffraction patterns of freshly dissected rat sciatic and optic nerves. (These and subsequent patterns were all obtained using CuKα radiation at a specimen to film distance of 140 mm in an evacuated camera.)

Fig. 3.—Comparison of the low angle X-ray diffraction pattern of a freshly dissected giant toad sciatic nerve with that obtained from the same specimen after freezing and thawing.

Fig. 4.—Low angle X-ray diffraction patterns of dried sciatic and optic nerves from rat.

Fig. 5.—Low angle X-ray diffraction patterns of rat sciatic and optic nerves after fixation for 4 hours in buffered 1 per cent osmium tetroxide.

counter technique for serial recording of low angle diffraction patterns. These studies show that the lipid components first separate from the lipoprotein structure as a single phase giving a reflection in the region of 60 Å, and that this eventually differentiates further to give the several lipid phases already identified. This lipid has been previously referred to as the labile lipid component of peripheral nerve myelin [1]. In the case of dried optic nerve (Fig. 4) there are reflections in the region assigned to lipid phases, but there are no clear indications of a residual lipoprotein component. However, there is other evidence to suggest that a protein component is also involved in myelin of central origin [10], though the lipid-protein association must differ appreciably from that in peripheral nerve myelin.

EFFECTS OF FIXATION

From the point of view of this presentation, it must be stressed that a breakdown of structure to give several lipid and lipoprotein phases will occur if the nerve is simply dried without any initial fixation. In preparing tissue for viewing in the electron microscope it has to be dried, and it is desirable that this structural breakdown which accompanies normal dehydration should be prevented by fixation. Thus our criterion of fixation from the point of view of molecular structure is that it shall preserve unity of structure during dehydration, and the success or failure of any fixative can be readily assessed from the low angle diffraction pattern of the dried specimen. So far, only buffered osmium tetroxide solution has produced the desired fixation of lipoprotein structures [6], though preliminary experiments with potassium permanganate solutions [14] suggest that this too may, under certain conditions, produce a satisfactory fixation. Thus, if one wishes to visualise something representing the intact structure in the electron microscope the preparation must be treated with buffered osmium tetroxide before dehydration. This treatment does, however, introduce extensive modifications into the structure in the way of shrinkage and drastic alterations in the distribution of scattering power within the structural unit. These modifications, which are complete within about four hours in the case of nerve bundles one half to one millimetre in diameter [6], can be readily appreciated by comparing the diffraction patterns reproduced in Figs. 2 and 5, and 3 and 6. In all cases, the shrinkage of the radial unit on fixation with osmium tetroxide is by about 20 Å. The first order reflection, which is very weak or absent in the diffraction pattern of the fresh material, is greatly strengthened to become the dominant reflection in the pattern of the fixed preparation. Referring again to the two lipoprotein layers suggested to form the fundamental structural unit in peripheral nerve myelin, this means that there is a very strong difference factor with respect to reactivity of the layer components with osmium tetroxide, and this applies both to peripheral nerve myelin and to myelin of central nerve fibres.

The difference factor in terms of reactivity with osmium tetroxide is not necessarily the same as that which distinguishes the layers with respect to diffraction in the normal structure. In the case of optic nerve myelin the osmium tetroxide reaction reveals a difference between layers which is not apparent in the fresh material. However, in spite of this emphasising of the difference between alternate layers in the myelin multilayer in all systems, a variation in the detailed density distribution in the myelin of amphibian and mammalian peripheral nerve and of optic nerve preparations is still evident. Frog sciatic nerve, and both frog and rat optic nerves, show an approximately linear decrease in intensities of reflections with increasing diffraction order, but whereas the fourth order reflection is normally clearly seen in the optic nerve pattern it is never detected in the case of a frog sciatic nerve preparation examined under the same conditions. The diffraction pattern of the osmium tetroxide fixed rat sciatic nerve shows an unusually intense third order reflection, and long exposures bring up a fifth order reflection without revealing the fourth order. Such variations in density distribution in the different types of myelin might be visualised in the electron microscope and might eventually help to establish real differences between the systems. It is also possible to affect the density distribution in these systems by modifying the structure before fixation. Of particular interest in this respect is the modification produced by the freezing and thawing of fresh peripheral nerve. This treatment obliterates the difference factor which is apparent in the diffraction pattern of the fresh preparation. When the preparation is subsequently fixed with osmium tetroxide, several significant features are apparent in the low-angle diffraction pattern (Fig. 6). The intense general scatter at low angles suggests an extensive breakdown of structure so that much of the osmium is distributed in an irregular fashion. The second order reflection is, however, greatly intensified, indicating that in the parts of the structure that remain intact the density distribution in the two layers constituting the fundamental unit is more nearly equal than was the case with the normal fixed preparation. Another interesting modification is that produced by partially drying before fixing with osmium tetroxide. When the preparation is fully dried before fixation, examination by X-ray diffraction reveals a very heavy low angle scatter in which it is difficult to identify any

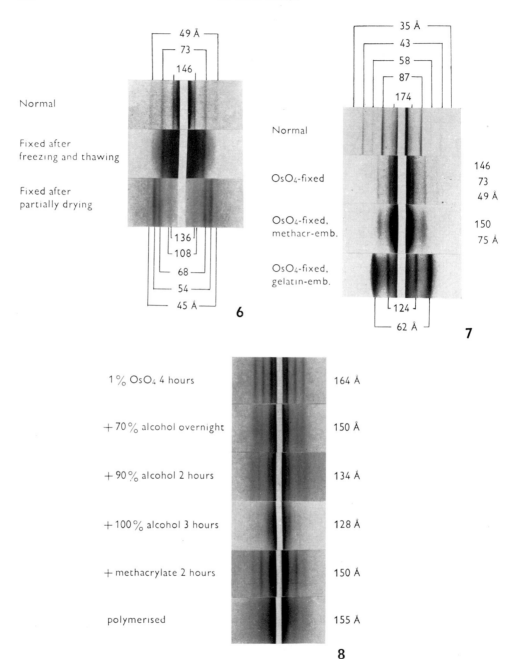

Fig. 6
Normal
Fixed after freezing and thawing
Fixed after partially drying
49 Å / 73 / 146
136 / 108 / 68 / 54 / 45 Å

Fig. 7
Normal
OsO₄-fixed
OsO₄-fixed, methacr-emb.
OsO₄-fixed, gelatin-emb.
35 Å / 43 / 58 / 87 / 174
146 / 73 / 49 Å
150 / 75 Å
124 / 62 Å

Fig. 8
1 % OsO₄ 4 hours — 164 Å
+ 70 % alcohol overnight — 150 Å
+ 90 % alcohol 2 hours — 134 Å
+ 100 % alcohol 3 hours — 128 Å
+ methacrylate 2 hours — 150 Å
polymerised — 155 Å

precise reflections. Fixation at intermediate stages of drying have led to the recording of some interesting diffraction patterns. The drying process can be followed using the Geiger counter recording, and the preparation fixed at a certain selected stage of drying. It is found that at a certain stage two components can be identified from the X-ray reflections (Fig. 6). The point at which the extra component appears seems to coincide with the limit of reversibility of the drying process. There is little doubt that the two components correspond to the labile lipid and the residual lipoprotein components, and it would be of great interest to try to identify these two components in the electron microscope.

EFFECTS OF DEHYDRATION AND EMBEDDING

In order to study the osmium tetroxide fixed myelin in the electron microscope the specimen must be thin sectioned, and it must be dehydrated. So far, three techniques have been used successfully in visualising the layered structure in the electron microscope. The earliest success was achieved using the freeze-sectioning method [3]. It has been shown that the process of freezing and thawing produces no further change in the structure after it has been fixed with osmium tetroxide, and it is therefore anticipated that the specimen prepared for the microscope by the freeze-sectioning method would not differ much from a simple air-dried preparation. The diffraction pattern of such a preparation reveals a further shrinkage of the structural unit by about 30 Å making about 50 Å in all as compared with the myelin of fresh nerve. There is also a marked intensification of the second order diffraction so that it becomes much stronger than the first order. Lower orders are no longer detected. The dehydration would thus appear to make the density distributions in the two layers that constitute the fundamental unit more nearly alike than is the case in the moist material. The diffraction pattern obtained from an osmium tetroxide fixed preparation, dehydrated and embedded in gelatin, is almost identical with that of the air-dried specimen, but material

Fig. 6.—Comparison of low angle X-ray diffraction patterns of OsO$_4$-fixed giant toad sciatic nerve and specimens modified either by freezing and thawing or by partially drying before fixation.

Fig. 7.—Comparison of low angle X-ray diffraction patterns of normal giant toad sciatic nerve, OsO$_4$-fixed nerve, and of OsO$_4$-fixed nerves which have been embedded either in 30 per cent gelatin containing 5 per cent glycerine, or in butyl methacrylate after alcohol dehydration.

Fig. 8.—Series of low angle X-ray diffraction patterns of rat sciatic nerve recorded at various stages in the methacrylate embedding procedure.

embedded in methacrylate shows a radial repeating unit very similar to that of the freshly fixed moist preparation, and there is no intensification of the second order diffraction, the first order remaining dominant (Fig. 7). If a little glycerine (2 to 5 per cent) is added to the gelatin to facilitate the cutting of thin sections, the structural unit is expanded by a few Ångström units, but there is little change in diffraction intensities. There are thus marked differences in size of structural unit and distribution in density between gelatin embedded material and methacrylate embedded material.

The similarities of the layer spacings measured in the electron micrographs of thin sections of osmium tetroxide fixed and methacrylate embedded specimens and the X-ray spacing of the freshly fixed material has been noted in the case of retinal rods and chloroplasts [12], and there has been speculation as to whether the technique of methacrylate embedding prevents contraction of structure and maintains the original distribution of scattering material. The first part of the question can now be answered from the results of a detailed study of the effects of each stage of the methacrylate embedding procedure on the structure of the myelin sheath. Low angle diffraction patterns were recorded after each step in the preparation. One set of results is reproduced in Fig. 8, and these bring out several important features of the preparative procedure. During dehydration in a graded alcohol series, the structural unit does shrink almost as much as in simple air-drying, but the first order reflection remains dominant throughout. In most patterns obtained at these stages the third order reflection is partially obscured by what appears to be an independent reflection in the region of 50 Å. This could be associated with a lipid component which is being extracted in spite of the preliminary fixation with osmium tetroxide. When the alcohol dehydrated specimen is eventually immersed in methacrylate the myelin structure quickly expands, and the diffraction bands improve in definition until, after two to four hours in the monomer, the diffraction pattern resembles very closely that of the original freshly fixed specimen. When the methacrylate is polymerised there is a further expansion of the structural unit by a few Ångström units, and the diffraction bands broaden thus indicating a distortion of structure.

SIGNIFICANCE OF DENSITY DISTRIBUTIONS REVEALED BY ELECTRON MICROSCOPY

These preliminary observations, which refer simply to the preparative procedures which have been commonly used for electron microscope studies of nerve and other tissues at IVNIC, brings up some interesting points in relation to the interpretation of electron micrographs in terms of the normal tissue structure. In order to consider these points it is necessary to anticipate some of the electron microscopy, but this can be reduced to simple diagrammatic form for general considerations, and details can be left for discussion when the electron microscope data on myelin has been presented in full by Dr. Fernández-Morán. There is now no doubt about the correspondence of the layer repeat observed in the electron micrographs of myelin preparations and the fundamental radial unit deduced from low angle X-ray diffraction patterns of osmium tetroxide fixed and embedded nerve fibres, though it turns out that in every case there is a discrepancy of as much as 10 to 20 Å between the measurements made using the two methods. The discrepancy is probably due to a further shrinking of the structure during sectioning and examination in the electron microscope.

Outstanding features in the electron micrographs of myelin are two narrow dense bands separated by regions of low density. One is invariably very dense and about 30 Å wide but the other, the intermediate band, can be relatively light and much narrower (15 Å) in the case of the normal methacrylate embedded specimen, but is intensified and broadened in the case of the gelatin embedded specimen and also in the specimen which had been frozen and thawed before osmium tetroxide fixation and methacrylate embedding. An impression of the density distributions in these three types of preparation can be gained from the diagrammatic representations given in Fig. 9. This interplay of the relative densities of the two principal bands is undoubtedly reflected in the variations of relative intensities of first and second order reflections in the low angle X-ray diffraction patterns. Thus it is possible to predict the general form of the density distribution to be visualised in the electron microscope from the intensities of the X-ray reflections. The definition of the diffraction bands will give some idea of the structural variations and distortions, whilst the amount of low angle general scatter superimposed on the diffraction pattern indicates the extent of structural breakdown effected by the preparative procedure. The low angle X-ray diffraction pattern of the embedded material can thus be used to gain an overall impression of the state of the structure, a very small part of which is subsequently examined in the electron microscope. The diffraction data from the intermediate stages of preparation emphasise the modifications introduced by the preparative procedures, and provide a link with the normal structure which assists in trying to interpret the features seen in the electron micrograph in terms of normal structural components. The diffraction studies also provide evidence to suggest that the density variations in myelin reflect to a

great extent the deposition of osmium compounds in the myelin layers. The
OsO$_4$-fixation greatly increases the X-ray scattering power of the system, and
also markedly alters the density distribution within the layers. The latter effect
could arise from addition to or subtraction from the structure, but the simplest
and most satisfactory explanation would be that osmium compounds are
added to the system in quantities sufficient to dominate the density distribu-

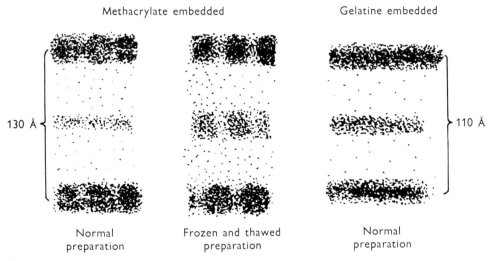

Fig. 9.—Diagrammatic representation of the density variation in myelin layers as seen in electron micrographs of three different types of preparation of giant toad sciatic nerve.

tion. In the absence of chemical evidence to the contrary it is therefore assumed that osmium deposition features largely in the density variations observed in the myelin layers by electron microscopy.

One of the most interesting points for consideration is the relative merits
of the gelatin and methacrylate embedding procedures. An obvious advantage
of the gelatin is that it is used in aqueous solution, and therefore there is
no risk of extracting lipid components during the embedding procedure. In
alcohol dehydration and methacrylate embedding there are definite indications that some lipid is extracted even after osmium tetroxide fixation. The
gelatin method thus promises to be of value in attempting to use fixatives
which are less effective than osmium tetroxide, and preliminary experiments
with permanganate fixation show better results with gelatin embedding than
with methacrylate. However, there still remains the fact that the diffraction
pattern of the osmium tetroxide fixed and methacrylate embedded myelin
resembles very closely that of the freshly fixed material, and may therefore

give a truer picture of the structure than does the gelatin embedding procedure. The diffraction patterns show that the myelin contracts and expands again during methacrylate embedding, and there is the obvious possibility that the contraction and expansion take place at different locations in the structure. Thus, if the contraction reflects the removal of water from an ionic interface it is by no means certain that the methacrylate would eventually re-expand the ionic region. On the contrary, the chemical nature of the methacrylate would suggest that it is more likely to penetrate and expand the non-ionic regions of the structure. There are, however, strong indications that the contraction of structure observed when the osmium tetroxide fixed specimen is dried does not simply reflect the removal of water from ionic interfaces. Fresh myelin contracts by about 20 to 25 Å per fundamental radial unit when dried, and this is the extent of contraction that takes place during osmium tetroxide fixation and during a number of other treatments which might be expected to effect a tighter binding of the ionic interfaces. In fact, our general experience gained from X-ray diffraction studies of modifications of nerve myelin leads us to suspect that the direct contribution of water to the size of the radial repeating unit is probably very small after osmium tetroxide fixation, and that any further contraction after fixation is probably due to a rearrangement of lipid or protein components. A contraction of the lipid layer through a tilting of the long axes of the lipid molecules could produce the observed effect. If the methacrylate treatment were then simply to reverse this process the close similarities in size of structural unit and density distribution when compared with the freshly fixed material would be readily understood. Such an explanation of the contraction and expansion taking place during methacrylate embedding is also in keeping with the fact that there is nothing in the electron micrographs that could be identified with a 20 to 30 Å layer of methacrylate. Although the evidence is far from conclusive this would seem to be the most likely explanation of the observations, and the combination of osmium tetroxide fixation and methacrylate embedding may be a very favourable one for observing lipoprotein structures in the electron microscope in spite of the possibility of a partial extraction of the lipid component.

There are several puzzling features about the differences in the appearance of the myelin when embedded in gelatin and when in methacrylate. The differences in densities and dimensions of the intermediate bands might be expected to be a direct result of the contraction of structure in the gelatin embedded material but the density outside the intermediate band in the methacrylate embedded myelin would appear insufficient to produce the intensification of intermediate band apparent in the gelatin embedded specimen. Lipid extraction during methacrylate embedding might account for some of the difference but then one would also have to bring into consideration the observation that the intermediate band can be intensified in a methacrylate embedded preparation by freezing and thawing prior to fixation. Detailed explanations of the observations must await further experimental data, but it is tempting to make some preliminary speculations as to the chemical significance of the density distribution in the lipoprotein layers of myelin. The general choice for the sites of heavy osmium deposition would seem to be between ionic interfaces and regions of unsaturation in the lipid hydrocarbon chains. Despite the traditional histological beliefs, available evidence seems to point to ionic interfaces as the principal sites of osmium tetroxide interaction in this organised structure. The degree of contraction of structure produced by osmium tetroxide fixation approximates to that which would be expected to result from the closer binding of ionic interfaces and expulsion of the intervening water. The stabilisation of the lipid-protein association would seem to suggest that extra binding has been introduced at the lipoprotein interfaces. Such ionic interfaces are well-defined, and could be very satisfactorily related to the narrow bands of relatively high density observed in the myelin structure. The dense, thirty Ångström band would span the two lipoprotein interfaces on either side of the suggested protein layer (see Fig. 1) and thus cover the entire ionic region. If the dense band does in fact represent one lipoprotein region then the intermediate band would be expected to mark the second region of lipid-protein interaction, and would thus support the location of a difference factor at the protein layer. The significance of the observations that the intermediate line can be intensified on the one hand by embedding in gelatin rather than methacrylate and on the other by freezing and thawing prior to fixing cannot yet be fully appreciated. The first observation would suggest that the difference factor is partly a variation in the distribution of osmium compounds, the effect of which is decreased when the structure contracts, and the second that a protein interaction is involved, for the process of freezing and thawing would hardly be expected to affect the organisation of the lipid chains directly. The latter effect might possibly be one of removing a blocking agent from reactive sites so as to intensify the subsequent interaction with osmium tetroxide.

All these points support the suggestion that the primary reaction with osmium tetroxide is ionic, but they do not amount to proof, and in relation to some of the points made it must be admitted that the stabilising effect of the osmium tetroxide and the heaviest staining are not necessarily at the same sites. Against such a conclusion is the undoubted tendency for osmium tetroxide to react with unsaturated lipids. However, there is appreciable density in the light band of the myelin structure, and this may be related to a relatively small amount of osmium deposition among predominantly saturated myelin lipids and the possibility that reactive groups may not be readily available to osmium tetroxide in a liquid crystalline structure. There is also the demonstration by electron microscopy of a regular density variation, possibly due to osmium deposition, in a purely lipid system, but the work is very preliminary and there is no possibility yet of determining whether the osmium deposition is at the ionic interfaces or among the lipid chains.

The nature of the difference factor still eludes us. In the case of the optic nerve, the difference factor revealed by osmium tetroxide interaction has no effect on the fresh nerve pattern and is therefore suggested to involve chemical groups which have insignificant scattering power for X-rays. In peripheral nerve, the observation that the freezing and thawing treatment obliterates the difference factor of the fresh nerve structure and also modifies the subsequent osmium tetroxide interaction indicates that in this system the difference factor for osmium may also be the factor which is responsible at least in part for the prominence of the odd order reflections in the fresh nerve diffraction pattern. Groups which might produce both effects are $-SH$ groups which react very strongly with osmium tetroxide and also are sufficiently strong X-ray scattering units to have an appreciable effect on the diffraction from this structure. In support of the involvement of $-SH$ groups in distinguishing alternate layers in this structure is the observation that treatment of the myelin with mercuric chloride will also strengthen the first order diffraction, and that this action is at least partially blocked by dinitrofluorobenzene [15].

These preliminary X-ray diffraction studies of the preparative techniques for electron microscopy indicate the possibility of a closer integration of X-ray diffraction and electron microscope studies of myelin structure, and the observations may also be of value in relation to electron microscope studies of lipoproteins in general.

SUMMARY

Polarised light and X-ray-diffraction studies of nerve tissue have facilitated detailed predictions concerning the molecular architecture of fresh nerve myelin. An extension of the diffraction studies to the preparative procedures used in electron microscopy has shown that a change in the dimensions of the fundamental structural unit of myelin and a marked alteration of the electron density distribution take place before the structure is viewed in the electron microscope. Information is provided which is of value in relating the electron microscope observations to the unmodified structure.

I wish to thank Dr. H. Fernández-Morán for the kind invitation to carry out these studies at *IVNIC*, and for his cooperation in all aspects of the work. I am grateful to the University of Birmingham for granting leave to enable me to accept the invitation.

REFERENCES

1. ELKES, J. and FINEAN, J. B., *Discussions Faraday Soc.* No. **6**, 134 (1949).
2. —— *Exptl. Cell Research* **4**, 69 (1953).
3. FERNÁNDEZ-MORÁN, H., *Exptl. Cell Research* **1**, 309 (1950).
4. FINEAN, J. B., *Exptl. Cell Research*, **5**, 202 (1953).
5. —— *International Colloquium on Biochemical Problems of Lipids. Brussels, 1953*, p. 82.
6. —— *Exptl. Cell Research* **6**, 283 (1954).
7. —— *Nature* **173**, 549 (1954).
8. —— *Second International Conference on Biochemical Problems of Lipids, Ghent, 1955*, p. 127. Butterworth, London.
9. —— *Second International Neurochemical Symposium, Aarhus, 1956*. Metabolism of the Nervous System, p. 52. Pergamon Press, London.
10. FINEAN, J. B., HAWTHORNE, J. N. and PATTERSON, J. D. E., *J. Neurochem.* **1**, 256 (1957).
11. FINEAN, J. B. and MILLINGTON, P. F., *J. Biophys. Biochem. Cytol.* **3**, 89 (1957).
12. FINEAN, J. B., SJÖSTRAND, F. S. and STEINMANN, E., *Exptl. Cell Research* **5**, 557 (1953).
13. GEREN, B. B., *Exptl. Cell Research* **7**, 558 (1954).
14. LUFT, J. H., *J. Biophys. Biochem. Cytol.* **2**, 799 (1956).
15. MILLINGTON, P. F., Thesis. University of Birmingham, 1957.
16. SCHMIDT, W. J., *Z. Zellforsch. mikroskop. Anat.* **23**, 657 (1936).
17. SCHMITT, F. O., Multiple Sclerosis and the Demyelinating Diseases, **28**, 247 (1950).
18. SCHMITT, F. O., BEAR, R. S. and PALMER, K. J., *J. Cellular Comp. Physiol.* **18**, 31 (1941).

Experimental Cell Research, Suppl. **5**, *33–57 (1958)*

AXON–SATELLITE CELL RELATIONSHIPS IN PERIPHERAL NERVE FIBERS[1]

F. O. SCHMITT

Biology Department, Massachusetts Institute of Technology, Cambridge, Mass., U.S.A.

GREAT advances have been made in recent years in the field of electro-physiology, particularly with respect to the more precise localization and characterization of the electrical properties of nerve fibers by the use of microelectrodes in conjunction with a giant fiber such as that of the squid. Equally striking advances in our knowledge of nerve ultrastructure have been made possible by the application of polarization optics, X-ray diffraction and, most recently, by high resolution electron microscopy. These rapidly moving developments have set the stage for a direct determination of the chemical properties and the structure, at or near the molecular level, of that region of the nerve fiber which lies between the axoplasm and the extracellular fluid. It is in this region that the "excitable membrane" is thought by many nerve physiologists to exist.

Although it has long been known to neurohistologists that the peripheral axon is everywhere enclosed by Schwann or satellite cells, this fact has become particularly significant as a result of recent electron microscope studies of various types of fibers. These studies, in conjunction with Geren's [21] ingenious explanation of the origin of the myelin by infolding of the Schwann cell membrane, have clarified the concept of myelination. This concept had become badly confused both because of misleading early terminology and because of limitations of light-microscope resolution. This matter will be reviewed in the present paper and it will be seen that the structural characteristic which is present in all fibers so far studied ("myelinated" or "unmyelinated") is the Schwann or satellite cell which, with its varying amount of lipid-protein membranous differentiation, appears everywhere to enclose the axon.

This situation poses an important problem because the "excitable membrane", traditionally supposed to lie in or near the limiting envelope of the axon, is also thought to be exposed to extracellular fluid. The propagated

[1] These studies were aided by a research grant (B-24) from the National Institute of Neurological Diseases and Blindness, of the National Institutes of Health, U.S. Public Health Service; by a contract between the Office of Naval Research, Department of the Navy, and the Massachusetts Institute of Technology (NR-119-100); and by grants from the Trustees under the Wills of Charles A King and Marjorie King, and from Mr. Louis E. Marron.

action potential wave is considered by many to result from rapid changes in permeability of "the membrane" to K and Na on a background of differential ion distributions which depend ultimately on the ability of the fiber to "pump" these ions against an activity gradient. It is therefore necessary to examine the satellite cell investment of the axon, including the structure at the node, with the highest resolution of the electron microscope in order to determine whether the junctions of the satellite cells or perhaps their intraprotoplasmic membranes may provide aqueous channels through which solutes, including ions, may freely flow, thus bringing the extracellular fluid effectively to the axon surface membrane. Progress in the investigation of this point is accelerated with each advance in the resolution obtainable in electron micrographs of thin sections. The evidence presently available is summarized in this paper.

Whatever the eventual solution of the problem of the structural and functional relationship of the axon to the satellite cells, it seems clear that we are here dealing with very thin, interlamellar capillary systems whose physical chemical properties may not be immediately predictable from those of bulk solutions. The desirability of careful investigation of the physical and chemical properties of such systems is emphasized by the fact that current electron microscope investigations demonstrate that similar membranous structures are characteristic not merely of nerves but of cells and tissues generally.

THE CONCEPT OF MYELINATION
THE ROLE OF THE SATELLITE CELLS AND THEIR PERIAXONAL LIPID-PROTEIN LAMELLAR SYSTEMS

Few subjects in the history of neurology have been more confused with respect to terminology and conceptualization than that of myelination, i.e., the nature of myelin, the criteria by which certain fibers are called myelinated (or medullated) while others are called unmyelinated (or unmedullated), and the morphogenesis and physiological role of myelination. The term myelin, applied first by Virchow [57], was unfortunate: like its German equivalent "Mark", it implied a marrow, i.e. a centrally located material. Although this may have been applicable in the macroscopic sense to the lipid-rich white substance in the brain, the lipid-rich material is, of course, cortical rather than medullary in individual nerve fibers. A chemical connotation soon became implicit also, because Virchow discovered the myelin by observing the tubular, contorted forms which issued from nerves and other tissues after they had been cut or macerated in water. Myelin forms,[1] which could readily be made by wetting various types of lipids, were later carefully studied as examples of the newly discovered mesomorphic or paracrystalline state [28, 29, 16, 32].

The discovery by Max Schultze and Ranvier that the myelin sheath is blackened by OsO_4 caused histologists of the time to consider this property a criterion for the presence of myelin. This led to drawing sharp distinctions between myelinated and unmyelinated fibers.[2] Another criterion was of course the presence or absence of nodes of Ranvier and of the Schmidt–Lanterman incisures. Although the able neurohistologists of the time were fully aware of the presence of the Schwann cell investments and had described them carefully, even in Remak fibers, the so-called unmyelinated fibers, particularly in the invertebrates, came to be considered by physiologists as essentially naked axons. Since such supposedly naked axons conduct impulses the surface membrane of the axon, as the "excitable membrane", was made to bear the full responsibility for the processes underlying impulse propagation. Thus is illustrated how histological concepts have in the past been used (or misused) as guides to physiological thinking; a detailed investigation of the chemistry and ultrastructure of nerve is even more vital today in providing a satisfactory basis for biophysical and biochemical studies of nerve function.

In the further evolution of our knowledge of myelination, micromanipulation experiments [37] and time lapse photomicrography of regenerating fibers [51] gave important information. These studies emphasized the apparent fluidity of myelin, the close organic adhesion of the myelin to the axon and the probability that in the laying down of myelin both the axon and the Schwann sheath cells are cooperatively involved.

Particularly valuable were the polarization optical and X-ray diffraction studies of myelin organization. It had been concluded [42] that the myelin behaves as though it were composed of alternating layers of lipid, with long axes radial in the sheath, and proteins with long axes tangential. Quantitative studies of Schmitt and Bear [45] suggested that, so far as ultrastructure is concerned, the transition from heavily myelinated to unmyelinated is continuous rather than abrupt and discontinuous as had been supposed from the supposition that, at diameters below 2 μ, fibers are unmyelinated

---

[1] "Myelin forms" connote a general type of ultrastructure characteristic of hydrophilic lipids when treated with water and should not be confused with forms of nerve myelin although there is close similarity in the ultrastructure of the two.

[2] Göthlin [26] commented on the inappropriateness of the terms "myelinated" and "unmyelinated" and suggested that in their place the terms "light or dark rimmed" ("randig") be used.

(see [9]). The chief variable in determining the net birefringence is the ratio in amount of radially oriented lipid to tangentially oriented protein.

Examination of invertebrate nerves, long considered to be unmyelinated, proved very profitable. These experiments hark back to the trail-blazing work of Göthlin [26] whose paper is of classical importance. Various kinds of unmyelinated nerves, vertebrate and invertebrate, had been studied in polarized light since the earliest work by Valentin [55, 56] and v. Ebner [10]. However, the almost simultaneous appearance of the papers by Apathy [2], Friedländer [17] and Ambronn [1] supported the view that the sheaths of these fibers have an ultrastructure qualitatively similar to that of myelinated fibers. These studies provided a basis for the more definitive work of Göthlin. When it is realized that these investigations were done before the discovery of form birefringence [58] one cannot but be impressed with the acuity of the investigators.

On the basis of their optical properties Göthlin divided nerve fibers into the following types.

Myelotropic.—In these the lipid-dependent birefringence (i.e., positive with respect to the radial optic axis) preponderates over the protein-dependent birefringence (i.e. negative with respect to the optic axis) both in serum and in glycerine (i.e. the birefingence is independent of the refractive index of the medium). Myelotropic fibers occur in the peripheral fibers of vertebrates and in certain shrimps and nerve cords of some annelids.

Metatropic.—In these the lipid-dependent birefringence is much weaker than in myelotropic fibers and can be elicited by immersion in glycerine. Most invertebrate fibers belong in this class.

Proteotropic.—In these only the protein-dependent type of birefringence can be observed even after immersion in glycerine. Examples are Remak fibers and certain invertebrate fibers.

Atropic.—No birefringence of any kind can be demonstrated in these, possibly because the small size makes detection difficult or because protein- and lipid-dependent types of birefringence balance each other out. Many invertebrate fibers belong in this class.

By a re-interpretation of Göthlin's data, Bear and Schmitt [4] proposed that metatropic fibers have the same kind of lipid-protein ultrastructure as do myclotropic fibers; the difference is primarily in the ratio of the oriented lipid and protein components. Thus a basic similarity exists in the molecular organization of all fibers, myelinated and unmyelinated, vertebrate and in-vertebrate [46]. This was paraphrased as "all nerve fibers are to some extent myelinated".

Such concepts made myelin even more ambiguous, for if a myelinated fiber is one possessing a lipid-containing sheath, then all fibers would qualify because in the last analysis the surface film of any fiber probably contains at least a bimolecular leaflet of lipid or "myelin". On the other hand, if the presence of nodes of Ranvier is a criterion, then clearly many fibers, particularly in invertebrates, are unmyelinated. This distinction is the one in current usage, particularly among neurophysiologists (some of whom have in recent years been studying the special properties of the node).

The thread of the myelin story continues with electron microscopy. Polarization optical analysis had indicated that the oriented lipid-protein system responsible for the metatropic effect was a "sheath" which lay immediately external to the Schwann cell and inside the connective tissue investment [5]. However, electron microscope studies of the squid giant fiber revealed no sheath in this location but instead emphasized the possible significance of dense osmiophilic double-edged layers seen to course through the Schwann cell preponderantly in planes parallel to the fiber surface [24, 25]. On the assumption that these layers contain lipid and protein molecules oriented as in the myelin sheath, it could be demonstrated that they might well account qualitatively and quantitatively for the metatropic effect. The myelin-like material would then have to be *inside* the Schwann cell rather than external to it. Such a situation was consistent with the important concept of the origin of myelin proposed by Geren [21] at about the same time. According to her hypothesis the myelin layers, predicted to exist from small-angle X-ray diffraction data and directly visualized by electron microscopy, are not strictly concentric as was previously supposed but are in fact spirally wrapped about the axon. The membranes form by an infolding of the outer plasma membrane of the Schwann cell, thus explaining the requirement of the X-ray data that the unit repeating layer contains *two* rather than one bimolecular lipid leaflet.

These advances not only explain myelin structurally and chemically and localize it properly in relation to the Schwann cell but also make possible a generalization far more significant for nerve theory than the original concept of myelination, as will now be briefly outlined.

From Geren's hypothesis, now confirmed by many investigators, myelin is composed primarily of the substance of the Schwann cell plasma membrane. Besides a bimolecular leaflet of mixed lipids, this includes a thin layer, probably protein in nature, on the inner and possibly also on the outer side of the membrane. It is the entire plasma membrane that infolds and gets wrapped around the axon. It is possible that minor changes in the content and packing of the molecules in the layers occur as the spirally wrapped layers become condensed by the expulsion of Schwann cell cytoplasm from between the layers.

It has thus become clear that the axons of all fibers, heavily myelinated A fibers, "unmyelinated" C fibers and invertebrate fibers alike, are enclosed to widely varying extents by periaxonal membranes (of "myelin") and that these membranes are components of the Schwann cells with which all peripheral nerve fibers are intimately associated. For purposes of simplification and without commitment regarding any chemical, structural and physiological differences which may be demonstrated to exist between central and peripheral fibers, we may refer to the periaxonal cells simply as "satellite" cells.

The generalization which thus emerges to replace the confusing concept and terminology of myelin is that *all nerve fibers are enclosed by satellite cells which possess lipid-protein membranes in varying amounts and types of structural and biochemical differentiation.* The membranes are parts of metabolically active satellite cells which enclose the axon and, in the microscopic if not in the molecular sense, separate the axon from extracellular space. By shifting the emphasis from the partial system, i.e. the membranes (or myelin layers), to the system as a whole, i.e. the entire population of satellite cells upon an axon and their relation to the axon and to each other, the above concept opens up new vistas of biophysical and biochemical research that may greatly advance our understanding of nerve function.

STRUCTURAL RELATIONS BETWEEN AXON AND SATELLITE CELLS

It will be profitable to examine the structural relations between axon and satellite cells in the three distinctive fiber types which have thus far been examined in some detail. These will be listed according to Göthlin's classification, as previously defined, thereby avoiding use of words like myelinated and unmyelinated in the present context.

Myelotropic fibers

The classical histologists described the Schwann cell layer as completely enclosing the axon even at the nodes. Nageotte [31], whose study of nodal structure was particularly penetrating, believed that the Schwann cells form a syncytium over the nodes. Cajal [7] on the other hand considered the Schwann cells to be in apposition but unfused at the node and to form a fenestrated membrane about the axon. The more recent studies of the Hortega school, of Tello [53] and De Castro [8] are in general agreement in favoring the view that Schwann cell sheath covers the entire axon; however even at the limit of resolution of the light microscope, it might be impossible to prove that cells are not merely in intimate contact rather than in syncytial relationship.

Electron microscopy has revealed some of the details of structure in myelotropic fibers but it must be admitted that only a beginning has been made in this study. The inner Schwann cell membrane is closely applied upon the axon membrane and is continuous under the incisures. The region of the incisure is subject to great distortions during removal and fixation of the fiber and also by manipulation when the nerve is subjected to electrophysiological study. Luxoro [30] observed that, at the edges of the incisure, the double membranes turn acutely outward, i.e. radially, joining the condensed layered system at some distance radially on the other side of the incisure. The incisure is thus not an aqueous channel through which ions may freely diffuse. Rather it is bridged over by many, possibly most, of the myelin layers forming a diffusion barrier probably little different from that through the bulk of the myelin. Being only about 150 Å thick these layers could, of course, not be seen with the light microscope except where they had been caused to aggregate by the preparative technique.

At the node the myelin layers were seen by Hess and Lansing [27], by Luxoro [30] and by Robertson [40, 41] to turn inwards peeling away from each other, describing an arc of a half circle and ending individually upon the axon membrane. In fresh fibers Göthlin [26] observed that, where the myelin bends in at the nodes, the interference colors change so as to form half, or a little more, of a positive polarization cross. This is consistent with the electron microscope finding because the myelin layers, which contribute positivity with respect to directions perpendicular to the planes of their surfaces, describe a similar circular course. It may be noted in passing that one reason why polarization optical studies of the thin membrane structure at the node in fresh fibers have not been made is that the relatively strong interference of the inturning myelin near the node reduces contrast in the nodal region.

At the ends of the infolded myelin layers where they are applied on the inner membrane Luxoro and Robertson observed small pockets or sacs representing the separation of the individual membranes at the ends of the folds.

The detailed structure at the node is not yet sufficiently understood to provide definitive answers to crucial questions about membrane structure and diffusion pathways from axoplasm to extracellular space in the nodal region. Many investigators are now turning their attention to this important problem and important advances may soon be expected. However, at the time of writing the situation may be briefly summarized as follows.

Gasser [18] found the protoplasm of the Schwann cell to be continuous over the node. The mitochondria of the Schwann cell cytoplasm are densely packed in the region of the node. Luxoro [30] also described the outer Schwann cell membrane as extending across the node. The Schwann cell protoplasm was found to be relatively dense due to a concentration of contorted membranes and to profiles of vacuoles or cisternae, possibly corresponding to intracytoplasmic membranes ("endoplasmic reticulum"). He could not determine whether adjacent Schwann cells actually fuse over the node to form a syncytium or merely have their membranes in close apposition. Robertson [40] described the nodal region in frog fibers as being fairly completely invaded by slender protuberances from the Schwann cells on either side of the node. Some of these outpocketings are closely applied upon the axon membrane while others extend like fingers across the nodal region. According to this view the Schwann cells do not extend completely across the node but leave small capillary spaces of communication between the axon membrane and extracellular space. Uzman and Noqueira-Graf [54] studied the formation of the node during early development in the chick sciatic fibers. They found the Schwann cells firmly adherent to the axon membrane but separated from each other by short distances. As development proceeds the Schwann cells become closely adherent to each other. It may be said in passing that all electron microscope observations on the myelin sheath and the node are in good agreement with Geren's membrane theory of myelin structure.

The axon has been described as showing certain structural differentiations at the node. Luxoro observed outpocketings from the axon into the Schwann cell at this region. He also observed certain small oval bodies differing in internal structure from most particulates so far described and appearing chiefly in the nodal axoplasm. Robertson observed certain small vesicles in nodal axoplasm which he suspected to be differentiation products of axon filaments.

Metatropic fibers

As examples of this class we shall consider briefly the structure of the squid giant fiber and the fibers of the nerves of the walking leg of the lobster.

Contrasted with the very large diameter of the giant fiber (500 μ) the thickness of the Schwann cells is very small (about 1 μ except at the region of the nucleus). The volume of the Schwann cell layer is thus less than one per cent of the volume of the axon. The relative number of Schwann cells, their distribution and average area in the sheath has not been systematically studied. It is not unusual however to observe two and sometimes three sheath cell nuclei in a single histological section. So far as is known the axon is completely covered by the Schwann cell layer.

From Geren and Schmitt's [24, 25] electron microscope study of the squid giant fiber the following points are pertinent. The axon–Schwann cell boundary is seen as a dense double-edged structure representing the individual limiting envelopes. The outer surface of the Schwann cell facing the connective tissue is bounded by a relatively thick amorphous basement membrane. In addition to the usual particulates, the Schwann cell cytoplasm is seen to contain a number (usually three to six) of dense osmiophilic double edged membranes coursing predominantly in planes parallel to the fiber axis. Infoldings of the Schwann cell membrane occur, both on the side of the axon and of the basement membrane, continuous with the intraprotoplasmic system of layers. From data presently available it is impossible to state whether these respresent the boundaries of adjacent Schwann cells or infoldings of the surface membrane such as have been observed in many types of metabolically active cells, or may perhaps be comparable to the intracytoplasmic layered system ("endoplasmic reticulum" of Porter and Palade). The dense double-edged layers are 150 to 250 Å thick. Thus, together with the limiting membranes of axon and Schwann cell, they are thought to be responsible for the metatropic polarization optical effect. It was suggested that in sea water the negative lamellar form birefringence of the osmiophilic layers overbalances the positive intrinsic birefringence of the oriented lipid molecules in the layers; immersion of the fibers in media of higher refractive index (e.g. glycerinated sea water) reduces the form birefringence and brings out the lipid contribution.

The Schwann cells of lobster fibers are very thin (order of 0.1 μ) and the axon surface is very contorted [24, 25]. The axon is everywhere covered by the Schwann cells, the interface being seen as a dense double-edged structure. Dense membranes are much rarer than in the case of squid fibers and may represent primarily boundaries between adjacent Schwann cells rather than infoldings or intracytoplasmic layers. However, more detailed studies are needed on this point.

The axon interface of the Schwann cell frequently invaginates into the axon forming structures varying from small indentations to relatively large ovoid structures which are occasionally seen to be constricted at the Schwann cell surface to form particulates resembling mitochondria in internal structure. Other ovoid particulates which are very probably mitochondria are seen clustered in the axoplasm immediately under the axon–Schwann cell surface, the axis of the ovoids being normal to the surface membrane. It is possible that these may have had their origin from the Schwann cell as indicated above. The concentration of mitochondria at the Schwann cell surface suggested that energy utilization may occur there.

Atropic or proteotropic fibers

As examples of this type we shall consider briefly the vertebrate C fibers. Early workers in polarization optics had found these to be weakly proteotropic although myelin-like lipid could be extracted from them. Göthlin [26] found Remak fibers slightly negative (with respect to the radial direction) after immersion in glycerine. The amount of oriented lipid present in these fibers is apparently too small to overbalance the form birefringence of the protein components (which include the fibrous proteins of the axon and adhering collagen fibrils as well as that associated with the lipids in membranes).

In the C fibers the Schwann cells were considered by Nageotte to be syncytial, forming anastomosing tubes; whether the cells are in fact syncytial has not yet been clearly shown by electron microscopy. As described by Gasser [18, 19, 20] the C fibers travel in the Schwann tubes; each axon itself only 0.1 to 0.5 μ in diameter, is enfolded in Schwann cell membrane. The relationship resembles that shown by Geren [21] to characterize the first stage of myelination; the axon, enfolded by Schwann cell membrane is still connected to the external surface by the infolded double Schwann cell plasma membrane. Frequently the axons lie deep within the Schwann cell protoplasm and are then suspended in a fairly long double membrane. Gasser terms this infolded region of the Schwann cell the "mesaxon" while Robertson [39] refers to it as the "surface connecting membrane".

Gasser pointed out that the axons are enfolded in the Schwann cell membrane, the outer surface of which is in contact with the axon membrane. He concluded that the axon is therefore really external to the Schwann cell, i.e. in contact with extracellular space through the aqueous phase of the "mesaxon".

Very recently Robertson [41] in very high resolution electron micrographs, found both the axon membrane of the C fibers and the infolded plasma membrane of the Schwann cell to be double edged, the overall thickness of each double-edged membrane being about 75 Å. He concluded that these represent individual membranes each containing a double layer of mixed lipids and another substance, probably protein. This leaves a space of about 150 Å between the two double-edged structures which Robertson supposes to be filled with aqueous material presumably continuous with the ground substances of the connective tissue. Until the various factors involved in the production of such structures have been fully evaluated it would perhaps be best to withhold judgement as to the extent to which the structure represents the situation in the fresh state.

POSSIBLE PATHWAYS OF DIFFUSION OF SOLUTES BETWEEN AXON AND EXTRACELLULAR PHASE

Since the axon seemingly is everywhere enclosed by satellite cells, it becomes important to examine carefully the nature of the aqueous pathways between the axon membrane and truly extracellular space through which ions and other solutes may pass, at rest and during the propagation of the impulse. We shall want most carefully to define the situation in the nerve type in which it seems most certain that the axon membrane is everywhere covered over by satellite cells. Probably the best choice for this would be the types which were previously considered unmyelinated (and therefore supposedly exposing a bare axon surface) but which now are seen to be completely enclosed by satellite cells. These include many types of invertebrate fibers and vertebrate C fibers. Particular emphasis should perhaps be placed on the squid giant fiber because of the detailed electrophysiological data which have been collected for this form.

In order to bring the problem to a focus let us examine, as nearly as possible at the molecular level, the various possibilities which might be considered the situation prevailing in the three major fiber types previously discussed. These possibilities are illustrated diagrammatically in Fig. 1 and may be characterized as follows:

(1) The bare axon surface membrane is exposed to bulk extracellular phase, i.e. there are substantial gaps between satellite cells, leaving the axon fully exposed to extracellular fluid at these places (Fig. 1 a). This is the type of structure which has been tacitly assumed by neurophysiologists, especially in relation to electrical polarization and changes which occur with excitation.

(2) The axon is completely covered over by satellite cells but between the axon and satellite cell membranes, between adjacent satellite cells and possibly within the satellite cell protoplasm there are aqueous channels whose widths are large compared with ionic diameters and through which

ions may diffuse as through bulk solution. These channels are of the order
of 150–250 Å thick; they constitute merely *passive* diffusion barriers to ions
passing between axon and extracellular phase (Fig. 1 *b*).

(3) The same as (2) except that *active* biochemical interchange occurs
between diffusible solutes and the cells between which or through which the
channels extend. The channels could be located between axon and satellite
cells, between satellite cells or through the protoplasm of the satellite cells
(Fig. 1 *c*).

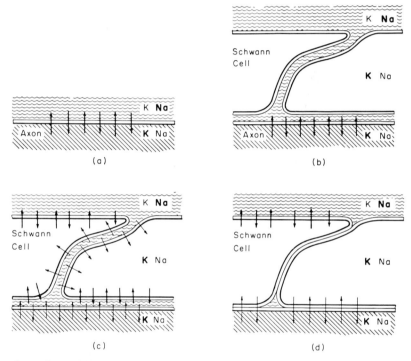

Fig. 1.—Several possible pathways for diffusion of solutes between axoplasm and extracellular fluid. K and Na concentration gradients shown by boldness of type. Active diffusion of
solutes and metabolites across membranes indicated by arrows. (*a*) Bare axon membrane is exposed to bulk extracellular phase. (*b*) Axon membrane covered everywhere by satellite cells
but space between limiting membranes of axon and satellite cells, between satellite cells and
possibly between the intracytoplasmic membranes within satellite cells is of the order of 150–200 Å
thick and is filled with extracellular fluid. Active interchange occurs only between axon membrane
and extracellular fluid immediately surrounding it; passive diffusion occurs in other channels
extracellular fluid immediately surrounding it; passive diffusion occurs in other channels and
satellite cell plays role chiefly as diffusion barrier. (*c*) Same as (*b*) except that active interchange
of metabolites and solutes occurs at all membrane surfaces; in this case satellite cell may participate actively in processes involving interchange between axon and extracellular phase. (*d*) Satellite cells and axon are essentially in molecular contact, leaving only very thin (12–15 Å) layers
of water between membranes, comparable to situation in compact myelin; interchange between
axon and extracellular phase occurs primarily through protoplasm of satellite cells.

(4) The same as (3) except that the aqueous layers are so thin (order of 10–20 Å) that they represent chiefly the solvate layers of the hydrophilic surfaces of adjacent membranes rather than channels through which fluid might flow. In this case transport of diffusible solutes between axoplasm and extracellular space would occur primarily through satellite cell protoplasm and across both satellite cell membranes (Fig. 1 *d*).

Before discussing the individual fiber types it will be perhaps desirable to indicate why these particular models of aqueous layers were chosen.

Fig. 1 *a* is obvious; it represents the hypothetical case where the axon is exposed either in highly restricted regions (nodes?) or over larger extents to frankly extracellular fluid.

Figs. 1 *b* and *c*, reflect the fact that electron microscopists have, with increasing frequency, reported that membrane separations of the order of 200 Å are found by them between free cell surfaces, between synaptic membranes and between infolded cell membranes.

Fig. 1 *d* reflects the small-angle X-ray diffraction analysis of nerve myelin, which is the only case in which it is possible to compare spaces observed in thin sections in the electron microscope with the same spaces as demonstrated in the fresh, unfixed material by small-angle X-ray diffraction.

From the data of Schmitt, Bear and Clark [47] and of Schmitt, Bear and Palmer [48] it was concluded that 25–30 Å of water exists in the 171 Å repeating layers of the myelin sheath in the radial direction. Since there are two aqueous interfaces in the repeating distance, there would be 12–15 Å of water at each if the water is equally distributed. This water probably is coordinated upon the thin protein layer which is thought to exist at the aqueous surface of each bimolecular leaflet of mixed lipid.

Similar data for the water layers were deduced by Finean [12, 13], Finean and Millington [14], and Fernández-Morán and Finean [11], who have made further detailed X-ray studies of nerve myelin structure and who have compared the spacings found from X-ray data with those seen in the electron microscope. From this work it is clear that fixation and subsequent preparation for electron microscopy reduce the apparent repeating period thickness. However their data confirm that, in the case of the nerve myelin, the aqueous channels are only 12–15 Å thick.

The infolding Schwann cell membrane forming the myelin is shown diagrammatically in Fig. 2. In this case there can be no doubt that, whatever the situation may be at the point of membrane infolding or in the mesaxon region, where the layers join the compact myelin, the water layers are definitely only 12–15 Å and not 150–200 Å thick in the compact myelin.

More recently Finean and Millington [14] found that exposure of frog nerves to hypotonic solutions may increase the radial repeating distance by as much as 75–100 Å due presumably to the intercalation of large amounts of water between one or both aqueous interfaces in the myelin. However this is a highly abnormal situation resulting from exposure to highly hypotonic solutions.

FORMATION OF MYELIN

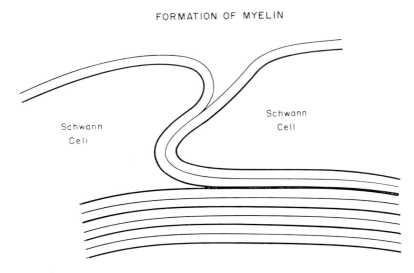

Fig. 2.—Infolding of Schwann cell membranes to form compact myelin after theory of Geren [21]. Inner surface of Schwann cell membrane different than outer surface leading to "difference factor" of Finean and 171 Å for full repeat distance as predicted by X-ray evidence of Schmitt, Bear and Palmer [48].

The X-ray data also indicate that the total protein in the repeating layers is about 25–30 Å or only about 12–15 Å per aqueous interface. This would seem to require that the proteins be present as monolayers. From the Geren [21] theory of the origin of the myelin layers it would be expected that the protein (i.e. non-lipid) material on the inside of the infolding Schwann cell membrane may be different than that on the outside.

In early electron microscope studies of nerve myelin the repeating layers were seen as one dark and one light band per fundamental repeating distance in the radial direction. The X-ray evidence clearly indicates that the light region must have represented primarily the hydrocarbon chains of the bimolecular leaflets of mixed lipids (together with the steroids, of course). With subsequent technical improvements it became possible to demonstrate also thin dense lines alternating with the heavy dense lines, corresponding to Finean's "difference factor" and representing the outer surface of the infolding Schwann cell membrane. This evidence supports the view that it is primarily the protein which reacts with the osmium tetroxide to produce relatively dense regions. Even though subsequent technical improvements were to show either one of the two types of dense lines in the myelin layers as doublets, this would have no effect upon the total thickness of the water

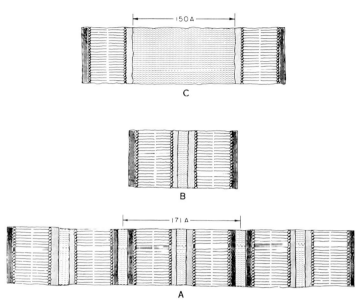

Fig. 3.—Possible molecular organization of membranes. *A*, Compact myelin structure. Bimolecular leaflets of mixed lipids bounded by very thin, possibly monolayer of "protein" on either side (different on one side than on the other) and separated by solvate layers having thickness of 12–15 Å. *B*, Structure at axon-satellite cell boundary or between satellite cells on assumption that they are in the same kind of molecular contact as are the layers in compact myelin. *C*, Molecular organization of membranes if satellite cells are not in molecular contact as in compact myelin but are separated by relatively thick (150–200 Å) aqueous layers. In this case factors must operate which prevent the close "molecular" adhesion of apposed membranes such as characterize the infolded Schwann cell membranes which form myelin; nature of such possible "long range" factors unknown at present.

(25–30 Å) in the total radial repeat distance or probably in the individual aqueous layers (12–15 Å).

In Fig. 3 are shown: in *A* the present concept of myelin structure; in *B* the nature of the aqueous space between adjacent membranes (axon–satellite cell, satellite cell–satellite cell or between infolded membranes of satellite cells) if these membranes were as compactly organized as in myelin structure; and in *C* the same if there were a space of 150–200 Å between the membranes, which presumably is filled with highly aqueous material; possibly continuous with connective tissue (extracellular fluid).

We may now consider which of the structures shown in Figs. 2 and 3 apply to the three types of fibers.

Myelotropic fibers

As representative of this category we shall discuss only the typical verte-brate A fiber. The invertebrate myelotropic fibers present features which would be very interesting in the present context, particularly the heavily myelinated fibers of the central nervous system of the prawns and shrimps in which nuclei occur on the axon side of the myelin and which early workers claimed showed periodic narrowing of the myelin but no true nodes. Un-fortunately too little information is at hand about these types to warrant inclusion here.

In our examination of possible pathways of interchange between axoplasm and extracellular fluid we may best begin at the outer surface of the axon membrane (axolemma). As shown by Geren [21], Robertson [39] and by all others who have examined the matter, the inner layer of the Schwann cell is closely adherent to the axon membrane throughout the internodal region. This is true also at the incisures, which are traversed by the helical layers where they may appear to jog a bit radially before continuing in the compact myelin, and hence do not constitute channels for solute diffusion from axon membrane to extracellular fluid [30]. Whether the axon–satellite cell interface, thus far characterized as two dense lines separated by a light space, will eventually be resolved as two double dense lines, leaving a sizeable distance (150–200 Å) between the two membranes which may repre-sent an aqueous channel remains to be seen. Present evidence suggests that the two membranes are in close, possibly molecular contact.

The structure at the node is unfortunately too poorly known at the present time to warrant extensive discussion much less to draw conclusions con-cerning diffusion pathways at this crucial region of the excitatory mechanism. The earlier electron microscope results already referred to, done on relatively thick sections and not at the highest resolution, suggested continuity of Schwann cells over the node without clear determination of whether the cells were joined in a true syncytium or were merely in close apposition at their boundaries. Robertson [40], in a preliminary note containing only a diagram, pictures an interdigitation of processes from adjacent Schwann cells which overarch the node and come to be applied upon the axon membrane in the nodal region. Until the details of this structure are published it will be impossible to determine whether the distances between adjacent Schwann cell processes are large with respect to molecular size, and whether in this case at least a fraction of the axon membrane at the node is exposed directly to extracellular fluid.

Metatropic fibers

Considering invertebrate peripheral fibers, such as the giant fiber of the squid or the lobster leg nerve as typical of this category, it may be said that, since in these cases the axon membrane is clearly everywhere covered by satellite cells, possibility *a* of Fig. 1 (i.e. axon membrane is directly exposed to the extracellular fluid) may be excluded from consideration. The problem then resolves itself into determining whether or not the distance between membranes (between axon–satellite cells, between adjacent satellite cells or between intracytoplasmic membranes) is sufficient to permit free diffusion of solutes and represents truly extracellular fluid. Micrographs of sufficiently high resolution from very thin sections have not yet been published to resolve this question. However, at this juncture the following points seem pertinent.

In a previous discussion of the interpretation of the membrane structure in the sheath of the squid giant fiber [44, 49] it was suggested that the relation between axon and satellite cells, between satellite cells and between intra-cytoplasmic membranes is similar to that between the helical layers in the myelin sheath (Fig. 1 *d*). The light space between the fairly diffuse dark bands would in that case correspond to the paraffin chains of lipid molecules rather than to aqueous "channels" several hundred Ångström units thick between the membranes. This would almost certainly be the situation if the adhesion between the respective membranes, particularly those of adjacent Schwann cells, is similar to that between helically wrapped myelin layers (which are themselves adherent pairs of Schwann cell membranes); the structure would then be that deducible by analogy from the X-ray analysis of myelin.

However what information is available suggests that the adhesion between the limiting membranes of cells may vary considerably from one cell type to another and in particular types under varying physiological conditions.[1] Such differences may be manifested in electron micrographs by variation in the space, presumably filled in life by an aqueous material, between the

---

[1] A large change in the solvation or intermembrane water content was visualized as accompanying heightened attractive interaction responsible for certain morphogenetic differentiation [43].

thin dense lines representing the boundaries of adjacent membranes. There remains the question, considered below, of the extent to which such aqueous spaces are faithfully preserved in the electron microscopic technique.

If for the purpose of discussion it be assumed that future high resolution work will show each of the edges of apposed membrane pairs as double, with large (150–250 Å) light spaces between them, the situation would be as pictured in b and c of Fig. 1.

In b the channels are shown as passive diffusion barriers between the axon membrane and extracellular fluid, a possibility suggested by Franken-haeuser and Hodgkin [15] to explain the time constants for diffusion of K required in their experiments. In this case the "channels" are assumed to be filled with extracellular fluid. The site of electrical polarization and of differences of ion patterns is then at the axon membrane. It should be pointed out that in this case a channel of the same sort as is assumed to pass between the satellite cells also exists between the satellite cells and the axon membrane and to pass through the protoplasm of the satellite cells. On this hypothesis of passive diffusion channels one must be able to account not only for the efflux of K during excitation but also for the influx of Na presumably through the same thin channels.

In Fig. 1 c, an active metabolic interchange is postulated between the fluid in the aqueous channels and the cellular material through which the channels extend. Such an exchange would of course also be related to the mechanism by which energy is made available to "pump" ions against an activity gradient.

Considerations similar to the above are thought to apply to lobster fibers except that the satellite cell layer is considerably thinner (order of 1000 Å) and membranes seen to traverse the satellite cell layer are much rarer than in squid. In addition there is the highly contorted nature of the inner surface of the satellite cell layer and its apparent relationship to the axoplasmic particulates.

Atropic or proteotropic fibers

Illustrative of this type is the mammalian C fiber. Suspended to a variable extent below the surface of the Schwann cell in a fold of the latter's plasma membrane (Gasser's "mesaxon", Robertson's "surface connecting membrane"), the situation with respect to the degree of membrane separation, i.e. thickness of water channels between axon surface membrane and Schwann cell membrane is similar to that in invertebrate nerve discussed above. The analysis of intermembrane aqueous channels was also similar, i.e. the situation was likened to that of the infolding Schwann cell membrane of the vertebrate A fiber and the compact layered structure of myelin. In this case the water layers between the infolded "mesaxon" membranes would be only 12–15 Å, in analogy to myelin structure. During preparation of this paper Robertson kindly communicated the results of his most recent studies of mammalian C fibers and permitted quotation of his results in the

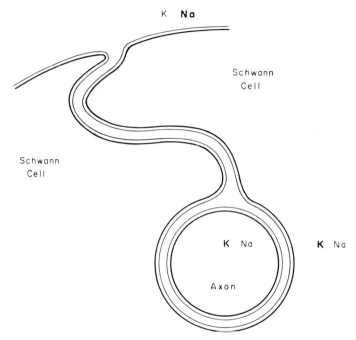

Fig. 4.—Axon–satellite cell relationship in C fiber on assumption of relatively thick (150–200 Å) water layers between membranes. After Robertson [41].

text of this paper. In these electron micrographs Robertson [41] clearly resolved each dark line (representing the axon surface membrane and the limiting membrane of the Schwann cell) into two fine lines (total thickness about 75 Å) which he thinks define the true membranes. The intervening 150 Å of light space between pairs of dark lines he considers may be an aqueous channel filled with extracellular material, continuous with the ground substance of the connective tissue (see diagrammatic representation in Fig. 4). This would be consistent with Gasser's interpretation that the C fiber lies "outside" the Schwann cell.

In passing it may be noted that, despite the small diameter of the Remak fiber and the fact that half a dozen or more C fibers may course through a given Schwann syncytium, the axons are of such small diameter that the ratio of Schwann protoplasm to axoplasm is high; in metatropic fibers on the other hand it is low (order ot one per cent or less) while in myelotropic fibers exclusive of the myelin itself, it may also be quite low.

Importance of artifacts of preparative techniques.—Because at the level of structure now under discussion we are dealing with matters which are of fundamental physiological as well as morphological significance, it is necessary to examine as critically as possible the degree to which the structure observed may actually exist in the fresh functioning fiber and to what extent they are artifacts of fixation, dehydration, embedding, sectioning and examination in the beam of he electron microscope.

There is actually very little factual knowledge on which to make such an analysis except the X-ray data on the myelin layers which, however, may be very much more condensed than the cellular membranes under discussion. The data of Bahr, Bloom and Friberg [3] may be pertinent. In these experiments shrinkage was observed to result from fixation. The authors point out, however, that what is observed in the bulk tissue may not apply to individual components (such as our membranes). One might suppose that, if anything, fixation, dehydration, etc. would result in an overall shrinkage and that therefore the distance between membranes in life might be even more than that seen in the electron micrographs. However, Bahr *et al.* point out that even when fixation occurs in hypertonic solutions there is swelling of the bulk tissue. It is not inconceivable that fixation may cause an abnormal distribution of water between cells and extracellular fluid and that the membranous structures are fixed, e.g. stabilized through combination with the fixative, in the abnormal condition. If, for example, the osmotic pressure of the space immediately surrounding the cell is not identical with that inside the cell (a situation not inconceivable in the steady state of a metabolically very active cell) then at the moment of fixation water might enter quickly the extracellular space if that region were hypertonic in the steady state or leave it if it were hypotonic. If fixation and electron microscope techniques then faithfully preserved the structure, the space between the axon membrane and satellite cell membranes would be correspondingly greater or less than was the case at the moment of fixation. There are as yet no data on which to evaluate the possible significance of such osmotic factors.

It is noteworthy in this connection that in all the published electron micrographs of such membrane systems (C fibers, synaptic junctions) the lines representing the edges of the apposed membranes run a strictly parallel course despite the fact that, as in the case of the C fiber deeply embedded in the Schwann cell, the course of the lines may be quite tortuous. One might have supposed that in fixation or in dehydration, removal of water would have caused collapse of the surfaces which, at least over part of their extent, would not have been fully replaced by embedding plastic. Satisfactory assessment of these factors must await the results of systematic studies designed specifically to provide answers to the problems posed.

PROPERTIES OF INTERMEMBRANE CAPILLARY SYSTEMS

The factors which determine the equilibrium separation in simple diphasic systems between charged layers of substances such as soaps have been fairly extensively studied although no satisfactory theoretical treatment has thus far been devised [52, 6]. The lipid-protein membranes with which we are here dealing represent a similar system in which a substantial fraction of the lipid groups presented at the aqueous interface may be electrically charged (negative phosphate oxygen atoms, positive nitrogen atoms of the quaternary ammonium residues). The charge density on the layers is an important factor in determining the separation between bimolecular leaflets, hence the water thickness between layers. The ionic strength is also important as was shown in the case of nerve lipids in aqueous dispersions by Palmer and Schmitt [48]; the presence of ions causes the water to be expelled from between the lipid double layers.

The nerve axon surface with which we are dealing is one at which ion movements are thought to occur. Changes in ion concentrations in the inter-membrane space between axon surface membrane and satellite cell membrane might be expected to change the thickness of the aqueous layer. This factor would gain in importance if, as depicted in Fig. 1 c, the aqueous layer is not a passive diffusion barrier but is a region of active interchange of metabolites from axon and satellite cells. The degree to which such changes may occur in the physiological range of conditions cannot at present be tested directly because the methods needed probably would themselves produce much larger changes.

Properties such as pH and ionic strength in such very thin capillary spaces differ markedly from customary concepts based on the properties of bulk solutions. Thus a solution that is isotonic with cells (say 0.1 M) would contain one molecule of solute or ion in a volume equal to that of a cube with an edge length of about 25 Å. Nor is it possible offhand to predict whether ions would be freely diffusible in such capillary spaces even if the aqueous layers are 150 Å thick. Interest in thin layered systems in cells is growing considerably with the discovery that this is a fairly common structural device. Examples are: (1) the intracytoplasmic lamellar system ("endoplasmic reticulum") which has been found to be widely distributed in cells and to be involved in various biosynthetic and other physiological activities [50, 33, 35, 36]. (2) The tendency for the plasma membrane to fold upon itself to form invaginations deep into the cytoplasm of the cell, frequently in association with mitochondria; this type of structure is seen particularly well in metabolically active cells [34]. In systems such as these there is little doubt that active interchange occurs between substances in the interlamellar spaces and the protoplasm surrounding the spaces. It seems entirely possible therefore that active interchange may occur between axon and satellite cells, between adjacent satellite cells and within the cytoplasm of satellite cells through aqueous layers of the kind here under discussion (Fig. 1 c). To what extent such a metabolic interchange may influence the diffusion of ions such as K and Na between axoplasm and extracellular fluid or play a role in other physiological processes remains to be demonstrated.

BIOCHEMICAL PROPERTIES OF SATELLITE CELLS

The stability of the axon depends upon its relationship with the cell body whose biosynthetic and regulatory activities are presumably presided over by the nucleus. However, the axon may extend far from the cell body (to distances sometimes thousands of times the diameter of the cell) and it seems improbable that reliance would be placed entirely upon the cell body for the maintenance of regions so remote from the metabolic center. The important evolutionary advance from unicellular to large multicellular organisms, which require rapid communication over relatively large distances, may in fact have depended upon solving this problem. Because of the ubiquitous presence of satellite cells enclosing axons it seems reasonable to suppose that this was the solution to the problem, the satellite cells helping to provide local metabolic energy and perhaps also the type of energy coupling necessary for ion pumping.

Biochemical and metabolic studies of peripheral nerve seldom consider the role of the satellite cells but attribute the effects entirely to the axons or "fibers". It would in fact be difficult except by inductive biochemistry to assess this role in any fibers other than the giant fibers of the squid which are large enough to study the isolated components. Recently a technique was developed in this laboratory by which the giant fiber may be slit open longitudinally, the axoplasm removed by gentle washing with an appropriate solution and the remaining sheath studied biochemically. Only preliminary results have been obtained so far but these support the view that the satellite cells are metabolically and enzymatically active.

Such slit sheaths consume oxygen at a rate which is linear with time for at least several hours after removal of the axoplasm. The respiratory rate, calculated on the basis of non-collagenous protein, is of the same order as that of the intact fiber. The sheath cells also maintain their cellular pattern of high potassium, low sodium. Poisoning with azide or dinitrophenol inhibits oxidative metabolism and ability to maintain ion patterns.

Sheaths and extruded axoplasm of squid giant fibers were assayed for their enzymatic activity by Roberts *et al.* [38]. Analyzing some ten enzymes it was found that axoplasm is well supplied with kexokinase and with enzymes involves in the three major pathways which begin with glucose-6-phosphate. Because of its low isocitric dehydrogenase activity axoplasm is probably relatively deficient in the citric acid cycle despite the presence of substantial amounts of malic dehydrogenase and glutamic-aspartic transaminase (which probably indicate ready conversion of glutamate to aspartate with the liberation of CO_2). Lactic dehydrogenase activity is relatively low. From the ratio of the activity of various enzymes in the sheath cells (not all of which are satellite cells) to that of hexokinase activity in the sheath it would appear that the citric acid cycle may be more prominent in sheath cells than in axoplasm. Whether, as these results suggest, there is an enzymatic differentiation between sheath cells and axoplasm such as to lead to integrated interaction at the surface is not known.

It is interesting that, with few exceptions, the enzymes in axoplasm and sheath cells appear to be similar, at least insofar as pH optima are concerned, as those in rabbit brain; the general enzyme pattern and relative concentrations also resemble those in rabbit brain. The studies of enzyme distributions is being continued. Here again specific localization of enzymes and cycles within narrow submicroscopic areas may reveal important biochemical and physiological mechanisms.

SUMMARY

The concept of myelination, which has been the subject of much confusion with respect not only to nomenclature but also to the mechanism of the process and the role of the myelin in physiological function, is critically reviewed in the light of recent electron microscope studies.

The structural relationship between axon and satellite (Schwann) cells is examined in the case of fiber types having relatively large, intermediate and small amounts of myelin (myelotropic, metatropic and proteotropic types).

In the light of these results the possible pathways for diffusion of solutes between the axon surface membrane and truly extracellular phase are considered. The point is made that the physicochemical properties of solutions in such capillary spaces may depart widely from those in bulk solution.

Brief reference is also made to the metabolism of the satellite cells and the possible role of these cells in the maintenance of the axon and in its physiological functions.

REFERENCES

1. AMBRONN, H., *Ber. Säch. Ges. Wiss. Leipzig. Math. phys. Kl.* **42**, 419 (1890).
2. APATHY, S., *Biol. Centralbl.* **9**, 638 (1889–1890).
3. BAHR, G. F., BLOOM, G. and FRIBERG, U., *Exptl. Cell Research* **12**, 3421 (1957).
4. BEAR, R. S. and SCHMITT, F. O., *J. Cellular Comp. Physiol.* **9**, 275 (1937).
5. BEAR, R. S., SCHMITT, F. O. and YOUNG, J. Z., *Proc. Roy. Soc. B*, **123**, 496 (1937).
6. BOOIJ, H. L. and BUNGENBERG DE JONG, H. G., *Protoplasmologia. Hdb. der Protoplasmaforschung* **1**, No. 2 (1956).
7. CAJAL, S. R., *Trabajos inst. Cajal invest. biol. Madrid* **10**, 221 (1912).
8. DE CASTRO, F., *Arch. histol. normal y pathol.* **3**, 317 (1946).
9. DUNCAN, D. *J. Comp. Neurol.* **60**, 437 (1934).
10. v. EBNER, V., Untersuchung über die Ursachen der Anisotropie organisierter Substanzen. Leipzig, 1882.
11. FERNÁNDEZ-MORÁN, H. and FINEAN, J. B., *J. Biophys. Biochem. Cytol.* **3**, 119 (1957).
12. FINEAN, J. B., *Exptl. Cell Research* **6**, 283 (1954).
13. —— *2nd Internat. Neurochem. Symp. Aarhus*, Pergamon Press, London (in press), 1957.
14. FINEAN, J. B. and MILLINGTON, P. F., *J. Biophys. Biochem. Cytol.* **3**, 89 (1957).
15. FRANKENHAEUSER, B. and HODGKIN, A. L., *J. Physiol.* **131**, 341 (1956).
16. FRIEDEL, G., *Ann. Phys. 9th Ser.* **18**, 273 (1922).
17. FRIEDLÄNDER, B., *Mitt. Zool. Station Neopel*, **9**, 205 (1889–1891).
18. GASSER, H. S., *Cold Spring Harbor Symposia Quant. Biol.* **17**, 32 (1952).
19. —— *J. Gen. Physiol.* **38**, 709 (1955).
20. —— *ibid.* **39**, 473 (1956).
21. GEREN, B. B., *Exptl. Cell. Research* **7**, 558 (1954).
22. —— *In* Cellular Mechanisms in Differentiation and Growth, P. 213. Princeton University Press, 1956.
23. GEREN UZMAN, B. B., and NOQUEIRA-GRAF, G., *J. Biophys. Biochem. Cytol.* **3**, 589 (1957).
24. GEREN, B. B. and SCHMITT, F. O., *Proc. Natl. Acad. Sci.* **39**, 880 (1954).
25. —— *In* Symposium on Fine Structure, P. 251. Leiden, 1955.
26. GÖTHLIN, G. F., *Kgl. Svenska Vetenskapakad. Handl.* **51**, 1 (1913).
27. HESS, A. and LANSING, A. J., *Anat. Rec.* **117**, 175 (1953).
28. LEHMANN, O., Die neue Welt der flüssigen Kristalle. Leipzig, 1911.
29. —— *Ergeb. Physiol.* **16**, 255 (1918).
30. LUXORO, M., Doctoral Dissertation, Massachusetts Institute of Technology. Cambridge, Massachusetts, 1956.
31. NAGEOTTE, J., *Arch. mikroskop. Anat. u. Entwicklungsmech.* **67**, 245 (1911).
32. —— Morphologie des gels lipoides. *Act. Sci. et industr.* No. 431, 1936.
33. PALADE, G. E., *J. Biophys. Biochem. Cytol.* **2**, Suppl. 85 (1956).
34. PEASE, D. C., *J. Biophys. Biochem. Cytol.* **2**, Suppl. 203 (1956).
35. PORTER, K. R., *Harvey Lectures Ser. 44*, **XX**, 175 (1956).
36. PORTER, K. R. and PALADE, G. E., *J. Biophys. Biochem. Cytol.* **3**, 269 (1957).

37. DE RENYI, G. S., *J. Comp. Neurol.* **48**, 293 (1929).
38. ROBERTS, N. R., LOWRY, O. and CRAWFORD, E. J. In preparation.
39. ROBERTSON, J. D., *J. Biophys. Biochem. Cytol.* **1**, 271 (1955).
40. —— *J. Physiol.* **135**, 56 P (1957).
41. —— *J. Biophys. Biochem. Cytol.* (in press) (1957).
42. SCHMIDT, W. J., Die Doppelbrechung von Karyoplasma, Zytoplasma und Metaplasma. Berlin, 1937.
43. SCHMITT, F. O., *Growth* **5**, 1 (1941).
44. —— *2nd Internat. Neurochem. Sympos. Aarhus,* 'The Metabolism of the Nervous System'', Pergamon Press, London, pp. 35–47, 1957.
45. SCHMITT, F. O. and BEAR, R. S., *J. Cellular Comp. Physiol.* **9**, 261 (1937).
46. —— *Biol. Revs.* **14**, 27 (1939).
47. SCHMITT, F. O., BEAR, R. S. and CLARK, G. L., *Radiology* **25**, 131 (1935).
48. SCHMITT, F. O., BEAR, R. S. and PALMER, K. J., *J. Cellular Comp. Physiol.* **18**, 31 (1941).
49. SCHMITT, F. O. and GESCHWIND, N., Progress in Biophysics and Biophysical Chemistry (in press), 1957.
50. SJÖSTRAND, F., *Physical Techniques in Biological Research* **3**, 241 (1956).
51. SPEIDEL, C. C., *In* Genetic Neurology, p. 66. Ed. P. WEISS. Univ. Chicago Press, 1950.
52. STUART, H. A., Die Physik der Hochpolymeren. Springer-Verlag, Berlin, 1955.
53. TELLO, J. F., *Trab. inst. Cajal invest. biol.* **36**, 1 (1944).
54. UZMAN, B. G. and NOQUEIRA-GRAF, G., *J. Biophys. Biochem. Cytol.* (in press) (1957).
55. VALENTIN, G., Die Untersuchung der Pflanzen und der Thiergewebe in polarisiertem Lichte. Leipzig, 1861.
56. —— *Z. rat. Med.* **14**, 122 (1862).
57. VIRCHOW, R., *Virchow's Arch. pathol. Anat. u Physiol.* **6**, 562 (1854).
58. WIENER, O., *Abh. Sächs. Ges. Wiss. math. phys. Kl.* **32**, 509 (1912).

STUDIES OF THE CHEMICAL COMPOSITION OF THE NERVOUS SYSTEM [1]

J. FOLCH, M. LEES and S. CARR

McLean Hospital Research Laboratories, Waverley, Mass., and Department of Biological Chemistry, Harvard Medical School, Boston, Mass., U.S.A.

In their attempts to elicit the intimate structure of living matter, chemists have historically progressed from the consideration of well-defined simple compounds to the study of substances of greater and greater molecular size and complexity. At the same time, the morphologists have started from the study of the readily observable features to the investigation of structures of ever-smaller size. At the present time, the two approaches appear to be reaching common ground in the study of macromolecules and sub-microscopic structures. Now that the sub-microscopic structure of the nervous system has become an important subject of research, a discussion of the chemical components of the tissue would seem to be justified.

The limitations of space restrict the present notes to structural components of the mammalian nervous system and, since our present knowledge of the subject is readily available in several recent reviews [20, 23], we will deal only summarily with most of the topics encompassed by the title of the present paper. This will serve as an introduction to a lengthier description of our own work. Since this has dealt mostly with the central nervous system, we will first present the pertinent results of its study and will then proceed to establish the validity of these observations for peripheral nerve.

The structural components of mammalian brain are lipides and proteins, mostly combined in different types of lipoproteins. Brain lipides can be classified as sterols, phosphatides, and sphingosides [20]. The main sterol is cholesterol, all of which is free cholesterol. Phosphatides are compounds containing phosphate esters and fatty acids among their constituents. According to the nature of the alcohol residue in the constituent phosphate ester, they are classified as phosphoglycerides, phosphoinositides, and phosphosphingosides. The known phosphoglycerides are lecithin, phosphatidyl ethanolamine, phosphatidyl serine, and plasmalogens, or acetal phosphatides. The first three have similar chemical structures: the two hydroxyls on

---

[1] This work has been aided by United States Public Health Service Grants B-130 and B-572.

the glycerol chain of glycerophosphoric acid are substituted by fatty acid residues and one phosphoryl radical is esterified with an amino alcohol. The amino alcohol is choline in the case of lecithin, ethanolamine in the case of phosphatidyl ethanolamine, and serine in the case of phosphatidyl serine. The structure of plasmalogens is still under discussion but they are known to include an aldehydogenic residue and to be otherwise fairly similar to the structure of the other phosphoglycerides.

Only one phosphoinositide has been demonstrated in brain, namely brain diphosphoinositide. Its structure has not yet been established but it appears to consist of inositol metadiphosphate, fatty acids and glycerol in equimolar proportions. Only one phosphosphingoside is known, sphingomyelin, which is monoacyl-sphingosyl-phosphoryl-choline.

The sphingosides, or sphingosine-containing lipides, can be classified as cerebrosides, sulfatides, and mucolipides. The cerebrosides are essentially n-acyl-sphingosyl-galactosides. What is known of the sulfatides suggests that they are simply mono-sulfate esters of cerebrosides. The name of mucolipides is given here to the group of substances having in common the presence of sialic acid among their constituents. To this group belong gangliosides and strandin which appear to be closely related and which consist of sialic acid, galactose, glucose, galactosamine, sphingosine, and fatty acids. They are substances readily soluble in water and undialyzable, whose detailed structure remains unknown.

Our knowledge of brain proteins is much scantier than that of brain lipides and most of it has been obtained by methods that are now obsolete, with the result that most of the information available will necessarily have to be confirmed. For the purposes of this discussion, we need only mention neurokeratin which is essentially the trypsin- and pepsin-resistant fraction of brain proteins and which will be discussed in some more detail later on.

The studies to be reported here have dealt with proteolipides, with neurokeratin, with sulfatides, and with the relationship between acidic lipides and mineral cations. In spite of the somewhat diverse nature of these four problems, the work carried out in each case has been the elaboration of leads uncovered in the course of a continuing investigation to determine optimal conditions for the isolation and purification of pure brain lipides with a minimum of change. This investigation [10] had shown at an early stage that, when the tissue is homogenized with twenty volumes or more of a 2:1 chloroform–methanol mixture, the extract obtained contains the tissue lipides and relatively small amounts of non-lipide substances. It had also been found that it was possible to separate lipides from the accompanying non-lipide substances by placing the extract under a large volume of water, upon which methanol diffuses from the extract into the water starting a complex sequence of events which is described elsewhere [10]. After a few hours, when the system had reached final equilibrium, it consisted of an upper methanol-water phase, a lower chloroformic phase and some material accumulated at the interface in the form of a "fluff". Analysis of the solids recovered from each phase and from the fluff had established that the upper phase contained the non-lipide substances and most of the strandin and that only chloroform–methanol soluble substances, i.e., lipides other than strandin were found in the lower phase and in the fluff. The fluff was freely soluble in chloroform–methanol, and could be brought into solution in the lower phase by the simple addition of methanol. The result was a solution of essentially pure tissue lipides. Since this procedure was much simpler and milder than the earlier methods of lipide extraction and purification, it was adopted in all our ensuing work.

Proteolipides

The study of the pure lipides thus obtained gave the first indication of the existence of proteolipides [13]. It was found that, when our extract of purified lipides was dried by vacuum distillation of the solvents, part of the residue had become insoluble in the same chloroform–methanol mixture, 2:1 by volume, used for the original extraction of the tissue. The part of the residue that had become insoluble in this solvent mixture as a result of drying was also insoluble in water. The chemical analysis of the material showed that it contained over 12 per cent nitrogen, that it gave a strongly positive biuret test and that, after acid hydrolysis, the bulk of the nitrogen could be recovered as free amino acids, i.e., the material was protein in nature. Further study established (*a*) that the amount of protein extracted with chloroform–methanol under the conditions used was always the same from the same tissue sample and that it remained constant in spite of freezing and thawing the tissue prior to extraction or carrying out the extraction at different temperatures within the range of $-15°$ to the boiling point of the solvent mixture (about $59°$); (*b*) that taking the extract to dryness, even under the mildest possible conditions, resulted invariably in rendering most of the protein present in the extract insoluble in the chloroform–methanol mixture; and (*c*) that washing the extract did not result in any removal of protein from the extract.

In view of what is known about the properties of proteins, the foregoing facts made it necessary to assume that the protein material being dealt with was not a free protein but that it was combined with lipides in such a way that the resulting compound or compounds offered an outside lipide surface. Chemically, these substances would be lipoproteins, i.e., they would consist of a lipide moiety and a protein moiety, but, while lipoproteins are usually soluble in water and insoluble in, or destroyed by, organic solvents, the postulated compounds (proteolipides) would be insoluble in water and readily soluble in chloroform–methanol. Of course, the only satisfactory proof of such a hypothesis would be the isolation of proteolipides. For this purpose, a procedure had to be devised which would not involve taking the extract to dryness since this invariably resulted in rendering most of the protein present insoluble in organic solvents. The procedure finally developed was an outgrowth of the washing procedure. It was based on the observation that the chloroform–methanol soluble protein concentrated in the fluff to a greater extent than did the other lipides. The fluff was collected and dissolved in about one-tenth as much chloroform–methanol as had been originally equilibrated with water and the solution placed at $-10°$. On standing overnight, a precipitate appeared (Proteolipide A) which was collected by filtration. The filtrate was mixed with an equal volume of acetone, and the mixture placed at 4°. On standing, a second precipitate (Proteolipide B) was formed which was collected by filtration. Both proteolipides were readily soluble in chloroform–methanol and insoluble in water. On analysis, it was found that Proteolipide A contained 15–25 per cent protein and Proteolipide B about 50 per cent protein. They accounted jointly for about half of the protein in the crude tissue extract. The balance of the protein could be recovered from the chloroform phase by simply drying it by evaporation of the solvent and treating the residue successively with acetone, ethyl ether, and ethanol. The remainder was readily soluble in chloroform–methanol, and contained over 75 per cent protein (Proteolipide C).

The foregoing had established the existence of proteolipides. It had also established that proteolipides were denatured by drying only from biphasic systems, and were not affected by drying from simple solutions.

Proteolipides are especially abundant in white matter where their protein moiety constitutes about 2 per cent of fresh tissue weight. They are absent in the fetal brain. They appear at the same time as histologically recognizable myelin and their increase in concentration parallels the progress of myelination. They are most likely constituents of central myelin and there is reason to believe that they are one of the antigens responsible for experimental allergic encephalomyelitis [27, 28].

Neurokeratin

The name of neurokeratin was given by Ewald and Kühne in 1877 [3] to a fraction of brain proteins which they isolated and which can be summarily described as a proteolytic enzyme-resistant residue obtained primarily from nerve tissue myelin. This fraction has traditionally been considered to be associated with the protein network of the myelin sheath and the name neurokeratin has loosely been given to this structure by histologists. The classical procedure for preparing neurokeratin consists essentially of two major operations: namely, the quantitative removal of lipides with organic solvents, and the subsequent treatment of the proteins thus obtained with digestive enzymes. The procedure takes several months, and involves such drastic steps as continuous extraction with hot ethanol for four weeks, digestion with pepsin in dilute hydrochloric acid for three weeks, and, in some of its versions, treatment with hot alkali. The product is a protein residue insoluble in water and in dilute acids and bases, rich in sulfur and resistant to the action of proteolytic enzymes. The preparations obtained by various workers differed somewhat in composition, and Block [2] concluded that neurokeratin is most likely an artefact derived from a definite group of substances specific to nervous tissue.

The work on neurokeratin carried out in our laboratory, mainly by Dr. F. N. LeBaron [19], started with an attempt to develop a method of preparation of neurokeratin less drastic than the classic procedure. A method was developed in which the lipides from brain tissue were extracted with chloroform–methanol, the lipide-free tissue residue treated with trypsin, and the trypsin-resistant residue extracted with dilute acid.

The final residue was a tan colored, hard powder. By the rationale of the method of its preparation, it should have been identical with classical neurokeratin. In fact, it was a protein material similar to classical neurokeratin in appearance, and in being rich in sulfur (1.76 per cent), insoluble in water and dilute alkalies and acids, and resistant to the action of pepsin, erepsin, and papain. However, it contained about 1.8 per cent phosphorus and over 3 per cent inositol, both of which are essentially absent from neurokeratin. The investigation of the nature of this phosphorus showed that it could not be extracted with neutral solvents, hence it was not lipide-phosphorus in the usual sense; that it was not acid-soluble, and that it was liberated quantitatively with dilute alkali at room temperature. However, the resulting solution showed no special absorption in the ultraviolet range. In other words, while the phosphorus in our material behaved like ribonucleic acid, it was not nucleic acid phosphorus. The phosphorus in these alkali extracts was finally identified as inositol phosphate. Our trypsin-resistant protein fraction (TRPR) contained combined fatty acids, and it had been observed that, on treatment with dilute alkali, fatty acids were liberated concomitantly with inositol phosphate. All this suggested the possibility that phosphorus in TRPR was part of a structure similar to, or identical with, brain diphosphoinositide [11]. This surmise was proven to be correct when it was found that, by treating the TRPR with acidified chloroform–methanol, a fraction was separated which accounted for about one-fourth of its weight and all of the phosphorus and inositol. After its separation from TRPR, the fraction was soluble in neutral chloroform–methanol and insoluble in water. It appeared to be a mixture of a new type of phosphatides, the *phosphatidopeptides* [8, 12]. These substances appeared to have as constituents inositol phosphates, mainly diphosphate, fatty acids, sphingosine, and short peptide chains.

In summary, TRPR appeared to be a lipoprotein in which the lipide and the protein moieties were combined by a salt linkage. In an effort to elucidate the relationship between neurokeratin and TRPR, it was found that when TRPR was submitted to the procedure of preparation of classical neurokeratin, most, if not all, of its phosphorus and inositol were removed. Therefore, it is very likely that neurokeratin is an artefact derived from TRPR.

Modification of the procedure of washing tissue lipide extracts

For all its simplicity the procedure of washing could not be conveniently adapted to micro scale operation because, with small volumes, the manipulations involved became awkward and the chances of contamination and errors in measurement were increased. Also, it had the disadvantage that, because of the denaturation of the proteolipides upon drying the washed extract, the aliquot used for dry weight could not be used for subsequent analysis. In an effort to obviate these drawbacks, it was found that effective washing could be obtained by simply adding to the crude extract one-fifth its volume of water [14]. After proper mixing, the system separated into two phases, without any interfacial fluff. The upper water-methanolic phase was found to contain all of the non-lipide substances and most of the strandin and only negligible amounts of lipides other than strandin. The lower chloroformic phase was found to contain essentially all of the lipides free of non-lipide substances. Since this method of washing depended on the distribution of solutes between two phases, it could be run at any scale which was otherwise technically feasible. This modified procedure also had the advantage that the lower phase could be taken to dryness without foaming and without denaturation of the proteolipides.

In the course of developing the modified procedure, it had been necessary to wash a lower phase repeatedly with aliquots of a mixture of solvent composition identical with that of the original upper phase. It was found that the successive "upper phases" thus obtained contained sizeable amounts of lipides. These lipides were mostly phosphatidyl serine and sulfatides, i.e., they were acidic lipides and their distribution between the two phases was according to a distribution coefficient of 2.7 in favor of the lower phase. Clearly, there was a factor or factors in operation during the original washing which altered the distribution coefficient of the acidic lipides so markedly that only negligible amounts of acidic lipides could be found in the upper phase. The factors were eventually found to be a small amount of mineral salts that were present in the crude extract and which were removed in the first washing. It was also found that the magnitude of the effect of the salts was directly proportional to the logarithm of their concentration. These observations afforded the leads for the successful isolation of sulfatides and provided a tool for the study of the relationship between acidic lipides and mineral cations.

Isolation of sulfatides

In spite of the fact that the occurrence of sulfur-containing lipides in brain has been known since the time of Thudichum, very little work has been done on these substances. The most significant contribution has been that of Gunnar Blix who, in 1933, isolated from brain with low yield a sulfur-containing lipide which he named cerebron sulfuric acid [1]. He did not establish its complete structure but his results suggest that cerebron sulfuric acid is the potassium salt of a sulfuric acid ester of a cerebroside.

At least one reson for the paucity of work on sulfatides had been the difficulty of separating them from other lipides and especially from cerebrosides. The distribution of sulfatides in the biphasic system described above provided a means of obviating this difficulty. In fact, small amounts of sulfatides could easily be recovered from the upper phases by simple solvent fractionation, but the procedure was awkward because of the large volumes of solvents involved.

The search for better conditions has resulted in the isolation of sulfatides from the crude tissue extract by a method of four "linked distributions" [21]. The crude extract is washed with one-fifth its volume of water as outlined above and the lower phase mixed with petroleum ether, methanol, and water, $1:0.5:0.75:0.2$ v/v. The system separates into two phases; the upper one is mixed with one-twelfth its volume of water, and the small lower phase that separates is discarded. The remaining upper phase is mixed with N aqueous KCl, methanol, and water, $1:0.04:0.02:0.1$ v/v. The resulting lower phase is a crude sulfatide fraction which contains over half of the lipide sulfur in the original extract, mixed with phosphatides, mainly phosphatidyl serine. From it, pure sulfatides can be readily obtained by precipitation at low temperatures, or by chromatographic separation.

Relationship between acidic lipides and mineral cations

It has been known for a long time [22] that nervous tissue contains smaller concentrations of mineral anions than do other tissues, and it had been postulated that the resulting "inorganic anion deficit" was made up by the presence of unusually large concentrations of unidentified organic anions. In the case of crustaceans it was established eventually that the organic acids involved were mainly free aspartic acid [24, 25, 26] and a new compound, iscthionic acid [18].

In the mammalian nervous tissue these substances are present only in small amounts if not altogether absent, and can therefore contribute no significant amount of anionic charges. Instead, it was pointed out at an early date [17] that lipides might constitute a substantial part of the organic acids of the tissue. This surmise was abundantly proven correct by the later identification, in brain tissue, of three different acidic lipides, namely, cerebron sulfuric acid, phosphatidyl serine [6], and brain diphosphoinositide [7]. All three, when isolated from the tissue by the use of neutral solvents, are obtained as neutral salts of Na, K, Ca, or Mg, and it was computed [5] that they might bind in salt linkage as much as one-fourth of the cations present in the tissue. More recently, it has been shown that the acidic lipides extracted from bovine central white matter with chloroform-methanol provide 27 milliequivalents of anionic charges per kilo of fresh tissue [15].

There remained a point on which no information was available. This was the question of the relative affinity of the different cations for the different acidic lipides. The effect of different salts on the distribution of acidic lipides between the two phases of the system tissue chloroform–methanol extract plus one-fifth its volume of water could possibly provide a means of arriving at some roughly quantitative formulation of such affinities and to establish whether or not the affinity of a particular cation for a particular lipide is so high that lipide and cation will combine with each other in the presence of any physiologically possible concentration gradient of another cation.

The basis of the possible study of this question was the supposition that the mechanism of the distribution-altering effect of salts was as follows. The acidic lipides which are extracted from the tissue as salts of Na, K, Ca and/or Mg are present in the upper phase in dissociated or partly dissociated form, and in the lower phase as undissociated salts. The addition of salts of the above cations (which remain in the upper phase) would decrease the dissociation of the corresponding salts of acidic lipides by a mass action effect, with a consequent shift of lipides to the lower phase. Since evidence already available showed that each cation could alter the distribution of all lipides present, it had to be assumed, if the foregoing hypothesis was accepted, that any one cation could displace other cations from combination with the lipides. Contrariwise, proof that any one cation could, in fact, displace other cations would constitute validation of the hypothesis.

Results of experiments designed to explore these different possibilities [15], showed that Na^+, K^+, Ca^{++}, and Mg^{++} could reversibly displace one another from combination with the lipides with relative affinities higher for Ca^{++} and Mg^{++} than for K^+ and Na^+, the difference between bivalent and monovalent cations being well beyond what could be expected from differences in valencies. The differences between Na^+ and K^+ were not significant, and those between Ca^{++} and Mg^{++} have, as yet, not been exactly formulated. While the work is still in progress, it is clear that there is no "absolute" affinity between any particular known lipide and any one of the cations studied. However, it must be mentioned that the experimental design used does not preclude the occurrence of small amounts of unidentified lipides which might exhibit such absolute affinities.

Composition of Mammalian Peripheral Nerve

The gross composition of mammalian myelinated nerve has been the subject of many investigations and the sizeable body of evidence thus gathered has resulted in the general acceptance of the concept that it is very similar to central white matter except for the presence of connective tissue which, in the central nervous system, is only present as part of vascular structures, while in the peripheral nerve it may constitute more than half of the solids of the tissue. In view of the ample documentation of this conclusion, our work on peripheral myelinated nerve has been advisedly limited to the study of points on which no evidence, or only insufficient evidence, was available, and we will discuss here only results bearing on proteolipides, neurokeratin, sulfatides, and acidic lipides.

Material and methods

Since our work on the central nervous system had been carried out mainly on cattle brain, bovine sciatic was the tissue selected for study. Sciatic nerves, collected at the time of slaughter, were chilled immediately, freed of connective tissue by gross dissection, frozen to the temperature of dry ice, and ground in a mortar maintained at the same temperature. The powder thus obtained was extracted with 2:1 chloroform–methanol mixture, and the extract and insoluble tissue residue separated by filtration [10]. The tissue residue was washed with water at 0° and the washed residue digested with trypsin. The chloroform–methanol extract was washed once with 0.05 N aqueous KCl and twice with "solvents upper phase" containing KCl at 0.05 N concentration [14]. The three washings were combined, dried by vacuum distillation of the solvents, the residue dissolved in water and the solution dialyzed exhaustively [14]. The undialyzable fraction was analyzed for strandin [9, 16]. The washed chloroform–methanol extract was concentrated to dryness by vacuum evaporation of the solvents. The residue was extracted twice with one-third as much acetone each time as chloroform–methanol had been used in the original extraction of the tissue. The acetone insoluble fraction was submitted to fractionation by the method of "linked distributions" for the separation of the crude sulfatide fraction.

In this experimental design, washing with KCl-containing solutions would replace all cations combined with the lipides with potassium [15] and the potassium content of the lipides would be a measure of the sum total of anionic groups; the treatment of the total washed lipides with acetone would presumably extract all of the neutral fats from the connective tissue in the anatomical nerve plus all the cholesterol, leaving, as an acetone insoluble residue, all the lipides from the strictly neural structures, minus cholesterol. The fractionation of the acetone insoluble fraction by the procedure of "linked distributions" would concentrate any sulfatides present and allow the accurate estimation of sulfur. Also, any lipide sulfur concentrated by such a procedure could reasonably be supposed to belong to substances of properties identical to those of sulfatides of the central nervous system. Finally, the trypsin-resistant fraction from the chloroform–methanol insoluble tissue residue could be assumed to correspond to the sum total of collagen, elastin, and neurokeratin present in the nerve.

Results

The results of a typical experiment on 117 g of bovine sciatic were as follows:

		% wt. fresh tissue
1. Solids in chloroform–methanol extract.		23.8
2. Wt. of insoluble tissue residue		12.6
3. Total tissue solids $(1+2)$.		36.4
4. Solids in washed lipide extract		23.0
5. Strandin and gangliosides		0.011

Composition of lipide mixture in washed extract

			% wt. fresh tissue
6. Proteolipide protein, % of lipides:	0.28		0.064
7. P	0.76		0.175
8. Phosphatidyl serine	2.86		0.66
9. Sphingomyelin P	0.40		0.092
10. Acetal phosphatides	3.8		0.87
11. Cerebrosides	4.5		1.03
12. K	0.186		0.043
13. Acetone insoluble lipides.			6.3

Composition of acetone insoluble lipide fraction

			% wt. fresh tissue
14. Proteolipide protein, % of fraction:	0.72		0.045
15. P	2.37		0.15
16. Phosphatidyl serine	9.3		0.59
17. Sphingomyelin P	1.22		0.077
18. Acetal phosphatides	6.2		0.38
19. Cerebrosides	16.8		1.06
20. K	0.62		0.039
21. Inositol	0.26		0.016
22. Crude sulfatide fraction	9.8		0.62

Composition of crude sulfatide fraction

			% wt. fresh tissue
23. S	% of fraction:	0.97	0.006
24. Galactose		5.53	0.034
25. Atoms S/moles galactose	ratio:	0.99	

Study of the Chloroform–Methanol Insoluble Tissue Residue

This material, amounting to 12.6 per cent of the weight of fresh tissue, was extracted four times each with 40-fold its weight of water at 0°. The first three extracts combined contained 5 per cent of the weight of the material; the fourth extract was essentially free of solids. The washed residue, which corresponded to nerve proteins, was then submitted to the action of trypsin [19]. One-half of its weight was recovered as a trypsin-resistant, water-insoluble residue with the appearance of crude collagen. It contained 0.13 per cent combined inositol and 0.1 per cent P. Attempts to prepare from it a trypsin-resistant residue similar to that obtained from central white matter by controlled digestion of the collagen by pepsin yielded a hard brownish powder containing 0.34 per cent combined inositol and 0.13 per cent P. As a check on the fate of collagen, hydroxyproline estimations were kindly run on our preparations by Dr. Jerome Gross of the Massachusetts General Hospital. The original total nerve protein preparation contained 10.7 per cent hydroxyproline and this value increased to 15.0 per cent after tryptic digestion. The product of our attempts to prepare TRPR contained 13.5 per cent hydroxyproline.

DISCUSSION AND CONCLUSIONS

From the results given above it is possible to reach an approximate estimate of the respective contributions of connective tissue, and of strictly neural elements, i.e., axons and satellite cells, to the anatomical nerve. Thus, from a quantitative point of view, it is safe to equate collagen with the trypsin-resistant proteins of nerve, the contribution of neurokeratin to the latter being negligible. Also, the acetone soluble fraction of lipides, which amounts to 16.7 per cent of the weight of fresh nerve, can be equated with connective tissue lipides, after making correction for the expected amount of cholesterol from neural sources, and the small amount of phosphatides present. Expressed in terms of weight of fresh tissue, these corrections amount respectively to 2 and 1 per cent. Thus, the amount of connective tissue lipides in the nerve can be computed to be 13.7 per cent of fresh weight, i.e., 60 per cent of total tissue lipides. This value checks with about half of the proteins being collagen and both results indicate that one-half or more of the tissue solids belong to connective tissue elements.

When the results obtained are corrected for this amount of connective tissue, the lipide mixture from the strictly neural elements of the anatomic nerve is very close to central white matter lipides. Thus, the phosphatide composition and cerebroside content of the acetone insoluble fraction could easily be that of central white matter lipides, corrected for cholesterol content. The yield of crude sulfatide fraction and its composition is similar to what is observed with white matter. The potassium content corresponds to 11 milliequivalents per kilo fresh sciatic and to about 27 milliequivalents after correcting for connective tissue present, a value which would be identical with that found in white matter. Hence, the strictly neural elements of sciatic nerve and central white matter can safely be assumed to contain identical acidic lipides, at essentially identical concentrations.

In the case of strandin (which includes gangliosides) [9], there is a marked difference between central white matter and sciatic, the former containing

8- to 10-fold the strandin content of the latter. Even after correcting for connective tissue present, a 3-fold difference remains. Of course, this difference may be without special significance and may simply reflect the fortuitous inclusion of gray matter elements in our sampling of central white matter.

The general similarity between peripheral nerve and white matter makes specially striking their marked difference in proteolipide content. The central white matter content of proteolipide protein, which averages about 2 per cent of the weight of fresh tissue, is 30-fold the content of proteolipide protein of sciatic nerve. Even after correction for connective tissue present, a 13-fold difference remains.[1] If, as much evidence indicates, proteolipides constitute a major element of the structure of central myelin, it is necessary to conclude that they are replaced by some other compound or group of compounds in peripheral myelin. The exact implications of such a qualitative difference between the two tissues cannot be foreseen but it is reasonable to assume that they will be of basic importance.

It should be mentioned that the determination of proteolipide protein at the concentration found in lipide extracts of sciatic nerve is a technically difficult problem, and the results reported are, at the most, maximal possible values which indicate only that small amounts of free alpha-amino acid groups are liberated by the acid hydrolysis of washed lipides. Such groups could also be derived from phosphatidopeptides [8, 12] and it will require further work to establish whether proteolipides, phosphatidopeptides, or a mixture of the two is present in the nerve. A point of inconclusive evidence obtained has been that acid hydrolysates of central white matter proteolipide protein give paper chromatograms quite different from those given by acid hydrolysates of sciatic nerve lipides. The only value of this observation is to point out the need of more comprehensive investigations.

The information obtained relating to the nature of neurokeratin from sciatic is too preliminary to warrant any conclusion.

SUMMARY

1. The composition of the central nervous system is reviewed and the work on proteolipides, neurokeratin, sulfatides and acidic lipides discussed in some detail.

2. The study of bovine sciatic nerve has shown that over half of its solids belong to connective tissue elements. The study of components of strictly

---

[1] Since the presentation of this evidence, Finean, Hawthorne, and Patterson [4] have published results which are in agreement with our own findings.

neural origin shows that the lipides are very similar in type and amount to those found in central white matter, with the important exception that, while central white matter contains 2 per cent of its fresh weight as proteolipide protein, sciatic nerve appears to be essentially free of proteolipides. Sciatic nerve also contains less strandin than does central white matter.

REFERENCES

1. Blix, G., *Z. physiol. Chem.* **219**, 82 (1933).
2. Block, R. J., *Arch. Biochem. and Biophys.* **31**, 266 (1951).
3. Ewald, A. and Kühne, W., *Verhandl. Naturhist. Med.* **1**, 457 (1877).
4. Finean, J. B., Hawthorne, J. N. and Patterson, J. D. E., *J. Neurochem.* **1**, 193 (1957).
5. Folch, J., *in* Psychiatric Research. Harvard University Monographs in Medicine and Public Health, No. 9, chapt. 2. Harvard University Press, Cambridge, Mass., 1947.
6. —— *J. Biol. Chem.* **174**, 439 (1948).
7. —— *ibid.* **177**, 505 (1949).
8. —— *in* McElroy, W. D. and Glass, B., Phosphorus Metabolism, vol. **2**, p. 195. Johns Hopkins Press, Baltimore, 1952.
9. Folch, J., Arsove, S. and Meath, J. A., *J. Biol. Chem.* **191**, 819 (1951).
10. Folch, J., Ascoli, I., Lees, M., Meath, J. A. and LeBaron, F. N., *ibid.* **191**, 833 (1951).
11. Folch, J. and LeBaron, F. N., *Federation Proc.* **10**, 183 (1951).
12. —— *ibid.* **12**, 203 (1953).
13. Folch, J. and Lees, M., *J. Biol. Chem.* **191**, 807 (1951).
14. Folch, J., Lees, M. and Sloane Stanley, G. H., *ibid.* **226**, 497 (1957).
15. —— *in* Metabolism of the Nervous System. D. Richter, Pergamon Press, London (in press).
16. Folch, J., Meath, J. A. and Bogoch, S., *Federation Proc.* **15**, 254 (1956).
17. Koch, W. and Pike, F. H., *J. Pharmacol.* **2**, 245 (1911).
18. Koechlin, B. A., *Federation Proc.* **13**, 80 (1954).
19. LeBaron, F. N. and Folch, J., *J. Neurochem.* **1**, 101 (1956).
20. —— *Physiol. Rev.* (in press).
21. Lees, M., *Federation Proc.* **15**, 298 (1956).
22. Manery, J. F., *in* The Biology of Mental Health and Disease, chapt. 10. P. B. Hoeber, New York, 1952.
23. Rossiter, R. J., *in* Elliott, K. A. C., Page, I. H. and Quastel, J. H., Neurochemistry, chapt. 2. C. C. Thomas, Springfield, Ill., 1955.
24. Schmitt, F. O., Bear, R. S. and Silber, R. H., *J. Cellular Comp. Physiol.* **14**, 351 (1939).
25. Silber, R. H., *ibid.* **18**, 21 (1941).
26. Silber, R. H. and Schmitt, F. O., *ibid.* **16**, 247 (1940).
27. Tal, C. and Olitsky, P. K., *Science* **116**, 420 (1952).
28. Waksman, B. H., Porter, H., Lees, M. B., Adams, R. D. and Folch, J., *J. Exptl. Med.* **100**, 451 (1954)

Experimental Cell Research, Suppl. **5**, *72–79 (1958)*

THE ROLE OF THIAMINE (VITAMIN B₁) IN NERVOUS EXCITATION

A. VON MURALT

The Hallerianum, Bern, Switzerland

THE role of thiamine in peripheral neurophysiology, as it was seen in 1947, has been summarized in an article in "Vitamins and Hormones" [8]. Since then our views have been enlarged by four new advances : (1) the development of the technique of single nerve fiber work, (2) the discovery and introduction of antimetabolites of thiamine, (3) the availability of labelled thiamine-S^{35}, (4) the use of *iso*-propane for quick freezing at $-190°C$. The fundamental problem: what is the role of thiamine in the chemical equilibrium of the neurone, remains still unsolved.

PREVIOUS WORK

The experimental evidence of the previous work may be summarized as follows: (1) From excised nerves, immersed in a bathing solution, 4–8 times more thiamine diffuses into the solution on excitation [5, 6]. (2) Shooting nerves into liquid air at 1 m/sec fixes the chemical status and on stimulation produces an accumulation of excitation waves [7]; with this technique it was found that the thiamine in the powder of frozen excited nerves is in such a state, that more can be extracted by Ringer solution, than can be obtained from a corresponding sample of powder of unexcited nerves. Excitation produces a shift from "bound" into "free" thiamine. This evidence has been tested with the following methods: bradycardia test [4], yeast fermentation test [18, 19], thiochrome method [16, 17], sensitizing effect on the leech muscle preparation [7], phycomyces test [9], polarographic determination [7, 14]. (3) In nerves poisoned with iodoacetate, about 50 per cent of the "free" thiamine disappears during stimulation into a compound X [18, 19]. (4) This "disappearance" is not evident if the yeast method is used. Yeast is able to use the compound X as well as thiamine for its respiration. These results may be represented in the following way:

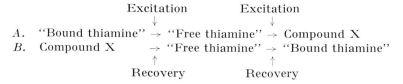

C.   Blocking glycolysis with iodoacetate blocks also reaction *B* (free thiamine disappears).

D.   Compound X + "free thiamine" can be synthesized by yeast to form cocarboxylase (thiamine diphosphate).

This was the situation as it presented itself in 1947. Since then new information has been gained by the following experiments.

EXPERIMENTAL

Single myelinated nerve fibers have the great advantage, that the action current or action potential of a single node of Ranvier can be studied. Under normal conditions such a node can be stimulated to deliver 50 excitations/sec for several hours, without showing any appreciable signs of fatigue. Test solutions can be applied to this node (method of Kunz [3] or Kilb and Stämpfli [2]) and their effect is very rapid, owing to the very short diffusion distances to the nodal membrane. For such studies 4 antimetabolites are of special interest: (1) oxy-thiamine, a competitor for cocarboxylase, (2) neopyrithiamine, a competitor for thiamine, (3) purified thiaminase, from carp intestines (*Chastek*-factor), (4) extracts from fern (*Pteris aquilina*). The latter two preparations destroy the thiamine molecule and have inactivation mechanisms different from the well known sulfite-cleavage (cf. [12]). On the water receptors of the frog tongue which are very close to the surface, thiaminase and fern extracts produce a block of receptor activity [10, 11]. The similar action of a fern extract on the action current of an isolated node of Ranvier of a myelinated fiber of frog is shown in Fig. 1. After one minute of action the threshold of the node is increased from 50 to 80 mV and then to 110 mV. The action current shows a significant change: the steepness of rise is smaller

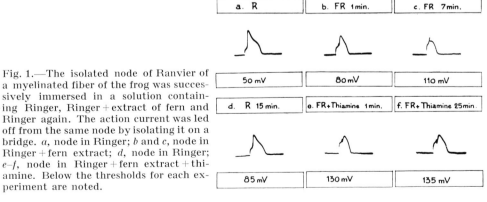

Fig. 1.—The isolated node of Ranvier of a myelinated fiber of the frog was successively immersed in a solution containing Ringer, Ringer + extract of fern and Ringer again. The action current was led off from the same node by isolating it on a bridge. *a*, node in Ringer; *b* and *c*, node in Ringer + fern extract; *d*, node in Ringer; *e–f*, node in Ringer + fern extract + thiamine. Below the thresholds for each experiment are noted.

A. von Muralt

and the amplitude is diminished (*b* and *c*). In *d* the node recovers after washing with Ringer solution. If now fern extract and thiamine are added the same effect occurs again (*e–f*), but the node remains excitable for more than 25 minutes, which is not the case if thiamine is withheld (experiment

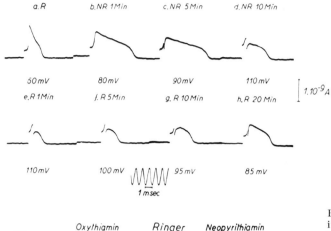

Fig. 2.—Same arrangement as in Fig. 1. *a*, node in Ringer; *b–d*, node immersed in a solution of Ringer + neopyrithiamine (NR); *e–f*, node was washed in Ringer again.

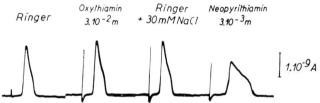

Fig. 3.—Same arrangement as in Fig. 1. On addition of oxythiamine (3×10^{-2} m) no effect is visible except a small increase of the spike. This is due to the increase of sodium, as can be seen from the addition of 30 mM NaCl. Neopyrithiamine has the same effect as in Fig. 2 at 1/10 concentration.

of Dr. Kunz). The same effects can be demonstrated with thiaminase from carp intestines, but owing to the large molecular weight the diffusion is slow and the effects are irregular. The activity of the fern and carp-intestine extracts is parallel to their activity in inactivating thiamine. This of course is not sufficient proof for a specific effect. Dr. Kunz [3] has therefore conducted a large series of experiments with competition antimetabolites. Fig. 2 shows a typical experiment with neopyrithiamine. After one minute the threshold has risen by 20 mV and the decrease in steepness of slope and a "plateau" in the action current is apparent. Such changes are typical for an increase of external Na concentration or inactivation of the sodium transport system. After 5 minutes the change is even more pronounced and after 10 minutes a block is beginning to set in (*b–d*). Washing the node produces after 20 minutes a partial recovery (*e–h*), especially with regard to the threshold of excitation (85 mV in *h*). The action of oxythiamine is quite different (Fig. 3). There is no action at all, even at 10 times the concentration, except for a small increase in the amplitude of the action current, due to a sodium effect and comparable to the addition of 30 mM NaCl to the outside solution. Neopyrithiamine applied to the same node shows again the effect of Fig. 2. These

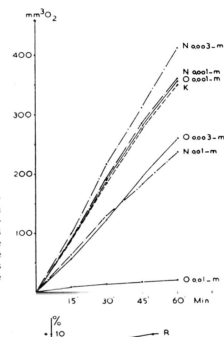

Fig. 4.—Influence of oxythiamine and neopyrithiamine on the pyruvate-oxydation of mitochondria prepared from rat-liver. *Ordinate*, oxygen consumption in mm³; *abscissa*, time in minutes. All samples contain 0.5 ml suspension of mitochondria, pyruvate 0.01 M, MgCl$_2$ 0.003 M, ATP 0.001 M, K-phosphate pH 7.5 0.005 M, KCl isotonic. N are the experiments with neopyrithiamine, O with oxythiamine, K is the control. (After Kunz [3].)

Fig. 5.—Steepness of rise of the action current in relation to the membrane potential of a single node, immersed in Ringer and neopyrithiamine-Ringer. *Ordinate*, steepness of rise; *abscissa*, membrane potential recorded with zero at the level of the resting potential. The measurements were made 5 minutes after changing the solutions. The membrane potential was biassed with the aid of a conditioning rectangular impulse of 20 msec. The test impulse at threshold had 10 msec. (After Kunz [3].)

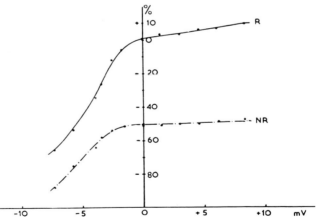

findings are consistent and opposite to the effect these two antimetabolites have on rat-liver mitochondria respiration in a pyruvate substrate (Fig. 4). Here oxythiamine blocks respiration by competition with cocarboxylase, but neopyrithiamine has no effect and increases respiration slightly. The further analysis of the neopyrithiamine effect on peripheral nerves has given the following information. The sodium-transport system can be studied according to Hodgkin and Huxley [1] and Weidmann [14] by measuring the steepness

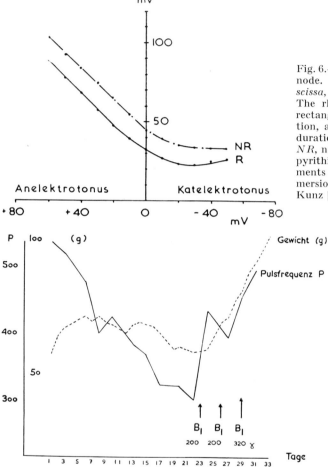

Fig. 6.—Electrotonic curves of a single node. *Ordinate*, rheobase in mV; *abscissa*, electrotonic potential in mV. The rheobase was determined with a rectangular impulse of 2 msec duration, after an electrotonus of 17 msec duration. R, node in Ringer solution; NR, node in Ringer solution with neopyrithiamine 0.003 M. The measurements were made 5 minutes after immersion in the new solution. (After Kunz [3].)

Fig. 7.—Experiment with avitaminotic rats. *Ordinate*, pulse-rate P and weight in grams; *abscissa*, time in days. From the first day onward a diet deficient in Vitamin B_1 was administered to the rats. The pulse-curve dropped from 550 to 300 (determined by electrocardiogram). The weight-curve came to a standstill and a slow drop. On the 23rd, 26th and 29th day radio-active Vitamin B_1 was injected. Note the rise in the pulse-rate and in the weight.

of rise of the action current as a function of the membrane potential. Fig. 5 (after Kunz [3]) shows in the unbroken curve the typical behaviour of the sodium-transport system, activated by the potential of the nodal membrane (conditioned by rectangular impulses of 20 msec duration). In NR the same experiment is carried through after the addition of 0.003 M neopyrithiamine. It is evident that the activation of the sodium-transport system reaches saturation at about 50 per cent normal. The resting potential of the node

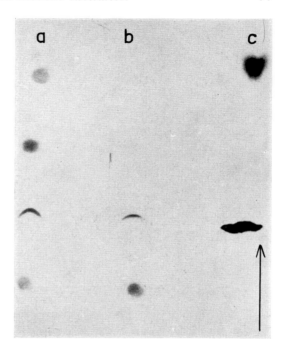

Fig. 8.—Autoradiogram of (*a*) extract of unstimulated nerves, (*b*) extract of stimulated nerves, (*c*) thiamine (6.4 *γ*) and thiazole.

however is not affected and the membrane resistance remains unchanged (measurements of Dr. Straub with the method of Stämpfli and Straub [13]), which is good evidence for the statement that the K-permeability is not influenced by the thiamine antimetabolite. Fig. 6 (after Kunz [3]) shows the electrotonic curves before and after addition of 0.003 *M* neopyrithiamine. The parallel upward shift of the curve is again a sign for partial inactivation of the sodium-transport system by neopyrithiamine, without effect on the resting potential. In all these experiments oxythiamine has no effect. The possibility that it does not diffuse into the node must be kept in mind, although it seems very improbable. We think that thiamine plays an important and immediate role, not in the resting metabolism of nerve, but in the activity cycle and is closely related to the sodium-transport system. In addition cocarboxylase might be important for metabolism, but if it is blocked the effect is not evident in short-time experiments.

In order to test this hypothesis from an entirely different angle, we have reintroduced the freezing method, but not with liquid air, but with isopropane at − 190°C. In our old experiments liquid air showed always a Leydenfrost phenomenon when the nerves were shot in. The heat given off from the nerve was sufficient to bring a certain amount of liquid air to the

boiling point. Iso-propane behaves differently. It has a boiling point of
−44.5°C and when cooled to −190°C lower than its boiling point. The heat
given off by the nerve is insufficient to produce boiling and the freezing
contact is therefore immediate. The nerves were loaded with labelled thiamine-

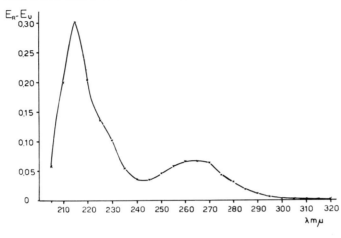

Fig. 9.—Ultra-violet absorption difference between the
alcoholic extract of excited
nerves (E_R) and the alcoholic extract of unstimulated
nerves (E_U) after freezing in
iso-propane at −190°C.

^{35}S by injection after having brought the animals into a pronounced avit-
aminosis. The right moment was chosen by following the weight curve and
the development of the bradycardia, typical for thiamine deficiency in the
rat. Fig. 7 shows the course of the experiment (averages of 10 animals).
On the 23rd day after applying a thiamine-deficient diet the weight curve
showed a tendency to drop and a bradycardia of 300 pulses/min had developed. Three injections of radioactive thiamine brought the pulse-rate
and the weight curve almost up to normal. At this stage the animals were
killed and the nerves shot into iso-propane, one group stimulated and the
symmetric nerves narcotized (ether vapour) in order to avoid the stimulus
of the cold iso-propane. Fig. 8 shows an autoradiogram of the alcoholic
extract of unstimulated and stimulated nerves and a control of 6.4 γ thia-
mine-^{35}S and thiazole-^{35}S obtained by the action of carp intestine thiaminase.
Both extracts of the nerves had initially the same counting rate for radioactivity, but in the paper the components of the resting nerve and the active
nerve behaved differently. This difference in the chemical composition of the
extracts is also obvious from the UV-absorption (Fig. 9). The stimulated
nerves contain at 265 mμ and at 220 mμ a greater amount of absorbing
material, although both extracts were prepared in an identical way. From
these experiments we conclude that the sequence of events which we are
studying now in great detail could be represented as follows:

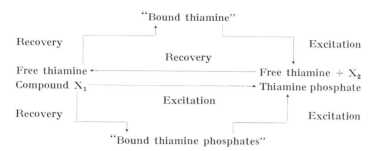

This is a very preliminary diagram, which will be the basis of further work, especially designed to identify X_1 and X_2.

SUMMARY

1. Thiamine is "liberated" during excitation of peripheral nerves.

2. Neopyrithiamine, as a competitor for thiamine, blocks nervous activity, oxythiamine has no effect.

3. Thiaminase from carp intestine and fern extracts have similar action, due to their anti-thiamine properties.

4. Thiamine in peripheral nerve is closely related to the functioning of the Na-transport system.

5. Labelled thiamine-^{35}S is differently distributed in resting and excited nerves. At rest a compound X appears together with thiamine, in the excited state it disappears and thiamine-phosphate appears instead.

6. Extracts from excited and unexcited nerves show a significant difference in UV-absorption at 265 and 220 mμ.

REFERENCES

1. HODGKIN, A. and HUXLEY, A. F., *J. Physiol.* **116**, 449 (1952).
2. KILB, H. and STÄMPFLI, R., *Helv. Physiol. Acta* **14**, 251 (1956).
3. KUNZ, H. A., *Helv. Physiol. Acta* **14**, 411 (1956).
4. LIECHTI, A., MURALT, A. VON and REINERT, M., *Helv. Physiol. Acta* **1**, 79 (1943).
5. MINZ, B., *Compt. rend. soc. biol.* **127**, 1251 (1938).
6. —— *Presse méd.* **76**, 1406 (1938).
7. MURALT, A. VON, *Pflügers Arch. ges. Physiol.* **245**, 604 (1942).
8. —— *Vitamins and Hormones* **5**, 93 (1947).
9. MURALT, A. VON and ZEMP, J., *Pflügers Arch. ges. Physiol.* **246**, 746 (1943).
10. MURALT, A. VON and ZOTTERMAN, Y., *J. Physiol.* **117**, 64 P (1952).
11. —— *Helv. Physiol. Acta* **10**, 279 (1952).
12. SOMOGYI, J. C., *Bull. Schweiz. Akad. Med. Wiss.* **10**, 446 (1954).
13. STÄMPFLI, R. and STRAUB, R., *Helv. Physiol. Acta* **12**, C 6 (1954).
14. WEIDMANN, S., *Experientia* **1**, 61 (1945).
15. —— *J. Physiol.* **127**, 213 (1955).
16. WYSS, F., *Helv. Physiol. Acta* **1**, C 70 (1943).
17. —— *ibid.* **2**, 121 (1944).
18. WYSS, A. and WYSS, F., *ibid.* **3**, C 30 (1945).
19. —— *Experientia* **1**, 160 (1945).

THE NERVE CELL MEMBRANE

Experimental Cell Research, Suppl. **5,** *83–100 (1958)*

TRANSPORT PROCESSES IN MEMBRANES IN RELATION TO THE NERVE MECHANISM

T. TEORELL

Institute of Physiology, The University of Uppsala, Uppsala, Sweden

Iɴ this paper the emphasis will be placed on an analysis of the driving forces of the ionic events in the nerve processes. This kind of approach will be mainly physico-chemical and necessarily subject to many shortcomings. It permits the following formulation of some of the neurophysiological problems.

The resting ionic composition and ionic distribution (particularly the problem of potassium–sodium selectivity).

Ionic transfers in action ("fluxes" implying also analyses of energy-supplying chemical processes).

Electrogenesis. This is linked to the two preceding ones (as well as to those following). It concerns the formation of (*a*) the *resting potential* and (*b*) the *action potential. The action current* Is of equal importance to the potential. Related to this are the so-called impedance properties (see below).

Rhythmicity (in the form of the "frequency modulated" action spikes). Related problems have to deal with "local response" and electrotonic phenomena, which leads to the next point.

Threshold properties. A certain amount of energy (electrical, chemical, mechanical etc.) has to be introduced in order to release the nerve or receptor action, i.e. the change from the resting state into the rhythmical response. Another way of restating the problem is to label it "triggering" and "accommodation".

Transducing problems. This implies in general the mechanism by which the receptors are able to transform other physical quantities into electricity, e.g. light, pressure or temperature, etc., into electrical signals.

Impedance properties. This implies ohmic *resistance, capacitance* and *inductance.* It is well known that the resistance changes concomitantly with the action potential and that most living tissues have a remarkably high capacity (of the order of several microfarads per cm^2). There is quite a spectacular occurrence of inductance under special conditions (according to Cole and other workers). All these three impedance components are certainly closely related to *rectification*, which can also be found to a greater or lesser degree in living matter.

Propagation. This is the most conspicuous nerve phenomenon, which is certainly closely linked with the problem of stability–instability and which lies behind the general mechanisms of rhythmicity or oscillatory behavior of nerve action. It is one of the very first observations of electrophysiology, but it is the one least rationally explained.

All the problems stated tentatively above under different headings have to be covered by a decent physico-chemical theory, or theories. Of course, it is impossible in the present state of knowledge to achieve this, and it might well be a foolish misconception to attempt it. Nevertheless it seems advantageous to look upon all of these problems from a unified point of view and not think about them individually, or in combinations of a few. Most recent papers in this field have defined the nerve problem in terms of *transport of ions*. This is certainly a fruitful approach, although it is important not to forget the biochemical aspect, which, after all, must lie behind all the dynamic events that we encounter in the nerve mechanism.

After this statement of the main problems we will first briefly review some formulations of the kinetics of the problems and then consider more fully the problem of rhythmicity.

SURVEY OF TRANSPORT KINETICS

For simplicity we start with *Ohm's law*, i.e. the flow of current is equal to 1 over the resistance times the potential:

$$\underbrace{\frac{\text{Current}}{\text{(I)}}}_{} = \underbrace{\frac{(1/\text{Resistance})}{(1/R)}}_{} \times \underbrace{\frac{(\text{Potential difference})}{(\varphi_2 - \varphi_1)}}_{}$$

where $(1/Resistance) = Conductance$ $(G) =$ Sum of (Conc. $\times$ Mobility) over all the different ionic species. This is an elementary formulation, but may emphasize the three main parameters in electrophysiology, namely *potential*, *current* and *conductance*. Accordingly one ought not to confine the measurements only to the potential, as is often the case. We can never discuss neurophysiological mechanisms with profit unless we expand our measurements to all these three variables. Later on we will add a fourth one, the *pressure*, which may be quite important.

Ohm's law of current flow is nothing but a transcription of the so-called *flux equation* for the transport of ions:

Flux-equations

Electrical "flux":

$$\text{Current} = \frac{\text{Potential difference}}{\text{Resistance}},$$

$$\text{Current} = \text{Conductance} \times \text{Potential difference}.$$

Molecular flux (Fick's law):

$$\text{Flux} = K \times \text{Mobility} \times \text{Concentration difference}.$$
$$\phi \qquad (u) \qquad\qquad (C_2 - C_1)$$

Ionic flux (Behn's law):

$$\text{Flux} = K \times \text{Mobility} \times (\text{Electrochemical activity difference}),$$
$$\phi = K \times u \times (C_2 \xi - C_1),$$

where $\xi = e^{\frac{\varphi_2 - \varphi_1}{25}}$ and $(\varphi_2 - \varphi_1)$ is the "transmembrane potential". The flux ϕ is the number of ions passing through a certain membrane in the time unit, K is a constant, u is the mobility of an ion and C_1, C_2 are "inside" and "outside" concentrations. Strictly speaking, it is not these "bulk" concentrations we ought to work with but rather those prevailing at the interfaces of the membrane, because concentration jumps can under certain circumstances appear right at the membrane surfaces. This is due to the fact that the biological membranes in all probability contain chemical groups, positive and negative as the case may be, which are *fixed* in the stationary membrane matrix (the "fixed charge theory"). The presence of these fixed charges introduces a number of extra complications in the theories and enter the calculations in the constant K as a function of a symbol (ωX), where ω signifies the sign of the fixed group charges (being carboxyl groups or amino groups etc.) and X is their density or volume concentration.

These flux equations are actually the basis for all quantitative "permeability" theories. From them one can deduct the potential in terms of the concentration inside and outside, the mobility of cations and of anions and maybe other factors. Such potential formulations are well-known as Nernst or Planck's diffusion potential formula, or offsprings or extensions of formulas by Henderson, Teorell–Meyer–Sievers, Schlögl, Ussing, Hodgkin *et al.*, and many others.

Besides expressions for the electrical potential, which commonly interest neuro-physiologists, one can also derive whole sets of formulas covering such other interesting aspects as ionic fluxes, membrane conductances, rectification properties etc. (Such formulations can be found in the literature; see for example [1].) Again we emphasize the simple basic fact that transport or flux is proportional to the driving forces and inversely proportional to the resistance encountered. In a general fashion the flux equation can be written as

Generalized flux equation

Rate of Transport = Conc. × Mobility × Sum of Driving Forces

"Permeability" in strict sense	$[f_1(C) + f_2(E) + f_3(P)]$ "superposition principle"

1. *Ion factors:*
 	
   size, hydration, solubility etc.
 	
2. *Membrane factors:*
 	
   pore size, chem. composition (charge, solvent action etc.)
	1. Conc. (activity) gradients "chemical potential", C.
	2. Electr. potential gradient, E.
	3. Hydrostatic pressure gradient, P.

One observes that in the scheme the inverse of the resistance (or friction) has been called "mobility". The mobility is dependent both on properties of the penetrating ions and factors arising from the membrane structures. The mobility corresponds to the "permeability" in the actual, narrow sense. It is not a transport as such, because this is also dependent on the sum of the direction and magnitude of the driving forces. If this sum happens to be zero there will be no transport although the ions may be fully "permeable". Such a state of affairs constitutes what we have called "apparent impermeability" [5].

DIFFERENT TRANSPORT PROCESSES IN RELATION TO THE

DRIVING FORCES

In the scheme above for ion fluxes one finds *concentration* gradients and gradients of *electrical* potential as driving forces. The combination of these two has been increasingly appreciated in all modern theories of nerve action (in particular those of the Cambridge school). The special consideration of the *pressure* difference as a driving force is not, however, very common. By pressure we mean the difference in hydrostatic pressure between the inside and the outside of the membrane, or the cell. The pressure factor is usually employed in discussions of fluid transport across blood capillaries, but it is not often discussed in relation to a cell or tissue and its environment. This might appear strange, as we here have to deal with a driving force, which can be applied to the transport of water, or tissue fluid. If one could somehow measure pressure differences across the cell or nerve membrane, one might find a hydrostatic pressure difference with the excess pressure in-

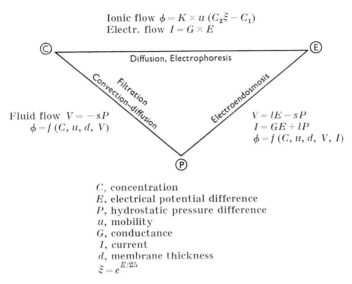

Ionic flow $\phi = K \times u\,(C_2\xi - C_1)$
Electr. flow $I = G \times E$

Diffusion, Electrophoresis

Convection
Filtration
Convection-diffusion

Electroendosmosis

Fluid flow $V = -sP$
$\phi = f\,(C, u, d, V)$

$V = lE - sP$
$I = GE + lP$
$\phi = f\,(C, u, d, V, I)$

C, concentration
E, electrical potential difference
P, hydrostatic pressure difference
u, mobility
G, conductance
I, current
d, membrane thickness
$\xi = e^{E/25}$

Fig. 1.—*Scheme of transport processes* arising from the three main driving forces encountered in biological systems (chemical potential, electrical potential, hydrostatic "potential"). The corresponding transport equations ("flow") are given along the sides of this "transport triangle".

side the cell. The pressure is likely to be there for several reasons, which will be discussed later on. The order need not be very large; perhaps only one or a few millimeters of mercury. We may challenge biologists to find if this is true or not.

It might be instructive to assemble the three driving forces, which we place as the corners of a triangle, being differences of *concentration C*, *electrical potential difference E* and hydrostatic *pressure difference P*, see Fig. 1.

The scheme is not free from objections, but it can help to show the different phenomena arising from the interplay between any pair of the three forces. In this scheme are also assembled some of the expressions for flux or flow. Note that we are always working with flow, force and resistances. It is instructive to observe that we have to deal with *three* different "permeability coefficients", namely *u* representing the mobility or the *ionic* permeability, *s* signifying the *hydrostatic* permeability and *l* being the *electro-osmotic*

T. Teorell

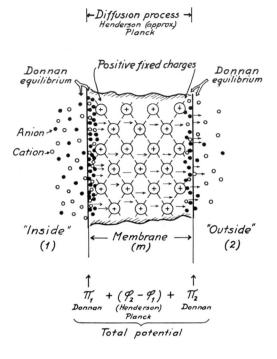

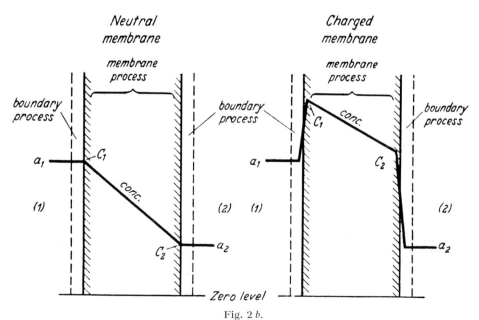

Fig. 2.—*Some features of the "fixed charge theory" of membrane permeability.* (a) The basic concept of the ionic distribution at a positively charged membrane, also showing the composite nature of the total transmembrane potential. (b) The shape of the concentration "profile" at a "neutral" and a "charged" membrane (note the jumps at the membrane boundaries in the latter case). (c) The fixed charge theory applied to a single electrolyte HCl. The diagram shows the course of the ion concentrations and of the electric potential. (d) Concentration profiles in a case of interdiffusion of a mixture of various electrolytes. In this case there will occur a transport "against the concentration gradient" of the K ions (note that the intramembrane profile of K is sloping from side (2) to side (1)). (From ref. [2]).

Fig. 2 a.

Fig. 2 b.

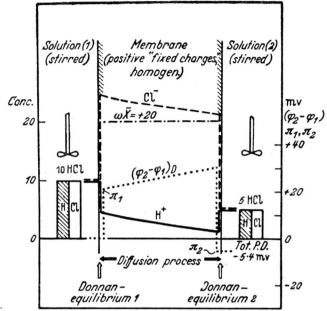

Fig. 2 c.

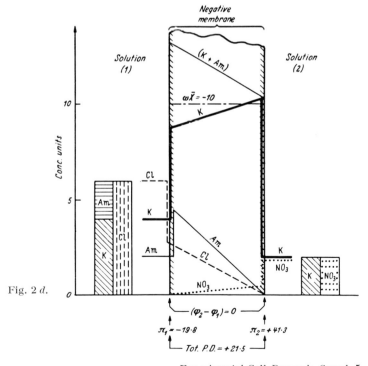

Fig. 2 d.

permeability (*s* is related to the porosity and *l* to the fixed charge density of the membrane). We wish especially to draw attention to the new symbol *V* denoting the velocity of flow of the fluid. In the presence of only a pressure difference the flow is proportional to this difference, $V = -sP$. This is just the law of *filtration*. If, however, an electrical potential is simultaneously present, there will be an additional term, lE, to the velocity of flow (provided *l* is not zero, which simply means that the membrane is "charged"). This cooperation between pressure and electrical force constitutes the well-known phenomenon of *electro-endosmosis*.[1]

To recapitulate, the operation of the three driving forces in superposition leads to different processes of flow, namely *flow of solutes* (="flux"), *flow of water* (="flow") and *flow of electricity* (="current"). The cooperation between the three forces may, at first sight, have as a consequence some unexpected transport phenomena. This is particularly true if the membrane carries a "fixed charge", as probably most biological membranes may do because of their chemical composition, built up, as they are, of a framework of proteins, lipoids and so on. One can thus predict the appearance of (*a*) more or less unique selectivity for cation or anion permeability, (*b*) transport against concentration gradients and (*c*) the appearance of very marked unequal individual ionic distributions inside and outside the cell membrane. We will not dwell on these particular aspects here as they have been described in great detail in several previous works. (The basic ideas and some consequences may be visualized with the aid of Fig. 2 *a–d* (for a review see [1, 2]). We wish to turn to some new aspects arising from a special consideration of the pressure force and its connection with the transport of water across the membranes. This approach leads to some new aspects of *rhythmicity*, which might be of interest in connection with the discussions on the mechanism of nerve and receptor actions.

RHYTHMICAL TRANSPORT PHENOMENA IN MEMBRANES

The special aspects of rhythmical or oscillatory phenomena to be described refer to experiments on models with artificial membranes and the theories attempting to explain the phenomena are purely physico-chemical and

---

[1] The additive law for electroendosmotic flow has to be supplemented with an equation describing the electric flow, i.e. the current, *I*. This leads again to Ohm's law, but with the introduction into this of an additive term, *lP*, allowing for the so-called streaming current. As one can notice from the scheme, this leads to the appearance of *l* as a "cross-coefficient". This is an interesting feature because it is exactly what can be derived by means of irreversible thermodynamics, which has been developed in the past 15 years, and which has helped a great deal in obtaining sharp formulations of biological transport phenomena.

mathematical. We have not the slightest idea as to whether our ideas are applicable to biological systems or not. This point should be emphasized very strongly. For the purpose of this symposium we will venture to shape the presentation somewhat in neuro-physiological terms. It might lead to objections and discussions, or ideas leading to the design of further experiments on living objects—it will then have served a useful purpose.

The basic philosophy behind our reasoning is this: It is probably an error to assume, as so often has been done in the past, that the water is immobile or "frozen" in biological tissues. The water molecules are certainly highly mobile and driving forces certainly exist in the form of osmotic and hydrostatic pressure gradients and as an electro-osmotic force. The last item requires, as we already have mentioned, two things: first that the membrane pores carry fixed charges, and secondly that there exists a potential gradient. The existence of pores, which carry electrical charges along their walls, seems to be a reasonable assumption from what is known about the chemical composition of biological membranes. As to the potential, it certainly is present, but it has also to be maintained. This means that we have to assume flowing electrical currents, but these seem to exist, at least "in action", when more or less "active" ionic migration occurs. There is finally a third provision which has to be allowed, namely that the membrane separates ionic solutions of different conductance inside and outside. This amounts actually to saying, in general terms, that the membrane exhibits a *rectification* for D.C.

EXPERIMENT WITH THE "MEMBRANE OSCILLATOR"

Let us now construct a model which exhibits the features we have assumed exist in some living membranes and study its behaviour. The *experimental model* was built up according to the scheme depicted in Fig. 3 (see also reference [3]).

In the centre is a membrane of porous glass or porcelain containing silicic acid ions, which gives it a negative charge. On purpose it is rather thick, about 1 mm, and is also rather porous. There is an assymmetry across the membrane, in this case created by having $N/10$ sodium chloride on one side and $N/100$ on the other side. This is the simplest method of achieving rectification in the membrane. It can obviously be created in other ways too. The important thing now is to introduce electro-osmosis by a constant electric current flowing across the membrane. This is done by adding a battery in the external circuit; the constancy is maintained experimentally by adding a high resistance in series. By aid of the arrangements seen in the figure one can now record (*a*) the potential drop across the membrane, (*b*) the membrane resistance, and (*c*) the pressure difference across the membrane (by means of a differential manometer). All the variables are simultaneously recorded on a multipoint recorder.

In this model we inject the chemical energy at a constant rate from the
battery through the electrodes in the inside and outside solutions, which means
that we supply a constant D.C. current. How Nature would do it in living
membranes we do not know, but it is certainly a coupling between chemical

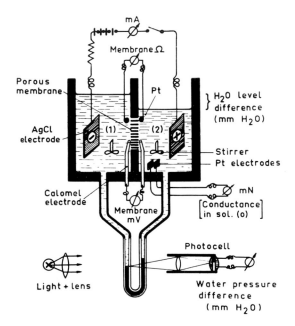

Fig. 3.—*Scheme of the experimental set
up of the "membrane oscillator"* (from
reference [3]).

processes and ionic events. This coupling is in fact one of the most important
problems to be solved in the future. It amounts to revealing the mechanism
of what has been called "active transport" or ion "pumps".

Some *typical results* are shown in Fig. 4 (cf. reference [3]). If we first
examine the experiment with the lowest current density ("1 mA") one
observes that a hydrostatic pressure head is built up (the heavy black line).
This is caused by a flow of water across the membrane towards the negative
pole (because the water behaves as if it were positive in relation to the
fixed negative charge of the membrane). This is straight-forward *electro-
endosmosis,* and one would perhaps expect that the attainment of a constant
difference of level would be the end of it (representing a steady state where
the water pressure balances the electric drive). But as the figures reveal,
this is not the case, at least not if we "stimulate" with the higher current
densities (2 and 3 mA/cm²). Instead one gets oscillatory curves, first a
damped and then an undamped response, just as if there was a "threshold"

around 2.5 mA/cm². The potential "spikes" (the dotted line) might appeal to the neuro-physiologists. Their shape is far from sinusoidal and more like so-called relaxation oscillations, somewhat similar to the actual nerve action potentials.

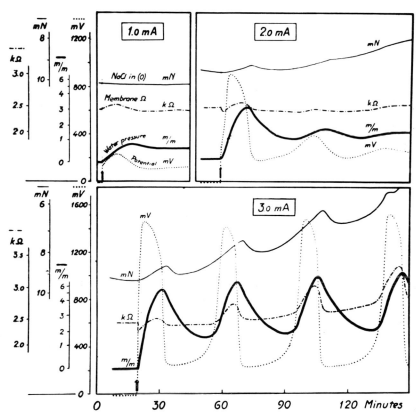

Fig. 4.—*Results obtained with "membrane oscillator" at different, constant current densities* (1, 2 and 3 mA/cm² respectively). Note the undamped oscillations released at a "threshold" between 2 and 2 mA/cm². The oscillations are of a relaxation type, particularly the potential "spikes" at "3 mA".

To summarize: what the membrane arrangement is doing is transforming the D.C. into an A.C. as regards the potential, so we actually have here a kind of "membrane oscillator". The most conspicuous feature is the *periodic transport of water* forward and back across the membrane. Whether this is something that happens in nerves concomitantly with spikes, we do not of course know, but it would be of interest if somebody started to search for such water movements. Another interesting feature of this membrane oscil-

lator is that it shows a definite *threshold behavior* as regards the effect of stimulation with increasing currents, just as the excitable tissues show. We will
return to this aspect somewhat later when discussing "triggering".

We have not said much about the membrane resistance. Actually it shows
an inverse behavior to the potential, which means, as the current is kept
constant, that Ohm's law is approximately obeyed.

These are the experimental findings and one might now ask for an explanation as to how all of these oscillatory phenomena are brought about. On this
occasion we have to refrain from giving more than a sketch of the main ideas
behind the physico-chemical and mathematical reasoning. A tentative theory
can be found in another publication [4].

The theoretical background of the membrane oscillator

The basic ideas of the quantitative theory rest (*a*) on the *rectification*, or
rather the resistance changes, exhibited in our model system, and (*b*) on a
time lag in these resistance variations.

In order to elucidate first how the resistance can change we will resort to
Fig. 5. In this we have a diagrammatic presentation of what variation of the
pressure, or rather the bulk flow, does to the membrane resistance. The
attention should be focused on the "concentration profiles" within the membrane. The bulk flow will distort the straight line profile of the pure diffusion
case A (velocity $V = 0$) to a bent curve. From these "maps" of the concentration distribution within the membrane one realizes that the membrane
resistance will be roughly inversely proportional to the shaded areas under
the concentration profiles in the sections A, B, and C. The quantitative relation between the direction and magnitude of flow, V, as induced by the
pressure difference and the corresponding *steady state* resistance of the membrane, R^∞, can be seen in the bottom section of Fig. 5. In mathematical abbre-
viation we can express this function $R^\infty = f(V)$. This somewhat S-shaped relation between velocity of flow and resistance is actually the key function of
these oscillatory phenomena. If there appears an extra force affecting the
velocity of flow, introduced by applying an electric potential, we get the
electro-endosmotic system discussed earlier in this paper with an additive
electric term. (Again using mathematical symbols one can state that $V = -sP$
(pressure term) $+ lE$ (electric term)). So much for the relation between the
fluid flow across the membrane and its electrical resistance in the steady
state or equilibrium.

Now for the second point regarding the time delay. This is more difficult
to appreciate in a brief presentation but can be hinted at as follows. First

we imagine that we have attained a steady state of matter (as depicted in section *B* of the scheme of Fig. 5) with a very bent, almost L-shaped concentration profile. If we then, by some means, suddenly achieve an arrest of the flow of the fluid across the membrane, the bent concentration profile

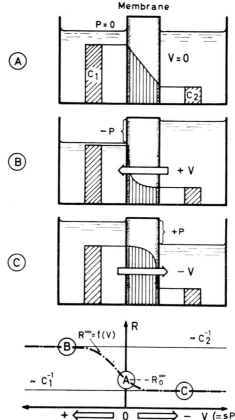

Fig. 5.—*Concentration profiles in a porous membrane* at different velocities (*V*) of bulk flow. (The bottom section shows the relation between membrane resistance (R^∞) and velocity of bulk flow (*V*) at the steady state.)

will strive to revert to the straight line profile (corresponding to section A, where $V = 0$). This adjustment is a diffusion process, but diffusion is a slow process and will therefore require some time, i.e. a *time delay* will appear. Very much the same will now happen for *any* change of the velocity of the flow; there will be a kind of competition between the effect of the flow and that of the diffusion. (In mathematical terms this time delay of change of *R* can be expressed as dR/dt and roughly be put proportional to the "divergence from the equilibrium value", i.e. $-dR/dt = k(R-R^\infty)$.)

We have now, at last, collected the necessary information about our model system to enable us to work out an understanding of its behavior as regards possible oscillations. This information can be summarized in the following system of equations:

$$
\begin{cases}
V = -sP + lE & \text{(electro-osmotic flow velocity)} & (1) \\
E = IR & \text{(Ohm's law)} & (2) \\
R^{\infty} = f(V) & \text{(resistance-velocity relation)} & (3) \\
-dR/dt = k(R - R^{\infty}) & \text{(time delay function)} & (4) \\
V = q \cdot dP/dt & \text{(geometry requirement)[1]} & (5)
\end{cases}
$$

It is perhaps not easy to understand off-hand how the concepts laid down in these five equations above may lead to a solution showing oscillations with time with regard to the variables of interest. However, by an appropriate treatment of the five expressions one can arrive at a system of two simultaneous differential equations of the following type (where for easier recognition we substitute y for the potential difference E and x for the pressure difference P).

$$
\begin{cases}
dy/dt = ax + by \\
dx/dt = cx + dy
\end{cases}
$$

An equation system of this type is in our case best solved graphically (by means of the so-called "isocline" method, for which reference may be made to textbooks). An analogue computer machine is also highly useful.

The solutions turn out to be *cyclical functions of x and y with time*, provided certain conditions are fulfilled which we cannot enter into now.

In order to hint at the type of procedure used and results obtained reference is made to Fig. 6, which is a rather composite figure. It starts actually with the relations between the resistance R and the flow velocity V in the oblique section to the right above. From this is calculated the interrelation between the potential E and the pressure P in form of a "path" which, in this particular case, will move along into a so-called limit cycle (the black "spiral" in the centre section). Actually, the path would strive to move to a point Q inside this cycle, which is the "equilibrium point" where the system would be at rest. However, if the current is strong enough, as it is here, one can show that the cycle will stay outside the equilibrium point, which means that one gets an undamped oscillation. On the E–P path one can now by a rather simple procedure insert points of equal time intervals and then replot E or P or V against time as can be seen at the edges of the figure.

---

[1] The fifth equation just describes the fact that the velocity of flow is proportional to the rate of change in pressure as demanded by the geometry of the experimental arrangement of Fig. 3.

If one compares these theoretical E versus t and P versus t curves with the potential and pressure curves which were obtained experimentally, as in Fig. 4, one finds a reasonably good agreement between theory and observation.

THE MEMBRANE OSCILLATOR AS AN ELECTRO-MECHANICAL
TRANSDUCER MODEL

(1) In the experimental and theoretical model which we have discussed so far, we have actually regarded the pressure as being set at zero at the time $t = 0$. This can be seen in the composite diagram (Fig. 6) where the $E - P$ path starts at $P = 0$. Furthermore, it was assumed that the potential and the pressure could, so to speak, follow one another in a "voluntary" manner. It would, however, equally well be possible to have this system "pre-set" at a

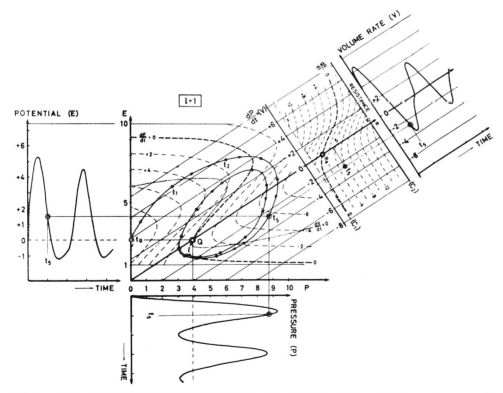

Fig. 6.—*A composite chart illustrating a graphical solution* of the equations for the membrane oscillator (see text). The theoretically predicted curves are the three sections at the edges where "Time" is the abscissa.

certain pressure difference at the very start of the application of the "stimulating" current and by some arrangement maintaining the pressure constant
at the pre-fixed level. Fig. 7 may hint at what could be expected from such
a system. We have three different conditions *a*, *b*, and *c* fixed at three different

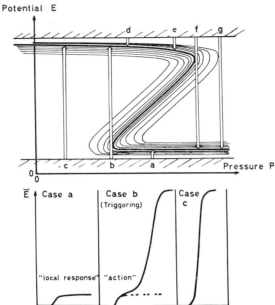

Fig. 7.—*A scheme showing how various
"pre-set" pressure differences ($P = a$, b,
or c) result in several types of electrical
potential response* (Cases *a*, *b*, and *c*
respectively). Note the similarity to
neurophysiological "local response"
and its transition into a full "action".

alternatives of pressure. In the figure some dE/dt "isoclines"[1] are drawn
very schematically (the "Z-shaped" curves). The heaviest line makes the
isocline = 0, which means that the potential here stays constant with time.
If to these three conditions respectively one applies the "stimulus", i.e. the
current, one obtains three different types of electric potential response as
indicated in Fig. 7 (case *a–c*). The main idea in this demonstration is to
point out the possibility that a small difference in the initial pressure is of
decisive importance for the outcome of the electrical response. This means
that a decrease, or increase, as the case may be, of the pressure may release
or trigger this response. We actually have here *a coupling between "mechanical" pressure and electrical events.*

(2) In the triggering mechanism just mentioned the shape of the $dE/dt = 0$
isocline was of primary importance for the outcome of the potential events.
One notices that the Z-shaped form of the potential isoclines made triggering
of the potential spikes possible at the "corners" of the Z (case *b* or *f*). We will

---

[1] An "isocline" is a locus for all points having the same rate of change, say dE/dt = a constant.

now pursue these concepts a little further. The theory shows that the inclination of the sloping part of the *Z*, among other things, determines whether one obtains a damped or undamped oscillation. Imagine that one has a section of the isoclines which has a somewhat less steep inclination just around

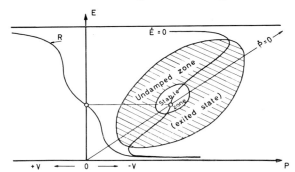

Fig. 8. *A hypothetical scheme of a possible triggering mechanism* of an electric potential response (*E*) by means of changes of a pressure difference (*P*). For details, see text.

the equilibrium point as is shown in Fig. 8. Then one can reason that this area (the unshaded area in the centre) would represent a "damped" or stable region with regard to potential and pressure, tending to a final stability. The system will here prefer to attain and maintain a "resting state". This state could, however, be upset by increasing, or decreasing, the pressure enough to come outside of the stable zone (unshaded). In the shaded zone, concentric with the stable one, the isocline conditions are such that the *E–P* variation will form a "limit cycle" and hence continuous undamped oscillations of potential and of pressure will appear. However, another external pressure change can again force the system back into the central zone of stability. The system would, in other words, behave as a *pressure sensitive triggering device, i.e. as a mechano-electrical transducer.* Of course, these ideas are very vague, but they may indicate something which might operate in living matter.

FINAL REMARKS

The kind of reasoning which has been applied here to the coupling of two physical factors (electrical potential and pressure) can be expanded in various ways. It should be remembered that we have to explain in electrophysiology, rhythmicity, triggering action, threshold action etc., and it means that one has to deal with systems which show an inherent tendency towards instability. Such a condition can actually be achieved in the membrane oscillator system proposed in this paper. It is tempting to assume that systems of this type, which can be made unstable, may also show properties of propagation, perhaps the most conspicuous characteristic of the nerve mechanism. We have not as yet, however, pursued this aspect as regards our membrane oscillator.

Again, it should be emphasized, that the rough similarity that the behavior of our artificial membrane system sometimes shows with some features of living cells does not imply that we suggest that the same mechanims are actually operating there. Our intention has merely been to show a mode of attack in our attempts to elucidate the nerve mechanism. Some practical consequences of these intentions could be summarized as a kind of "recipe": in a rational electro-physiology one ought to determine not only the electrical potential (E), but also the resistance (R), the concentration changes (C), the resting or action currents (I) and, above all, possible changes of pressure differences across the active membranes (P). This *recipe* is a logical, maybe somewhat artificial, result of our mode of looking upon the nerve phenomena as transport processes caused by the operation of well-defined physical forces acting in superposition.

SUMMARY

The main problems concerning the electrical events in the nerve processes are stated and a survey of the kinetics of possible underlying transport mechanisms is given.

An analysis of the effect of including the hydrostatic pressure as a driving transport force in addition to that arising from a difference in electro-chemical potential is presented. It is shown that the mutual interaction of electro-chemical and hydrostatic "pressure" differences can result in oscillatory membrane phenomena revealed by periodic variations of the membrane potential, the membrane conductance and the pressure difference (and of the bulk flow). Some necessary conditions for these rhythmicity phenomena are the presence of a fixed charge and of an electric current flow in a porous membrane.

Some experimental and theoretical aspects of these "membrane oscillators" are discussed. Finally some possible implications are presented relating to electro-physiological "triggering" and "transduction".

REFERENCES

1. TEORELL, T., *Z. Elektrochem.* **55**, 460 (1951).
2. —— Progress of Biophysics. Vol. 3, p. 305. Pergamon Press, London & New York, 1953.
3. —— *Exptl. Cell Research, Suppl. 3*, 339 (1955).
4. —— *Acta Soc. Med. Upsaliensis* **62**, 60 (1957).
5. —— *Ann. Rev. Physiol.* **11**, 545 (1949).

Experimental Cell Research, Suppl. **5,** *101- 117 (1958)*

HISTOCHEMICAL DEMONSTRATION OF PHOSPHATASES IN THE CENTRAL NERVOUS SYSTEM OF THE RAT

G. H. BOURNE

Department of Anatomy, Emory University, Emory, Georgia, U.S.A.

THERE are very few detailed histochemical studies of the distribution of phosphatases in the central nervous system. Naidoo and Pratt have recorded a series of investigations on the distribution of phosphatases hydrolysing various esters at different pH values [3, 4, 5] and the present author has published a brief note [2].

The present study deals with the distribution of enzymes in the cerebrum and cerebellum of the rat which hydrolyse a variety of phosphate esters at a pH of 9.0.

METHODS

Rat brains on removal from the animal were sliced transversely and the central slice passing through both cerebral hemispheres and the brain stem and a slice passing through the cerebellum and brain stem, were fixed in ice cold acetone for 12 hours. Their dehydration was then completed, they were cleared in methyl benzoate, embedded in paraffin wax and sectioned at 10 μ.

The standard Gomori substrate mixture was used for incubation purposes. In some cases the substrate was β glycerophosphate, in others it was either oestrone, hexoestrol or cortisone phosphate, glucose-1-phosphate, fructose-1-phosphate, galactose phosphate, riboflavin-5-phosphate, pyridoxal phosphate, carbamyl phosphate, ethanolamine phosphate, phosphorylated hesperidin and carboxy-phenyl phosphate (a synthetic, non-natural, substance).

Only microgram amounts of the steroid phosphates were soluble in the incubation mixture so that long incubation times had to be used with these substrates (8 hours). Other substrates were readily soluble in the amounts used (25 mg per cent). Incubation times with these were 30 minutes in all cases.

Sections were visualized by the standard technique using cobalt chloride and ammonium sulphide and mounted in balsam. No counterstains were used.

It is not known whether phosphorylated steroids have any metabolic significance; the significance of sugar phosphates is of course well-known. Riboflavin and pyridoxal phosphates are of course co-enzymes; carbamyl phosphate is an intermediary in urea metabolism; the role of ethanolamine phosphate is uncertain but it is believed to play some part in lipoid metabolism; phosphorylated hesperidin is of doubtful physiological significance, and carboxy-phenyl phosphate is a compound which living tissues would not normally encounter since it is synthetic.

RESULTS

Glycerophosphate

With this substrate the first elements to give a reaction (which is intense) were the whole capillary system in both cerebrum and cerebellum, and the pia mater. With slightly longer incubation an area of the cortex immediately under the pia, which appears to correspond with the plexiform layer, gave a strong diffuse reaction (Fig. 1). The cytoplasm of the cells in this region was difficult to distinguish but the nuclei of these cells were intensely positive. In the case of the cerebellum the other structures which showed up at this stage (30 minutes incubation) were the nucleoli of the Purkinje cells. There is at this stage also, in the outer half of the cerebral cortex, a faint diffuse reaction in the intercellular[1] tissue. Further incubation led to an increase in this reaction. The pyramidal cells in the cortex all showed negative cytoplasm and dendritic processes but slightly positive nuclei. The negative reaction by many of these cells is due in part to the presence in the cytoplasm of large vacuoles, due no doubt to the solvent action of the acetone used for fixation. However, it is noteworthy that the strands of cytoplasmic material which remain are also negative. Also, not all the cells show these large vacuoles and in those in which they do not occur the cytoplasm has no phosphatase reaction. In some cases there appeared to be an aggregation of phosphatase positive material along the membranes of the dendrites but this was more obvious with other substrates. The intercellular tissue in the middle portion of the cortex, even at half an hour was much darker than the outer portion

---

[1] The term "intercellular tissue" is used to refer simply to the tissue between the cell bodies. It is used only as a literary convenience.

Fig. 1.—Outer portion of cerebral cortex of rat. Substrate: glycerophosphate. Note positive pia mater, plexiform layer, capillaries and intercellular substance, and "negative" cell bodies (due partly to vacuolation of cells by acetone treatment) with slightly positive nuclei.

Fig. 2.—Outer portion of cerebral cortex of rat. Substrate: carbamyl phosphate. Note reactions of various elements similar to Fig. 1, *except* that all nuclei positive and most capillaries negative or slightly positive. Concentration of positively reacting material along the dendritic membranes which are themselves negative.

Fig. 3.—Outer portion of cerebral cortex of rat. Substrate: glucose-1-phosphate. Reaction fundamentally similar to glycerophosphate but not so broad in plexiform layer.

Fig. 4.—Outer portion of cerebral cortex of rat. Substrate: pyridoxal phosphate. Reaction similar to glycerophosphate, *except* that many cells with positive cytoplasm and nuclei are scattered among "negative" cells.

Fig. 5.—Ventro-lateral end of cerebral cortex. Substrate: glycerophosphate. Note intense reaction of intercellular material, positive nuclei and "negative" cell bodies.

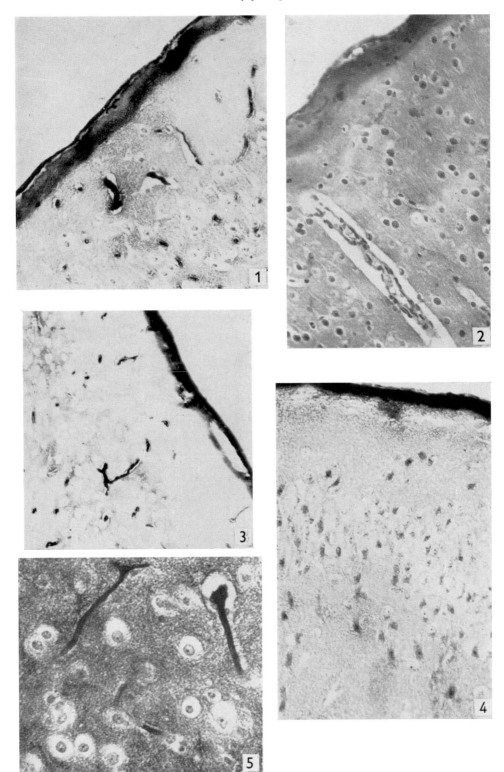

though not as dark as the plexiform layer (Fig. 6). The innermost portion of the cortex at this stage remained completely negative and even after long incubation showed very little reaction. However, in the brain stem itself various structures gave a strong reaction. The nuclei and particularly the nucleoli of the hippocampal cells gave a strong positive reaction and the tissue in between and surrounding the lateral ventricles was moderately positive. A strongly positive area was also found in the floor of the third ventricle (Figs. 27, 28). The intercellular tissue in the ventro-lateral ends of the cerebral cortex were intensely positive and all the cells present showed a positive nucleus and completely negative cytoplasm (Fig. 5). Another strongly positive structure was the striatum globus (Fig. 23). Both the transverse and the longitudinal fibres were positive to about an equal degree. There are certain elongated cells associated with the transverse fibres which had a positive cytoplasm and an intensely positive nucleus. A number of other cells were present in both groups of fibres in which the nucleus and particularly the nucleolus were positive and the cytoplasm completely negative. There was a moderate reaction by the ground substance of the lateral geniculate bodies (Fig. 31). In the cerebellum the white layer was a little more positive than the gray matter but even in the former the reaction was very slight. The choroid plexus was intensely positive, particularly in the stroma (Fig. 19).

Sugar phosphatases

With both glucose-1-phosphate (Fig. 3) and galactose phosphate the pia gave an extremely strong reaction but with fructose-1-phosphate it gave only a slight reaction. However, with all three substrates the plexiform layer was strongly positive. Only a slight reaction was given by the intercellular material of the cerebral cortex at 30 minutes incubation but it became more positive with

---

Fig. 6.—Deeper part of cerebral cortex of rat. Substrate: glycerophosphate. Note positive nucleoli, intercellular substance and capillaries with "negative" cell bodies and dendrites.

Fig. 7.—Deeper part of cerebral cortex of rat. Substrate: ethanolamine phosphate. Note reaction similar to glycerophosphate but nuclei intensely positive, intercellular material very positive and strong positive reaction along membranes of dendrites.

Fig. 8.—Deeper part of cerebral cortex of rat. Substrate: oestrone-3-phosphate. Reaction similar to ethanolamine phosphate. Note strong reaction along membranes of dendrites.

Fig. 9.—Deeper part of cerebral cortex of rat. Substrate: pyridoxal phosphate. Only a few positive cells present. Positive nucleoli in most cells. "Negative" cell bodies and positive intercellular material.

Fig. 10.—Deeper part of cerebral cortex of rat. Substrate: carboxy-phenyl phosphate. Reaction similar to ethanolamine phosphate but nuclei only slightly positive and capillaries positive.

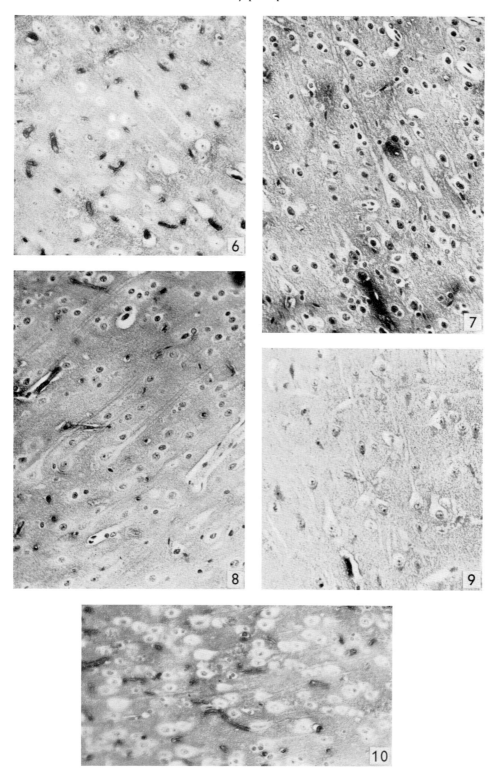

longer incubation times. The majority of the pyramidal cells again showed negative cytoplasm and positive nucleoli, although deeper in the cortex, with all three substrates; a number of pyramidal cells, i.e. those with angular rather than rounded bodies, had positive nuclei, positive cytoplasm and positive processes (Fig. 16). There appeared to be more of this type of cell in the fructose-1-phosphate preparations. The capillaries were strongly positive with the galactose and glucose preparations but only moderately so with fructose phosphate (Fig. 18). The choroid plexus was strongly positive with all substrates.

The structures, viz. lateral geniculate bodies, floor of the third ventricle, striatum globus and ventro-lateral ends of the cerebrum, which were shown to be positive with glycerophosphate, were also positive with these three substrates.

The cerebellum showed considerable individual variation in the reaction of the capillaries even with the same substrates—this is unlike the reaction given with glycerophosphate where they all gave a very intense reaction. With the three substrates the nucleoli of the Purkinje cells were all strongly positive, but with galactose phosphate there was a moderate reaction by the cell body.

Steroid phosphates

The reactions given by the use of oestrone and cortisone phosphates as substrates were very similar. In each case the pia mater was positive, this being due largely to the strong positive reaction given by the nuclei, the plexiform layer was positive and the capillaries were variable in their reaction but in none was the reaction strong. All the pyramidal cells in the outer and middle cortex had completely negative cell bodies and dendrites—all dendrites showed extremely well a strong reaction associated with their membranes (Fig. 8). The nuclei of all these cells and also those of the microglia

---

Fig. 11.—Inner part of cerebral cortex of rat. Substrate: carbamyl phosphate. Some "negative" pyramids with positive nuclei can still be seen. The intercellular substance is also strongly positive.

Fig. 12.—Inner part of cerebral cortex of rat. Substrate: pyridoxal phosphate. Note strong positive reaction in intercellular material and strongly positive, small pyramidal-shaped and smaller cells.

Fig. 13.—Inner part of cerebral cortex of rat. Substrate: riboflavin-5-phosphate. Note moderately positive cells and strongly positive nucleoli.

Fig. 14.—Inner part of cerebral cortex of rat. Substrate: carbamyl phosphate. "Negative" and positive pyramidal cells can be seen.

Fig. 15.—Brain stem underlying cerebral cortex of rat. Substrate: phosphorylated hesperidin. Note positive cells and axons.

Fig. 16.—Deeper part of cerebral cortex of rat. Substrate: fructose-1-phosphate. Note strongly positive capillaries and scattered moderately positive cells.

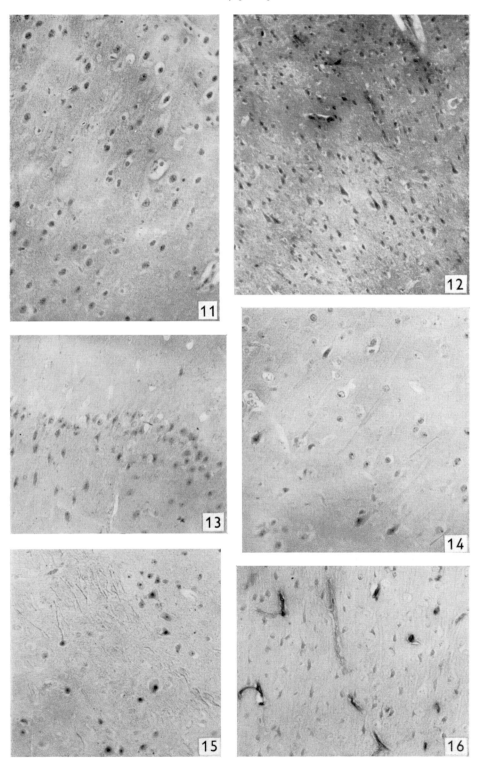

were strongly positive. With cortisone phosphate the reaction was in the nuclear membrane, the chromatin and the nucleoli; with oestrone phosphate
it was confined to the nuclear membrane and the nucleoli. In the deeper
parts of the cortex a number of angular-shaped pyramidal cells were seen
which gave a strong positive nuclear and cytoplasmic reaction with both
substrates. In such cells the axon as well as the dendrite was positive. Positive cells and axons were also seen in the spindle-cell layer of the cortex
with both substrates. In the striatum with oestrone phosphate the transverse
fibres gave a strong reaction, the longitudinal fibres giving a moderately
strong reaction (Fig. 22); with cortisone both fibres, and in fact all fibres in
the brain stem, gave a strong reaction and with both substrates a number of
small granules were present which were also positive—many of these were
associated with cell membranes and appeared similar to "boutons terminaux". With both oestrone and cortisone the inter-cellular tissue of the outer
half of the cortex gave a reaction—it was also present (to a stronger degree)
in the lateral geniculate bodies (Fig. 32), in the floor of the third ventricle
(Figs. 29, 30) and in the ventro-lateral ends of the hemispheres. The choroid
plexus gave a strong positive reaction largely in the nuclei and cytoplasm of
the cells (Fig. 21).

In the cerebellum all the capillaries, with both substrates, were very positive. The fibres in the white matter gave a definite reaction and so did the
nuclei of the cells in this region, all the cell bodies being negative. The cytoplasm of the Purkinje cells was negative or only slightly positive, the nuclei
were moderately positive and the nucleoli intensely so. The bases of the
Purkinje cells were enveloped in a basket work of positive fibres and a
number of positive "bouton"-like endings were in contact with the cell
membrane. When hexoestrol phosphate was used as a substrate to compare
with oestrone phosphate the reaction given by the two was found to be very
similar; however, with hexoestrol there appeared to be more positive cells

---

Fig. 17.—Spindle celled layer, cerebral cortex of rat. Substrate: cortisone phosphate. Note positive
nuclei and positive intercellular material. Positive axons may also be seen. One cell may be seen
(arrowed) in which the positive axon passes through a "negative" cell body to end in a positive
cap around the nucleus.

Fig. 18.—Inner part of cerebral cortex of rat. Substrate: fructose phosphate. Note positive nuclei
in negative cells, moderately positive intercellular material and a few scattered positive cells.

Fig. 19.—Choroid plexus of rat brain. Substrate: glycerophosphate. Positive stroma.

Fig. 20.—Choroid plexus of rat brain. Substrate: phosphorylated hesperidin. Positive nuclear
membranes, slightly positive cell bodies.

Fig. 21.—Choroid plexus of rat brain. Substrate: cortisone phosphate. Strongly positive nuclei—
slightly positive cytoplasm.

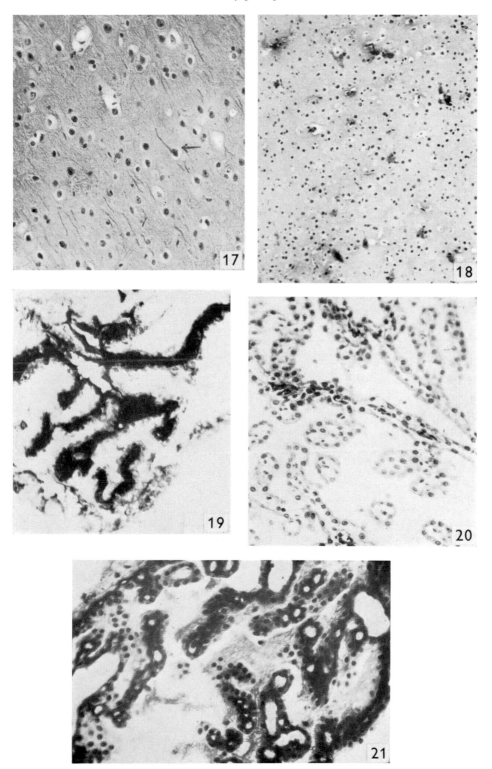

deep in the cortex and some cells showed a positive cytoplasmic membrane reaction.

Vitamin phosphates

With pyridoxal and riboflavin phosphates the pia mater was positive but only in patches with the latter substrate; the plexiform layer was strongly positive with both and so was the intercellular material of the cortex (Fig. 9). The large flask-shaped pyramidal cells and their dendrites were negative as with other substrates and there was an aggregation of positively reacting material along the dendritic membranes. With riboflavin phosphate all the capillaries were strongly positive as with glycerophosphate, but with pyridoxal phosphate only a few gave a reaction, and a weak one at that. With the latter substrate a number of positive cells were found scattered through all the layers of the cortex except the plexiform and the outermost part of the cerebral cortex (Fig. 4); in these cells nucleus and cytoplasm stained with more or less equal intensity. Strongly positive cells were also found deeper in the cortex (Fig. 12). In the striatum, with pyridoxal phosphate, both transverse and longitudinal fibres were equally positive (Fig. 25), all cell bodies were negative and all nuclei positive, but with riboflavin phosphate, while the cells gave the same reaction and the transverse fibres were positive, the longitudinal fibres were completely negative (Fig. 26). Deeper in the cortex with this latter substrate cells were also found which had positive nuclei and cytoplasm (Fig. 13).

In the cerebellum the reaction with riboflavin phosphate was indistinguishable from that of glycerophosphate, but with pyridoxal phosphate there was

---

Fig. 22.—Striatum globus of rat brain. Substrate: oestrone-3-phosphate. Note strongly positive transverse fibres, moderately positive longitudinal fibres—"negative" cell bodies and positive nuclei.

Fig. 23.—Striatum globus of rat brain. Substrate: glycerophosphate. Both types of fibre are moderately positive. Moderately positive nuclei in "negative" cell bodies and some positive cells seen.

Fig. 24.—Striatum globus of rat brain. Substrate: carbamyl phosphate. Transverse and longitudinal fibres positive to about the same intensity. Positive nuclei and "negative" cell bodies. Diffusion from positive capillaries can be seen.

Fig. 25.—Striatum globus of rat brain. Substrate: pyridoxal phosphate. Distinction between the two types of fibres difficult to see—both stain with equal intensity. "Negative" cell bodies and positive nuclei present.

Fig. 26.—Striatum globus of rat brain. Substrate: riboflavin-5-phosphate. Note positive transverse fibres and completely "negative" longitudinal fibres, negative cell bodies and positive nuclei.

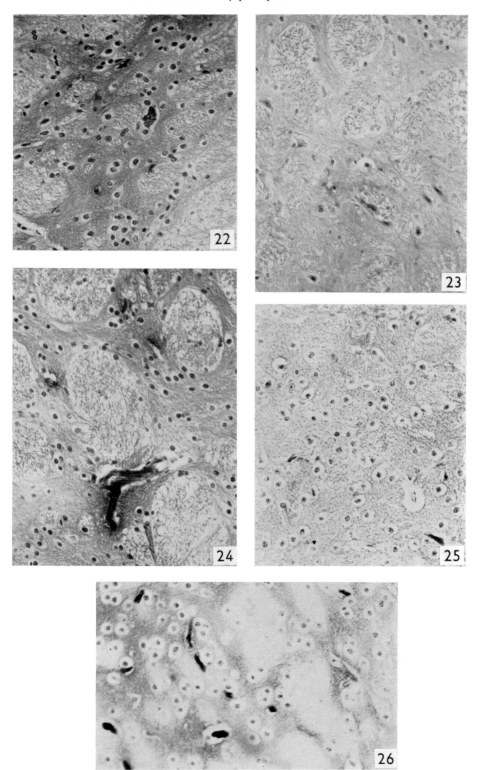

a general overall slight positive reaction by cells and fibres, the Purkinje cells were more intense in both nucleus and cytoplasm, with some there was even a positive Golgi region.

Miscellaneous Substrates

Ethanolamine phosphate, carbamyl phosphate, phosphorylated hesperidin and carboxy-phenyl phosphate.—The general pattern of reaction which has already been established for the cerebrum was characteristic of these substrates, i.e. positive pia mater, plexiform layer, intercellular material of outer two-thirds of cortex and negative large and medium pyramidal cells with an accumulation of positive material along the dendritic membranes. There were, however, grades of reaction with the various substrates: with carboxy-phenyl phosphate the reaction with the pia was very strong, with ethanolamine phosphate the outer part of the pia was strongly positive, but in the inner part only the nuclei were positive, whereas with carbamyl phosphate and hesperidin phosphate the pia was barely positive (Fig. 2). The reactions with nuclei of the various cells in the cortex also varied with the substrate; with phosphorylated hesperidin the nucleus gave a diffuse moderate positive reaction with an intensely positive nucleolus. A similar result was given by carbamyl phosphate (Fig. 11) and carboxy-phenyl phosphate (Fig. 10). Ethanolamine phosphate produced negative nuclear membranes but all the chromatin and the nucleoli were intensely positive (Fig. 7). Cells with positive cytoplasm and processes were present in the deeper layers of the cortex with all substrates (Fig. 14). There was a strong reaction by both fibres in the striatum with carbamyl phosphate (Fig. 24) and with the other substrates. The bodies of the cells in this area were negative and the nuclei positive. Capillaries were only strongly positive with carboxy-phenyl phosphate, although a few were positive with carbamyl phosphate. In the brain stem positive cells and axons were present with all substrates e.g. phosphorylated hesperidin (Fig. 15).

The capillaries in the cerebellum gave the same reactions with the various substrates as in the cerebrum. All nuclei including those of the Purkinje cells and all nucleoli, were strongly positive. Some Purkinje cells showed a moderate positive cytoplasm and in some it was negative. In some of these cells the nucleus was negative too. All substrates gave a very strong reaction in the choroid plexus. For reaction with phosphorylated hesperidin see Fig. 20. The reaction is mostly in the nuclei, particularly in the nuclear membranes and is slight in the cytoplasm.

DISCUSSION

It should be admitted at once that criticism may be levelled at this work because of the use of acetone as a fixative. Most phospholipids are soluble in this substance and it must dissolve out a considerable amount of brain substance as indeed it appears to do with the pyramidal cells; this may result in shifts of enzyme either by translocation or diffusion. A study of the sections suggests however that diffusion does not play a significant part in producing these results although translocation may play a part and this can only be decided by repeating this work with frozen dried material. The evidence against diffusion playing a part is as follows:

The large and medium pyramids are situated in an intercellular material which gives a strong positive reaction with all the substrates, yet the cytoplasm of these cells is strikingly negative and the boundary between the cell and the surrounding material is extremely sharply defined. It may be argued that the positive nuclei in such cells may be due to diffusion from the matrix, but the nuclei are negative when the substrate is glycerophosphate and the matrix is positive, but they are positive when ethanolamine phosphate and carbamyl phosphate and the vitamin phospates (at the same time of incubation) are used and the matrix is positive to the same degree. The nuclei are similarly positive with the steroid phosphates though with longer periods of incubation.

The metabolic significance of these results is difficult to assess, particularly since the function of alkaline phosphatases in soft tissues is relatively obscure. Furthermore there is no evidence that substrates such as cortisone and oestrone phosphates are of any physiological significance, yet it is of interest that they are effectively dephosphorylated by enzymes which appear to be in different sites of the cell and in different parts of the nervous system, from those which dephosphorylate glycerophosphate and the sugar phosphates; it may be that phosphorylation and dephosphorylation of steroid hormones may play a part in the metabolism of these latter compounds. It may be noted that aneruin is freely diffusible across cell membranes, but that cocarboxylase (aneurin pyrophosphate) is not—possibly phosphorylated sterols are more effectively retained in cells. The role of ethanolamine phosphate, though it is present in significant amounts in the central nervous system, is uncertain. A suggestion has been made that it plays a part in phospholipid metabolism.

Carbamyl phosphate is an intermediary in urea synthesis, riboflavin and pyridoxal phosphates are co-enzymes and phosphorylated hesperidin has had, as yet, no metabolic significance attributed to it. This uncertainty makes the interpretation of the results just described extremely difficult. However, regions of active and general dephosphorylation are fairly certain to contain high energy phosphates and it may not be too incorrect to ascribe to these areas some ability to release free energy. In the light of this suggestion therefore it becomes of great interest to note that the general dephosphorylating activity is well shown in those parts of the brain where many synapses occur. This is particularly well demonstrated by the strong reaction given by the plexiform layer with all substrates—this is a region where axons from many sources and dendrites passing back to the inner cortex establish contact. Further, many synapses probably occur along the dendrites of the pyramidal cells and it has been shown that a variety of substrates are dephosphorylated along the dendritic membrane; if the small positive granules detected in contact with a number of cells and their processes when some substrates are used, are in fact "boutons terminaux" then this supports the general thesis. The lateral geniculate bodies are also regions of many synapses and a number also occurs in the intercellular material between the pyramidal cells; this too is uniformly positive with a variety of substrates. These facts suggests that phosphatase activity must be taken into account in a consideration of the mechanism of impulse transmission at synapses. It is of interest that we have obtained no evidence that phosphatase is present in motor endplates.

The positive reaction given by most of the fibres in the striatum globus, the positive pyramidal cells lying deeper in the cortex and the unidentified cells which dephosphorylate pyridoxal phosphate and which are widely scattered through the cortex cannot be adequately interpreted. It is of interest that all neurones which are present at the site of origin of nerve roots have a cytoplasm as well as a nucleus which is strongly positive with a wide variety of phosphate substrates; furthermore the processes and particularly the axons

---

Fig. 27.—Floor of 3rd ventricle of rat brain. Substrate: glycerophosphate. General positive reaction in ground substance and strongly positive capillaries.

Fig. 28.—Floor of 3rd ventricle of rat brain. Substrate: glycerophosphate. Slightly positive cell nuclei present. (Higher power than Fig. 27.)

Fig. 29.—Floor of 3rd ventricle of rat brain. Substrate: cortisone phosphate. Note positive nuclei and moderately positive capillaries.

Fig. 30.—Floor of 3rd ventricle of rat brain. Substrate: oestrone-3-phosphate. Note positive nuclear membranes and moderately positive capillaries.

Fig. 31.—Lateral geniculate body of rat brain. Substrate: glycerophosphate. Body is only slightly positive.

Fig. 32.—Lateral geniculate body of rat brain. Substrate: oestrone-3-phosphate. Note strongly positive intercellular substance and "negative" cell bodies.

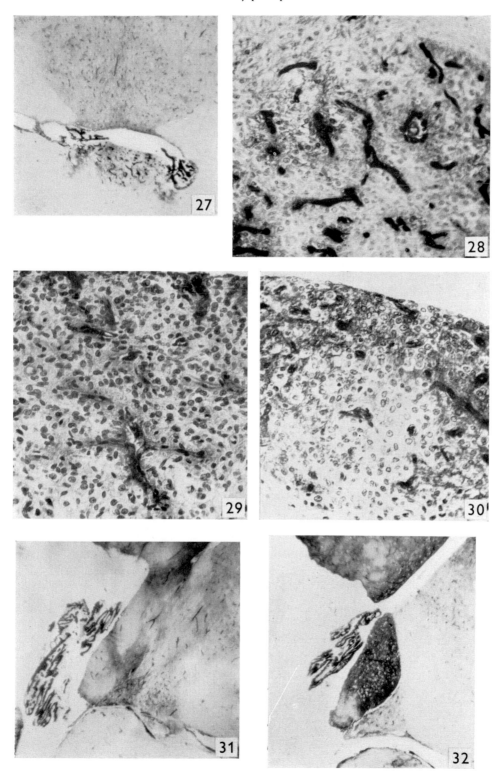

of such cells are also positive. In some cells a positive axon was seen to extend up to the cell body and then a positive area continuous with it passed through the negative cell body ending in a positive cap surrounding one end of the nucleus.

Another suggestion concerning the role of phosphatases is that they play some part in the synthesis of proteins. Nucleoli have been claimed as centres of protein synthesis and perhaps the association of every type of phosphatase with the nucleolus may be of some significance in this connection.

It has been observed consistently that with phosphatases, and with esterases too, there are a number of Purkinje cells in the cerebellum which give a positive reaction but that interspersed with these are a number which are virtually negative. It is always the large well-rounded cells which are negative and it is the smaller, more shrunken cells which give the positive reaction. This may suggest that the Purkinje cells work in relays, interspersing periods of activity with periods of quiescence. However, the present author has noted increased hydrolytic enzyme activity in senescent cells, and since the rats used for this work were mature animals and since it has been shown by various authors (see [1]) that from maturity on there is a continuous loss of Purkinje cells and other neurones from the brain, it may be that these Purkinje cells, and possibly some of those in the cerebrum with more active hydrolytic enzyme activity, are senescent.

Naidoo and Pratt in a series of papers [3, 4, 5] have studied the histochemical distribution of enzymes dephosphorylating glycerophosphate, aneurin pyrophosphate and adenosine tri- and di-phosphates at different pH values. Most of their incubations were carried out at acid pH values and in this region there is predominantly a reaction in the cells, although with adenosine monophosphate many fibres stained strongly. With aneurin pyrophosphate at pH 9.1 the reaction was claimed to be similar to that obtained at pH 6.9; in other words, all cell bodies reacted strongly—which is of interest in view of the fact that the aneurin pyrophosphate molecule dissociates at alkaline pH values. Glycerophosphate at 9.1 gave a reaction only in the capillaries, the cells being all negative. Although the tissues appear to have been incubated for times varying from 20 to 200 minutes, the authors make no reference to "ground substance" (intercellular material) reaction. This may have been due to the fact that they used frozen dried sections and placed them straight into the incubation mixture after dewaxing and without passing through absolute alcohol. It is known that there is considerable loss of protein material if absolute alcohol is not used and it may be that the intercellular phosphatase is lost under these circumstances.

SUMMARY

The dephosphorylating activity of the central nervous system for a variety of substrates has been demonstrated in the brain of the rat. Blood brain barriers such as the pia mater, the choroid plexus and the capillaries have strong dephosphorylating activity; this may be related to the permeability of these membranes since phosphatases are also associated with other membranes across which solutes must pass. Synaptic regions such as the plexiform layer of the cerebral cortex, the general intercellular tissue in the cortex, the membranes of the dendrites of pyramidal cells and the lateral geniculate bodies, have strong dephosphorylating activity. It is suggested that a possible role of phosphatases in synaptic transmission should be considered. The two functions of phosphatases which would be represented by the presence of these enzymes at blood brain barriers and at synaptic sites may perhaps be reconciled by the suggestion that in each case they are responsible for alteration of permeability or supply of free energy.

All nucleoli of all cells appear to have strong dephosphorylating activity.

REFERENCES

1. BOURNE, G. H., *in* Modern Trends in Geriatrics. Butterworth & Co., 1956.
2. — *Nature* **179**, 1247 (1957).
3. NAIDOO, D. and PRATT, O. E., *J. Neurol. Neurosurg. Psychiat.* **14**, 287 (1951).
4. —— *ibid.* **15**, 164 (1952).
5. —— *Enzymologia* **XVI**, 19 (1953).

118   *Experimental Cell Research, Suppl.* 5, *118–152 (1958)*

EXPERIMENTS ON CURRENT FLOW AND IONIC MOVE-
MENTS IN SINGLE MYELINATED NERVE FIBERS

P. MÜLLER[1]

Physiological Institute, University of Cologne, Germany

MEASUREMENTS of membrane resting and action potentials have been most useful for the investigation of bioelectric phenomena in nerve and muscle. When making such measurements, either directly with microelectrodes (e.g. [13, 10]) or by indirect methods [3, 16], great care is taken to avoid any short circuit current flow through the membrane.

In the present investigation myelinated fibers were studied under the condition of maximal current flow through the nodal membrane, with the aim of obtaining more information on the origin of bioelectric phenomena from the characteristics of these currents and their correlation to ion movements.

Maximal resting and action currents through one node of Ranvier were obtained by cutting the fiber at the two neighboring nodes. Single dissected myelinated nerve fibers from frogs were used because of their favorable geometry, since (1) the active membrane area is confined to a very small region, the node, and (2) relatively long electrical leads in the form of the external fluid and the axoplasm extend from this region.

The analysis of the current flow would be of more significance if it were known which ions had transported the current and how the current checks quantitatively with ionic movements. To obtain such knowledge it would be necessary to measure the ionic concentrations in stretches of a single fiber not longer than 1 or 2 internodal lengths, i.e. 1–5 mm. Because of the extremely small amounts present in this volume (under certain conditions less than (1×10^{-12} mol.) this seemed, at first sight, impossible. It turned out, however, that the requirements can be met by a relatively simple method. The first section of this paper gives a detailed description of this method together with measurements of the normal Na and K content of the single fiber. In the second section the results of the combination of current measurements and ion determination are presented and discussed.

---

[1] Present address: Eastern Pennsylvania Psychiatric Institute, Henry Avenue and Abbotts-ford Road, Philadelphia 29, Pa., U.S.A.

DETERMINATION OF SODIUM AND POTASSIUM IN DISSECTED
SINGLE FIBERS

So far measurements of Na and K concentrations in single fibers have been made only in giant axons of sepia and squid [6]. For these valuable determinations Keynes and Lewis used the method of activation analysis which consists of irradiating the samples with neutrons and taking the activity of the radioisotopes formed as a measure of the amounts of the parent elements present in the sample. Although the sensitivity of this method is already very high (in the order of 1×10^{-8} mol.), it is not sufficient by far for the single myelinated fiber.

Another method for the determination of sodium and potassium is flame photometry. This method is very sensitive when it comes to measuring low concentrations in a large volume. However, the commercially available flame photometers require relatively large amounts of fluid to give an exact reading. This is as much due to the slow reaction of the recording system as to the fact that the individual atom emits light for only a very short time— the time it passes through the flame.

Accordingly, there are two possibilities of increasing sensitivity with respect to the minimum amount measurable. (1) The atom could be forced to radiate for a longer period. This could be done for instance by evaporating the sample in a very small evacuated quartz tube, applying a suitable potential between electrodes inside the tube in order to activate the evaporated atoms which will then send out light on their characteristic wavelength. (2) The other possibility is to raise the frequency response of the recording device and to bring the whole sample at one instant into the flame. Both methods were tried. The latter turned out to be much the simpler and more reliable. Since it was used for all determinations reported below, a description of the first method is omitted.

METHODS

If a small amount of sodium or potassium salt is placed on a platinum wire and suddenly brought into a gas flame, the atoms of the salt will evaporate and move upwards through the flame with a speed which mainly depends on the temperature of the burning gases. This temperature, and hence the speed, will be different at the center of the flame from that on the outside. However, because of the large number of Na or K atoms involved, there will be an average time, (t_0) for which the individual atoms stay within the flame and emit their characteristic spectrum. The atoms leave the platinum wire as soon as their temperature has reached the necessary value, so that the form of a Gaussian distribution curve might be expected for the amounts of atoms present in a cross section of the flame at successive moments after the sample is placed in it.

Let the intensity of the light emitted by the individual atom be I_0, then the output of the photocell V_0 is related to the amount of light given by the single atom by the expression

$$V_0 t_0 C = I_0 t_0, \tag{1}$$

where C is a constant depending on sensitivity, amplification and type of filter used. Since also

$$\Sigma I_0 t_0 = \Sigma V_0 t_0 C \tag{2}$$

and since $I_0 t_0$ is small compared to $\Sigma I_0 t_0$, the total number of atoms passing through the flame should be linearly proportional to the integrated value of the output of the photocell.

Description of the Instrument

The experimental layout was simple (Fig. 1). A small flame, fed with city gas, came out of a metal tube of 0.4 mm inner diameter. The flame height was adjusted to 2 cm, the widest diameter was 5 mm. The main problem was to prevent light emitted by the glowing platinum wire from reaching the photocell; with the high amplification used this would have made any reading impossible. Several methods of shielding were tried, the final one adopted is illustrated by Fig. 1. The burner tube was placed inside a small square metal box, the tip of the tube reaching 1.5 mm below the top of the box. The flame

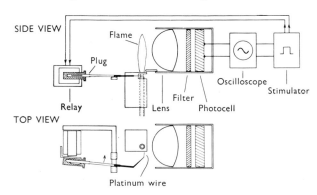

Fig. 1.—Diagram of flame photometer (see text).

was allowed to burn through a small hole, 1.5 mm in diameter, the edge of which was made as sharp as possible in order to avoid reflection. The hole was placed in one corner of the box top. Outside and inside the box was blackened. At one corner of the box opposite the short part of the flame burning inside there was a slit, 1.5 mm high and 3 mm long, which extended round the box corner. Through this slit the sample could be brought into the flame. The slit was extended to the second side of the box in order to allow enough air to reach the flame which otherwise did not burn smoothly through the hole.

The samples were brought into the flame after placing them on a 100 μ thick and 6 mm long piece of platinum-iridium wire (30 per cent iridium). This alloy was chosen because it keeps its elastic tension even after the longest periods of glowing, so that the necessary handling during the collection of the samples did not bend the wire. This was of importance because the tip of the wire with the attached sample had to be placed exactly into the small part of the flame between burner tip and box top. The platinum wire was attached to a holder which could be fitted snugly, and in only one position, into a connector which in turn was soldered to the anchor of a relay. In this way the holder with the platinum wire could be removed from the relay, the sample collected, and the holder placed in exactly the same position as before. The relay pulled the holder towards the flame. In order to control direction and the end point of this rather fast movement, the holder was supported near its end by a metal bar on which it could slide back and forth, limited at the ends by pieces of rubber mounted on the bar. The operation of the relay was controlled by a stimulator which in turn was synchronized with the oscilloscope sweep.

The light emitted by the flame was focused through a filter on a selenium photoelement, which was directly connected to a high-gain wide-band DC amplifier (AEL). The output of the amplifier was displayed on an oscilloscope screen. Maximal amplification used was 10 μ V/cm deflection on the screen. Photocell, flame burner and relay were mounted on separate adjustable stands.

Calibration of the instrument

In order to distinguish between sodium and potassium which are both present in the sample, suitable filters must be used. Through these filters should pass a very large proportion of the light emitted by the atom to be measured, 589 mμ for Na and 769 mμ for K, while in the range of the other atom it should pass not more than 1 per cent. For the potassium meaurements

a standard dark red-colored glass filter (Leitz) was found to have these
properties (pass at 769 mμ, 84 per cent; at 589, <0.5 per cent). For sodium
an interference filter (Schott + Gen. AL 590) had to be used, since all color
filters have a relatively high transmission in the infrared region. The transmission of the interference filter was 54 per cent at 590 mμ and 0.5 per cent
at 769 mμ.

Calibration was made by measuring small droplets of a solution containing
a known concentration of the ion in question. The droplets were placed in a
dish containing paraffin oil, out of which they were drawn up with the platinum wire.

The drops were prepared in the following way: a 2 mm wide capillary tube
(pyrex glass) was pulled out so that the diameter of the tip was of the order of
10 μ. The capillary was then washed and filled with the testing solution
from a syringe. The open end of the capillary was connected via a plastic
tube filled with oil to a driving syringe of an electrically operated micromanipulator. By moving the plug of the driving syringe forward at a very
slow rate a constant flow of testing solution came out of the capillary tip.
The tip was held into the paraffin. Approximately 25 per cent of the testing
solution in the capillary was discarded in order to make sure that uncon-
taminated solution of the proper concentration was flowing out. The capillary
was then quickly pulled back and forth in the paraffin with the tip 1–2 mm
below the surface. In this way small droplets of the testing solution were
formed which floated free in the paraffin. The size of the droplets varied
between 10 and 250 μ. It could be easily adjusted by the speed of movement
through the paraffin, the flow rate of the solution and the size of the capillary.
At periods when the speed of movement was constant, droplets of equal size
were formed. The dish was placed on a microscope stage, illuminated from
below (blue filter to prevent heating and movements of the droplets) and a
droplet drawn out under microscopic control with the platinum wire, after
its size had been measured at higher magnification ($\times 160$). The flame photometer reading was made between 20 sec and 1 min after the drop was removed
from the oil. Various sizes of the drops and various concentrations of the
testing solution (0.1–100 mM/l) were used.

Potassium calibration

Fig. 2 shows some oscillograph records from droplets containing 1–17 $\times$
10^{-12} moles of potassium. Each record was simultaneously taken at fast and
slow sweep speed in order to allow more accurate integration of the curves.
It should be noted that the record has a fast phase which shows the expected

shape of a distribution curve and a small slow phase. No exact reason can be given for the occurrence of the slow phase but it was tentatively assumed that the small quantity of paraffin attached to the wire burned very fast before the wire itself reached the proper temperature and that this paraffin

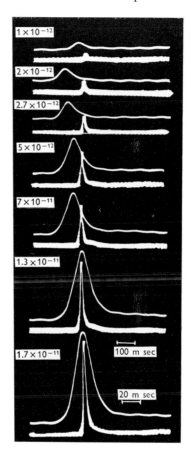

Fig. 2.—Flame photometer records from small drops of a KCl solution containing amounts of K as indicated for each record. Each record was taken simultaneously at fast and slow sweep speed. Note the small hump at the foot of the slow records.

"explosion" evaporated the major part of the potassium. Indeed small droplets of paraffin burn in a quick, explosive manner, which itself of course is not recorded by the instrument. The bigger the droplet of the testing solution, the greater is the amount of paraffin attached to it when it is removed from the dish. This would explain why small drops also show these two phases.

10^{-12} mol. is considerably below the upper limit of sensitivity for the potassium readings. The smallest amount measurable is of the order of 1×10^{-14}

mol. This means that the sensitivity of the method for potassium is 10^5–10^6 times greater than the sensitivity of activation analysis.

The values obtained by mechanical integration of the records (in mV msec) were plotted against the amount of potassium in the drops. The entire

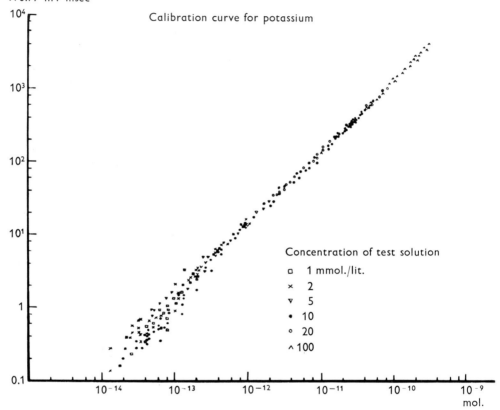

Fig. 3.—Potassium calibration curve. *Abscissa*, amount of potassium; *ordinate*, integrated value of flame photometer record, expressed in mV·msec.

calibration curve for potassium obtained in this way for the range of 10^{-14} to 10^{-9} mol. is shown in Fig. 3. From 10^{-13} to 10^{-9} mol. the curve is linear and the values are close enough to omit application of statistical calculation.

Sources of error

Below 10^{-13} mol. a considerable scatter occurs and in addition the curve deviates from the straight line. One reason for the scattering is obvious. Very small droplets have to be used in this region, and the error made in determining the drop diameter has a greater effect since the volume–diameter relation becomes very steep in this range. Another reason might be the loss of K to the surrounding paraffin and into the air which might vary from drop to drop. The loss of K to paraffin might also be the reason for the deviation of the curve in the lower region. In the first place, if a constant very small

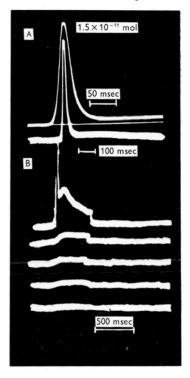

Fig. 4.—Flame photometer records from drops of a NaCl solution containing 1.5×10^{-11} mol. NaCl. Records in (*A*) were taken with similar sweep speed and amplification as in Fig. 2. (*B*) Records taken from a drop of equal size as in (*A*) but at higher gain and slower sweep speed to show the time course of the slow component. The sample was put into the flame 5 times during 5 successive sweeps, each time for 500 msec. Due to high gain most of the fast phase is cut.

amount of K is lost to the paraffin or during evaporation of the water, this amount will be detectable only when the total amount inside the drop is also very small. Secondly, it was found that with test solutions which had a very low concentration, 0.1 mM, the calibration curve showed an even greater deviation in the range from 10^{-13} to 10^{-14} mol. so that the curve had a much steeper slope in this range. One plausible explanation would be this: for the testing solution of low concentration larger droplets have to be used to give the same amount as is contained in a small drop of a more concentrated solution. The surface which comes in contact with the paraffin and consequently the loss of K into the paraffin is therefore much bigger. As a result the values are lower than the ones obtained with the more concentrated solution. At amounts above 10^{-13} mol. the values from a 0.1 mM solution check with those from the other solutions, probably because (*a*) the total amount present is large compared to the lost amount, and (*b*) because the relation of surface to volume decreases so that the oil–solution interphase is relatively smaller.

The small errors for the bigger amounts are due mainly to mistakes in the determination of droplet size and to mistakes connected with the integra-

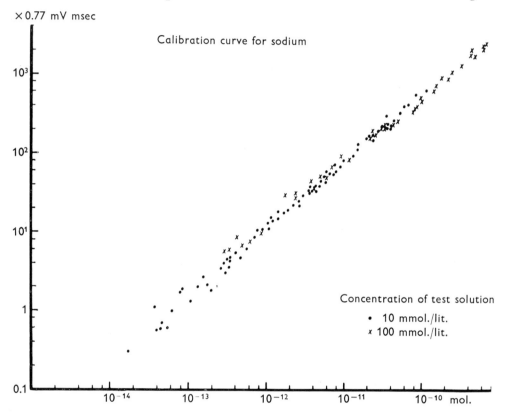

Fig. 5.—Sodium calibration curve. *Abscissa*, amount of Na; *ordinate*, integrated record of flame photometer.

tion. A mechanical integrator—Aristo planimeter—was used for this procedure which introduced errors of $\pm$ 5 per cent. More exact determination of droplet size by means of higher magnification and electrical integration could probably reduce these errors.

The instrumental error is in fact very small. Droplets which had come out one after the other from the capillary and had practically the same diameter gave records of equal size.

Sodium calibration

Records from sodium samples are slightly different from those from potassium. The first phase of the records is the same as with potassium but the second phase appears much later and lasts for a much longer time (up to 5 sec (Fig. 4)). At higher amplification one can see that the second phase displays a second maximum. The reason for this long phase is unknown. It might be that some of the sodium is adsorbed to the platinum wire and requires a higher temperature to evaporate. This late phase introduced some errors in the integration procedure which find their expression in the somewhat larger scatter of the calibration values (Fig. 5).

For greater accuracy a recording procedure was used in which the slow phase was recorded separately at higher gain and for several sweeps, placing the platinum wire for 0.5 sec into the flame during each sweep (Fig. 4, B).

RESULTS

The normal sodium and potasssium content of single fibers

Material used.—Sciatic nerves from male and female frogs (*Rana temporaria*) were used. The frogs had been kept outdoors (temp. 6–16°) and later at room temperature for 1–24 hrs before dissection. Before dissecting the fibers the nerves were kept from 10 min. to 3 hrs in Ringer's solution of the following composition: 110 meq/l NaCl, 5 meq/l KCl, 9 meq/l $CaCl_2$; no buffer, pH 6.8.

Method.—The procedure of recording the K and Na content of a single fiber was as follows:

The fiber was dissected over two internodes, i.e. 4–5 mm. The fiber diameter was measured at several points of the internode with a magnification of 900 × (water immersion objective). Average values varied between 10 and 13 μ. The fiber was then placed on a recording stage so that the internodes extended through paraffin oil while the three dissected nodes were in small Ringer's pools. Action potentials were tested by stimulating and recording from the middle node. Only fibers which gave good all-or-none action potentials were used for analysis. The fiber was then pulled to the side so that its entire length extended through the oil. (Careful checks were made to see whether the oil affected the function of the node. No such effect was found. Full size action potentials could be recorded from a node hanging free in oil for one hr and more.) In order to remove the external K and Na the fiber was now washed for 10 sec with 0.1 M dimethyldiethanolammonium-

P. Müller

chloride (DDA) by moving a 300 μ drop of this solution back and forth along the fiber. The holder of the flame photometer was fixed in such a position that its platinum wire touched the fiber. A measured fiber stretch was cut (usually two internodes), wound around the wire, and burned in the flame.

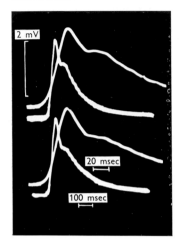

Fig. 6.—Flame photometer records of the potassium content of 5 mm stretches of two single fibers dissected from the two sciatics of the same frog.

Errors.—The main error is introduced when measuring the fiber diameter. This error is of the order of ± 10 per cent and is the major error of the whole method. Since the fiber is cut under oil, there can be no loss either of Na or of K escaping from the axon after cutting, because all fluid stays attached to the fiber and is analysed. A very small amount might be lost to the cutting forceps which had a tip diameter of less than 10 μ.

The potassium content.—Fig. 6 shows the flamephotometer records of the potassium content of two fibers taken from contralateral sciatic nerves of the same animal. The records differ from records of a potassium–water solution in so far as the slow phase is much more pronounced. This is probably due to the large molecules (proteins, lipids) present in the fiber which have to be broken up and evaporated together with the potassium. Table I gives the potassium content of 20 fibers. Two facts deserve being mentioned. One is the great variation of the values—between 51 and 145 meq/l—and the other, that fibers from the same animal have a very similar potassium content. Simon and Szelöczy [15] found in whole rabbit sciatics great variations of the K content from animal to animal while the two nerves from the same animal had very similar contents. Also the figures of Keynes and Lewis [6] indicate that there are great differences from fiber to fiber.

TABLE I. *Internal potassium concentration of single dissected fibers.*

Fiber No.	Frog No.	Fiber diameter (μ)	Internodal distance (μ)		Internal potassium (meq/l nerve)
			left	right	
22	11	12	1950	1800	79
23	11	11	1750	1830	85
24	12	11	2320	2100	81
25	13	12.5	1980	2050	89
26	13	11	2050	2100	75
27	14	10	2010	1835	142
28	14	11	1700	2100	145
29	15	12.5	1920	2500	128
30	15	11.5	2070	2220	139
31	16	13	2150	2810	131
32	16	12	2790	2980	136
33	17	10	1970	2320	54
34	17	12.5	2250	2240	51
57	29	12	2050	1950	65
58	29	12	1870	2030	68
60	30	12	1650	1820	135
61	30	11.5	2750	2400	85
62	31	10	2100	2050	99
63	32	11	2200	2100	98
64	32	12	1900	1600	83

The fibers might have lost some of their K to the Ringer's solution, but according to Fenn *et al.* [1] this loss is zero when the Ringer's solution has a potassium concentration of 5 mM/1. It therefore seems more likely that the differences of the potassium content represent a true individual variation. The fact that all fibers gave good action potentials is no obstacle to this conclusion, since it is shown below that they give action potentials even after the internal potassium concentration is of the order of 10 mM/1.

The sodium content.—The fibers in which Na was measured were treated in the same way as those for the potassium analysis. As in the calibration records, the long component is more pronounced than in potassium records. The individual variation for the normal fiber is not as wide as for potassium.

TABLE II. *Internal sodium concentration of single fibers.*

Fiber No.	Frog No.	Fiber diameter (μ)	Internodal distance (μ) left	right	Internal sodium (meq/l nerve)
66	34	11.5	2150	2000	51
67	34	10.5	2350	2300	57
68	35	12.5	2350	2350	78
69	35	12	2460	1850	73
70	36	12	2300	2320	56
71	36	11.5	2450	2150	102^a
72	37	10.5	2300	2020	72
73	37	11	1700	1780	85
75	38	12	2000	1980	63
78	40	11.5	2100	2150	19^b

[a] Fiber which had conducted 500,000 impulses at a rate of 100/sec.
[b] Fiber which had been kept in Na-free DDA (0.1 M) for 1 hr. before analysis.

(Table II). The height of the values is surprising. It is, however, in agreement with recent determinations of Lorente de Nó (personal communication), who found a value of 70 mM/l in desheathed trunks. The figures disagree with those of Fenn, Cobb, Hegnauer and Marsh [1], who suggested an Na concentration of 10.1 mM/l inside the fiber. This conclusion was based on the fact that all but this amount of the Na escapes from the fibers when soaked in Na-free solutions. However it can be shown that also the single fiber loses Na from the inside when kept in a Na-free medium (see below).

In order to show the upper and lower limit of the Na concentrations in undamaged fibers, two fibers are included in the table with which experiments were carried out to raise or lower the Na content. One fiber was stimulated for 83 min at 100/sec. Two nodes had been activated and had carried 500,000 impulses each. The net gain of Na in comparison with the contralateral unstimulated fiber was 2.0×10^{-11} mol. for two internodes, which would give 1.0×10^{-17} mol./imp./node, while on the bases of current flow approximately 2×10^{-17} mol./imp./node must enter the fiber. If these figures are correct a great part of the outward current must have been carried by sodium. For a nodal membrane surface of 75 μ^2 the Na entry, per cm² of membrane would be 2.6×10^{-9} mol./imp., while 1.3×10^{-9} mol./cm²/imp. leaves the fiber. Compared to sepia axons with 4.4×10^{-12} mol./cm²/imp. net gain [6], these figures are very high. Obviously they are due to a higher current density at the node.

In order to demonstrate the loss of Na, a dissected fiber was placed for one hr in 0.11 *M* DDA before analysis. In accordance with the observations of Fenn *et al.* [1] made with trunks, the fiber lost a large percentage of its Na content into the Na-free medium.

Regarding the results of these K and Na determinations with respect to the function of the fiber, it is too early to draw definite conclusions. Above all it is not known in which part of the fiber the Na and K is located. It might well be that almost all the K is in the axoplasm while the content of myelin is very small. On the other hand the greater part of the sodium could be in the myelin or, more probably, in the mitochondrial system. There might also be a longitudinal distribution with higher or lower concentration of either electrolyte near the node. The described method is sensitive enough to detect such an unequal distribution, but measurements have not yet been made.

More information is obtained when ion determinations are combined with measurements of current flow. The results of such measurements are reported in the following section.

EXPERIMENTS ON CURRENT FLOW

Demarcation current

If a single fiber is cut at two points 3–5 mm apart so that the cut stretch contains one node of Ranvier, located at the center, current starts flowing outward through the nodal membrane to both sides in the external fluid layer around the fiber, enters the axon at the cut ends and flows back towards the node inside the axon. The amplitude of the current flow will depend on

(1) the potential across the membrane (V_M),
(2) the internal resistance of the nodal membrane (R_M),
(3) the sum of the external longitudinal resistance (R_e) and
     the internal longitudinal resistance of the axoplasm (R_i).

All three factors are subject to changes due to internal and external causes of which the major ones have been investigated.

Method

A single fiber was dissected over more than two internodes so that 3 nodes were freed from the surrounding fibers. After measuring diameter and internodal distances the fiber was placed on a recording stage, so that all three nodes were in Ringer's solution while the internodes were suspended

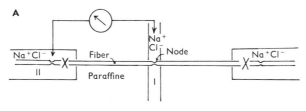

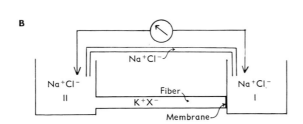

Fig. 7.—(A) Diagram of method used to measure demarcation current from a single fiber. The fiber was cut in the two side pools (crosses). (B) Diagram of geometrical and electrochemical situation corresponding to Fig. 10 A. Two large volumes of NaCl are connected by a tube (the axis cylinder). At one end the tube is closed by a membrane (the nodal membrane), the other end is open (where the fiber is cut). An NaCl bridge corresponding to the fluid layer around the fiber, connects both NaCl pools (for further explanation see text).

in oil (see Fig. 7 A). The width of the middle Ringer's pool was 300 μ. The action potential was tested by applying square waves from a stimulator across the right internode while the developing electrotonic potential and the action potential were recorded across the left internode. The fiber was then cut within the left and right pool either directly at the two side nodes or some 50 μ towards the central node. The two trunks were removed from the side pools so that now only a 3–5 mm long piece of the fiber containing one central node and the two attached internodes was lying on the recording stage.

The current which started flowing immediately after cutting was measured separately across both internodes by recording the voltage drop across the resistance of the external conductor (R_e). Silver–silverchloride-sat. KCl agar electrodes were used and the recording made by first placing both electrodes in the middle pool (which gave the base line) and then placing one electrode in either side pool. In this way the small potential difference of the electrodes was cancelled out. The DC amplifier (AEL) had an additional differential cathode follower input with a tube, selected for low grid current ($<10^{-12}$ amp).

Measurements of external and internal resistance

In order to calculate the amount of current flow, the resistance of the external conductor (R_e) must be known. Since it cannot be measured unless the internal longitudinal resistance (R_i) is known, and also for calculations of R_M and V_M, R_i must first be measured. A rough calculation of R_i on the bases of the conductivity of a 120 mM KCl sol., and an average axon diameter of 6 μ, gave 50 MΩ/2 mm. A probably more correct value is obtained in the following way:

First, the total resistance of a fiber stretch of one internode was measured with all nodes intact and the internode under oil. Then both nodes at the side of the internode were cut and the total resistance of the fiber stretch was again measured.

In this way two values of total resistances (R_{t1} and R_{t2}) were obtained which are connected to R_e, R_i and the resistances of the two side nodes, R_{M1} and R_{M2}, by the following equations:

$$\frac{1}{R_{t1}} = \frac{1}{R_e} + \frac{1}{R_{M1} + R_{M2} + R_i}, \tag{3}$$

$$\frac{1}{R_{t2}} = \frac{1}{R_e} + \frac{1}{R_i}. \tag{4}$$

Solution of these equations for R_i gives:

$$R_i = -\frac{R_{M1} + R_{M2}}{2} + \sqrt{\left(\frac{R_{M1} + R_{M2}}{2}\right)^2 - \frac{R_{M1} + R_{M2}}{1/R_{t1} - 1/R_{t2}}}. \tag{5}$$

The resistance of a resting node is known to be 40 MΩ [17]. R_{t1} and R_{t2} were measured in the following way: A square pulse was applied over a 20 MΩ series resistance (R_c) to the open grids of the amplifier, and measured on the oscilloscope screen. The same pulse was then measured with the electrodes in contact with the two Ringer's pools so that the R_t of the fiber stretch to be measured formed a shunt for the pulse applied to the grids. When the relation of the latter pulse to the former is U_A then the total longitudinal resistance of the fiber stretch is

$$R_t = \frac{R_c}{1/U_A - 1}. \tag{6}$$

Determination of R_i by this method gave values between 37 and 48 MΩ/2 mm fiber, which are slightly lower than the above estimate.

Knowing the values of R_t, R_i and R_M, the true value of R_e for an intact internode can be calculated in first approximation by

$$\frac{1}{R_e} = \frac{1}{R_t} - \frac{1}{R_i + R_{M1} + R_{M2}}. \tag{7}$$

R_e, of course, depends largely on the length of the fiber stretch under oil; it also increases during the course of an experiment and therefore has to be measured several times during each experiment.

Results

Maximal value of demarcation current.—The current reaches a maximum immediately or a few minutes after the fiber is cut. The current can be expressed either in terms of the individual longitudinal currents of the two internodes or as total membrane current which is equal to the sum of both longitudinal currents.

The maximal values show appreciable variations. The highest values for total membrane current were between 1.2–1.3×10^{-9} amp. Most values lie between 7 and 10×10^{-10} amp.

Membrane potential and resistance.—Due to the short circuit between internal and external conductor, the membrane potential drops immediately after the fiber is cut. As a result of this depolarisation also the membrane resistance decreases. From simple network analysis it follows that the membrane resistance

$$R_M = 0.5 \frac{R_e}{V_e} - \left(\frac{R_i + R_e}{2} \right), \tag{8}$$

where R_e is the external longitudinal resistance of one internode, R_i the corresponding internal resistance and V_e the potential across R_e expressed as a fraction of the normal resting potential. It is assumed that R_e and R_i of the one internode is equal to R_e and R_i of the other internode. Since R_e, R_i and V_e are known, R_M can be calculated assuming a normal resting potential of 70 mV [3]. Eight determinations gave values for R_M between 31 and 38 MΩ/node, which is about 10–25 per cent less than the resting value determined by Tasaki and Freygang [17] with 40–42 MΩ. Knowing R_M, the potential across the membrane V_M can be calculated.

Calculated values of V_M at the time of maximal current flow varied between 28 and 39 mV.

Time course of the demarcation current.—After reaching its maximum, the current decays along a curve which in the ideal case is exponential. Such a curve is seen in Fig. 8. The decay should be expected if one considers the geometrical and electrochemical situation which is demonstrated in Fig. 7 *B*. The small volume of the axon cylinder of the internodes is presumably filled with potassium ions and anions unknown in character. It is separated by the nodal membrane from the large fluid volume in the middle pool which

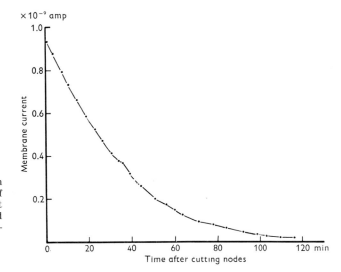

Fig. 8.—Total current through nodal membrane as function of time after the fiber was cut at both sides. Curve was obtained by adding the longitudinal currents in the two internodes.

is filled with Ringer's or NaCl. The other end of the axon is open and in connection with the large volume of NaCl in the side pools. There is also a salt bridge connection, corresponding to the fluid layer around the fiber, between the two NaCl pools which allows the current to flow.

If it is now assumed that the K ions are free to move through the membrane, and there is considerable evidence for this assumption (e.g. Keynes [5]), while internal anions and external Na ions are not, then current will flow caused by the potassium ions diffusing out through the membrane into the middle pool. At the open end positive charges (Na) will move into the axon. At the same time some potassium will diffuse out against the potential gradient and exchange for Na. As a result of both potassium movements, the potassium concentration inside the axoplasm at the membrane will decrease and the potential and thus the current will decay. Current can flow only as long as there is potassium inside the axon and the total amount of current given by the system should depend on the amount of K initially present inside the two internodes.

These assumptions were tested thus: (1) Experiments were performed concerning the total amount of current flow. (2) Other experiments concerned the current amplitude and the factors on which it depends.

The total amount of demarcation current.—If the above assumptions about the origin of the current were correct, the total amount of current given by the two internodes should check with the amount of K ions originally present

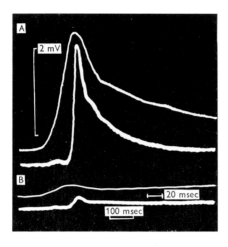

Fig. 9.—(A) Flame photometer record of the potassium content of an untreated fiber stretch of 5.5 mm. (B) Same as (A), but at the end of demarcation current flow and from 4.4 mm of fiber.

in this volume. Rough calculations based on the internal K concentrations reported above indicate already that this indeed could be so. Integration of the demarcation currents of 3 different fibers gave 2.45, 2.34 and 2.57×10^{-6} amp. sec., which correspond to a flow of 2.54, 2.41 and 2.66×10^{-11} mol. of univalent ions. The potassium content of an 11 μ thick fiber, assuming a 0.1 M concentration is 1.12×10^{-11} mol./mm. The fibers were 3450, 3600 and 3740 μ long and 11 μ thick, which means they contained between 3.8 and 4.0×10^{-11} mol. of potassium. The internal content of potassium is thus more than enough to account for the current flow. As a matter of fact, the figures indicate already that some of the potassium has leaked out of the open ends of the two internodes.

More exact information is obtained if the amount of potassium which had left the fiber is measured. Fig. 9 shows flame photometer records from a 5.5 mm stretch of a normal untreated fiber and from two internodes (4400 μ) of the contralateral fiber which had given demarcation current until exhaustion. There is still some potassium left which amounts to approximately 15 per cent of the initial content.

As an example the figures are given for fiber No. 48. The total amount of current given by this fiber was 2.21×10^{-6} amp. sec, which corresponds to

2.29×10^{-11} mol. univalent ions. The reference value for the initial potassium content was taken from a fiber from the contralateral sciatic of the same animal. To be more correct the determination should have been made with another stretch from the same fiber. However, regarding the results from Table I the figure should come very near to the true value. For fiber No. 48, the initial potassium content of the two internodes (3300 μ) was calculated as 3.43×10^{-11} mol. After the current flow had reached zero, the rest of potassium inside the fiber was measured with 0.41×10^{-11} mol. which corresponds to a concentration of 11.8 meq/l. The fiber had thus lost a total amount of 3.02×10^{-11} mol. potassium, while only 2.29×10^{-11} mol. had contributed to the current flow. The rest of 0.73×10^{-11} mol. has most probably been lost by diffusion out of the open ends.

Approximately 10–15 per cent of the internal potassium does not leave the fiber (see Fig. 14). This amount cannot be removed even if strong longitudinal currents are passed through a fiber stretch which contains no node (isolated internodium) so that the current can pass freely through the axoplasm (both ends of the internode in pure NaCl). Whether this amount is retained in the axoplasm or in the myelin cannot be decided, but the figure tallies with the conclusion reached by Hodgkin and Keynes [2] that approximately 90 per cent of the internal potassium is free to exchange with the external potassium.

One should be able to increase the total amount of current by making more potassium available to diffuse out through the nodal membrane. Considering the geometrical situation of Fig. 7 this could be done by filling the two side pools with 0.1 M KCl. The amount of potassium available to the fiber is then practically infinite and the current flow should not decay.

Fig. 10 demonstrates such an experiment. Immediately after the KCl is applied to the two side nodes, current starts flowing out of the middle node. This current increases as the two side nodes are cut (due to the short circuit between internal and external conductor) and stays practically constant at this high level. (There is a slow decay which seems to be due to the accumulation of K outside the membrane, since it can be prevented by washing the middle node with fresh Ringer's solution; see arrows in Fig. 10.) When the middle node is cut after $3\frac{1}{2}$ hrs, the current drops to a negative value and from there to zero. The small opposite current after cutting of the middle node must be attributed to internal longitudinal polarisation (see below).

Intergration of the current in Fig. 10 shows that 1.3×10^{-10} mol. univalent ions have left the fiber through the node which is approximately 4 times the amount of potassium initially present in this fiber stretch. Fig. 11 illustrates a similar experiment, but instead of cutting the middle node, the KCl in the two side pools was exchanged for Ringer's after 3 hrs of steady current flow. As was expected, the current decays to zero in the usual exponential fashion.

There is another possibility of checking the validity of the assumption that the amount of potassium present inside the fiber is responsible for the total amount of current flow. If 0.1 M KCl is applied to the middle node the current flow stops, presumably because the potassium concentrations inside and outside the membrane and thus the fluxes in both directions are equal.

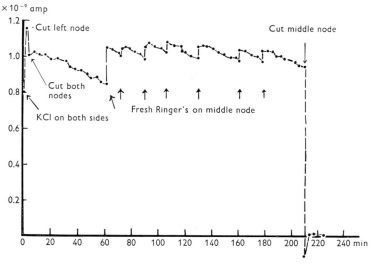

Fig. 10.—Membrane current as function of time when both side pools are filled with 0.1 M KCl. Values corrected for liquid junction currents.

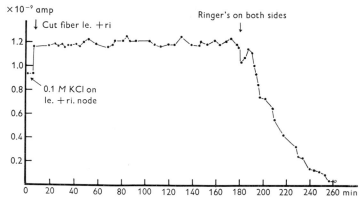

Fig. 11.—Membrane current as function of time. Both sides filled first with 0.1 M KCl, then with Ringer's.

Even if the KCl is left on the node for a long time, the total amount of potassium inside the fiber should not decrease considerably and the current should come back to the original level, when the KCl on the middle node, is exchanged for Ringer's. Fig. 12 illustrates this experiment. The current shows the expected behavior. The situation is somewhat complicated by the fact that there might be some inward diffusion of sodium from the open ends, so that the potassium concentration will be slightly lower than expected. This might be the reason, why the current does not reach its initial value

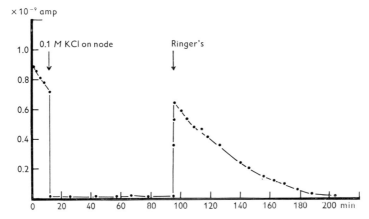

Fig. 12.—Membrane current as function of time. Side pools filled with Ringer's. Ringer's in middle pool exchanged with KCl (0.1 *M*) for 45 min.

again after the KCl has been removed from the middle node. It is, however, possible to refill partly the internodes with potassium through the middle node even after it has been completely emptied by the current flow (see Fig. 20).

Current flow and movement of sodium

The potassium leaving the fiber through the middle node has to be replaced by other cations entering the axon from the side pools. Since Na is the only cation present in these pools, some of this Na will go into the fiber. If all the internal anions were fixed, i.e. could not diffuse out of the open end, each potassium ion leaving the fiber would have to be replaced by a Na ion. There is not much information available concerning the mobility of the internal anions. Although a large fraction of the anions in squid axoplasm was found to be dialysable [7], their mobility in the intact axoplasm is not known. The total gain of Na can be measured in the first approximation in

TABLE III. *Sodium and potassium concentration of single fibers which had been cut and had given demarcation current until exhaustion.*

Fiber No.	Internal concentration after demarcation current had become zero (meq/l nerve)	
	Na	K
82	141	
83	138	
86	145	
87	133	
89	161[a]	
90	128	
40		10.4
41		9.1
42		15.2
43		22.6
44		15.8
48		11.8
51		12.6
55		11.2

[a] Fiber which had been stimulated at 100/sec for 1 hr after the demarcation current had become zero.

the same way as the loss of potassium. If all lost potassium had been replaced by sodium, the total sodium concentration of the fiber would have to be considerably higher than that of Ringer's because the initial sodium content of the fiber is already between 50 and 70 meq/l.

The sodium concentrations of 6 fibers measured after the demarcation current had become zero are collected in Table III, together with the potassium concentrations of 8 other fibers measured also at the end of current flow. Taking 60 mM as the normal Na content the fibers gained between 68 and 100 mM/l Na, while they had lost between 60 and 120 mM/l K assuming an initial potassium concentration of 70–140 mM/l.

The exact quantitative relationship between K loss and Na gain can, of course, be established only by further experiments in which initial and final concentration of Na and K have to be measured simultaneuosly in the same fiber.

The sodium figures in Table III, however, indicate that the Na concentration inside the fiber exceeds the concentration of Na in the surrounding medium. But this fact alone does not allow the conclusion that the Na concentration in the axoplasm becomes equal to the prior K concentration, because a large amount of the Na might be stored by the numerous mitochondria present on the outside of the fiber, especially near the node.

The amplitude of the demarcation current

While the total amount of current seems to depend only on the amount of potassium available, the current amplitude is determined by several factors. The main ones are:

(1) the potential across the membrane,
(2) the membrane resistance,
(3) the external longitudinal resistance,
(4) the internal longitudinal resistance.

Each of these can vary independently.

(1) The membrane potential is known to vary with the external potassium concentration (e.g. [3]). Raising the external potassium concentration at the middle node causes an immediate decrease of the current amplitude. Fig. 13 shows the relationship between the external potassium concentration and the membrane current. The relation of the internal potassium concentration (assumed as 120 mM) to the external concentration is plotted logarithmically versus the membrane current. The straight line is drawn assuming a variation of the membrane potential of 58 mV per tenfold increase of the external concentration. (Original membrane potential assumed as 70 mV.)

If the membrane potential depends on the ratio of the internal/external K concentration, there should be a relationship between the measured internal potassium concentration and the initial membrane current given by the fiber immediately after the two sides are cut. Fig. 14 indicates that this relationship exists. The values were obtained in the following way: The fiber was suspended as usual under oil; both side-nodes were cut and the current was measured over both internodes. Immediately afterwards, the fiber was moved to one side of the recording stage, so that its entire length (two internodes) was hanging free in the oil. After a brief washing with DDA it was then placed on the platinum wire and analysed for potassium. It took about 2 min from the time the fiber was cut until it was taken out of the oil.

Although the other factors—especially internodal distance and fiber diameter—which also influence the current amplitude have not been accounted for in the plot, there is a definite increase of current amplitude with internal potassium concentration. On the average the concentrations are somewhat lower than those in Table I, indicating that some potassium had already diffused out of the open ends during the few minutes the ends were in the side pools after the fiber was cut.

(2) A decrease of the membrane resistance should increase the current flow. Removal of calcium from the surrounding medium is known to decrease the membrane resistance of the node. Application of a Ca-free Ringer's to

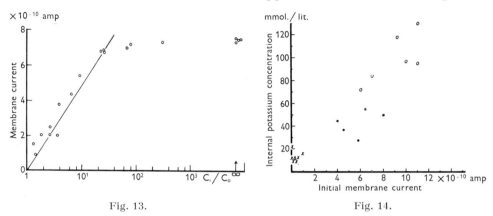

Fig. 13.   Fig. 14.

Fig. 13.—Amplitude of membrane current as function of the log. of internal/external potassium concentration. Both side pools filled with 0.1 M KCl. Straight line gives current amplitude calculated for an increase of membrane potential of 58 mV per tenfold increase of C_i/C_o.

Fig. 14.—Internal potassium concentration plotted versus membrane current immediately after the fiber was cut. Circles, fibers with good action potential. Dots, fibers which were slightly depolarised and gave full size action potentials only with external hyperpolarisation. Crosses, internal potassium concentration after the demarcation current had flowed for 100 min and was almost zero. Triangle, fiber through which was passed additional longitudinal current from external source after the end of demarcation current.

the middle node in fact increases the current flow. Also brief current pulses from a stimulator of either direction through the membrane cause a decrease of the membrane resistance and an increase of current flow.

(3) An increase of the external resistance can be brought about e.g. by washing the internode with glucose. The resulting decrease of current flow requires no comment.

(4) More consideration must be given to changes of the internal resistance. The electric behavior of the axoplasm as the internal conductor of longitudinal currents has not been given much attention in the literature. The only extensive study was made by Lorente de Nó [11] who concluded that the axoplasm must be the seat of a longitudinally polarisable structure. The effect of core polarisation can be seen already in Fig. 10. When the middle node is cut after the current has flowed for some time, the current does not

fall to zero, but flows for a short time in the opposite direction. The amplitude of this polarisation counter current is usually not greater than 10–15 per cent of the maximal demarcation current. It decays exponentially with a time constant of 1–3 min. The experiment illustrated in Fig. 15 provides further evidence that the seat of the polarisable structure is in fact the internal conductor. The fiber was cut in the usual way and the longitudinal current flow

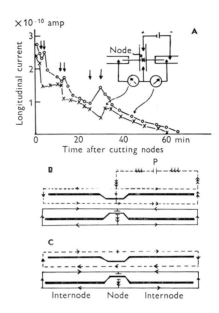

Fig. 15.—(*A*) Longitudinal current in left and right internode as function of time. *Between arrows*, hyperpolarisation from an external source was applied across the right internode (see insert). (*B*) Diagram of current flow through node and both internodes. *Broken line*, current flow due to the external hyperpolarisation. *Full line*, demarcation current. (*C*) As in (*B*), but broken line gives direction of polarisation counter current after the external hyperpolarisation was turned off.

in the external conductor recorded over the left and right internode. An additional inward current was passed through the middle node from an external source (see insert, Fig. 15 *A*). Direction and distribution of the two current components, namely the demarcation current proper and the polarising current from the external source, are illustrated in Fig. 15 *B*. If the polarising current is interrupted after it has flowed for some time and the longitudinal current measured, it turns out that the current is increased in the right segment while it is decreased in the left internode, so that the two curves which normally run parallel to each other are more or less separated according to how strong the external polarisation is and for how long it has lasted. This behavior of the total current can only be explained by a polarizable structure oriented longitudinally inside the axon. As can be seen in Fig. 15 *C*, a polarisation counter-current inside the axon would oppose the demarcation current in the left internode, thus decreasing the total current, while in the right internode it will flow in the same direction as the demarcation current and thus increase the total current in this segment. A measurement of the total current in both internodes made by placing the recording electrodes in the left and right pool confirms these assumptions. This current is usually near zero since current flow is opposite in both internodes. However, after the end of a few minutes of hyperpolarisation (electrode position as in

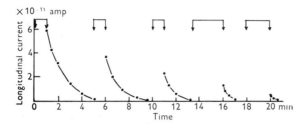

Fig. 16.—Longitudinal currents of a single internode (both nodes cut). *Between arrows*, current from an external source was applied longitudinally through the internode. The curves give the resulting polarisation counter current. This current decreases with each period of external current.

Fig. 15 A) there is a net current from left to right which again follows from the flow of counter current in the axon cylinder.

The great amount of this polarisation current is remarkable, requiring as it does the accumulation of a large number of ions at the poalrizable structure (concentration polarisation; see e.g. [14]).

The phenomenon seems to be bound to some axon constituent. It is independent from the species of the cation present inside the axon, i.e. it can be observed not only when the axon still contains its normal amount of potassium but also after this potassium has been replaced by Na, DDA or Ca by means of the demarcation current. However, the polarisability can be exhausted. After excessive and repeated current flow no internal core polarisation can be observed (see Fig. 16). This indicates that some ionic component of the axoplasm plays an important role in polarisation.

Longitudinal polarisation is only one factor causing changes of internal resistance. Another factor which is equally important is discussed in connection with experiments on the action currents.

Behavior of the action current

It was mentioned above that after the fiber is cut, the membrane potential drops to less than 50 per cent of its resting value. Accordingly, it should be expected that an action potential could be elicited only after the membrane potential was brought back to the resting value by external polarisation. To some extent this expectation is confirmed. Fig. 17 shows records of the longitudinal current in one internode for square pulse stimuli applied to the middle node at various times after the external hyperpolarisation was turned on (rec. 1 and 2) and after it was turned off again (rec. 3–5). It is remarkable that the hyperpolarising current has to flow for a considerable time (sometimes up to 5 min) before the action current has regained its full amplitude. Once the action current has recovered, much less polarisation is necessary

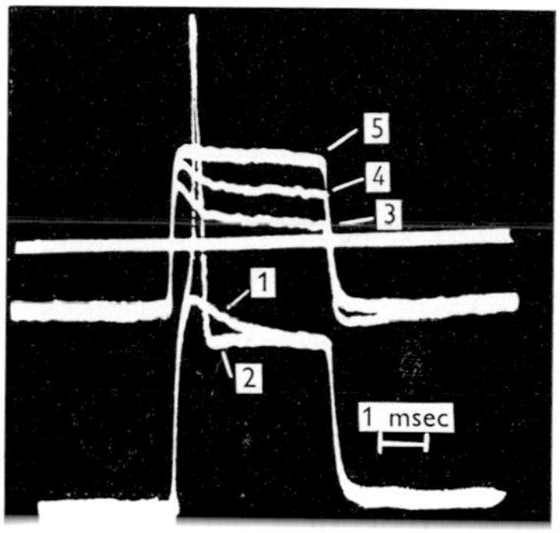

Fig. 17.—Electrotonic and action currents in response to square pulses applied to the middle node after the fiber was cut at both sides. Five sweeps superimposed with 10 sec interval between each sweep. Numbers indicate sequence of sweeps. Rec. 1 was taken 5 sec after application of constant hyperpolarisation, rec. 2, 10 sec later. Rec. 3–5 taken after the external hyperpolarisation was turned off.

to keep its amplitude at the full value. Similar observations were made by Lorente de Nó [11] in the whole trunk.

Immediately after the hyperpolarisation is turned off, the membrane resistance has a low value, judging from the height of the electrotonic current. Recovery also takes up to several minutes.

At short times after the fiber has been cut, the ionic composition of the axoplasm under the nodal membrane is presumably still unaltered and the ability of the system to give full size action currents is not surprising. The upshot is that the system still gives an action current after the demarcation current has become zero, i.e. in a state where the internal potassium concentration is presumably very low and the Na concentration high. In addition, no external hyperpolarisation is required. The phenomenon is illustrated in Fig. 18. The side pools were filled with pure 0.1 M NaCl to make sure that only Na could enter the fiber. The middle pool contained a potassium-free Ringer's. The records inserted in Fig. 18 give the action currents at the times indicated by the arrows. Rec. 1–6 show the action currents at fast sweep speed. Shortly after the fiber is cut, considerable hyperpolarisation is necessary to allow a full size action current (rec. 2). Rec. 3 shows the action current without hyperpolarisation at that time. As the demarcation current decreases, the size of the action current increases, and at the end of the demarcation current curve the node gives a full-size action current without hyperpolarisation.

Before drawing any conclusions from this phenomenon the relation between the measured longitudinal current and the transmembrane potential must be considered. Both would be linearly proportional to each other if the internal conductor had only the properties of an ohmic resistance. However, it was demonstrated above that there is a large apparent capacity in

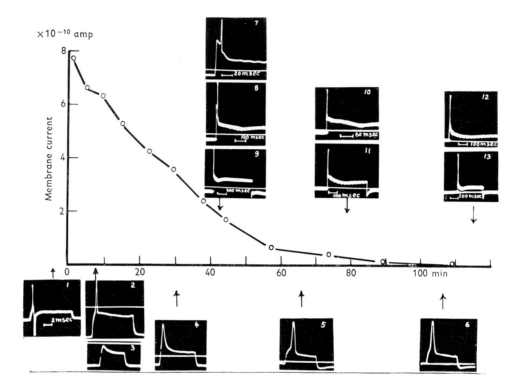

Fig. 18.—Action currents during decay of demarcation current. Arrows indicate time at which records were taken. Rec. 1 shows action current before cutting the fiber. Side pools were filled with pure 0.1 M NaCl.

the axis cylinder, presumably in parallel with its resistance which will allow transient potential changes to cause greater current variations than those which follow from changes of the steady value of the membrane potential. If the internal longitudinal resistance in parallel with the capacitance became infinite, there could exist a steady membrane potential in the absence of external current flow, while an action potential would still give the same amount of current as normally.

There is, indeed, experimental evidence that the internal resistance increases considerably as the sodium enters the axon. Some of the evidence can be taken from rec. 7–13 of Fig. 18, which give longitudinal currents in response to square pulses at various times during the decay of the demarcation current. Large capacitative maxima and overshoots can be seen already in rec. 7–9. These capacitative peaks and overshoots increase in proportion to the constant level of current flow as the demarcation current decreases (rec. 10–11; see also rec. 5 and 6). Finally in rec. 12 and 13 the current in the steady state is very small. The amplitude of the action current, however, is practically unchanged. Also the stimulating voltage necessary for threshold excitation increases considerably, indicating that less current flows through the membrane due to the increased internal resistance.

On the other hand, the internal resistance does not become infinite, as witness the amount of steady current flow in rec. 12 and 13. Furthermore, there are two more pieces of evidence suggesting that there is in fact no appreciable potential difference across the membrane after the demarcation current has become zero. One is the fact that the substitution of Ringer's for potassium in the middle pool at the end of the demarcation current flow is able to recharge the axon to a certain extent with KCl, which results in a new flow of demarcation current and the necessity to hyperpolarise in order to obtain full action currents. This would indicate that the axoplasm immediately under the membrane is empty of potassium—and thus the transmembrane potential zero—at the end of the demarcation current flow.

The second point is this: If there were any appreciable membrane potential after the current is zero, the longitudinal core capacity would have to be charged and should discharge, if the middle node were cut, at the same rate as those capacitative maxima and overshoots in rec. 7–13, Fig. 18. This discharge, should give a longitudinal current with an amplitude approximately half that of the action current. No such fast discharges were seen when the middle node was cut under oscillographic control. There is only the very small and slowly decaying current of longitudinal polarisation.

Thus the question whether or not the node gives an action current at the end of the demarcation current flow, without there being a full resting potential across the membrane, must be left open. If the NaCl solution in the two side pools contains some KCl (5–10 mM), the internal longitudinal resistance increases much less. In this case, the external hyperpolarisation is necessary before a full action current can be elicited at the end of demarcation current flow. However, the action current still goes far beyond the zero membrane current line, indicating that there is still a reversal of the membrane potential.

Since the sodium concentration at this time inside the fiber should be at least 0.1 M, it becomes difficult to explain the action potential as the result of a simple inward diffusion along a concentration gradient, unless one accepts the fact that most of the internal sodium is combined, or that there is some mechanism which keeps the immediate region under the node free of Na.

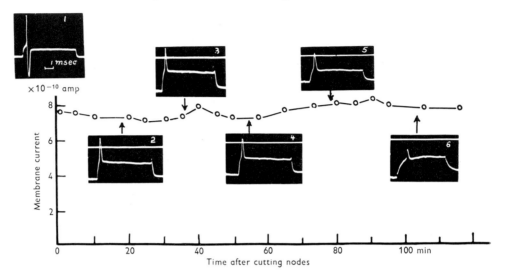

Fig. 19.—Action currents during constant flow of demarcation current. Rec. 1 was taken before fiber was cut. Side pools filled with 0.1 M KCl. Middle pool filled with K-free Ringer's.

In fact, there are indications that the ability of the system to give full action currents is more sensitive to other factors than the internal concentration of Na or K. In Fig. 19 an experiment is illustrated in which both side pools were filled with 0.1 M KCl so that there was a continuous and steady flow of demarcation current. No Na could enter the fiber. As a result, there is no increase of the internal resistance, judging from the electrotonic currents, and there will also be no considerable change of the internal K concentration. Yet the amplitude of the action current decreases continuously and finally becomes zero in spite of the supposedly normal ion distribution. Due to the current flow, some axon, or membrane, constituent seems to be removed or altered, which is of vital importance for the ability of the system to give a normal action current.

Further evidence that at least the internal K concentration plays no role for the action current is provided by Fig. 20. In this experiment both side pools were filled with DDA (middle pool with Ringer's). It appeared that the decay of the demarcation current is considerably faster than in Na and also that the internal longitudinal resistance does not increase. Both facts are probably due to a high mobility of the DDA in the axoplasm. This higher mobility will allow the DDA to diffuse into the axis cylinder and exchange for K at a much higher rate than the Na. Action currents can be

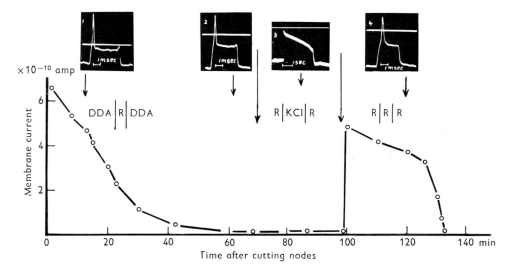

Fig. 20.—Action currents during flow of demarcation current. Inserted letters indicate the solutions in the three pools. DDA = Dimethyldiethanolammoniumchloride (0.1 M). Note the long-lasting action current when middle pool is filled with KCl.

elicited only after external hyperpolarisation, which has to be maintained for several minutes before the action current attains its full size. However, even after the demarcation current was zero and the internal potassium concentration correspondingly low, the action current has its initial amplitude.

Some other interesting points can be taken from Fig. 20. After the demarcation current had reached zero, 0.1 M KCl was applied to the node in combination with external hyperpolarisation. Upon stimulation by brief cathodal currents, the node gives now very long-lasting action currents, which are typical for a fiber in high external KCl, and obviously the fiber is refilled with K through the node since it again gives a large demarcation current after the KCl is replaced by Ringer's. The action current is then normal again. The subsequent decline of the demarcation current has an unusual form which must be attributed to the fact that the external hyperpolarisation was continued.

CONCLUSION

The experiments provided evidence for the following major points.

(*a*) The demarcation current through the nodal membrane is due to an outward diffusion of K ions along a concentration gradient. No energy source other than a concentration difference is necessary for a steady flow of demarcation current.

(*b*) The process underlying the action potential is independent of the presence of internal potassium ions and of the outward diffusion of K ions in so far as the potential difference across the membrane (resting potential) established by this diffusion can be replaced by a potential difference from an external source. The resting potential might well be established at another membrane or structure than the action potential, which is also indicated by the fact that a large number of agents interfere with the action potential without altering the resting potential. For instance, even a strong fixative like formaline does not affect the demarcation current.

(*c*) There exists in the axoplasm a structure which is highly polarisable by longitudinal currents and allows the accumulation of rather large amounts of ions (concentration polarisation), which then result in a prolonged polarisation counter current.

(*d*) The most important fact is the apparently extremely low mobility of Na ions inside the axoplasm. A rough estimate based on the change of the internal resistance gives a conductance of $(1000 \ \Omega \ cm)^{-1}$ as compared to a normal value of approximately $(100 \ \Omega \ cm)^{-1}$, a figure which might be even on the high side since there is always some internal potassium left. The low mobility of Na in the axoplasm might be of importance for selective ion accumulation as well as for the mechanism of the action potential itself. The low mobility of Na in the axoplasm need not necessarily be due to the formation of a complex between Na and internal anions. Ling [8, 9] worked out a theory which accounts for the preferential accumulation of K in the axoplasm. From the theory it follows that within a system of fixed negative charges which by virtue of their field strength preferentially absorb potassium, the mobility of Na ions would be considerably smaller than that of K ions.

In this connection it is interesting to note that the relation of the mobilities of Na and K within the axoplasm is of the same order of magnitude as within the membrane, namely $\frac{1}{10} - \frac{1}{20}$, although the absolute values differ by a factor of 10^5.

SUMMARY

1. By means of a special flame photometer method measurements of the sodium and potassium content of single myelinated nerve fibers of frogs were made. The potassium concentration in the total fiber varied from animal to animal. Values between 50 and 145 mM/l nerve were found. Sodium concentrations varied between 50 and 80 mM/l.

2. In a second series of experiments single fibers were cut, leaving only the node and the two neighbouring internodes intact and the flow of demarcation current through the nodal membrane was measured and quantitatively correlated with the concentrations and movements of potassium and sodium ions.

3. The experiments provided evidence in favor of the assumption that the demarcation current is caused by outward diffusion of K ions through the nodal membrane. The total amount of demarcation current depends on the amount of potassium ions available for diffusion through the nodal membrane.

4. Action currents were tested at various times during the flow of demarcation current. From their behavior the following conclusions were drawn: (*a*) The ability of the node to give normal action potentials is not dependent on the concentration of potassium under the nodal membrane; (*b*) There are indications that the action potential is also independent of the internal sodium concentration.

5. Na ions entering the axoplasm cause a large increase of the resistivity of the internal conductor. The same is true for Ca ions. Potassium ions and some quaternary ammonium ions like DDA do not cause this increase of the internal resistance.

6. Evidence is provided for the presence of longitudinally polarisable structures inside the axoplasm.

The author is indebted to Mr. K. Deck for technical assistance and helpful discussion.

REFERENCES

1. FENN, W. O., COBB, D. M., HEGNAUER, A. H. and MARSH, B. S., *Am. J. Physiol.* **110**m, 74 (1934).
2. HODGKIN, A. L. and KEYNES, R. D., *J. Physiol.* **119**, 513 (1953).
3. HUXLEY, A. F. and STÄMPFLI, R., *J. Physiol.* **112**, 476 (1951).
4. —— *ibid.* **112**, 490 (1951).

5. KEYNES, R. D., *J. Physiol.* **114**, 119 (1951).
6. KEYNES, R. D. and LEWIS, P. R., *J. Physiol.* **114**, 151 (1951).
7. KOECHLIN, B. A., *J. Biophys. Biochem. Cytol.* **1**, 6 (1955).
8. LING, G. N., *Symposium on Phosphorus Metabolism.* Johns Hopkins Univ. Press, Baltimore. **II**, 748 (1952).
9. —— *Am. J. Phys. Med.* **34**, 89 (1955).
10. LING, G. and GERARD, R. W., *J. Cellular Comp. Physiol.* **34**, 383 (1949).
11. LORENTE DE NÓ, R., A Study on Nerve Physiol. Studies from the Rockefeller Inst. for Med. Res., New York, Vol. II, 1947.
12. —— personal communication.
13. NASTUK, W. L. and HODGKIN, A. L., *J. Cellular Comp. Physiol.* **35**, 39 (1950).
14. NERNST, W. and RIESENFELD, E. H., *Ann. Physik* **8**, 600 (1902).
15. SIMON, A. and SZELOCZEY, J., *Biochem. Z.* **193**, 393 (1928).
16. STRAUB, R., *Helv. Physiol. Acta* **14**, 1 (1956).
17. TASAKI, I. and FREYGANG, W. H., *J. Gen. Physiol.* **39**, 211 (1955).
18. WEIDMANN, S., *J. Physiol.* **114**, 372 (1951).

Experimental Cell Research, Suppl. 5, 153–167 (1958)

AN ATTEMPT TO DETERMINE THE ORIGIN OF
SYNAPTIC VESICLES

V. L. VAN BREEMEN, E. ANDERSON and J. F. REGER

Department of Anatomy, University of Colorado Medical Center, Denver, Colorado, U.S.A.

SYNAPTIC vesicles have been described by a number of investigators [6, 1, 7, 9]. Characteristics of the vesicles may be summed up as follows: They are semi-dense homogeneous bodies, bounded by a simple membrane; they vary from 200 to 600 Å in diameter; they are generally considered to be spherical in definitive form, but they may vary from spherical to ovoid, or they may be somewhat irregular in shape.

Fernández-Morán [2] briefly mentioned vesicular structures as they appeared in whole mounts of nerve fibers. Hess and Lansing [3], in studying sections of peripheral nerves, found endoplasmic reticulum scattered throughout the axoplasm, ranging in diameter from 300 Å upward. Thornburg [10] also mentioned endoplasmic reticulum as a component of axoplasm. Axonal endoplasmic reticulum was described by Thornburg and De Robertis [11] as strands of canaliculi and vesicles about 300 to 400 Å in diameter scattered along the axon cylinder.

In a report of studies of synapses in frog and earthworm, De Robertis and Bennett [1] stated: "The close geometric association of synaptic vesicles with endoplasmic reticulum ... suggests that the ergastoplasm may have a role in the synthesis of vesicular contents." Only in Palay and Palade's [8] very careful description of the fine structure of neurons was a distinction drawn between granular and agranular endoplasmic reticulum as they appeared in the neuron. The consensus of writings on the axon is that agranular reticulum (not ergastoplasm, granular reticulum nor Nissl substance) appears in the axons and at or near the synapses. Though there must be structural and functional relationships between the granular and agranular reticulum, as pointed out by Palay and Palade [8], the one is clearly not synonymous with the other. It may even be helpful, in interpretation of structure and function of the neuron, to relate the agranular reticulum with the classical descriptions of the Golgi apparatus in the neuron (perikaryon), as an irregular interlacing network.

The following report deals with an attempt to trace the synaptic vesicles to their source.

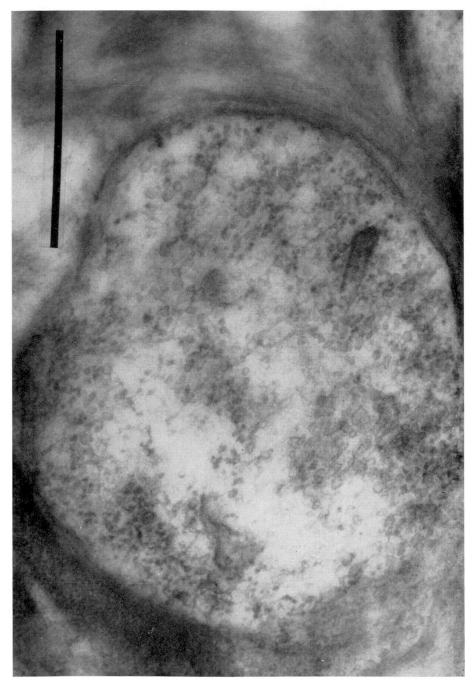

Fig. 1.—Normal frog. Section of axon in sarcolemmal groove, very near definitive neuromuscular synapse. Axoplasmic vesicles almost fill the axon; a few tubules are present. The bar measures 1 micron.

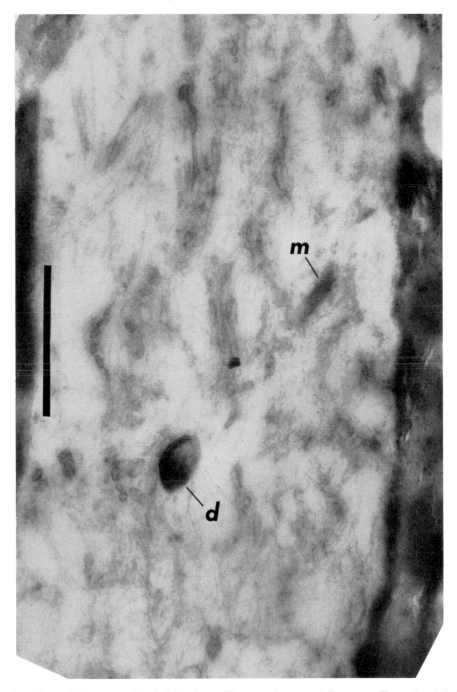

Fig. 2.—Frog sciatic nerve, ligated 20 days. The axoplasm contains neurofilaments, tubules (mostly in groups), vesicles, a mitochondrion (*m*) and a dense body (*d*). The bar measures 1 micron.

MATERIAL AND METHODS

Electron microscopic investigations of frogs (*Rana pipiens*) were divided
into three phases, as follows: studies of (1) normal neurons (perikarya,
axons, neuromuscular synapses), (2) dammed axons of sciatic nerves and
(3) perikarya (in spinal ganglia) and axons after malononitrile treatment.

Sciatic nerves from 18 normal frogs were studied. Sciatic nerves of 24 frogs were
ligated with cotton thread or fine plastic tubing. After 3 to 30 days, the axons at the
sites of the ligatures were removed and fixed. The micrographs presented here were
from axons dammed for 20 days. Several dozen frogs were given varied amounts of
malononitrile solution, by intraperitoneal injection, 6–40 mg/kg of body weight. Ten
frogs were given 40 mg/kg, and spinal ganglia were removed 1 hour after injection.
Electron micrographs presented here are from this group.

For orientation, representative specimens were fixed in Bouin's solution, embedded
in paraffin, sectioned at 2 μ and stained with a chrome–alum hematoxylin stain.
Most of the specimens were fixed in acetate-veronal buffered 1 per cent osmium
tetroxide (pH 7.6–7.8) for 15–25 minutes, dehydrated in methanol and embedded
in *n*-butyl methacrylate. Servall cantilever ultramicrotomes were used for sectioning,
and the sections were studied with a Philips electron microscope (EM-100-A).

RESULTS AND DISCUSSION

As a working hypothesis, one could say that synaptic vesicles probably
originate in the perikaryon of the neuron, which is highly active and productive. This seems plausible when one considers evidence for axoplasmic
flow, distad from the perikaryon, as presented by Weiss and Hiscoe [12].
Then, from our morphological point of view (in electron microscopy) we
would expect to see structures comparable to the synaptic vesicles, not only
in the axon, but also in the perikaryon.

Studies of normal frog neuromuscular synapses revealed a multiplicity
of round vesicles, 200–500 Å in diameter, dispersed through the terminal
axoplasm (Fig. 1). Contents of axons of normal frog sciatic nerves have
been found to consist of very fluid axoplasm containing scattered neurofilaments, few mitochondria, scattered round or elongate vesicles (200–400
Å in diameter) and rarely occurring large dense bodies. The round or
elongate vesicles were sufficiently numerous and were of the right order
of size to be related to synaptic vesicles. The large dense bodies were usually

Fig. 3.—Frog sciatic nerve, ligated 20 days. The axoplasm contains neurofilaments (periodicity
is evident), tubules and vesicles. Note the group of vesicles in the lower right corner. The bar
measures 1 micron.

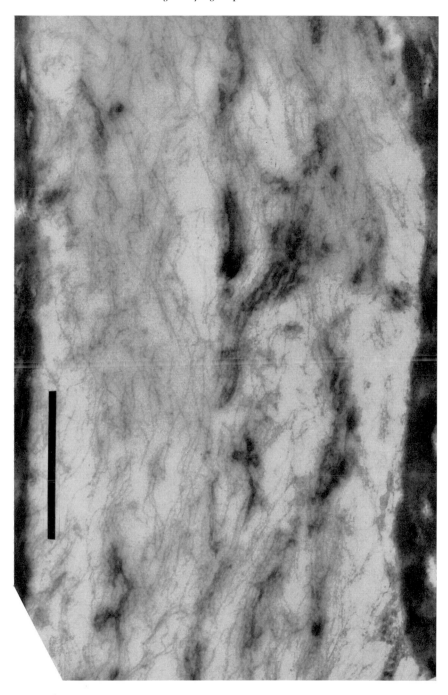

partially enclosed by a membrane and usually contained small granules (100–150 Å) and sometimes small vesicles (100–150 Å) in a dense matrix. The dense bodies in the axoplasm were not found to be intact, when compared to comparable structures in the perikaryon; their granules were sometimes found disseminated through the nearby axoplasm; single granules of the same size were found widely scattered through the axoplasm. These granules may be related to those described by Thornburg and De Robertis [11] as a dense particulate component of the axoplasm. Very few vesicles of the size of those in the dense bodies (100–150 Å) were seen as separate entities in the axoplasm, and they were apparently too few in number and too small in size to be related to the synaptic vesicles.

Ligation of the sciatic nerves was followed by axonal swelling proximal to the ligature, comparable to the results reported by Weiss and Hiscoe [12]. With damming of the axoplasm, there was an increase in the amount of normal axonal components, which appeared as follows (Figs. 2, 3, 4): fluid axoplasm, higher-than-normal concentration of filaments, few mitochondria (non enlarged, but still thin and elongate as in normal axons), many round or ovoid vesicles (usually in groups), many elongate vesicles (tubules or lamellae; occurring singly or often in groups), and rarely occurring large dense bodies (as previously described; Fig. 2). Accumulation of axoplasmic components in the swelling proximal to axonal ligation substantiates the idea that the axoplasm flows distad from the perikaryon.

The round or ovoid vesicles that occur singly or in groups in the ligated axons are directly comparable in size and structure to the synaptic vesicles, measuring approximately 150–200 Å in one dimension and 200–400 Å in the long dimension. Much elongated vesicles (tubules or lamellae) appear only in longitudinal or tangential sections. Groups of round or ovoid vesicles appear in these axons whether the axons are cut longitudinally, transversely or tangentially; therefore it is assumed that these actually represent spherical or ovoid vesicles. These axoplasmic vesicles may become the synaptic vesicles, which may also be formed by pinching off from the elongated vesicles; indications of such a phenomenon have been observed in the synaptic axoplasm.

Fig. 4.—Frog sciatic nerve, ligated 20 days. Among other things the axoplasm contains two groups of vesicles, at the arrow and in the lower right corner. At *a* is indicated the axolemma, as being distinct from the myelin sheath. The bar measures 1 micron.

Fig. 5.—An enlargement of the myelin sheath and axolemma indicated at *a* Fig. 4. The axolemma is again indicated by the letter *a*. A granular layer separates the axolemma from the myelin sheath. The bar measures one-fourth micron.

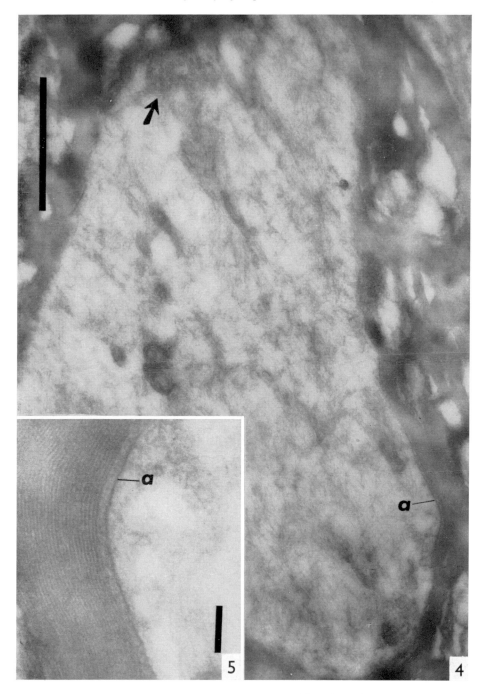

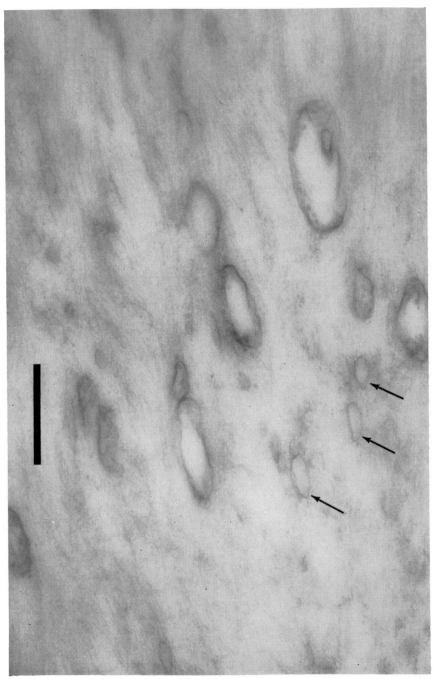

Fig. 6.—Malononitrile-treated frog (40 mg/kg). Portion of an axon near a spinal ganglion. The arrows indicate enlarged agranular vesicles. Other smaller vesicles may be seen in the axoplasm. The large vacuolated bodies are probably mitochondria. The bar measures 1 micron.

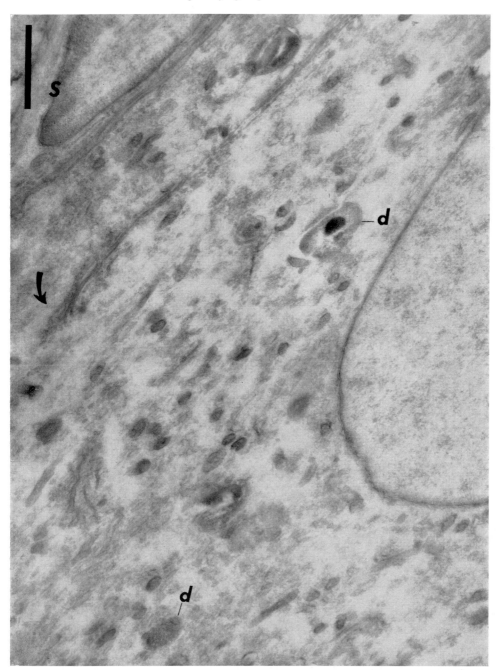

Fig. 7.—Normal frog ganglion cell. Portion of nucleus of neuron is at the right. Dense bodies are indicated by the letter *d*, one with a very dense core. The arrow indicates the terminal tubules and vesicles of the Golgi complex. A portion of a satellite cell (*s*) appears in the upper left corner. The bar measures 1 micron.

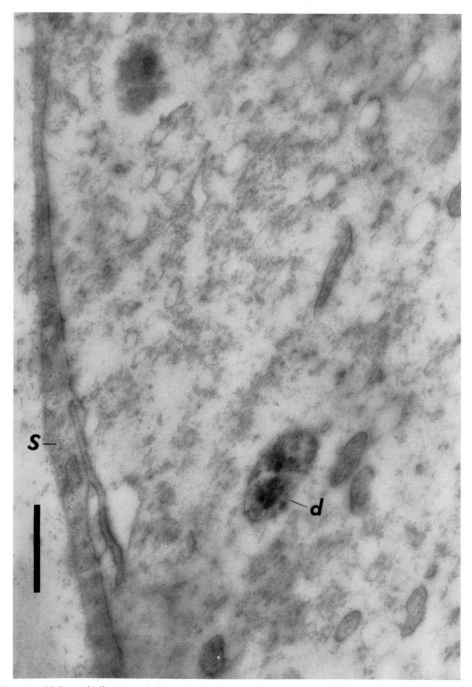

Fig. 8.—Malononitrile-treated frog. Portion of perikaryon of ganglion cell, with neighboring portion of satellite cell (s). A somewhat enlarged dense body is indicated by the letter d. Mitochondria are seen in the cytoplasm. Swollen vacuoles are seen associated with the granular endoplasmic reticulum. The bar measures 1 micron.

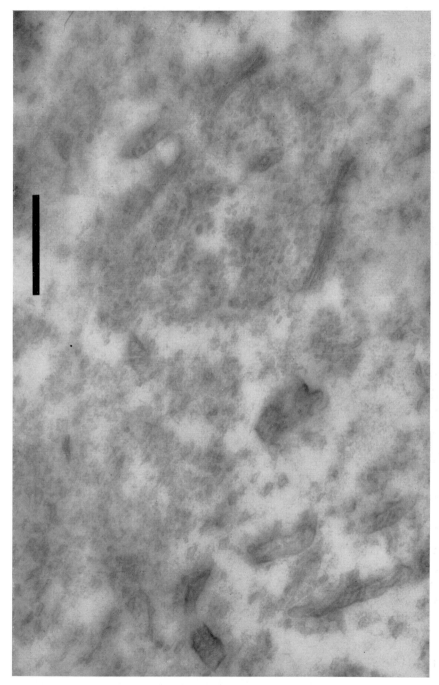

Fig. 9.—Malononitrile-treated frog. Portion of perikaryon of ganglion cell. Mitochondria are seen in the cytoplasm. Especially noticeable are the Golgi complexes with many associated vesicles. The bar measures 1 micron.

Noticeable in many dammed axons was the increase in amount of neurofilaments, probably reflecting their role in the sol-gel relationships of the axoplasm. The high concentration of neurofilaments in the axonal swellings would indicate an increased viscosity of the axoplasm, in view of the statement by Maxfield [5] that the neurofilaments are reversibly polymerized axoplasmic proteins. It seems to us that the neurofilaments have no relationship to the formation of synaptic vesicles, as was suggested by Robertson [9].

In the normal perikaryon (Fig. 7), there are round or ovoid vesicles (200–300 Å in diameter) associated with the agranular endoplasmic reticulum (Golgi apparatus). Palay and Palade [8] describe these structures as follows: "Like the endoplasmic reticulum, the second system of membrane-bound cavities described in this paper apparently consists of broad, flattened cisternae, which arborize into tubules and fragment into smaller vesicles at their extremities." We believe that this is a very likely source of the vesicles and tubules that appear in the axoplasm and eventually pass into the synaptic area to become the synaptic vesicles. These same vesicular structures appeared in the few axon hillocks that we have observed.

In the normal perikaryon, we have also observed groups of vesicles (each vesicle being 200–350 Å in diameter) surrounded by membranes. Palay and Palade [8] described such formations and interpreted them to represent villous invaginations from the surface membrane of the vacuole and to be related to the agranular reticulum. However, we would like to suggest another possible interpretation, that such structures may be derived from the satellite cells, the cytoplasm of which also contains many vesicles that range in size from 200 to 400 Å. It may be that these vesicles move into the neuron perikaryon, either singly or in groups, directly or by invagination; subsequently the groups could retain a single or multiple enclosing membrane. This is another possible source of the synaptic vesicles, though we present it as only a suggestion. On the other hand, it could be that these vacuoles (with enclosed vesicles) temporarily store materials supplied to the neuron by the satellite cells.

In the perikaryon were seen scattered large dense bodies (Figs. 7, 8), usually enclosed by a membrane, probably being the source of the dense granular bodies found in the axoplasm. These bodies were ovoid in shape, with a dense central core surrounded by small dense granules (100–150 Å),

---

Fig. 10.—Malononitrile-treated frog. Portion of perikaryon of ganglion cell. The arrow indicates a Golgi complex with swollen terminal tubules. The bar measures 1 micron.

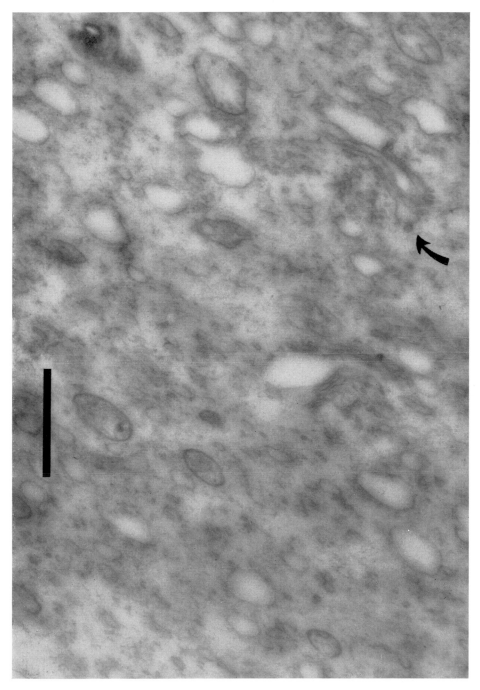

small vesicles (100–150 Å) and occasional larger vesicles (300–800 Å). These bodies may be related to those described by Palay and Palade [8]; however, there apparently are some differences, which may be species differences. That these large dense bodies were found in both the perikaryon and the axoplasm may indicate a functional relationship; the function of these bodies, with their granules and small vesicles, is obviously uncertain at this time.

Malononitrile treatment was followed by an increase in the number of vesicles (200–400 Å) associated with the Golgi complex (Fig. 9). In some ganglion cells, there was an enlargement of the cisternae in the granular reticulum (Fig. 8) as well as an enlargement of the vesicles associated with the Golgi complex (Fig. 9). However, only the enlarged *agranular* vesicles were found in the axons. Only once in the many observations that were made on malononitrile-treated or ligated axons was granular reticulum seen in the axon. It is apparent, then, that the Golgi tubules and vesicles relate directly to the agranular tubules and vesicles that appear in the axon and in the synaptic axoplasm. Awaiting further evidence, we tentatively conclude that the synaptic vesicles originate in the Golgi complex.

SUMMARY

Electron microscopic observations of frog neurons revealed the morphologic similarity of vesicles (200–500 Å diameter) found in the perikarya of spinal ganglion neurons, in the axoplasm of sciatic axons and in the axoplasm (synaptoplasm) at the neuromuscular synapse.

When frog sciatic nerves were ligated, axonal swellings appeared proximal to the ligatures. Axoplasmic accumulation in the swellings is compatible with the idea that axoplasm flows along the axons distad from the perikarya. Vesicles, being a normal axoplasmic component, accumulated in the axonal swellings. This was accepted as evidence that the vesicles moved with the axoplasm down the axons from the perikarya.

In the perikarya, vesicles were found in association with the agranular reticulum, which, in the opinion of the authors, should be properly called the Golgi apparatus, or Golgi complex.

The authors suggest that the synaptic vesicles may originate in the Golgi complex.

REFERENCES

1. DE ROBERTIS, E. D. P. and BENNETT, H. S., *J. Biophys. Biochem. Cytol.* **1**, 47 (1955).
2. FERNÁNDEZ-MORÁN, H., *Exptl. Cell Research* **3**, 282 (1952).
3. HESS, A. and LANSING, A. I., *Anat. Rec.* **117**, 175 (1953).
4. HYDÉN, H. and HARTELIUS, H., *Acta Psychiat. et Neurol., Suppl.* **48**, 1 (1948).
5. MAXFIELD, M., *J. Gen. Physiol.* **37**, 201 (1953).
6. PALADE, G. E., *Anat. Rec.* **118**, 335 (1954).
7. PALAY, S. L., *J. Biophys. Biochem. Cytol.* **2**, 193 (1956).
8. PALAY, S. L. and PALADE, G. E., *J. Biophys. Biochem. Cytol.* **1**, 69 (1955).
9. ROBERTSON, J. D., *J. Biophys. Biochem. Cytol.* **2**, 381 (1956).
10. THORNBURG, W., *Anat. Rec.* **118**, 362 (1954).
11. THORNBURG, W. and DE ROBERTIS, E., *J. Biophys. Biochem. Cytol.* **2**, 475 (1956).
12. WEISS, P. and HISCOE, H. B., *J. Exptl. Zool.* **107**, 315 (1948).

THE FINE STRUCTURE OF ELECTRIC TISSUE

J. H. LUFT[1]

Department of Anatomy, University of Washington, Seattle, Wash., U.S.A.

THE ability to pump and accumulate ions seems to be a fundamental feature associated with the function of living cells. It would be of considerable value to cellular biology to identify this electrical activity with some structural component of the cell. Powerful and highly developed biological ion-pumping mechanisms occur in the electric organs of various fishes. In the belief that the structures associated with ionic transfer might be likewise highly developed in these specialized tissues, electric organs of 4 species of electric fish have been examined with the electron microscope. In this report the characteristic morphological features of electric tissue are described, and a possible mechanism is suggested, correlating structure with function. Calculations are presented indicating that the postulated mechanism is compatible with a type of ion transport in which electrolytes move by transfer within and from vesicles.

MATERIAL AND METHODS

Electric tissue was obtained from vigorous specimens of 4 varieties of electric fish, namely the "electric eel", *Electrophorus electricus*, the torpedo ray, *Torpedo occidentalis*, several unidentified species of *Mormyrus* from the Nile, and the Egyptian electric catfish, *Malapterurus electricus*. Several large (1 meter) specimens of *Electrophorus* were obtained from Dr. David Nachmansohn of Columbia University and Mr. C. W. Coates of the New York Zoological Society Aquarium. Two specimens of *Torpedo* (about 15 kg) were obtained at the Marine Biological Laboratories, Woods Hole, Massachusetts. Small specimens (6–10 cm) of *Mormyrus*, *Malapterurus*, and *Electrophorus* were obtained through tropical fish importers. All were found to be fully active electrically by physiological or electrical tests before fixation.

The tissue was fixed for electron microscopy by immersion in 1 to 2.5 per cent osmium tetroxide buffered at pH 7.4, for one hour at 0°C [23]. The tissue blocks were then rapidly dehydrated in ethanol, embedded in *n*-butyl methacrylate, and sectioned in the usual fashion. The sections were examined in an RCA EMU 2 A microscope.

[1] This project was initiated at the Anatomy Department, Harvard Medical School, under a National Research Council Fellowship in the Medical Sciences, for which funds were provided by the Rockefeller Foundation. It was completed at the University of Washington supported by a grant from the Muscular Dystrophy Association.

OBSERVATIONS

The resulting electron micrographs confirmed previous observations with the light microscope [2, 4, 22]. In all instances the electric tissue was seen to be composed of an aggregation of large, flattened units called electroplaques, electroplates or electroplaxes. These are the unit electrical elements which are stacked in series like a pile of dinner plates (in neat columns in the case of *Electrophorus*, *Torpedo* and *Mormyrus*, but less well ordered in the case of *Malapterurus*). Each plate is separately innervated at one surface only and hence is polarized [4]. The properties of the electroplate have been well studied with microelectrodes only in *Electrophorus* and the Skate [18, 1, 17]. In these forms at rest the intercellular spaces on each side of the electroplate are at the same potential, but during activity the space adjacent to the innervated surface becomes negative by about 40 (Skate) to 150 (eel) millivolts with reference to the space adjacent to the non-innervated surface. In *Malapterurus*, however, the surface presenting to the nerve becomes positive. The innervation is strikingly different in each of the 4 genera, but these variations will not be described here. In each form, the electric tissue seems to have an independent evolutionary origin [9].

In contrast to the variations in innervation, the electroplates have one feature in common, namely a highly developed system of caveolae, or cave-like blind tubules, and vesicles. The caveolae are blind, elongated sac-like indentations of the plasma membrane of the cell (Figs. 3, 6 and 8). They may be branched. They can be regarded as elaborations of small vesicles and caveolae seen along the surface of many cells [29, 25]. Associated with the caveolae in the electroplate are many vesicles with a diameter approximately equal to that of the caveolae (500 to 1000 Å). These vesicles are completely intracellular, and are bounded by a membrane similar in appearance to the plasma membrane. As seen in the electron micrographs the contents of the vesicles do not communicate with the extracellular space. These features have been briefly described for *Electrophorus* and *Torpedo* [21]. In *Electrophorus*, the system of tubules is easily visible collectively with the light microscope, and has been called the "striate margin" [22]. Furthermore, vague outlines of the individual caveolae can just be detected with this instrument. They were called "Stäbchen" in the older literature [2]. However, the caveolae and vesicles cannot be resolved and recognized as such with the light microscope.

Fig. 2 illustrates an electroplate (*EL*) from *Electrophorus* under relatively low magnification, illustrating the caveolae (*C*) on both innervated and non-innervated surfaces. (The innervated surface is at the bottom, and this orientation is maintained in all figures.) Figs. 3 and 4 show more details of the tubular systems of the non-innervated face and innervated face respectively. In both Figs. 3 and 4 it is seen that the caveolae (*C*) extend from the limiting plasma membrane (*PM*) into the interior of the electroplate (*EL*). In all forms but *Malapterurus* the system of caveolae and vesicles is more elaborately developed at the non-innervated surface (Fig. 3) than at the innervated surface (Fig. 4). Associated with the caveolae are outlines of vesicles (*V*) within the cytoplasm, occasionally lined up in rows (Fig. 3).

Fig. 5 illustrates several electroplates (*EL*) from *Torpedo*, again demonstrating the system of caveolae and vesicles. Figs. 6 and 7 respectively illustrate the blind tubules of the non-innervated and innervated surfaces. Here, the main feature is the pronounced branching of the caveolae. They are more extensive on the non-innervated surface (Fig. 6) than on the innervated surface, where they are sparse (Fig. 7).

Figs. 8, 9 and 10 are from *Malapterurus*. Fig. 8 shows both surfaces of one electroplate (*EL*), with a nucleus (*N*) and several mitochondria (*M*). Figs. 9 and 10 show the caveolar system. The sacs and vesicles appear to be about equally well developed on both surfaces. If there is any difference it is slightly in favor of greater development upon the surface presenting to the connecting nerve branch.

Figs. 11, 12 and 13 in like manner represent respectively a whole electroplate and the non-innervated and innervated surfaces of the electroplate of *Mormyrus*. The caveolar system is highly developed with many ridges and clefts, but these are nearly obscured by numerous mitochondria (*M*), which are very closely packed. In this form again, the system of blind tubules is more elaborate on the non-innervated surface, where it is adorned with more vesicles. The mitochondria are likewise more numerous close to the non-innervated surface (Fig. 12) than near the opposing innervated surface (Fig. 13).

DISCUSSION

The first 3 electric fish herein described (Figs. 2 through 10), *Electrophorus*, *Torpedo*, and *Malapterurus*, can each generate sufficient electrical power to stun their prey or to defend themselves, and consequently display only occasional and intermittent violent electrical activity. *Mormyrus*, on the other hand, produces only a feeble discharge, insufficient for offense or defense, but which apparently is used in conjunction with some sensory receptor for exploring the conductivity of its environment. *Electrophorus*

has a special electric organ (of Sachs) which produces similar weak explo-
ratory pulses. These forms consequently produce rapid and frequent weak
pulses more or less continuously, as do several other fish [19, 5]. The large
number and close packing of mitochondria in the electric organ of *Mormyrus*,
and in the organ of Sachs in *Electrophorus* [22] seems to be associated with
frequent, repetitive use of these electric organs. Here, the mitochondria are
always found in close proximity to the caveolar system.

Strong electric fish, such as *Electrophorus* and *Torpedo*, are remarkable
for the large quantity of electric power which they can produce. *Electrophorus*
can generate a peak power of about 50 watts (0.25 amp. at 150 to 200 volts)
whereas *Torpedo* can produce several kilowatts (60 amp. at 100 volts)
[7, 6]. Keynes and Martins-Ferreira [18], and Altamirano *et al.* [1] have
obtained by microelectrode techniques, information regarding the specific
electrical changes occurring in the individual electroplate. These studies
indicate that activity in the electric organ of *Electrophorus* is similar in
mechanism to the generation of bioelectric potentials in nerve or muscle
[14]. With microelectrodes, a resting potential of about 80–90 millivolts is
measured across the cell membrane between the cytoplasm of the electroplate and the extracellular space. The authors mentioned above report
that upon arrival of the exciting impulse at the innervated surface of the
electroplate, the cell membrane undergoes a sudden change with the appearance of an action potential or "spike". The measured resting potential
across this membrane, normally positive outside and negative inside (av. 84
mV for *Electrophorus*), suddenly decreases toward zero, overshoots [18]
with reversal of polarity (to an average of 67 mV [18]), and returns to its
original voltage, all within several milliseconds. This is the same sequence,
and nearly the same voltage change as observed in nerve or muscle [14].
Keynes and Martins-Ferreira [18] have shown in the eel that the spike
potential can be decreased or eliminated by varying the sodium concentration
in the extracellular environment. They suggest that the membrane change
upon stimulation is associated with a sudden influx of sodium ions at the
innervated face. They relate the voltage of the action potential to differences
in intra- and extra-cellular sodium ion concentrations, and the current to the
number of ions crossing the membranes, (see [15] for similar reasoning with
respect to squid nerve.) Microelectrodes across the non-innervated membrane
show the same resting potential, which decreases only a few millivolts during
the spike. Since a considerable ionic current moves across this membrane
with such a small voltage drop, if one assumes that the membrane behaves
like an ohmic resistance, the conductance across this membrane would be

remarkably high, corresponding to a positive, ohmic resistance of only 0.23 ohms/cm² for the eel [18]. From the data and illustrations presented by these authors, it would appear that this non-innervated membrane adds its voltage to that of the innervated surface, completing the circuit to the next electroplate by permitting either influx of anions or efflux of cations, or both. They suggest that it is an exit of potassium.

As seen with the electron microscope, the characteristic feature of the electroplate is the system of caveolae and vesicles, which, in *Electrophorus*, *Torpedo*, and *Mormyrus*, are especially well developed on the non-innervated surface. This extreme specialization of the cell membrane is the only common structural feature seen in all the electric organs so far examined. It is conceivable that these specialized structural features might have an important role in the physiological specialization of the electric organ. In that event, the highly developed system of caveolae and vesicles would be important in ion pumping and transfer. Bennett [3] has already suggested a mechanism whereby vesicles and caveolae might function in active transport of ions. As applied to the electroplate, these mechanisms can be invoked as is seen from Text-fig. 1.

According to this hypothesis, ion transfer at both innervated and non-innervated surfaces could occur by the formation and reopening of vesicles. Although ions would pass from one side of the plasma membrane of the cell to the other, the membrane would at all times be an intact, continuous sheet without perforations or pores [3]. In Fig. 1 A the electroplate is represented in its resting state with the usual high concentration of sodium in the extracellular space, and a high concentration of potassium within the cytoplasm, as indicated by Keynes and Martins-Ferreira [18]. It is postulated that these concentrations are maintained by ion pumps operating at leisure, as outlined by Hodgkin and Keynes [15] for squid nerve. Some of the intracellular potassium is envisioned as occurring in vesicles near the blind ends of the caveolae of the non-innervated surface. The caveolae of the innervated surface would contain sodium at the extracellular concentration. In Fig. 1 B, the electroplate is represented just after stimulation. Vesicles containing sodium at extracellular concentration are shown as pinching off at the ends of the caveolae of the innervated surface, assuming an intracellular position as a result of this process. Fig. 1 C represents the electroplate in its active, conducting state. The vesicles just admitted at the innervated surface are shown as having opened, releasing sodium at high concentration into the interior of the cytoplasm. This would produce a reversal of polarity at this membrane. Simultaneously, or immediately thereafter the potassium-laden vesicles at the

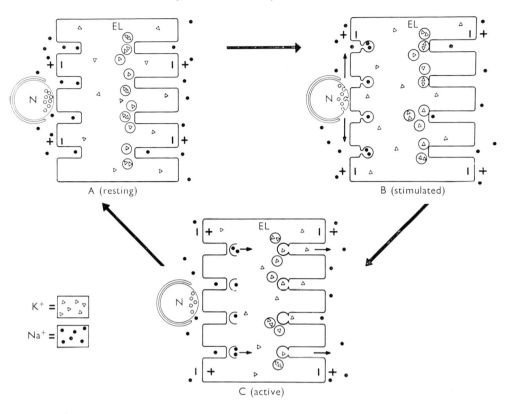

Text-fig. 1.—Schematic diagram of the electroplate of the eel (*Electrophorus*), utilizing the hypothesis of ion transport by vesicles to account for the generation of the electric impulse. An electroplate (*EL*) is represented in 3 phases of activity: *A*, the resting or inactive state, *B*, just after
stimulation, and *C*, in the active conducting phase in which voltage and current is generated.
The electroplate is simplified to show a single nerve fiber (*N*) in synapse with the innervated surface
of the electroplate. Within the nerve are synaptic vesicles. Sodium ions (solid dots) are randomly
distributed in the extracellular space, and potassium ions (triangles) are present within the cytoplasm of the electroplate. Some of the potassium is represented as being segregated within vesicles
near the caveolae or tubules of the non-innervated surface. A resting potential is illustrated
across the cell membrane. At stage *A* this is equal in voltage but opposite in sign across the
whole electroplate. In stage *B*, the nerve is represented as having been activated by the opening
of some synaptic vesicles at the synapse, perhaps releasing acetylcholine in the vicinity of the
innervated surface. A wave of activity sweeps over the innervated surface, and vesicles are pictured as pinching off at the tips of the caveolae of this surface, enclosing some sodium ions from
the extracellular space, thus transferring the ions to an intracellular position. In stage *C*, the
sodium-filled vesicles are represented as having pinched off and broken open, discharging their
contents to the intracellular environment, with reversal of charge at this surface. The potassium-
containing intracellular vesicles are pictured as having fused to the non-innervated caveolae,
opening and releasing their contents to the extracellular space. At this stage voltage on both
innervated and non-innervated surfaces is alike in polarity, adding voltages and passing current.
The electroplate then returns to the stable resting stage *A*, restoring its former intra- and extracellular ionic concentrations by ion pumps, and forming new vesicles.

non-innervated surface are thought to fuse with their caveolae, to open to the exterior and to release potassium to the extracellular space. The electroplate then returns to the resting condition (Fig. 1 A). The numerous vesicles seen near the non-innervated surface are thought of as a store or reservoir or reserve supply of segregated potassium ions maintained near the caveolae of that surface. These reserve potassium-filled vesicles can be called upon in case the cycle is repeated immediately. Volumes and concentrations of the intracellular and extracellular compartments are such as to permit some hundred thousand shocks with only about 5 per cent change in the respective ion concentrations of the compartments.

Some interesting features of this model may be pointed out. First, ions would be travelling in vesicles, i.e. packages where the movement of one ion is associated with the movement of many other similar ions in the same direction. Hodgkin and Keynes [16] present evidence that potassium moves in *Sepia* axons in a manner which suggests that the individual ions are not independent of each other, but move as groups. While they did not specifically consider ion transport in vesicles, such movements may be compatible with their findings.

Secondly, vesicles have received some attention in recent discussions of neuromuscular transmission. Del Castillo and Katz [10] present a recent review on this subject. They point out that since 1938 it has been realized

---

The solid line in each figure represents one micron. In each figure this line is placed in the extracellular space.

Figs. 2, 3 and 4.—Electron micrographs of the main organ of the electric eel, *Electrophorus*. *Fig. 2* shows a portion of an electroplate (*EL*), with several nuclei (*N*) and nearby clumps of mitochondria (*M*). Caveolae are seen at *C*. The innervated surface of the electroplate is at the bottom of the illustration and this orientation is maintained in all figures. × 3100. *Fig. 3* shows a portion of the non-innervated surface of the electroplate (*EL*) showing caveolae (*C*) continuous with the plasma membrane of the cell. In addition, there are groups of vesicles (*V*) closely associated with the caveolae. In some instances they appear to be oriented in rows like a string of beads. × 13,800. *Fig. 4* illustrates a portion of the innervated surface of the electroplate, including a nerve ending (*NE*) containing some synaptic vesicles (*arrows*). The membrane lining the caveolae (*C*) is clearly continuous with the plasma membrane (*PM*). In addition, there are a few vesicles (*V*) near the blind ends of the caveolae. × 17,400.

Figs. 5, 6 and 7.—Electron micrographs of the electric organ of *Torpedo*. *Fig. 5* shows at low magnification portions of 6 electroplates with several nuclei (*N*), and some small groups of mitochondria (*M*). The caveolar system (*C*) is highly developed on the non-innervated surface of each electroplate. The lower, innervated surface has few caveolae, but has a wealth of nerve endings (*NE*). × 15,600. *Fig. 6* demonstrates the caveolar system at the non-innervated surface. The tubules are highly branched, and the oval outlines represent both caveolae in cross section, and vesicles. × 12,000. *Fig. 7* represents a nerve ending (*NE*) indenting the innervated surface of the electroplate (*EL*). The caveolae are simple tubes. The neural elements of the ending seem to penetrate well into some of the caveolae. × 12,800.

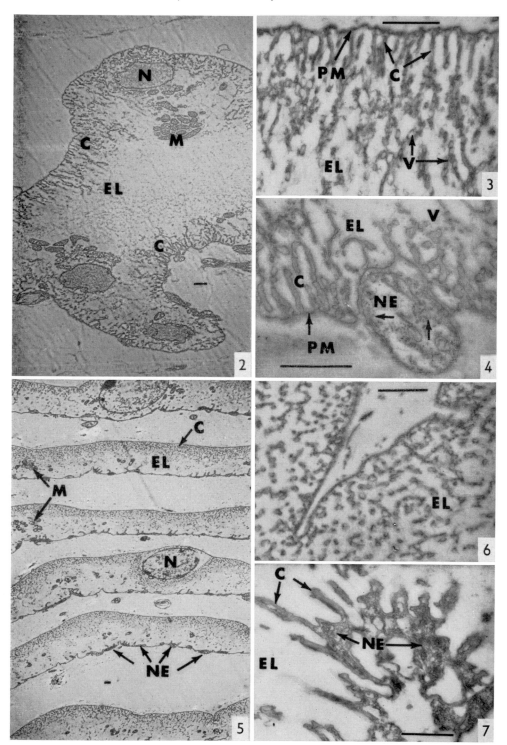

that acetylcholine exists in nerve in a "bound" form. Fatt and Katz [13] postulated that acetylcholine was released from motor end plates in discrete and rather constant amounts or "quanta". This deduction was based upon electrical recording of minute potentials at the motor end plate, random in frequency, but nearly equal in size. These were detected even in the resting condition. When the motor nerve and its end plate were stimulated, activity was revealed as an increased frequency of release of these quanta, which summed to give the standard end plate potential. Calcium and magnesium ions altered the frequency of discharge of these miniature end plate potentials when the motor end plate was stimulated, but did not alter their amplitude. Independently, vesicles had been described in electron micrographs of synapses and motor end plates [24, 26, 27, 11, 12, 28]. Del Castillo and Katz [10] suggest that the discharge of individual synaptic vesicles seen in the electron microscope may account for the packets or quanta demonstrated by them with purely electrical methods. The synaptic vesicles of synapses and the motor end plate are similar in appearance to the vesicles present in the electroplate, but tend to be smaller. Del Castillo and Katz [10] suggest that the synaptic vesicles of the motor end plate contain acetylcholine. If this be so, and if the present hypothesis of a high potassium concentration in the electroplate vesicles be correct, then synaptic vesicles and electroplate vesicles would be analogous in that both contain a high concentration of cation, and both are postulated to function in vesicular transport across the membrane by fusion and opening. The reasoning employed by del Castillo and Katz [10] concerning the statistics of the release of the acetylcholine quanta may well apply to the release of vesicles at the non-innervated surface of the electroplate.

Finally, the question arises as to whether such a vesicular transport system is reasonable in terms of the known electrical data relating to electric fish. It is possible to calculate roughly how many vesicles would be required to participate in each electric impulse of the eel. The following calculation

Figs. 8, 9 and 10.—Electron micrographs of electric tissue from *Malapterurus. Fig. 8* illustrates a portion of an electroplate showing both surfaces. The stimulating impulse arrives at the lower surface. The nucleus (N) has numerous mitochondria (M) associated with it. Membranes and vesicles typical of the Golgi complex are present at G. Caveolae (C) and vesicles are seen on both surfaces. Many of the caveolae are seen to be open to the extracellular space. The limiting membrane of the caveolae is continuous with the plasma membrane (PM). ×5800. *Fig. 9* shows further detail of the electroplate surface which does not receive the nerve. A nucleus (N) is present in the lower left corner, associated with mitochondria. The caveolar system (C) is well demonstrated. ×16,500. *Fig. 10* shows the surface which presents to the incoming nerve. The caveolae (C) are well seen. Within the cytoplasm are clumps of Palade's particles (P), frequently associated with delicate thread-like strands about 50 Å in thickness. ×25,700.

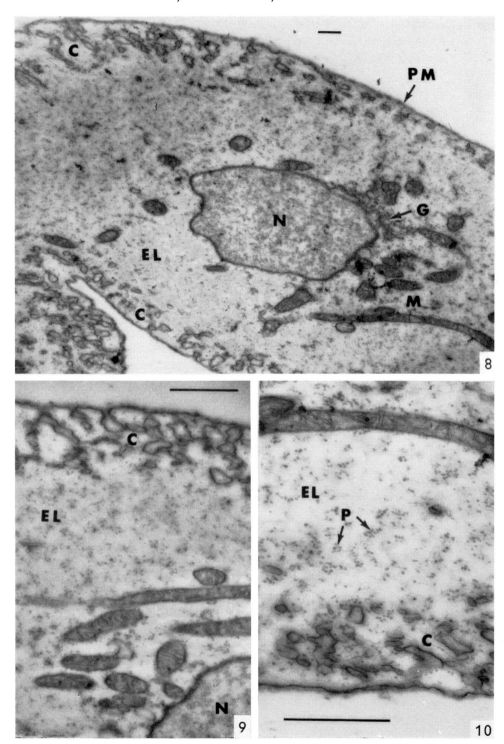

has been carried out for the non-innervated surface of the eel electroplate, where measurements and caveola counts are relatively easy. The geometry of the caveolae in the innervated surface is more complex, making measurements and counts more difficult here. However, such rough measurements and counts as can be made indicate that the number of caveolae per electroplate on the innervated surface is approximately equal to that on the non-innervated surface, but may be somewhat less. Thus the following quantitative argument can be applied to either surface, within the margin of error of the values employed. The calculations show that the postulated mechanism of vesicular transport could operate reasonably utilizing the vesicles and caveolae associated with either or both surfaces. The argument follows:

Cox, Coates and Brown [8] present electrical data on electric eels. For 8 eels averaging 67 cm in length, they find the average moving charge in the main organ to be 19 microcoulombs per impulse per cm^2 of cross section of electric organ. This represents (19×10^{-6}) $(6.28 \times 10^{18}) = 119 \times 10^{12}$ unit charges/cm^2/impulse. Since the surface of the electroplate is grossly convoluted, presenting many papillae [22], the true surface available for ionic transfer is greater than the cross section of the organ considered by Cox, Coates and Brown [8]. Linear measurements of profiles of the non-innervated surface, not allowing for the caveolae, show the gross profile following the papillae to be about 2.5 times the shortest linear dimension across the electric organ. It follows that the cross-sectional area of the non-innervated surfaces, allowing for papillae but not caveolae is 2.5^2 or about 6.5 times the cross-sectional area of the electric organ mentioned above. Correcting for this factor, the current density per unit area of non-innervated electroplate membrane would be

---

Figs. 11, 12 and 13.—Electron micrographs of the electric tissue from *Mormyrus*. *Fig. 11* illustrates a portion of one electroplate. Narrow zones of extracellular space (*ES*) are seen at the upper and lower margins of the figure. The plate itself is seen to consist of three zones. The two marginal zones are densely packed with large numbers of mitochondria associated with the caveolar systems. The non-innervated surface (*NS*) is more elaborately developed and shows more mitochondria (*M*) than the lower, innervated surface (*IS*). Separating these two zones is a less dense, central zone containing several myofibrils of striated muscle. The Z bands of the myofibrils are noted at *Z*, with a wide A band (*A*) between them. ×8700. *Fig. 12* demonstrates the complexity of the non-innervated surface. A nucleus (*N*) is in the lower corner. Mitochondria (*M*) densely populate this zone. In between them, the faint outlines of the caveolae (*C*) may be seen, forming an elaborate system associated with many vesicles. ×9200. *Fig. 13* illustrates the simpler, innervated surface of the electroplate (*EL*). Caveolae are present in various sections at *C*. A myofibril may be seen near the top containing normal-appearing myofilaments (*F*). There are also many Palade's particles near the myofibril. ×24,000.

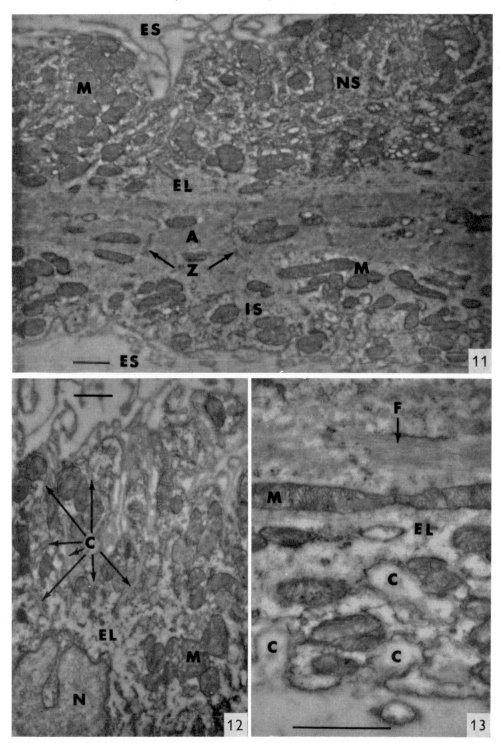

$$\tfrac{119}{6.5} \times 10^{12} = 1.83 \times 10^{13} \text{ unit charges/cm}^2/\text{impulse}$$

$$= 1.83 \times 10^5 \text{ unit charges}/\mu^2/\text{impulse}.$$

In electric eels of the size used by Cox, Coates and Brown [8], there are 15 to 25 caveolae per μ^2 of non-innervated membrane. Taking an average of 20 channels per μ^2 one finds

$$\tfrac{1.83}{20} \times 10^5 = 9.2 \times 10^3 \text{ unit charges/channel/impulse}.$$

The vesicles associated with the caveolae of the non-innervated surface measure about 700 Å in diameter. Hence the volume of a single vesicle would be about

$$\tfrac{4}{3}(3.14)(3.5 \times 10^{-2})^3 \; \mu^3 \quad \text{or} \quad 1.8 \times 10^{-4} \; \mu^3.$$

If the concentration of potassium within the electroplate is taken at 150 meq/liter, which is a common value for intracellular potassium concentration [20], which is in turn assumed to be a reasonable value for the potassium concentration within the vesicles themselves, then

$$(0.15)(6.06 \times 10^{23}) = 0.91 \times 10^{23} \text{ K}^+ \text{ ions/liter}$$

$$= 0.91 \times 10^8 \text{ K}^+ \text{ ions}/\mu^3$$

or $\qquad (1.8 \times 10^{-4})(0.91 \times 10^8) = 1.63 \times 10^4 \text{ K}^+ \text{ ions/vesicle}.$

The observed current density could be produced by

$$\tfrac{9.2 \times 10^3}{1.63 \times 10^4} = 0.56 \text{ vesicles/channel/impulse}.$$

Thus, according to this reasoning, one vesicle rupturing into each caveola of the non-innervated surface per impulse would more than account for the current density of the electric eel. Correspondingly, at the innervated surface, the conversion of the tip of each caveola into a vesicle 700 Å in diameter would about account for the sodium current thought to traverse this membrane during an impulse.

Although the above calculations in no respect prove that ion transfer occurs via vesicles, they indicate that such a mechanism of vesicular electrolyte transport is at least compatible with the observed electrical characteristics of the eel and known ionic concentrations within and outside cells. Electrical data on other fish are insufficient to permit similar calculation.

Malapterurus is peculiar in that the polarity of its electroplates is reversed, with the surface receiving the impulse becoming positive during activity, rather than negative as in the other fish. Keynes [17] suggests that reversed membrane polarity or ion movement may account for its unusual behavior. However, there are some special features regarding its innervation which may make it conform to the general mechanism suggested for the other tissues, including the vesicular transport of ions.

Nearly all the work concerning bioelectric phenomena implies movement of ions from one side of a cell membrane to the other. Although special properties are frequently assumed for these membranes, such as perforation by long, narrow tunnels, or pores, or such as the existence of an electric charge at a pore, as in an ion-exchange membrane, free diffusion of the ions themselves is usually assumed [14]. It is a purpose of this paper to suggest an alternate mechanism, namely vesicular transport. Although vesicular transfer may be more difficult to treat mathematically than free ionic diffusion, vesicular movement may possess many interesting properties in regard to flexibility of control by intracellular regulatory mechanisms. It is hoped that this suggestion may lead to productive approaches in the future.

SUMMARY

1. The electron microscope has been used for a study of electric tissues from 4 genera of electric fish, namely the electric eel (*Electrophorus electricus*), the torpedo ray (*Torpedo occidentalis*), the electric catfish (*Malapterurus electricus*), and several species of *Mormyrus*.

2. Although there is considerable variation in nerve endings and in wealth and density of mitochondria, all the electroplates show one structural feature in common.

3. This constant and recurring feature is a system of blind tubules, continuous with the plasma membrane, and projecting into the cytoplasm of the electroplate. These tubules are called *caveolae*, from terminology applied to such blind pouches elsewhere in the electron microscope literature.

4. Associated with the caveolae are vesicles. An hypothesis is presented invoking these vesicles and the caveolae, to account for ion transport in electric tissue.

5. Calculations are presented, based on the above hypothesis, which indicate that the known current density produced by the eel would not require an unreasonable number of vesicles per impulse.

REFERENCES

1. ALTAMIRANO, M., COATES, C. W. and GRUNDFEST, H., *J. Gen. Physiol.* **38**, 319 (1955).
2. BALLOWITZ, E., *Arch. mikroskop. Anat.* **50**, 686 (1897).
3. BENNETT, H. S., *J. Biophys. Biochem. Cytol.* **2**, Suppl., 99 (1956).
4. BIEDERMANN, W., Electrophysiology, Vol. II, p. 357. Translated by F. A. WELBY, London, 1898.
5. COATES, C. W., ALTAMIRANO, M. and GRUNDFEST, H., *Science* **120**, 845 (1954).
6. COATES, C. W. and COX, R. T., *Zoologica* **27**, 25 (1942).
7. COATES, C. W., COX, R. T. and GRANATH, L. P., *ibid.* **22**, 1 (1937).
8. COX, R. T., COATES, C. W. and BROWN, V., *Ann. N.Y. Acad. Sci.* **47**, 487 (1946).
9. DAHLGREN, U., *Am. Naturalist* **44**, 193 (1910).
10. DEL CASTILLO, J. and KATZ, B., Progress in Biophysics and Biophysical Chemistry, Chapter 5. Ed. by J. A. V. BUTLER. Pergamon Press, 1956.
11. DEROBERTIS, E. D. P. and BENNETT, H. S., *Federation Proc.* **13**, 35 (1954).
12. —— *J. Biophys. Biochem. Cytol.* **1**, 47 (1955).
13. FATT, P. and KATZ, B., *J. Physiol.* **117**, 109 (1952).
14. HODGKIN, A. L., *Biol. Rev.* **26**, 339 (1951).
15. HODGKIN, A. L. and KEYNES, R. D., *J. Physiol.* **128**, 28 (1955).
16. —— *ibid.* **128**, 61 (1955).
17. KEYNES, R. D., *Endeavour* **15**, 215 (1956).
18. KEYNES, R. D. and MARTINS-FERREIRA, H., *J. Physiol.* **119**, 315 (1953).
19. LISSMAN, H. W., *Nature* **167**, 201 (1951).
20. LOWRY, O. H., *Biol. Symposia* **10**, 233 (1943).
21. LUFT, J. H., *J. Biophys. Biochem. Cytol.* **2**, Suppl., 229 (1956).
22. —— *J. Morphol.* **100**. In press.
23. PALADE, G. E., *J. Exptl. Med.* **95**, 285 (1952).
24. —— *Anat. Rec.* **118**, 335 (1954).
25. —— *J. Biophys. Biochem. Cytol.* **2**, Suppl. 85 (1956).
26. PALAY, S. L., *Anat. Rec.* **118**, 336 (1954).
27. —— *J. Biophys. Biochem. Cytol.* **2**, Suppl., 193 (1956).
28. ROBERTSON, J. D., *ibid.* **2**, 381 (1956).
29. YAMADA, E., *ibid.* **1**, 445 (1955).

THE NEURONS

Experimental Cell Research, Suppl. **5**, *185–200 (1958)*

THE PRODUCTIVE CAPACITY OF THE NEURON IN RETROGRADE REACTION [1]

S.-O. BRATTGÅRD, J. E. EDSTRÖM and H. HYDÉN

Department of Histology, The University of Göteborg, Sweden

THE possibility of obtaining biochemical information on the central nerve changes during regeneration has up to now been severely restricted due to the lack of suitable methods.

The changes are bound to the nerve cell bodies and possibly to glia cells. Of a small volume of nerve tissue the nerve cells usually constitute a minor part. Any bulk analysis of this sample is therefore of little value, if the aim is to determine as well as to localize a given substance.

Quantitative methods now available permit analysis of individual neurons on the cytoscale. Therefore, it has been possible to raise more direct questions concerning the primary process in the re-establishment of the neuron during regeneration.

Regeneration implies the spinning out of a nerve cell process and its development to a functioning axon, capable of conducting nerve impulses [40, 42]. Of this complex problem we have studied the correlation between the quantitative changes in the nerve cell components and the outgrowth of the axon as well as the changes in the cell body volume [8]. Since the method used in this study allows a correlation between cytology and cell chemistry we have also studied the question of the cytochemical correlation of chromatolysis, known since the early days of cytology [34, 18].

The restoration of morphological continuity in the severed nerve involves a considerable production of cell protein [26]. In view of the present knowledge of cell protein formation special interest must be focused on the relation between the nerve cell ribose nucleic acid (RNA) and the production of cell protein [13, 26, 27]. In this respect nerve regeneration can also be considered as a problem of growth and of chemical differentiation.

MATERIAL AND METHODS

In all, 69 rabbits weighing between 1.5 and 2.0 kg were used for the experiments. The hypoglossal nerve on one side was exposed and chrushed with forceps cooled

---

[1] These results have been published in a similar paper (*J. Neurochem.* **1**, 316 (1957)).

to − 70°C where it intersects musculus digastricus, which is at a point ⅔ from the periphery of the nerve. Analyses were made from two to ninety days after the trauma. It may be noted that the results from the regenerating cells are always compared with those obtained from the hypoglossal cells on the contralateral, non-operated side. In all 2650 quantitative measurements were made in this study.

Morphologically, the hypoglossal nucleus is composed of different groups of cells [12, 31]. The main part of the nucleus, however, consists of large nerve cells of practically uniform size and structure. We have used only these cells, and have investigated about three thousand. The hypoglossal nerve has only one maximum at 7–9 μ in its fibre spectrum [23]. The part containing the hypoglossal nucleus was removed as rapidly as possible and frozen in liquid nitrogen.

Analysis with X-ray Microradiography

The tissue was cut out in a special cryostat at − 20°C in 10 μ thick sections using a knife of a special steel, sharpened and controlled according to the method devised by Hallén in 1956 [24]. The sections were mounted on a 2 μ thick Al foil and dried at − 40°C in a slight vacuum over P_2O_5 in a small freezer built into the cryostat. In this way dried sections from fresh nerve cells are obtained. This material is then exposed at 8–10 Å for the determination of the amount of dry organic substance divided into a lipid and a protein fraction, as has been earlier described [16, 9, 10].

For the computation of the mass of whole, fresh and unfixed hypoglossal nerve cells of control rabbits the following procedure is used. The nerve cells are dissected out by hand in a Zeiss stereoscopic microscope a few minutes after killing the animal. In order to render the cells visible a drop of very dilute methylene blue solution in 0.88 M sucrose is applied to the section through the nucleus for approximately 2 minutes. The nerve cells then acquire a pale sky-blue staining and in about ten minutes are available for dissection. The free cells are sucked up in a micro-pipette and applied to the 1 μ thick Al foil of the preparation holder. From a drop of the solution containing the free cells each nerve cell is taken and placed on the Al-foil covering the slit of the holder. Each cell is carefully and rapidly washed free from sucrose. It was possible during all these manipulations to dispense with the micromanipulator and thus shorten the time considerably before the cell material was exposed or frozen down.

The contact X-radiograms are evaluated photometrically [5, 29]. This instrument measures the distribution and amount of dry mass from many cells in a short time.

The X-ray analysis of sections gives results expressed as weight per unit area. In order to obtain the concentration value, the thickness of the section must be known. A new optical instrument for the determination of the latter has recently been devised by Hallén [24]. Furthermore, in our present study all results are based on a comparison between operated and control material from the same section.

Determination of RNA

For the determination of the content and concentration of RNA of the individual hypoglossal cells the microchemical method worked out by Edström [14] was used. The principle of the method is to determine RNA from single Carnoy fixed cells photographically and photometrically after enzymatic extraction.

The method for RNA determination is worked out for use on cells containing about 500 pg (1 pg $= 10^{-12}$ g). Normal hypoglossal cells from the rabbit were found to contain about 200 pg. For obtaining an ideal range the control cells were analyzed on the average three at a time. In three cases (2, 15 and 48 days) single cells were used from the control as well as from the operated side. Such a procedure of course demands a relatively large number of analyses. Three times four cells were investigated from each side at each period, and all cells taken from each animal were dissected from the same section, control and operated cells being from symmetrical areas.

Determination of the Cell Volume

X-ray microradiography carried out with the precautions referred to above gives the organic mass concentration. To obtain the RNA concentration the volume of the cell body was determined by optical three-dimensional reconstruction, as described by Edström [14]. Since information regarding both the amount of substance per cell and of the concentration are desirable, the determination of the cell volume has also been carried out.

For the volume determinations two independent methods were applied on Carnoy fixed material. A third method was used in order to check the two first methods.

About two hundred determinations were carried out on Carnoy fixed material according to Edström [14] (Table II). The second method included 1800 volume determinations on fixed cell sections. Since nerve cells, however, do not have the ideal form for such a method, a correction had to be applied for the error introduced by the nerve cell form using a three-dimensional reconstruction. The results from the two methods used showed satisfactory agreement.

The cytological procedure, including the fixation, is reported to give volume shrinkage (see e.g. [39]). Robins, Smith and Eydt [37] have especially studied the effect of formaldehyde fixation and found a volume shrinkage of about 80 per cent. For quantitative cytochemical studies Brattgård and

Hydén [9] emphasized the importance of using only untreated frozen material. Under certain circumstances, however, the use of fixed cell material which has undergone volume changes is unavoidable. In such cases a correction for volume changes may be used, provided the volume change caused by the particular fixative has been estimated for the cell material studied. In the present study Carnoy fixation was used for the RNA determinations. The histotechnical procedure, including the fixation, was found to give an average of 25 per cent in one dimension of a small piece of nervous tissue, i.e. 58 per cent volume decrease. When measured the Carnoy fixed hypoglossal cells showed a volume of $5.6 \cdot 10^3 \ \mu^3$. The average volume of the fresh cells can thus be calculated as $13.3 \cdot 10^3 \ \mu^3$.

In order to check the correction factor for the volume change, thus induced in the nerve cell, the following method was used. Fresh hypoglossal cells were dissected in Ringer solution and the volume was determined as described above. The volume of the fresh cells was found to be $13.1 \cdot 10^3 \ \mu^3$ which value agrees well with that given above. Data on nerve cells, in a condition as similar to the native state as can *pro tempore* be carried out, were obtained in this way.

Since, however, the main emphasis in our study is based on a change of the volume of the nerve cells on the operated side compared with that on the non-operated side, expressed as a quotient (See Table II, III), such corrections have no relevance for the conclusions.

Ultraviolet micrographs at 2570 Å were also performed on sections and staining with toluidine blue, methylene blue, gallocyanine and cresyl violet.

RESULTS

Control material

Table I gives the data obtained with hypoglossal cells from control animals. The average volume shows that the hypoglossal cells are rather small. The average dry weight of a fresh cell is 2770 ± 207 pg. The single fresh cell has a weight of 2770 pg and a mass concentration of $0.20 \ \mathrm{pg}/\mu^3$ gives a volume of the cell of $13.80 \cdot 10^3$ pg. The three values for the cell volume, i.e. 13.3, 13.1 and 13.8 respectively agree very well. The main part of the cell consists of proteins and a smaller part, 20 per cent or 550 pg of lipids,

TABLE I. *Analyses of hypoglossal cells from control rabbits.*

Volume	RNA	Dry weight	Lipids	Proteins	Axon mass
$13.3 \cdot 10^3 \ \mu^3$	200 pg	2770 pg	550 pg	2200 pg	0.06 pg/μ^3

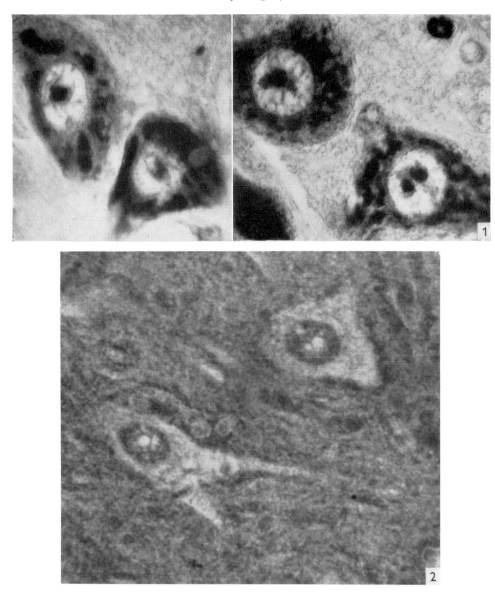

Fig. 1.—Hypoglossal cells from a contro lrabbit taken at 2570 Å. 2.5 mm monochromate, ocular
× 10.

Fig. 2.—High-resolution radiogram taken at 8–10 Å on a Kodak spectrographic emulsion 649 Å
of two Carnoy-fixed hypoglossal cells. Cell details well below 1 μ in size are resolved.

extractable with chloroform. The amount of RNA averages 200 pg and the concentration averages 1.5 per cent. Expressed as concentration it averages a value which is in agreement with that found in other types of motor nerve cells fixed in Carnoy solution [15]. Fig. 1 demonstrates four hypoglossal

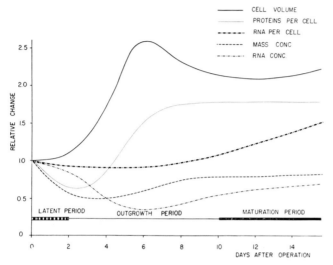

Fig. 3.—Table II. Diagrams of the quantitative nerve cell changes occurring from 1 to 12 days after the operation.

cells taken at 2570 Å. Fig. 2 shows a high-resolution radiogram taken at 8–10 Å of two Carnoy-fixed hypoglossal cells. Cell details well below 1 μ in size are resolved.

The statistical analysis performed showed that there is no significant difference in volume, amount of protein or RNA between the studied cells of the right and left hypoglossal nucleus. Also, the cell values within each nucleus are distributed along a Gaussian curve. Thus, this material proved to be suitable for our experiments.

Regeneration

The following division of the regenerating period into a latent outgrowth and maturation period is based on anatomical and chemical data. In such a continuous phenomenon as nerve regerneration all limits are naturally only approximate.

The latent period (1–2 days after nerve crush).—During this first period which is here called the latent period, a degeneration occurs of the central part of the nerve fibre proximally to the place of the crush. There can also be shown an outgrowth of numerous thin processes a few hours after the trauma. This, however, is a transient phenomenon. Processes which can structurally be defined as axons can be shown on the second day to appear in the degenerating central stump [11].

Our results (Tables II and III, the diagrams in Fig. 3 and 4) show that during the first two days the volume of the cells remains largely constant, as

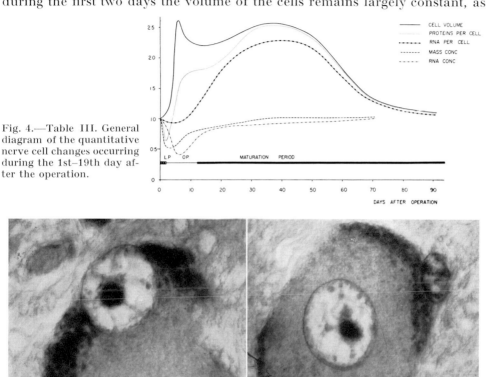

Fig. 4.—Table III. General diagram of the quantitative nerve cell changes occurring during the 1st–19th day after the operation.

Fig. 5.—Two hypoglossal cells taken at 2570 Å one week after the operation. Ocular × 10.

does the amount and concentration of RNA. The dry cell substance, including the proteins which are the main components, decreases by 30 to 40 per cent.

Within one day after the nerve crush the absorption at 2600 Å, characteristic for the RNA, is seen to decrease within a sector of the cytoplasm. This change manifests itself during the first week and eventually comprises all the cytoplasm with the exception of the parts near the cell membrane (Figs. 5 and 6). Furthermore the appearance of the absorbing collections containing

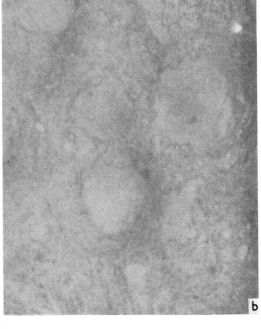

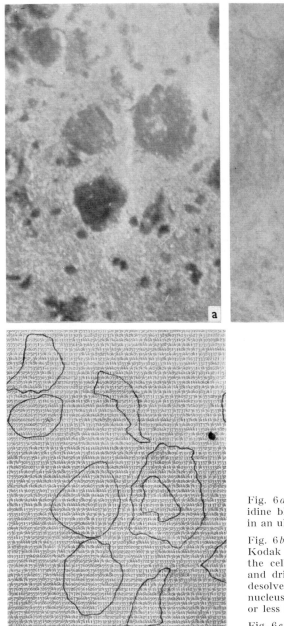

Fig. 6a.—Hypoglossal cells studied with toluidine blue and photographed after the analyses in an ultro-pak system.

Fig. 6b.—The same cells taken at 8–10 Å on a Kodak spectrographic emulsion 649 A. Since the cell section are taken from fresh, frozen and dried tissue no organic material has been desolved from the nucleus or the cytoplasm. The nucleus therefore does not show up as a more or less empty space in the cell.

Fig. 6c.—The picture in figures of the transmission values per every 5 μ^2 of the same cells given by the cell analyzer.

RNA changes to a finely dispersed, faintly absorbing configuration.[1] If stained according to the ordinary Nissl-staining methods the result is of course that of the well-known chromatolysis phenomenon. According to Gersh and Bodian [20] the reason for the chromatolysis picture may be a depolymerization of RNA.

The out-growth period (3–12 days after the nerve crush).—During this period the thin new axons grow out through "the degenerating and scar tissue". Thin sproutings occur within three hours after the trauma but these are abortive [35, 36, 11]. On the fifth day after crushing, the axons can be detected in the peripheral part and the rate of outgrowth has been found to be around 4 mm per day for motor nerves with very little variation [21]. We have computed the time for the completed outgrowth of the hypoglossal nerve in our experiments to be 12 to 13 days after the nerve crush.

During the 3rd to 6th day the volume increases 1.6 times and since the amount of RNA remains unchanged, the RNA concentration consequently decreases by 60 per cent. The protein concentration remains low. The net result is that the nerve cell body during these four days more than doubles its amount of proteins and lipids.

During the rest of the period the nerve cell volume decreases moderately. The amount and concentration of RNA and of proteins and lipids, on the other hand increase to a slight extent, the increase being not more than 20 per cent (Tables II, III).

The change in absorption at the nucleic acid maximum observed becomes continually more pronounced and maximal, and involves most hypoglossal cells.

The maturation period.—This period is characterized by an increase in the diameter of the newly established axons. The data presented covers in detail the first 2.5 months of this period. The axons grow slowly and after crushing the diameter reaches its normal value within a year [43, 22].

The full number of terminal branches in the motor endplates was reached around 90 days after the crush [21]. Signs of functional recovery were found within 12 days after the arrival of fibres at the endplates, i.e. 25 days after the crush in our experiments.

Our results show a volume increase of 1.5 fold of the nerve cell body, showing a maximum at 40 days, after which the volume slowly decreases and regains the original values after 90 days. The nerve cell more than doubles the amount of RNA which reaches values of 470 pg per cell. The

---

[1] The resolution of the UV-microscope using a monochromate 2.5 mm corrected for 2570 Å lies at 1000 Å.

TABLE II. *Analyses of RNA and volume of Carnoy-fixed hypoglossal cells.*

Days after oper- ation	Cell volume in $10^3 \mu^3$			pg RNA per cell		pg RNA operated side/non- operated side	
	op.	non-op.	op./non-op.	op.	non-op.	per cell	per μ^3
2	6.1	6.1	1.0	159	171	0.93	0.93
4	10.2	5.0	2.0	180	198	0.91	0.46
5	10.1	4.7	2.1	—	—	—	—
6	12.2	4.7	2.6	184	199	0.92	0.35
8	12.5	6.0	2.1	—	—	—	—
9	11.8	5.3	2.2	240	236	1.02	0.50
15	11.7	5.6	2.1	242	164	1.48	0.70
27	14.9	6.1	2.4	380	183	2.08	0.87
48	13.2	5.4	2.4	469	216	2.17	0.90
77	9.1	6.9	1.3	295	228	1.29	0.99

TABLE III. *Analysis of dry weight, lipids and proteins in fresh hypoglossal cells.*

Days after oper- ation	Volume op./non-op.	Mass/μ^3 in pg		Lipids/μ^3 in pg		Proteins/μ^3 in pg		Proteins op. side/non-op. side	
		op.	non-op.	op.	non-op.	op.	non-op.	per cell	per μ^3
0	1.00	—	0.20	—	0.04	—	0.16	1.00	1.00
2	1.10	0.14	0.21	0.05	0.05	0.09	0.16	0.62	0.56
3	1.40	—	—	—	—	—	—	—	—
4	1.69	0.15	0.21	0.05	0.05	0.10	0.16	1.06	0.63
5	2.30	—	—	—	—	0.09	0.17	1.22	0.53
6	2.60	—	—	—	—	0.10	0.17	1.53	0.59
7	2.47	—	—	—	—	0.12	0.17	1.73	0.70
8	2.30	0.15	0.21	0.03	0.05	0.12	0.16	1.73	0.75
15	2.20	0.15	0.20	0.03	0.04	0.13	0.16	1.78	0.81
30	2.50	0.20	0.21	0.04	0.05	0.16	0.16	2.50	1.00
42	2.50	—	—	—	—	—	—	(2.50)	(1.00)
90	1.10	—	—	—	—	—	—	(1.16)	(1.00)

RNA concentration is still low and reaches the original value after 70 days. The proteins and lipids per cell are further increased and reach their maximal values concurrently with the RNA. The original value of the mass concentration is restored as early as one month after the crush.

EVULATION OF THE RESULTS

The Magnitude of the Changes in Relation to Time

Let us consider the magnitude of the cell substance which is contained in the new axon. Taking the results, an average hypoglossal neuron in our experiments substitutes, during the regeneration period, organic cell material of approximately 10^5 pg, i.e. 50 times the amount of the material contained in the cell body. During the outgrowth period, however, the axons are thin averaging around 0.5 μ in diameter and the output per day will only average 50 pg and for these eight days this means approximately a mass of 500 pg.

During the latent period the only change observable in the cell body is the decrease in proteins. The change in the RNA towards a smaller particle aggregation, however, begins to manifest itself. The amount of RNA per cell remains constant during the out-growth period, but the RNA change in aggregation becomes more accentuated during the rest of the period and gives the nerve cells the typical chromatolytic appearance with a low absorbing capacity at 2600 Å. During two to five days the proteins and lipids of the cell double and are maintained at this level with only a slight increase during the rest of the out-growth period. The cell volume increases 1.6 times and the values show that this mainly depends on the water uptake in the cell body.

Concomitantly with the spinning-out of the axons in the first two days of the out-growth period there is an increase of more than 100 per cent in the proteins and lipids per cell. A hundred per cent increase in cell weight during such a short time means a vigorous protein production.

Regarding the maturation period which involves more than 95 per cent of the whole regeneration, the most conspicuous trait is the RNA increase per cell. Its maximum occurs at 40 days and averages 470 pg per nerve cell, i.e. 160 per cent increase. The RNA concentration, however, goes back slowly to the normal values. The fine dispersity of the RNA in the central part of the cytoplasm in the fixed sections, observed during the outgrowth period, is now gradually substituted by the intensely absorbing aggregations corresponding to the usual Nissl-picture. This happens during the short first part of the maturation period.

The RNA increase observed, parallels an increase in the amount of proteins and lipids per cell and is of a similar magnitude and course ending with a doubled cell body weight. This increase in substances can be correlated with the volume increase. It may be noted that the concentration of the cell material has returned to normal. Hence, the volume increase observed is due to a real increase in mass. Volume, RNA, protein and lipids of the regenerating nerve cell return slowly to their respective starting points during the maturation period.

The high content of RNA in all types of nerve cells hitherto analyzed averages 150 to 1000 pg RNA per cell and the high concentration (of 0.5 to 3 per cent—or around 20 per cent RNA computed) on the dry protein basis stresses an important characteristic of the nerve cell. It seems to be *the* RNA containing somatic cell *par préférence*. The only type of cell that can compete seems to be the pancreatic cell of small animals with a high metabolism.

The extensive quantitative changes during regeneration of RNA and solid matter—proteins and free lipids—of the nerve cell indicates a high protein and RNA metabolism of these cells. These conclusions have been drawn already on the basis of earlier microspectrographic studies on nerve cells during regeneration and various functional conditions [26, 25]. This hypothesis is strongly supported by recent studies of Geiger [19] of the RNA production in the cerebral cortex after stimulation. At present we are continuing the analysis of regenerating nerve cells using isotopes.

It is not an exaggeration to visualize the neuron as an enormous gland cell structure whose lively protein metabolism serves the specific nerve function.

Hypothesis on the Nerve Cell Mechanism

By now it seems to be proved that the RNA in a cell organism is a prerequisite for the formation of protein [1, 17], although the DNA of the nucleus controls the protein formation on a long term basis [6]. This conclusion has been drawn from instances where an increase in the amount of RNA can be correlated with a protein increase. During the maturation period this is exactly what we have found.

Our findings during the out-growth period of a protein increase while the amount of RNA remains constant seems remarkable from this point of view. The change in RNA aggregation from large microscopic particles to particles of submicroscopic size at a constant RNA level, however, gives a new aspect to this fundamental problem. We would like to advance the working hypothesis that the change in RNA aggregation to small particulates means a transformation from an active to a more active form. This results in its turn in a protein increase, necessary for the production of the new axon.

Furthermore, when this distribution of RNA in the cell prevails newly formed RNA occurs on the outer side of the nuclear membrane and a gradient of nucleoproteins has been shown from the nucleus to the nuclear membrane [26].

A nerve cell mechanism for the production of cytoplasmic nucleoproteins involving the activity of the nucleus and the cytoplasm simultaneously seems possible.

Previous studies on nerve regeneration using ultraviolet microspectrography [26, 20] gave as a result that RNA concentration in the chromatolytic area was diminished. This agrees well with the data now reported.

Analogy with nerve cells during embryonic development.—It has frequently been pointed out that the chromatolytic nerve cells in regeneration recall embryonic nerve cells [2]. Our data from the out-growth period confirm this view cytochemically.

The water increase in the cell body, the change in configuration with constant amount of RNA and the rapid increase in proteins and lipids are indicative of a close correspondence between the regenerating and embryonic nerve cells, earlier studied with our methods [38, 28], and not only a cytological resemblance.

If we turn to the changes during the maturation period the cytological observations are of little use. A closer analysis based on the data obtained in our study reveals the following. The returning aggregation of RNA and protein increase together with the volume increase show a strong resemblance to the motor neuron during the late embryonic stage.

The role of the functional re-establishment in the growth process.—The nerve regeneration can also be considered as a problem of differentiation. This process in itself cannot at present be explored. Only by different types of criteria obtained from cytological, chemical and physiological studies can the process of differentiation be recognized. The primary problem, however, lies at the level of gene action on the cytoplasm and the action of external or cell milieu factors back on the genes of the nucleus. As has frequently been pointed out the nucleus and the gene are surrounded by the cytoplasm from which raw material is provided to the genes. Since external conditions have been shown to affect gene action, a change in the internal cell milieu must be expected to give a detectable effect as a consequence of gene action i.e. the equilibrium in the expression of the genes must be changed.

In nerve regeneration such a phenomenon seems to be observable. Our results show that a most conspicuous change occurs around the 12th day in regeneration. At this time a second volume increase begins which is due to a

high increase in the amount of RNA, proteins and lipids. The volume increase during the out-growth period on the other hand depends mostly on a
water increase. The out-growth period is finished when the thin axon has
reached the periphery. This re-establishment of functional contact is presumably the factor which changes the course of the chemical processes in the
cell. The stimulus from the effector organ back to the cell probably represents
the change in the internal cell milieu which permits the effect of another
part of the genome to be expressed.

As discussed above the nucleo-cytoplasmic relationship is particularly
important in the nerve cell. If the relationship is disturbed, the nerve cell as
a subject for differentiation will react on this change in the milieu with chemical and morphological changes. In this context one might say that the effect
of gene activity is one, when the thin axon rapidly spins out, and another
during the maturation period. The re-establishment of the functional contact
between neuron and effector organ signifies the starting point of the considerable production of nucleoproteins during the maturation period.

It has repeatedly been shown how important it is for the neuron during
embryonic development and in regeneration to achieve contact with the
periphery in order to be fully differentiated chemically and morphologically
[25, 28, 33]. When functional stimulation is excluded, the growth process
in the nerve cells is also inhibited [7].

All evidence shows that the neuronal function is of great importance for
the highly differentiated neuron to develop chemically.

SUMMARY

Nerve regeneration has been studied in nucleus hypoglossus in rabbit
using ultramicrochemical and quantitative cytochemical methods for the
determination per nerve cell of ribonucleic acids (RNA) and dry weight
divided in a protein and a lipid fraction. The data observed are correlated
to the peripheral growth of the axon. The weight of the control, fresh hypoglossal cell soma averages 2770 pg (1 pg = 10^{-12} g) and the amount of RNA
per cell averages 200 pg. The RNA concentration expressed as weight per
volume averages 1.5 per cent and computed on a dry protein basis it lies
at 9 per cent. The volume of the cells was measured by three independent
methods. The fresh hypoglossal cell soma has a volume averaging 13,300 μ^3.

During the period of the out-growth of the axons the nerve cell changes are
characterized not only by an increase in volume and amount of lipids
and proteins, but also by an uptake of water, causing a decrease in the

concentration of the intracellular substance. The amount of RNA is kept constant during this period. The state of aggregation of RNA changes, however, resulting in small, finely dispersed RNA particles. The described changes form the chemical background for the chromatolysis in nerve regeneration.

The change in RNA aggregation is interpreted as a transition from an active to a more active form of RNA, operating during this period of rapid growth and serving as an initiator of the protein production which follows.

The maturation period starts when contact is re-established between nerve cell and periphery and is characterized by another type of growth process. The striking feature is the 100 per cent RNA increase and the volume increase of 100 per cent. The latter is explained by the increases in amounts of proteins and lipids per cell. The original RNA aggregation is eventually restored as are the concentration values. The functional re-establishment of the contact nerve cell-periphery is stressed as a factor of importance for the complete chemical reconstruction of the neuron.

The central mechanism operating in the nerve regeneration is discussed from a cytological point of view.

Financial support for this investigation has been received from the Rockefeller Foundation, the Swedish Medical Research Council and from the Swedish Society for Cancer Research.

REFERENCES

1. ALLFREY, V. G., DALY, M. M. and MIRSKY, A. E., *J. Gen. Physiol.* **37**, 157 (1953).
2. BIERVLIET, J. VAN, *Le Névraxe* **33**, 1 (1900).
3. BODIAN, D. and MELLORS, R. C., *J. Exptl. Med.* **81**, 469 (1945).
4. BOURGHARDT, S., BRATTGÅRD, S.-O., HYDÉN, H., JIWERTS, B. and LARSSON, S., *J. Sci. Instr.* **30**, 464 (1953).
5. BOURGHARDT, S., HYDÉN, H. and NYQVIST, B., *Experientia* **11**, 163 (1955).
6. BRACHET, J. *in* KITCHING, Recent Development in Cell Physiology, pp. 91–102. Butterworths Scientific Publications, London, 1954.
7. BRATTGÅRD, S.-O., *Acta Radiol. Suppl.* **96** (1952).
8. BRATTGÅRD, S.-O., EDSTRÖM, J. E. and HYDÉN, H., *J. Neurochem.* **1**, 316 (1957).
9. BRATTGÅRD, S. O. and HYDÉN, H., *Acta Radiol. Suppl.* **94** (1952).
10. —— *Internat. Rev. Cytol.* **III** (1954).
11. CAJAL, RAMON Y S., Degenerating and Regenerating of the Nervous System. Humprey Milford, London, 1928.
12. —— Histologie du système nerveux de l'homme et des vertebrés, **I**, Instituto Ramon y Cajal, Madrid, 1952.
13. CASPERSSON, T., *Naturwissenschaften* **29**, 33 (1941).
14. EDSTRÖM, J. E., *Biochim. et Biophys. Acta* **12**, 361 (1953).
15. —— *J. Neurochem.* (in press).
16. ENGSTRÖM, A. and LINDSTRÖM, B., *Biochim. et Biophys. Acta* **4**, 351 (1950).
17. GALE, E. F. and FOLKES, J. P., *Nature* **173**, 1223 (1954).
18. GEHUCHTEN, A. VAN, *La Cellule* **313**, 13 (1897).

19. GEIGER, A., YAMASAKI, S. and LYONS, R., Am. J. Physiol. **184**, 239 (1956).
20. GERSH, I. and BODIAN, D., J. Cellular Comp. Physiol. **253**, 21 (1943).
21. GUTMANN, E., GUTTMAN, L., MEDEWAR, P. B. and YOUNG, J. Z., J. Exptl. Biol. **14**, 19 (1942).
22. GUTMANN, E. and SANDERS, F. K., J. Physiol. **101**, 489 (1943).
23. HÄGGQVIST, G., Anat. Anz. **85**, 191 (1937/38).
24. HALLÉN, O., Acta Anat. Suppl. **25** (1956).
25. HAMBURGER, V. and LEVI-MONTALCINI, R., in WEISS, Genetic Neurology, pp. 128–160. University of Chicago Press, Chicago, 1950.
26. HYDÉN, H., Acta Physiol. Suppl. **17** (1943).
27. —— in WEISS, Genetic Neurology, pp. 177–193. University of Chicago Press, Chicago, 1950.
28. —— J. Embryol. Exptl. Morphol. **1**, 315 (1953).
29. HYDÉN, H. and LARSSON, S., J. Neurochem. **1**, 134 (1956).
30. KOLLER, P., (1956).
31. METTLER, F. A., Neurochemistry. C. V. Mosby Comp., St. Louis (1948).
32. MICKLEWRIGHT, H. L., KURNICK, N. B. and HODES, R., Exptl. Cell Research **4**, 151 (1953).
33. MOTTET, K. and BARRON, D. H., Yale J. Biol. **26**, 275 (1954).
34. NISSL, F., Allg. Z. Psychiatr. **48**, 197 (1892).
35. PERRONCITO, A., Beiträg. pathol. Anat. **42**, 354 (1907).
36. RANSON, S. W., J. comp. Neurol. **22**, 487 (1912).
37. ROBINS, E., SMIDT, D. E. and EYDT, K. M., J. Neurochem. **1**, 54 (1956).
38. SOURANDER, P., Acta Pathol. Microbiol. Scand. Suppl. **95** (1953).
39. STOWELL, R. E., Stain Technol. **16**, 67 (1941).
40. WEISS, P., in WEISS, Genetic Neurology, pp. 1–39. University of Chicago Press, Chicago, 1950.
41. —— J. Embryol. Exptl. Morphol. **1**, 181 (1953).
42. —— in WILLIER, WEISS and HAMBURGER, Analyses of Development, pp. 346–401. W. B. Saunders Co., Philadelphia, 1955.
43. YOUNG, J. Z., Physiol. Rev. **318**, 22 (1942).

Experimental Cell Research, Suppl. **5**, *201–220 (1958)*

ON UNDIFFERENTIATED NEURONAL SPREAD
OF EXCITATION

C. G. BERNHARD

Institute of Physiology, Karolinska Institutet, Stockholm, Sweden

THE "CORTICAL POTENTIAL PROFILE" AS A SIGN
OF SYNCHRONIZED NEURONE ACTIVITY

THE synchronization of cortical neurone activity resulting in rhythmical potential waves is a phenomenon which from the very beginning of the electroencephalographical era has attracted much attention. In recent years the feature of the cortical "potential profile" [24] and its significance for the cortical state of excitability have come into the center of interest in connection with studies of mechanisms underlying different states of alertness in physiological and pathological conditions as well as under the influence of neuropharmacological drugs. I refer to reviews by Bremer [15], Magoun [28, 29], and Moruzzi [31]. Investigations on the functional characteristics of the nerve cell membrane have given valuable contributions to the understanding of the intrinsic control of rhythmical neurone activity of basic importance for neurone action as well as for junctional transmission. Synchronization of rhythmical neurone activity into grouped activity is a common phenomenon at all levels of neuronal organization, from the peripheral nerve with its relatively regular orientation of fibres to the cerebral cortex with its complex neuronal network, and a great many experiments of various types have been designed for the analysis of the synchronization mechanisms. When discussing such mechanisms within the central nervous system we have to take into consideration the diverse geometrical orientation of several types of extensions of different nerve cells, and have also to take into account a great variety of junctional structures, the functional characteristics of which are more or less unknown. The complicated situation is well illustrated by recent electronmicroscopical pictures of central neurone structures which have already been discussed by other authors in this volume. It is evident that the mechanisms controlling the synchronization of the rhythmical neurone activity and its projection may be of a different order. Thus the coordinating mechanisms controlling, e.g., a synchronized cortical mass activity, for which the cortical "potential profile" in certain conditions is taken as an expression, are probably not uniform.

CORTICAL AFTER-DISCHARGE EVOKED BY REPETITIVE ELECTRICAL STIMULATION (POST-STIMULATORY AFTER-DISCHARGE)

I am well aware that our experimental approach may give one aspect of this intricate problem, an aspect which, of course, is strongly bound to the experimental methods used. We have studied some characteristics of the sustained rhythmical high voltage cortical activity following upon the cessation of a repetitive cortical stimulation (Fig. 1 B), which is to be regarded as a result of a synchronized activity and is described as equivalent to certai

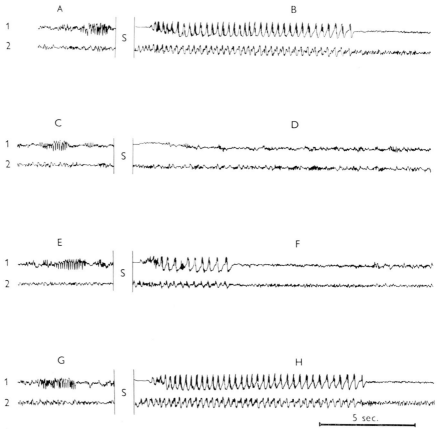

Fig. 1.—Effect of intravenous lidocaine (2 mg/kg) on the cortical after-discharge. Cortical activity led off from the frontal (tracing 1) and parietal (tracing 2) regions in cat before (A and B) and 2 (C and D), 20 (E and F) and 45 (G and H) minutes after the lidocaine injection. Records A, C, E and G show the pre-stimulatory corticograms and records B, D, F and H corticograms obtained after cessation of cortical stimulation (S). Stimulus frequency 25 per sec.; total duration 5 sec. (From Bernhard, Bohm and Wiesel [10].)

forms of epileptic activity. In the following account this sustained cortical activity will be referred to as post-stimulatory after-discharge (PA). Although the expression after-discharge is used to denote many different types of neuronal activity, I think we are justified by having defined the experimental situation to which it is referred.

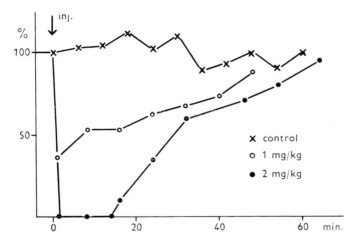

Fig. 2.—Duration of cortical after-discharge as a percentage of pre-injection values (vertical axis) plotted against time (horizontal axis) after intravenous injection of 1 mg/kg (open circles) and 2 mg/kg. (filled circles) of lidocaine. The crosses represent individual duration values of cortical after-discharge obtained during 60 min. before injections. (From Bernhard and Bohm [4].)

The shape, duration and projection to remote areas of the post-stimulatory after-discharge is primarily dependent on stimulus characteristics and cortical excitability. With low stimulus strengths the seizure activity may involve only the neurones in the vicinity of the cortical areas stimulated, as is also the case with strong stimuli when the animal is kept at a deep narcotic level (Fig. 4 *F* and *H*). Such a restricted experimental attack has been compared with the focal cortical seizure in epileptic patients (see, e.g., [34]). If the stimulus strength is increased the PA-duration increases and the convulsive activity projects to remote ipsilateral and contralateral areas where the after-discharge will go on as long as that in the cortical area stimulated (Fig. 1 *B*). It has been emphasized that the projection of the epileptiform activity, characterized by a simultaneous arrest of the after-discharge, should be differentiated from the spread of the epileptic seizure, in which case a self-sustained activity is set up in other areas of the grey matter which may continue in the secondary foci after the cessation of the after-discharge in the cortical area where it was started [34]. The PA is generally followed by a period of decreased cortical activity (Fig. 1 B). In order to obtain a PA with long duration and to avoid variations in the duration, the stimulus should be of sufficient strength and the stimulus characteristics kept constant. Further, the intervals between each cortical stimulation should be sufficiently long so that the excitability changes resulting from the preceding attack disappear. It is surprising that the PA duration tested with appropriate intervals shows remarkably small variations during several hours.

Concerning the building up and the spread of this synchronized high voltage activity in central structures, both transmission in anatomically defined pathways and activation by diffuse electrical field effects have been discussed. In a paper on the control of normal and convulsive brain potentials Libet and Gerard [24] discussed different possible mechanisms for synchronized high voltage rhythmical central neurone activity. Their experiments on the frog brain led to the conclusion that, besides transmission of nerve impulses along anatomically available fibre pathways, electrical field effects may cause a spreading activation. They argue that such a mechanism may prove of importance in the interpretation of, e.g., the massive convulsive action of the cortex in epilepsy. Analogous to Libet's and Gerard's finding [23], that high voltage coffeine waves can be transmitted from one part of the frog's brain to another adjacent part after transection, is Bremer's observation [14] that high voltage activity set up in the spinal cord by strychnine remains synchronous in the whole cord even after complete transection, provided that the severed ends are in contact with each other.

INFLUENCE OF LOCAL ANAESTHETICS ON THE
POST-STIMULATORY AFTER-DISCHARGE

I would like to point out that most of the investigations which serve as a basis for the following discussion were performed together with Dr. Einar Bohm [4–10]. Some of our animal experiments were made in collaboration with Drs. Kirstein [9], Valleala [11] and Wiesel [9, 10], and in some of the clinical investigations Drs. Höjeberg [7, 8] and Melin [8] took part.

Dr. Bohm and I happened to come across this problem when studying the influence of substances which are in common use as local anaesthetics [3, 4, 7], the central effects of which have hardly been investigated at all. From what is known about the blocking action on peripheral nerve fibres it is not surprising that a *local application* of, e.g., cocaine direct on the cortex

Experimental Cell Research, Suppl. **5**

is followed by a depression of the cortical activity [18, 30], and local anaesthetics are often used as a blocking agent in the analysis of cortical potentials (see, e.g., [17]). As to *intravenous injections*, allowing an action on the
whole central nervous system in minute concentrations, both general depressant and exciting effects have been described. Among the former may be
mentioned respiratory paralysis [22], central analgesic effects [12], and
potentiation of anaesthetic agents in narcosis [1, 19, 13, 39, 27]. On the
other hand, it is always pointed out in the current literature that intravenous
local anaesthetics have a convulsant effect, the electrocorticographic characteristics of which were first studied by Berger [2]. Later on they have been
further analyzed by several authors (see, e.g., [35]), as has the dysrhythmical
activity appearing after subconvulsive doses. Actually, in toxicological work
the convulsive dose (CD_{50}) of local anaesthetics is often used as a test.

However, in this presentation our electrophysiological data will be reviewed, which led to the somewhat unorthodox conclusion that local anaesthetics in subconvulsive doses have an exquisite anticonvulsive (antiepileptic) effect (Bernhard and Bohm [3], later confirmed by Yasukata *et al.*
[40], Tanaka [37], Tanaka *et al.* [38], French *et al.* [21]), on the basis of
which even a treatment of certain types of epilepsy with lidocaine has been
worked out [7, 5]. Further, the mechanism of this specific desynchronizing
action of local anaesthetics will be discussed on the basis of our recent
investigations on their effects on different transmission systems [11].

A small intravenous dose of a local anaesthetic, e.g. lidocaine (2 mg/kg),
causes a total abolition of the cortical after-discharge (Fig. 1 *D*). From what
is known about the rate of breakdown of lidocaine [36] and the duration of
its local anaesthetic action it is to be expected that the effect should be temporary. Thus, 20 minutes after the injection the PA can again be elicited but has
then a shorter duration (Fig. 1 *F*). In this stage of action the PA also stops
simultaneously in all areas, as is the case before the injection of the drug.
The effect of the drug gradually disappears and the duration of the PA
returns to the same value as before the injection (Fig. 1 *H*). Fig. 2 shows the
recovery of the PA estimated by testing the effect of cortical stimulation at
various intervals after two different intravenous injections of lidocaine.
The smaller dose does not produce a complete abolition but reduces the
duration of the PA to about 40 per cent of the pre-injection value and is
followed by a shorter recovery period.

The PA has been shown to be sensitive to intravenous injections of local
anaesthetics independent of its site. Thus, for example, the typical PA in
hippocampus elicited by hippocampal stimulation is abolished by the same

amount of a local anaesthetic. The same is the case in the isolated cortical
slab with intact blood supply [10].

As seen in Fig. 3, illustrating the effect of four different doses of procaine,
there is a relation between the dose of the local anaesthetic injected and the
maximal reduction of the PA. Naturally this relation can only be followed
up to a dose which is just big enough to produce a total abolition of the

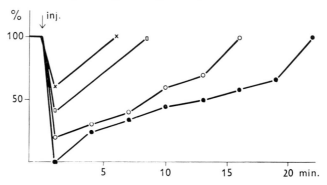

Fig. 3.—Duration of cortical after-discharge as a percentage of pre-injection value (vertical axis)
plotted against time (horizontal axis) after intravenous injection of various doses of procaine
(crosses, 2 mg/kg; open rectangles, 2.5 mg/kg; open circles, 4 mg/kg; filled circles, 5 mg/kg).
(From Bernhard, Bohm and Wiesel [10].)

after-discharge. Fig. 3 also demonstrates the regularity in the recovery of the
after-discharge as measured by its duration after the moment of maximum
effect. It has already been mentioned that the duration of the PA is dependent
on the stimulus strength, the duration of the seizure activity increasing to a
maximum with increasing stimulus strength. In the different experiments
referred to, supramaximal stimulation has been used. When a certain dose
of a local anaesthetic is given which reduces the seizure duration or causes a
total abolition of the PA, an increase of the stimulus strength does not alter
the situation, no matter which stimulus strength has been used [33]. In this
respect the effect of local anaesthetics differs from the action of most anti-
epileptics in clinical use (e.g. barbiturates), since the influence of these
drugs on the PA can be compensated for with an increase of the stimulus
strength. Thus, in the latter case the threshold for the elicitation of the
after-discharge can be used for the evaluation of their anticonvulsive effect,
which is not the case with local anaesthetics.

In order to illustrate further the specific AP blocking action of local anaesthetics some other important differences between these drugs and barbiturates should be mentioned. It should first be pointed out that the shortened

PA after local anaesthetics has the same general shape as before the injection, the reduction of the duration being the main effect. Further, it should be noted that after a total abolition the PA duration during the recovery phase (Fig. 1 F) is the same in all cortical leads, and there is also a simultaneous arrest of the seizure activity when doses are given which only cause reduction of the PA duration. A barbiturate like pentobarbitone influences the PA

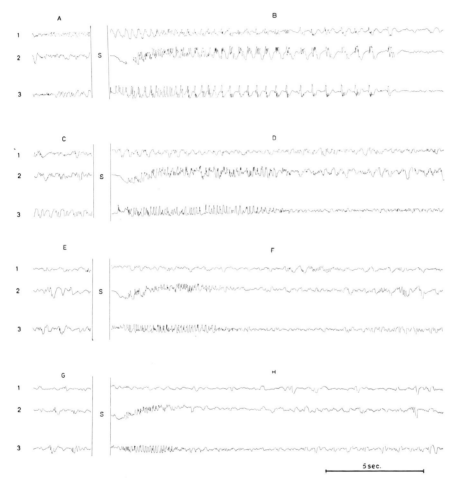

Fig. 4.—Effect of increasing doses of pentobarbitone on the cortical after-discharge in a monkey. Cortical activity led off from the ipsilateral post-central (tracing 2) and pre-central (tracing 3) areas and from the contralateral post-central area (tracing 1) before (A and B) and after 10 (C and D), 15 (E and F) and 20 (G and H) mg/kg of pentobarbital. Records A, C, E and G show the pre-stimulatory corticograms and records B, D, F and H the corticograms obtained after the cessation of the cortical stimulation (S). Stimulus frequency 25 per sec.; total duration 5 sec. (From Bernhard, Bohm, Kirstein and Wiesel [9].)

in quite another way (Fig. 4). Increasing doses of this drug profoundly alter the character of the PA and reduce its projection so that finally, after large doses, the PA does not appear in remote areas, whereas it remains within the cortical area stimulated. All these observations suggest important differences between the mode of action of local anaesthetics and, e.g., barbiturates. There are also other important differences which will be dealt with later.

EVALUATION OF ANTICONVULSIVE EFFECTS OF DIFFERENT LOCAL ANAESTHETICS

Since the main effect of small doses of intravenous local anaesthetics is a reduction of the duration of the PA and since, further, there is a constant relationship between the reduction of the duration and the dose injected, the PA duration has been used for the evaluation of the anticonvulsive effects of different local anaesthetics [10]. The dose–response relationship can be obtained by plotting the reduction of the duration of the cortical after-discharge at the moment of maximal effect (see Fig. 3) expressed in per cent of the pre-injection value against the dose injected (Fig. 5). From such dose-response curves the relative anticonvulsive effect of different local anaesthetics can be evaluated (Table I; column 1 with procaine as unit). Similar dose–response curves expressing the relation between dose and duration of effect give another aspect of the relative anticonvulsive effect (Table I; column 2). Superficially there seems to be a rough relationship between the local anaesthetic and the anticonvulsive effects, tetracaine and dibucaine in both

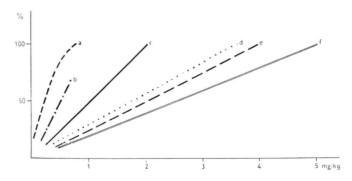

Fig. 5.—Dose–response relationship for seven different local anaesthetics. The reduction of the duration of the cortical after-discharge (one minute after the injection) as a percentage of pre-injection values (vertical axis) plotted against the varying doses (horizontal axis). *a*, tetracaine; *b*, dibucaine; *c*, lidocaine and diethoxine; *d*, piperocaine; *e*, buthetamine; *f*, procaine. (From Bernhard, Bohm, Kirstein and Wiesel [9].)

TABLE I

Substance	Anticonvulsive effect calculated from		Local anaesthetic effect		Toxicity	
	dose for 50 % block	dose for 20 min. effect	infiltration and block	surface	subcutaneous	intravenous
Procaine (taken as unit)	1	1	1	1	1	1
Buthetamine, Monocaine[R]	1.2	1	1.3–1.6	5	1.0–1.3	—
Piperocaine, Metycaine[R]	1.5	1	1.1–1.3	3	1.1	3
Diethoxine, Maxicaine, Intracaine[R]	2.5	2.7	1.3–1.5	8	1.4–1.5	—
Lidocaine, Lignocaine, Xylocaine[R]	2.5	2.7	2–4	8	1.2	2
Dibucaine, Cinchocaine, Nupercaine[R], Percaine, Cincaine	5	9	10–60	1300–2000	10–60	10–22
Tetracaine, Pontocaine, Amethocaine, Pantocaine[R], Decicaine[R]	12	23	5–20	375	10–30	10

cases being most effective, procaine, buthetamine and piperocaine having the weakest effect and lidocaine and diethoxine representing moderate effects. However, judging from the data given in the literature, dibucaine is more effective as a local anaesthetic than tetracaine, whereas, according to Table I, there seems to be a reversed relationship between the anticonvulsive effects of these two drugs. The reason is obscure but the observation may give an indication that the anticonvulsive and local anaesthetic effects of different local anaesthetics need not be related.

With the exception of lidocaine the substances listed in Table I are chemically related. As to the group of substances to which lidocaine belongs (alkyl-amino-acyl derivates), our investigations indicate that the anticonvulsive activity increases—as does the local anaesthetic action—with increasing size of the substituents in the aromatic nucleus. It has been claimed that the local anaesthetic action of lidocaine is related to 2.6 positions of the CH_3 groups [26] and this arrangement also seems to be important for its antiepileptic potency. Thus, we have investigated the anticonvulsive properties of about 17 homologues and isomers of lidocaine with varying positions of the substituents in the benzene nucleus, in the side chain and at the amino-N [10]. Those characterized by the CH_3 in 2.6 positions (10 compounds) have the same potency as lidocaine with the exception of two compounds. The low activity of these could be explained in one case by a rapid hydrolysis, in the other by the presence of further hydrophilic groups. A compound with the CH_3 groups in other positions in the benzene nucleus was found to be less active than lidocaine (7 compounds). With regard to the chemical constitution of the antiepileptic drugs in clinical use it has been pointed out that a basic chemical structure should be common to most of them. The local anaesthetics listed in Table I as well as the homologues and isomers of lidocaine tested do not seem to fit into this scheme at all. When dealing with neurophysiological principles it is worth while emphasizing the fact which has already been demonstrated, that the mode of action of the local anaesthetics differs from that of the substances built up on another basic chemical structure.

SPECIFICITY OF THE ANTICONVULSIVE ACTION OF LOCAL ANAESTHETICS

Before discussing further these differences and the possible mechanisms concerning the PA abolishing effect of local anaesthetics the specificity of their action will first be illustrated. It is not surprising that local application or intravenous injections of large doses may cause a general depression of central nervous functions (see above). This general blocking action, as well as the so-called convulsive effect of large intravenous doses, will be left out of the discussion; suffice it to say in this context that for some of them there is a large margin between the PA abolishing doses and the convulsive doses [10]. Our experiences with intravenous lidocaine treatment of human epileptic fits support this statement (see below).

The effect of small intravenous doses just big enough to cause a total abolition of the PA has been tested on several transmission mechanisms. It has been shown that they are without any significant effect on the transmission in the monosynaptic spinal reflex arc in decapitate and decerebrate preparations (cat); neither is there any influence on the unconditioned monosynaptic S_1 and L_7 ventral root reflex discharge evoked by stimulation of low threshold afferents from different muscles (Fig. 6), nor is there any influence on the post-tetanic potentiation within the same reflex systems (Fig. 7). In this connection it should also be mentioned that much larger intravenous doses of procaine are needed in order to obtain any effect on the myoneural transmission (up to 64 mg/kg according to Ellis *et al.* [20]) than those needed to abolish the post-stimulatory cortical after-discharge (for procaine about 5 mg/kg; see Fig. 3). Intravenous doses which totally abolish the PA are

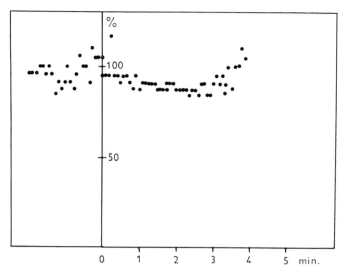

Fig. 6.—Amplitude of monosynaptic reflex before (to the left of vertical axis) and after (to the right of vertical axis) the injection of lidocaine (2 mg/kg) in a decerebrate preparation (cat). Amplitude values (in per cent of the average value obtained before the injection; 100 per cent on vertical axis) plotted against time in minutes after the injection (horizontal axis). (From Wiesel, unpublished observations.)

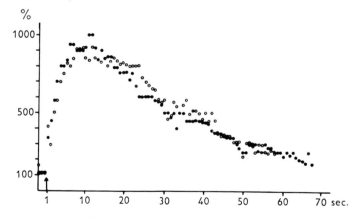

Fig. 7.—Post-tetanic potentiation of monosynaptic reflex discharge after repetitive stimulation at a frequency of 500 per sec for 2 sec. applied to the afferent fibres of the reflex pathway. Amplitude of the response plotted in per cent of the value obtained without preceding potentiating stimulation (100 per cent on vertical axis). Filled circles before injection and open circles after the injection of lidocaine (4 mg/kg). Decapitate preparation (cat). (From Wiesel, unpublished observations.)

also without effect on the cord dorsum potentials evoked by low threshold cutaneous fibres (Taverner, personal communication) as well as on the DR IV and V potentials led off from the dorsal root adjacent to that stimulated (Fig. 12). Intravenous doses which are large enough to abolish the cortical

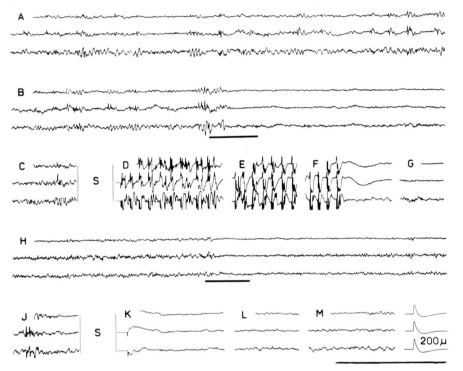

Fig. 8.—Effect of intravenous lidocaine (3 mg/kg) on the cortical activity in a monkey. Cortical activity led off from the post-central (upper tracings), pre-central (middle tracings) and frontal (lower tracings) areas ipsilateral to the stimulation (pre-central area) before (*A–F*) and after the lidocaine injection. *A*, pre-injection non-convulsive activity; *B*, pre-injection arousal reaction (heavy line signals auditory stimulation); *C*, activity before stimulation; *D–G*, post-stimulatory activity 1–5 sec. (*D*), 10–13 (*E*), 20–23 (*F*) and 35 sec. after stimulation (*S*); *H*, arousal reaction (heavy line signals auditory stimulation) after lidocaine injection; *J*, activity before stimulation, *K–M*, post-stimulatory activity 1–5 sec. (*K*), 10–13 (*L*) and 20–23 (*M*) sec. after stimulation (*S*). Calibration 200 μV. Heavy line below signals 5 sec. (From Bernhard, Bohm, Kirstein and Wiesel [9].)

PA have also been tested on ascending transmission systems and were found not to influence the cortical responses within the sensory areas I and II to single electrical stimulation of low threshold cutaneous fibres [4, 6].

Of more interest in this connection is the resistance of the transmission in the ascending diffuse activation system to PA abolishing doses, as judged from the tests on the arousal reaction in non-anaesthetized preparations (monkeys). Here again there is a striking difference between local anaesthetics and barbiturates [9]. While small intravenous doses of a local anaesthetic which cause a total abolition of the PA (lidocaine, 3 mg/kg; cf. Fig. 8 *D–G*

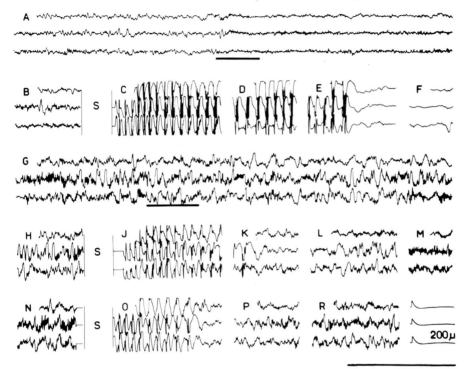

Fig. 9.—Effects of intravenous pentobarbitone on the cortical activity in a monkey. Leads as in Fig. 4. Non-convulsive (*A* and *B*) arousal reaction (*A*) and post-stimulatory activity 1–5 (*C*), 8–10 (*D*), 15–18 (*E*) and 25 sec. after stimulation (*S*) before injection of pentobarbitone. *C–M*, effect of 9 mg/kg of intravenous pentobarbitone on non-convulsive cortical activity (*G* and *H*), arousal reaction (*G*) and post-stimulatory after-discharge (*J*, 1–5, *K*, 8–10, *L*, 15–18 and *M*, 25 sec. after stimulation). *N–R*, effect of 15 mg/kg of pentobarbitone on non-convulsive activity (*N*) and post-stimulatory after-discharge 1–5 (*O*), 8–10 (*P*) and 15–18 (*R*) sec. after stimulation (*S*). Calibration 200 μV. Heavy line below signals 5 sec. (From Bernhard, Bohm, Kirstein and Wiesel [9].)

and *K–M*) have no effect whatsoever on the pre-stimulatory cortical activity (cf. Fig. 8 *A–B* and *C*, *H*, *J*) and on the arousal reaction (cf. Fig. 8 *B* and *H*), a small dose of pentobarbital produces well-known changes in the EEG (cf. Fig. 9 *A–B* and *G*) and abolishes the arousal reaction (cf. Fig. 9 *A* and *G*) but does not extinguish the PA. Even large hypnotic doses do not abolish the PA (cf. above). This is in accordance with the results of investigations

on humans which have shown that intravenous injections of 2–3 mg/kg
lidocaine break sustained grand mal attacks [7, 5] and shortens the electro-
shock seizure in non-epileptic patients [32], whereas doses up to 6 mg/kg
may be without any influence on the EEG and doses up to 8 mg/kg are not
followed by sedation in normal persons who had not received any other
drug (see [8]). In contrast to barbiturates there is thus a remarkable discrepancy between the dramatic action of small intravenous doses of a local
anaesthetic on pathological synchronized cortical activity and the lack of
influence on coordinated central functions, the integration of which takes part
in anatomically defined transmission systems. In this connection it should
be mentioned, for example, that the reactions appearing during hippocampal
stimulation in cats remain after doses which totally abolish the hippocampus
PA following upon the stimulation. Complex rhythmical integrated reflexes
like post-rotational nystagmus also remain uninfluenced by PA abolishing
doses. Finally, it is interesting that Jacksonian fits in humans are abolished
by intravenous doses of local anaesthetics without disturbances of the con-
scious state in cases which do not suffer from unconsciousness.

ON THE ROLE OF UNDIFFERENTIATED SPREAD OF EXCITATION
IN CONVULSIVE CORTICAL ACTIVITY

*Effect of local anaesthetics on the ephaptic transmission in
peripheral nerves*

The question therefore turned up concerning the mechanism of the central
action of the PA abolishing doses of local anaesthetics. Evidence for the view
that electrical field effects may play an important role in the synchronization
underlying certain types of high voltage cortical activity was briefly outlined
in the introductory section. Hence, it seemed to us to be of interest to investigate further the effect of small intravenous doses of local anaesthetics on
different types of undifferentiated neuronal spread of excitation [11]. Thus,
for example, the effect of PA abolishing doses of local anaesthetics on the
ephaptic motor-to-sensory nerve fibre transmission at the injured region of a
peripheral nerve in spinal cats has been tested (Figs. 10 and 11). In such
experiments it has been shown that small intravenous doses of local anaesthetics just large enough to block the PA are followed by a considerable
reduction of the response, transmitted ephaptically at the injured region of
the sciatic nerve, and recorded from the post-ephaptic sensory fibres in the

L₇ sensory roots (transected centrally near the cord), when the corresponding ventral root (also transected centrally) is stimulated, the pre-ephaptic spike response remaining uninfluenced.

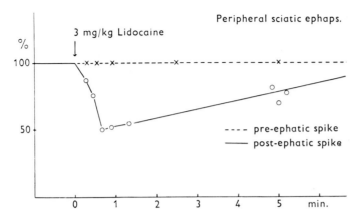

Fig. 10.—Effect of lidocaine on post-ephaptic sensory root response to motor root stimulation (open circles) in per cent of pre-injection values. Crosses, amplitude of pre-ephaptic response. (From Bernhard and Valleala [11].)

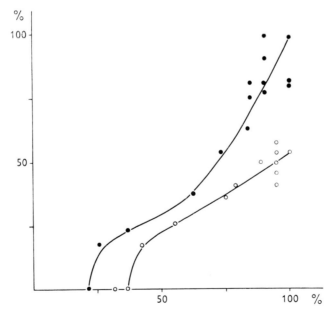

Fig. 11.—Amplitude of post-ephaptic sensory root response (vertical axis) plotted against amplitude of pre-ephaptic response (horizontal axis) in per cent of maximal value tested before (filled circles) and after 3 mg/kg of lidocaine (open circles) at increasing stimulus strength.

Effect of local anaesthetics on the dorsal root reflex

Of considerable interest in this connection is also the quite regular blocking action of corresponding doses of local anaesthetics on the dorsal root reflex. The effect on this special transmission system has been studied simultaneously with that on the dorsal root potentials (DR IV and V, according to the terminology of Lloyd and McIntyre [25]). Intravenous PA blocking doses of a local anaesthetic which produce a striking reduction of the dorsal root

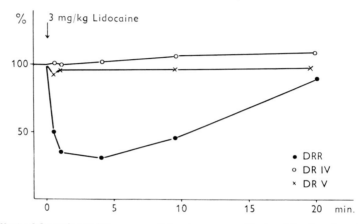

Fig. 12.—Effect of 3 mg/kg of intravenous lidocaine on amplitude of L_7 dorsal root reflex (filled circles), *DR* IV (open circles) and *DR* V (crosses). Amplitude values plotted in per cent of pre-injection value. (From Bernhard and Valleala [11].)

reflex (stimulation and recording from adjacent groups of filaments in the L_7 dorsal root) do not seem to have any significant effect on the DR IV and V potentials (Fig. 12). This negative finding as well as the above mentioned fact that the post-tetanic potentiation in the monosynaptic reflex arc is relatively resistant would indicate that the activity set up in the afferent terminals is not influenced by the treatment. That the unconditioned synaptic transmission in the monosynaptic pathways is also resistant to these doses of local anaesthetics has already been mentioned (Figs. 6 and 13). Before discussing the behaviour of the polysynaptic reflex under the influence of corresponding doses of these drugs, attention should be paid to the resistance of the dorsal root reflex to increasing doses of barbiturates. In the experiment illustrated in Fig. 14 up to 12.5 mg/kg of pentobarbitone are given without any significant influence on the dorsal root reflex. At this dose the polysynaptic reflex is abolished and the monosynaptic reflex significantly reduced.

The dorsal root reflex studies are to be regarded as model experiments

on the effect of local anaesthetics and barbiturates on a type of undifferentiated spread of excitation. According to current views (see, e.g., [16]) afferent
terminal interaction as well as interaction with interneurones play an important role for the spread of excitation in this system which would mean
that ephaptic mechanisms are involved. Thus, the peripheral nerve as well
as the spinal cord experiments strongly suggest that small intravenous doses
of local anaesthetics block the undifferentiated spread of excitation which is
due to electrical field effects rather than to specific synaptic processes.

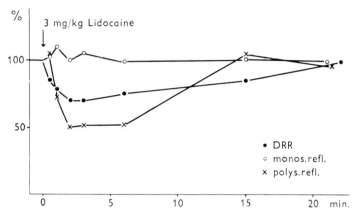

Fig. 13.—Effect of 3 mg/kg of intravenous lidocaine on amplitude of L_7 dorsal root reflex (filled
circles), monosynaptic reflex (open circles) and polysynaptic reflex (crosses). Amplitude values
in per cent of pre-injection values. (From Bernhard and Valleala [11].)

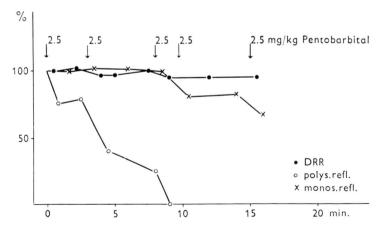

Fig. 14.—Effect of intravenous injections (arrows) of pentobarbital on L_7 dorsal root reflex (filled
circles), monosynaptic reflex (crosses) and polysynaptic reflex (open circles). Amplitude values
in per cent of pre-injection values. (From Bernhard and Valleala [11].)

*Comparison of anticonvulsive action of local anaesthetics
and their effects on ephaptic transmission*

Comparative studies on the PA abolishing effect (tested within the cortical
region stimulated) and on the effect on the dorsal root reflex of pentobarbitone
and a series of local anaesthetics of different potency have recently been

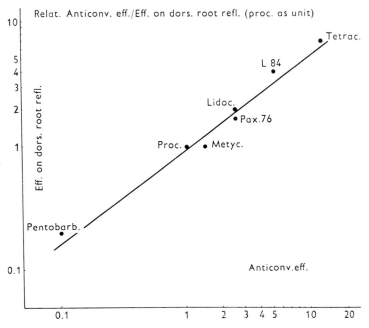

Fig. 15.—Relation between anticonvulsive effect and effect on dorsal root reflex of pentobarbitone
and a series of local anaesthetics (arbitrary scale with procaine as unit). (From Bernhard and
Valleala [11].)

made [11]. The direct relation between the anticonvulsive effect (i.e. the
PA abolishing effect) and the blocking effect on the dorsal root reflex (Fig.
15) is in favour of the view that electrical field effects play a basic role for
the synchronized post-stimulatory cortical after-discharge and that this
mechanism is very sensitive to local anaesthetics in low concentrations. In
this respect the pentobarbitone (when referring to mg/kg weight) is much less
effective than any of the local anaesthetics tested. Further, as has been pointed
out, pentobarbitone has a different mode of action on the PA; it reduces the
projection to remote areas instead of producing an instantaneous arrest of the
synchronized activity in all cortical regions, as do the local anaesthetics. The
significant influence of pentobarbitone on the spinal ventral root reflexes in
contrast to its lack of influence on the dorsal root reflex even in large doses

also indicates a different mode of action. Returning to the effect of small intravenous doses of local anaesthetics on the polysynaptic reflex, it usually undergoes a reduction in parallel with the reduction of the dorsal root reflex (Fig. 13). In analogy with the considerations made in the discussion concerning the effect of local anaesthetics, this would indicate that an ephaptic component should be involved. The effect of small doses of pentobarbital, on the other hand, may then indicate that this is not the only factor. One may argue that a synchronous volley elicited by a single electrical stimulation of a nerve or dorsal root favours an ephaptic activation in the reflex path which may not take part in the excitation process with natural asynchronous stimulation. The central transmission mechanism behind the electrically evoked postsynaptic response may, on the other hand, be the same as when natural stimulation is used, in which case one may ask if electrical field effects are involved for, e.g., axo-dendritic conduction in the more diffuse reflex system. It is quite plausible that the diffuse dendritic arborizations in the cortex play an important part in the synchronization of the post-stimulatory after-discharge which is so extremely sensitive to local anaesthetics.

SUMMARY

The main theme of this discussion concerns the possibility of producing a selective block of central neuron activity controlled by electrical field effects resulting in undifferentiated neuronal spread of excitation without influencing specific synaptic processes in anatomically determined pathways. The blocking effect of small intravenous doses of various local anaesthetics on the electrically evoked cortical convulsive activity was studied in relation to chemical constitution, and the difference in action between these compounds and barbiturates was demonstrated. In model experiments it was shown (cats and monkeys) that corresponding doses of local anaesthetics selectively block the ephaptic type of neurone interaction. Thus, small intravenous doses of local anaesthetics reduce the ephaptic motor to sensory fibre transmission at the injured region of peripheral nerve. Further, when given in doses of the same magnitude which usually do not influence the monosynaptic reflex, these substances block components in the dorsal root reflex response to synchronous afferent volleys, which components, according to current views, are of "ephaptic order", i.e. are due to potential fields set up by the afferent volley. Recordings of different spinal reflexes as well as of the dorsal root potentials demonstrate the selective effect of local anaesthetics on ephaptic processes. Using equivalent intravenous doses of these compounds, a correlation was found between their anticonvulsive action and their effect on the ephaptic type of central neurone interaction, which shows that ephaptic interaction is essential the building up and spread of rhythmic epileptic cortical activity.

REFERENCES

1. ALLEN, F. M., CROSSMAN, L. W. and LYONS, L. V., *Current Researches Anesthesia & Analgesia* **25**, 1 (1946).
2. BERGER, H., *Arch. Psychiat. Nervenkrankh.* **87**, 525 (1929).
3. BERNHARD, C. G. and BOHM, E., *Acta Physiol. Scand.* **31**, Suppl. 114, 5 (1954).
4. —— *Experientia* **10**, 474 (1954).
5. —— British Society Neurol. Surg. Trans. Meeting, Stockholm, 1956. In press.
6. —— *Brit. J. Pharmacol.* **10**, 288 (1955).
7. BERNHARD, C. G., BOHM, E. and HÖJEBERG, S., *Arch. Neurol. Psychiat.* **74**, 208 (1955).
8. BERNHARD, C. G., BOHM, E., HÖJEBERG, S. and MELIN, K. A., *Acta Psychiat. et Neurol. Scand.* **31**, 185 (1956).
9. BERNHARD, C. G., BOHM, E., KIRSTEIN, L. and WIESEL, T., *Arch. intern. Pharmacodynamie* **108**, 408 (1956).
10. BERNHARD, C. G., BOHM, E. and WIESEL, T., *Arch. intern. Pharmacodynamie* **108**, 392 (1956).
11. BERNHARD, C. G. and VALLEALA, P., to be published.
12. BIGELOW, N. and HARRISON, I., *J. Pharmacol. Exptl. Therap.* **81**, 368 (1944).
13. BITTRICH, N. M., *J. Am. Med. Assoc.* **141**, 766 (1949).
14. BREMER, F., *Arch. intern. physiol.* **51**, 211 (1941).
15. —— Neurophysiological problem of sleep, *in* Brain Mechanisms and Consciousness, pp. 137–162. Blackwell, Oxford, 1954.
16. BROOKS, CH. McC. and KOIZUMI, K., *J. Neurophysiol.* **19**, 61 (1956).
17. CHANG, H.-T., *J. Neurophysiol.* **14**, 1 (1951).
18. CLAES, E., *Arch. intern. Physiol.* **48**, 181 (1939).
19. EDMONDS, G. W., COMOR, W. H., KENEDY, J. D. and TAYLOR, I. B., *J. Am. Med. Assoc.* **141**, 761 (1949).
20. ELLIS, C. H., WNUCK, A. L., DE BEER, E. J. and FOLDES, F. F., *Am. J. Physiol.* **174**, 277 (1953).
21. FRENCH, J. D., LIVINGTON, R. B., KÖNIGSMARK, B. and RICHLAND, K. J., *J. Neurosurg.* **14**, 43 (1957).
22. HILL, E. F. and MACDONALD, A. D., *J. Pharmacol. Exptl. Therap.* **53**, 454 (1935).
23. LIBET, B. and GERARD, R. W., *J. Neurophysiol.* **2**, 153 (1939).
24. —— *Am. J. Psychiat.* **96**, 1127 (1940).
25. LLOYD, D. P. C. and McINTYRE, A. K., *J. Gen. Physiol.* **32**, 409 (1949).
26. LÖFGREN, N., Studies on Local Anesthetics, Xylocaine a New Synthetic Drug. Ivar Hægg-ströms Boktryckeri AB, Stockholm, 1948.
27. MAYKUT, M. O. and KALOW, W., *Canad. Anaesthet. Soc. J.* **2**, 109 (1955).
28. MAGOUN, H. W., *in* Brain Mechanisms and Consciousness, pp. 1–20. Blackwell, Oxford, 1954.
29. —— Ascending reticular system and anesthesia *in* Trans. Mary Fond. 1st Conf. on Neuro-pharm., 1955.
30. MORUZZI, G., *Arch. intern. Physiol.* **49**, 33 (1939).
31. —— *in* Brain Mechanisms and Consciousness, pp. 21–53. Blackwell, Oxford, 1954.
32. OTTOSSON, J. O., *Experientia* **11**, 453 (1955).
33. —— (1957) in course of publication.
34. PENFIELD, W. and JASPER, H., Epilepsy and the Functional Anatomy of the Human Brain. Little; Brown and Company, Boston, 1954.
35. SOREL, L. and LEJEUNE, R., *Arch. intern. Pharmacodynamie* **102**, 314 (1955).
36. SUNG, CHEN-YU and TRUANT, A. P., *J. Pharmacol. Exptl. Therap.* **112**, 432 (1954).
37. TANAKA, K., *Soc. Exptl. Biol. Med.* **90**, 192 (1955).
38. TANAKA, K., YASUKATA, M. and OTSUBO, Z., *Jap. J. Pharmacol.* **5**, 42 (1955).
39. WRIGHT, G. V. S., *Anesthesia* **5**, 201 (1950).
40. YASUKATA, M., *J. Yonago Med. Assoc.* **6**, 72 (1955).

Experimental Cell Research, Suppl. 5, *221–233 (1958)*

THE APPROACH TO UNITARY ANALYSIS OF NEURON RESPONSE

D. P. C. LLOYD

The Rockefeller Institute for Medical Research, New York, N.Y., U.S.A.

In examination of the behavior of motoneurons in any given circumstance of activation two reasons present themselves for studying individual members of the motoneuron pool rather than the population: because the individuals may yield information that cannot be extracted by measuring the response of the population, or because one is forced to study individuals by the very nature of one's experimental method. In either event unless the individuals of a population are essentially alike in behavior, as examplified by the response of muscle fibers to motor nerve volleys [5], or the unit is the population, as is the stretch receptor cell studied by Eyzaguirre and Kuffler [3, 4] and Kuffler and Eyzaguirre [12], the question of representative sampling must be faced, and its importance respected, lest the information gained prove misleading.

A way to the desired end of representative sampling was found by Hunt in his study of the receptor origin of afferent fibers arising in muscle [6]. Briefly put, Hunt's technique was to examine systematically every isolated strand of dorsal root for afferent fibers from the muscle in question in order to detect, as far as possible, every afferent fiber from that muscle. In searching, electrical stimulation of the muscle nerve was employed rather than natural stimulation which latter method favored isolation of the larger fibers yielding the larger spike potentials [9]. Each fiber encountered was studied with respect to conduction velocity and then with respect to the functional quality of its peripheral termination. Utilizing the conversion factor of Hursh [10] to obtain fiber diameter from velocity measurement Hunt was able to show that the method of serial examination of individuals yielded, for the range from 4 μ diameter upward, a "fiber spectrum" substantially identical to that obtained by histological survey of afferent fiber distribution [17]. With the question of representative sampling settled Hunt was able to give a quantitative accounting for the Group I and Group II afferent fiber bands in terms of A (muscle spindle) and B (tendon organ) type endings.

Faced with a question concerning motoneuron response, in the circumstance of monosynaptic reflex action, that could not be answered by the motoneuron pool acting as a population, and encouraged by the success of Hunt's method of serial examination, McIntyre and I undertook, employing similar principles, a study of the monosynaptic reflex responses of individual motoneurons [19]. We evolved a battery of tests and applied them to each individual gastrocnemius motoneuron we came upon by serial examination of filaments of the seventh lumbar and first sacral ventral roots. One or more of these tests asked the questions we hoped the individuals would answer, that the natural pool could not. The assembly of individuals we collected, in number 110, was designated a synthetic motoneuron pool and an item of prime concern to us was whether or not this synthetic pool would be representative of the natural pool in circumstances of monosynaptic reflex activation. It was our hope that some of the other tests applied would tell us the answer.

NATURAL AND SYNTHETIC MOTONEURON POOLS

The number of motoneurons engaged in monosynaptic reflex response to a series of identical afferent volleys varies in magnitude from one trial to another due to temporally random fluctuation in the responsivity of the individual motoneurons [19, 7, 22]. Some motoneurons are so strongly excited as never to fail in response, others so feebly excited as never to respond. Between these extremes is a segment of the population excited within a critical range that permits fluctuation to determine whether or not response will occur on a given trial.

Response of populations is gauged by finding the mean response in a series of trials and, according to this, apportioning the population arbitrarily into responding and non-responding fractions. Change in response is expressed by varying ratio of numbers in the two fractions. Change in status among individuals is measurable only as an individual lies in the range between the always responding and the never responding conditions. This "intermediate" range, which is dispensed with in studies of populations is the focus of attention in study of "individuals".

The performance of a motoneuron, necessarily in terms of yes or no answers, can be expressed by means of a "firing index" which is given by:

$$\frac{\text{No. responses}}{\text{No. trials}} \times 100.$$

For pictorial representation of the monosynaptic reflex behavior of a synthetic motoneuron pool a plot is constructed in which the individuals are ranked in order of decreasing firing indices. Fig. 1 contains two such plots representing behavior of the synthetic pool in two circumstances of stimulation. In each circumstance of stimulation it is seen that some motoneurons responded to every trial ($Fi = 100$), some did not respond to any test ($Fi = 0$)

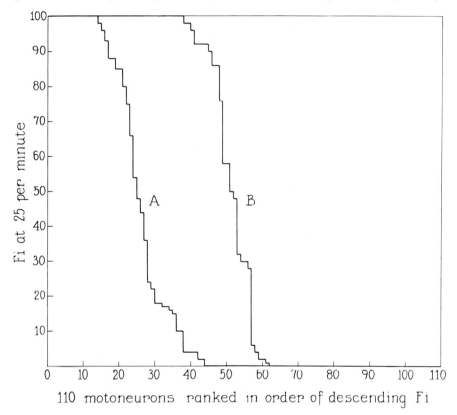

110 motoneurons ranked in order of descending Fi

Fig. 1.—Graphical representation of a synthetic motoneuron pool. In all 110 motoneurons are represented in terms of their firing indices, being ranked in order of decreasing Fi. Curve A represents the pool when activated by standard maximal homonymous afferent volleys, curve B when activated by standard maximal volleys in the entire afferent supply of the synergic unit, triceps surae. (From Lloyd and McIntyre [19].)

and some responded in an intermediate percentage of trials ($Fi < 100$ and > 0). I might point out that the $Fi = 0$ motoneurons although not responding at the given level of excitation are identified as being part of the synthetic pool by virtue of response at a higher level of input, or by virtue of response in the period of potentiation following a period of high frequency stimulation [15]. For some purposes it is desirable to have a numerical value for the mean monosynaptic reflex response of the synthetic pool in a given circumstance of activation. This is given by

$$\frac{\sum\limits_{Fi=1}^{100} f(Fi)}{100}$$

and has been dubbed the "fictitious monosynaptic reflex".

A TEST FOR REPRESENTATIVE SAMPLING

The principle employed for testing the ability of serial examination of motoneurons to produce a representative sample is that the sum of the individual behavior patterns in some well known circumstance of change should reproduce the behavior of a pool in identical circumstance. The pool illustrated in Fig. 1 was tested by observing the response of its individual members during the period following high-frequency stimulation of the afferent nerve (so-called post-tetanic potentiation).

When, in a low-frequency series of monosynaptic reflex responses, a

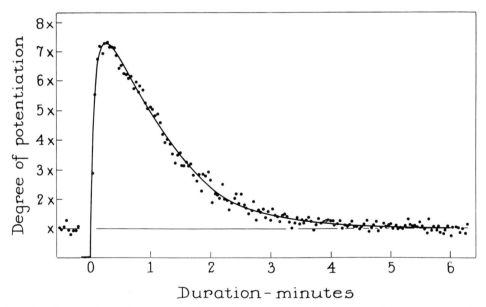

Fig. 2.—Course of post-tetanic potentiation in a natural motoneuron pool (triceps surae). The base-line X represents the mean reflex amplitude at a repetition rate of 25 per minute. The time scale on the abscissa begins at the close of a 12 second tetanus at 555 per second. The ordinates represent reflex amplitude expressed in multiples of the mean pre-tetanic reflex amplitude. (From Lloyd [15].)

high-frequency stimulation, of perhaps 500 per sec. for 10 seconds, is directed
to the nerve afferent for the reflexes in question, the responses, fairly uniform
prior to the high-frequency burst, augment to reach a ceiling in magnitude,
that may be many times the control value, in approximately 20 seconds,
after which the responses decline in magnitude and return after some minutes

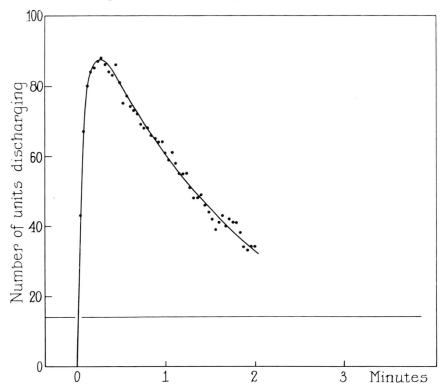

Fig. 3.—Synthetic curve of post-tetanic potentiation constructed by summation of the post-
tetanic response patterns of individual motoneurons. *Ordinates:* the number of units that responded to any given post-tetanic test stimulation. The base-line is given by the number of $fi = 100$
motoneurons. *Abscissae:* time in minutes. (From Lloyd and McIntyre [19].)

to normal [15]. Fig. 2 depicts the temporal course of this post-tetanic potentiation of response in a natural motoneuron pool.

Now clearly each of the individual motoneurons can be subjected to the
identical procedure and the patterns of their responses recorded. Those that
respond to every trial in the otherwise resting state cannot naturally increase
their response, but those in the intermediate zone can and those in the never
responding zone can be brought to the condition of responding for a certain

number of trials following the tetanus. Knowing from one's oscillographic recordings the exact pattern of response by each neuron subjected to precisely the same conditions one can then simply add up the number of motoneurons that responded to the first post-tetanic test, the second and so on. Fig. 3 presents the result in graphical form extending over two minutes of the post-tetanic period, the ordinates representing the number of individuals in the synthetic pool that responded on any given post-tetanic test interval.

That the synthetic curve of post-tetanic potentiation reproduced in Fig. 3 duplicates the course of post-tetanic potentiation in the natural pool is reason to suppose that the method of serial examination is adequate to procure a representative sample.

ANOTHER SYNTHETIC MOTONEURON POOL

It is all very well to say that a given assemblage of individual motoneurons was representative of the natural pool, but it is fair to ask whether the same procedure applied on another occasion would have the same degree of success in securing a representative sample. Actually, with another problem in mind another synthetic motoneuron pool has been assembled [16]. The problem concerned the influence of repetition rate upon response in the monosynaptic reflex pathway [21].

The synthetic motoneuron pool assembled upon this occasion was smaller than the original pool studied by McIntyre and myself [19, 20]. Serial examination of motoneurons was practiced until an "intermediate zone" of the same numerical magnitude as that of the original pool was obtained. By the time this was done a slightly smaller number of $Fi = 100$ motoneurons has been encountered. The number of $Fi = 0$ motoneurons is not significant for decision had been made not to enter all the $Fi = 0$ motoneurons that could be identified with the aid of post-tetanic potentiation, this because the phenomenon under observation was a depression of response and hence concerned not the already $Fi = 0$ motoneurons.

Fig. 4 constructed in the manner of Fig. 1 represents this second synthetic motoneuron pool. To the left is plotted by the solid line this pool as it was constructed from observations made at a repetition rate of 30 per minute. Repetition rate for the study of the original pool was 25 per minute, the difference being related to the requirements of the later series of experiments and to replacement, in the interim, of obsolete equipment. Plotted by the broken line is the original synthetic pool adjusted for difference in the number of $Fi = 100$ motoneurons, this to allow comparison between the intermediate zones of the two synthetic pools. The intermediate zone of the second pool by comparison with the original is a little short in the range from $Fi = 70$ to $Fi = 90$ and a little high in the range from $Fi = 50$ to $Fi = 70$. The general character of the intermediate zone, however, is as well preserved as it is within a single pool at different levels of excitation (Fig. 1) or at varied frequency which latter influence is depicted to the right of Fig. 4.

On the right of Fig. 4 is seen the response behavior of the second synthetic pool at three frequencies of stimulation. These plots, reading from left to right represent behavior at 10 per second, 2 per second and 30 per minute

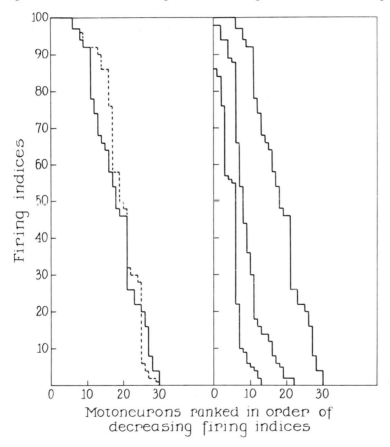

Motoneurons ranked in order of decreasing firing indices

Fig. 4.—Graphical representation of another synthetic motoneuron pool, constructed as was Fig. 1. On the left the solid line plots this pool according to its behavior at a stimulus repetition rate of 30 per minute, stimuli being applied to the entire afferent supply of triceps surae. Broken line plots, for comparison, the intermediate zone as it was in the synthetic pool of Lloyd and McIntyre (cf. Fig. 1 *B*). On the right are representations of the synthetic pool behavior at three stimulus repetition rates. (From Lloyd [16].)

respectively. It is of some interest to compare behavior of a pool at three
frequencies, input level being held constant, with the behavior of another
pool, illustrated in Fig. 5 at three levels of input, frequency being held constant.

ANOTHER TEST FOR REPRESENTATIVE SAMPLING

Again the test for representative sampling by serial examination is that the
sum of the behavior of the individuals should reproduce that of a natural
pool. The phenomenon under study is that known as low-frequency depression of monosynaptic reflex response [11, 21, 1].

Fig. 6 illustrates the relation between afferent stimulation frequency and
mean monosynaptic reflex output from the medial gastrocnemius motoneuron
pool at two levels of afferent input. It is presented at this time not for the

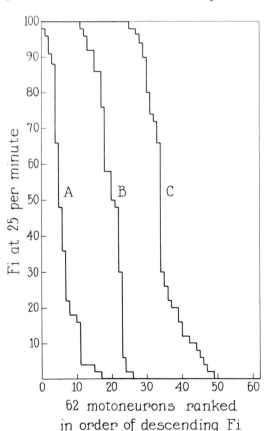

Fig. 5.—A synthetic motoneuron pool represented at three levels of afferent input.
A, standard maximal homonymous input.
B, standard maximal entire input. C,
standard maximal entire input set upon
a background of long spinal reflex excitation. Stimulus repetition rate 25 per
minute. (From Lloyd and McIntyre [19].)

purpose of discussing the nature of low-frequency depression, but rather to serve as an example of pool behavior in a given set of circumstances with which to compare synthetic pool behavior in the same set of circumstances.

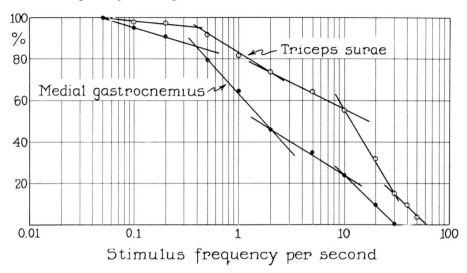

Fig. 6.—Relation between frequency and mean monosynaptic reflex amplitude from a natural motoneuron pool. The relation is shown for the medial gastrocnemius motoneuron pool when the entire triceps afferent supply is stimulated and when afferent stimulation is restricted to the medial gastrocnemius component. From Lloyd and Wilson [21].)

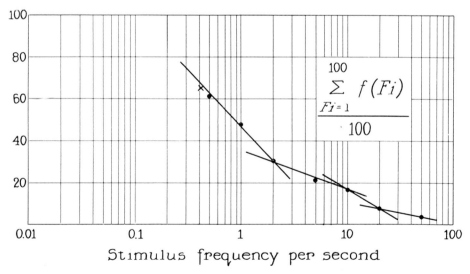

Fig. 7.—Mean discharge zone (the fictitious monosynaptic reflex) of a synthetic motoneuron pool plotted as a function of stimulation frequency. (From Lloyd [16].)

Experimental Cell Research, Suppl. **5**

From the data contained in Fig. 5, and similar data obtained employing other frequencies of afferent stimulation, it is possible to calculate, for each frequency examined, the fictitious monosynaptic reflex of the synthetic motoneuron pool. The result is shown in Fig. 7 which relates amplitude of the mean fictitious monosynaptic reflex to frequency. Since this relation is a close match for the type of relation displayed by natural motoneuron pools one may suppose that the method of serial examination again has proven adequate to secure representative sampling.

AN EXAMPLE OF THE UTILITY OF A SYNTHETIC POOL

In all ordinary circumstances the monosynaptic reflex response engendered by stimulation of a given muscle nerve, in conformity with the nature of the stretch reflex which it represents, appears only in that nerve, and not in the nerves even of synergists acting upon the same joint [13]. To be specific an afferent volley in the nerve to gastrocnemius medialis will engender a monosynaptic reflex response among the motoneurons of gastrocnemius medialis (that is to say the homonymous motoneurons) but not among the (heteronymous) motoneurons of gastrocnemius lateralis, this despite the fact that heteronymous connection can be shown to exist between the afferent fibers from one head of the muscle and the motoneurons of the other head [14, 2]. In certain circumstances, however, and this was discovered more or less simultaneously in several laboratories (cf. [18] for references), heteronymous transmission will occur and a few heteronymous motoneurons will respond in the monosynaptic reflex tempo. Fig. 8 illustrates an example of heteronymous reflex transmission occurring during the peak of its potentiation by a prior high-frequency tetanization of the afferent nerve. Alternative inter-

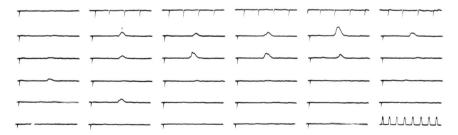

Fig. 8.—An example of heteronymous monosynaptic reflex transmission occurring, following tetanization of the afferent pathway, from the afferent fibers of medial gastrocnemius to the motoneurons of lateral gastrocnemius. Records made every two seconds before, during (top row) and following (second and subsequent rows) a 10 second tetanus at ca. 500 per sec. Time at bottom right in milliseconds. (From Lloyd, Hunt and McIntyre [18].)

pretations immediately suggest themselves and observation of the pool is powerless to indicate preference. Thus one might suppose that the moto-neurons possess a wide range of threshold and that those of low threshold are susceptible to the action of potentiated but normally feeble heteronymous

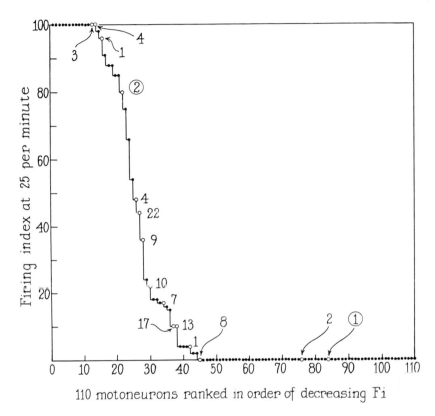

Fig. 9.—The same synthetic motoneuron pool as that represented in Fig. 1. In this instance the motoneurons that did respond to heteronymous volleys during the period of post-tetanic potentiation are identified by open circles. The number associated with each such identified motoneuron tells the number of responses so yielded at a test stimulation repetition rate of 25 per minute. (From Lloyd and McIntyre [20].)

connections. Or, one might chose the alternative view that motoneuron thresh-old is fairly uniform, and that details of presynaptic organization might determine which motoneurons were predisposed to heteronymous response. It was, in fact, this impasse that led Dr. McIntyre and me to the study of individual motoneurons. Initial surmise was that the former alternative, if true, would result in a high degree of correlation between homonymous firing index of a motoneuron and the incidence of heteronymous response during potentiation, whereas the latter alternative, if true, probably would not.

Fig. 9 illustrates our finding [20] with respect to motoneurons subjected to homonymous afferent volleys and to potentiated heteronymous afferent volleys. The synthetic motoneuron pool is that illustrated in Fig. 1, but in this presentation each individual is identified by a circle, filled to represent those that would not respond to potentiated heteronymous volleys, open to represent those that did. The number associated with each open circle represents the number of responses yielded by each motoneuron to iterative stimulation at 25 per minute during the post-tetanic period.

It is evident that most of the motoneurons that responded at all to post-tetanically elicited heteronymous afferent volleys are to be found in the intermediate zone with respect to response to homonymous afferent volleys, and that of these the individuals that responded with the highest incidence were in the range below $Fi = 50$. Consonant with this result is the finding by Hunt [8] that the individual motoneurons most powerfully facilitated by heteronymous afferent volleys were to be found in the range of intermediate firing indices with respect to homonymous response.

The foregoing would appear to dispose of the notion that variation in motoneuron threshold is a significant factor in the readiness of motoneurons to respond in monosynaptic reflex action, be it homonymous or heteronymous in origin. Difference, then, must be considered a consequence of presynaptic organization.

CONCLUSION

A tremendous expansion in the study of individual neurons having taken place following introduction of the intracellular microelectrode technique the problems of representative sampling would appear to merit the most careful attention. The systematic serial examination of every motoneuron one comes upon apparently will secure a representative sample of the population in which one is interested. Of course, it is possible to ask specific questions of a synthetic pool that might require for solution only the observation of $Fi = 100$ neurons or, perhaps, only the $Fi = 0$ neurons. Without some specific question of that sort in mind, however, it could well be dangerous to discard any individual one comes upon.

SUMMARY

Methods are described for obtaining a representative sample of a population of motoneurons and for testing the adequacy of the sampling procedure. The individuals studied are collected into a 'synthetic' motoneuron pool some specific property of which, obtained from the properties of the individuals, can be compared with the same property as evidenced by a 'natural' pool of motoneurons. Examples are given as is an example of the utility of the procedure in securing information unobtainable from study of a natural pool.

REFERENCES

1. BESWICK, F. F. and EVANSON, J. M., *J. Physiol.* **135**, 400 (1957).
2. ECCLES, J. C., *J. Neurophysiol.* **9**, 87 (1946).
3. EYZAGUIRRE, C. and KUFFLER, S. W., *J. Gen. Physiol.* **39**, 87 (1955).
4. —— *ibid.* **39**, 121 (1955).
5. FATT, P. and KATZ, B., *J. Physiol.* **115**, 320 (1951).
6. HUNT, C. C., *J. Gen. Physiol.* **38**, 117 (1954).
7. —— *ibid.* **38**, 801 (1955).
8. —— *ibid.* **38**, 813 (1955).
9. HUNT, C. C. and KUFFLER, S. W., *J. Physiol.* **113**, 298 (1951).
10. HURSH, J. B., *Am. J. Physiol.* **127**, 131 (1939).
11. JEFFERSON, A. A. and SCHLAPP, W., *in* The Spinal Cord. A Ciba Foundation Symposium. P. 99. G. E. W. WOLSTENHOLME, editor. Boston, Little, Brown and Company, 1953.
12. KUFFLER, S. W. and EYZAGUIRRE, C., *J. Gen. Physiol.* **39**, 155 (1955).
13. LLOYD, D. P. C., *J. Neurophysiol.* **6**, 293 (1943).
14. —— *ibid.* **9**, 421 (1946).
15. —— *J. Gen. Physiol.* **33**, 147 (1949).
16. —— *ibid.* **40**, 435 (1957).
17. LLOYD, D. P. C. and CHANG, H. T., *J. Neurophysiol.* **11**, 199 (1948).
18. LLOYD, D. P. C., HUNT, C. C. and McINTYRE, A. K., *J. Gen. Physiol.* **38**, 307 (1955).
19. LLOYD, D. P. C. and McINTYRE, A. K., *ibid.* **38**, 771 (1955).
20. —— *ibid.* **38**, 789 (1955).
21. LLOYD, D. P. C. and WILSON, V. J., *ibid.* **40**, 409 (1957).
22. RALL, W. and HUNT, C. C., *ibid.* **39**, 397 (1956).

COMPONENT ANALYSIS OF ACTION POTENTIALS
FROM SINGLE NEURONS[1]

G. SVAETICHIN

Department of Neurophysiology, Venezuelan Institute of Neurology and Brain Research (IVNIC), Caracas, Venezuela, and the Department of Physiology, Karolinska Institutet, Stockholm, Sweden

IN connection with extra- and intracellular recordings from vertebrate neurons of the central nervous system it has not yet been possible to determine accurately the recording position of the microelectrode in relation to the active cell. Hence, the conclusions concerning the origin of the action potential and its different components are based on indirect evidence, as is also stated by Eccles ([12], pp. 5, 6, 49): "When inserting a microelectrode, by far the largest target is presented by the soma and the adjacent large dendritic branches. In all but a few exceptional experiments we may, therefore, assume that the microelectrode is implanted therein. ... Furthermore, in analogy with muscle fibres and giant axons, it is probable that the intracellularly recorded electric potentials arise across the surface membrane of a nerve cell. ... This identification of the origin of the IS spike has been based on the likelihood of a block in antidromic transmission at the axon hillock, where there is a large expansion in the surface membrane to be invaded." In order to point out the uncertainty of the conclusions regarding the origin of the action potential components, it can be mentioned that Fatt [15, 16], who worked in Eccles' laboratory reached the conclusion that the prepotential seen on the intra- or extracellularly recorded action potentials of anti- or orthodromically activated motoneurons originates in the cell body, and the subsequent larger response in the dendrites, while Eccles himself [12] is of the opinion that these components (IS and SD) originate in the non-myelinated segment and the cell body plus dendrites respectively.

Svaetichin [35] described experiments in which the perikaryon membrane of a spinal ganglion cell (frog, cat) was punctured with a microelectrode

---

[1] The main result of the present study were presented at the Scandinavian Physiological Congress in Helsingfors 1954 and were also discussed at the International Physiology Congress in Brussels 1956.

(less 1 μ) under simultaneous microscopic inspection. A resting potential of 50–90 mV and a (depolarization) action potential, of about the same size, was obtained. This observation was concluded to represent direct evidence that the perikaryon membrane participates in the impulse activity. At that time (not reported) a prepotential also was observed and the blocking between it and the subsequent larger component. The blocking was commonly seen shortly after a puncturing with a large electrode. It appeared reasonable to believe that the prepotentials seen in both extra- and intracellular recordings had the same origin. Later, comparative studies were made between the extra- and intracellular recordings, and these studies are reported in this paper.

Since it is considered valuable to make analogies between recordings from invertebrate giant nerve cells and myelinated vertebrate neurons, I think it might be even more reasonable to generalize the observations obtained on vertebrate spinal ganglion cells and try to apply this information when interpreting, for instance, the components of extra- and intracellular action potentials obtained from neurons of the central nervous system.

The dorsal root ganglion cell does not possess dendrites like the motoneuron, whereas the anatomical structure and the relative dimensions of the myelinated axon (M), the initial non-myelinated segment (I) and the perikaryon (P) are very similar for both types of neurons. Thus, when a motoneuron is antidromically stimulated or a dorsal root ganglion cell is activated from its peripheral axon, the course of the impulse conduction towards the cell body would be expected to be more or less identical. Any differences possibly found in the configuration of the action potentials, recorded from the two different types of neurons, would then be caused by the absence of a "dendritic component" in the recording from the dorsal root ganglion cells.

In experiments on dorsal root ganglion cells it was possible to make recordings during simultaneous microscopic inspection, making the neurons visible by vital staining. It was also possible to activate one cell only by stimulating its peripheral sensory ending. Working with neurons, having their cell bodies situated at the exposed surface of the dorsal root ganglion, the location of the recording electrode could be determined in relation to the perikaryon and the axon. In the spinal ganglion of frog, the axon generally leaves the perikaryon at the pole opposite to the surface of the ganglion; in the few exceptional cases where the axon hillock was directed towards the surface of the ganglion, the axon hillock and the initial segment could be detected after staining with methylene blue.

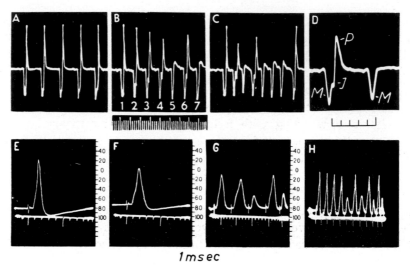

Fig. 1.

ORIGIN OF COMPONENTS OF THE ACTION POTENTIAL

The responses recorded by intra- and extracellular electrodes from single spinal ganglion cells were generally obtained with the electrode tip situated at the perikaryon pole opposite to the axon hillock. Extracellular recordings of this type are seen in the upper row of Fig. 1 (*A–D*, negativity upwards, from Svaetichin [35]), whereas the records below (*E–H*) were intracellularly obtained by puncturing the perikaryon pole opposite to the axon hillock. The records are similar to those obtained by Crain [10] from cultured spinal ganglion cells. As appears from Fig. 1, repetitive stimulation splits the action potential into sub-components. It was shown [35] that the M-deflection could follow stimulus frequencies maximal for myelinated frog fibres, whereas the I- and P-components were blocked. A corresponding block between the M-component and the I–P complex could be created by exerting pressure by the electrode against the cell body (Fig. 2) and by all other means which lowered the membrane potential of the perikaryon. The records in Fig. 2 are from an experiment in which a block was caused by local pressure with the microelectrode against the perikaryon (*A–F*), and where the response again was rebuilt when the pressure was released (*G–M*). By a light pressure against the perikaryon was it also possible to stimulate the neuron and the evoked discharges which often were repetitive showed the usual configuration starting with the M-component. According to the interpretation given [35]

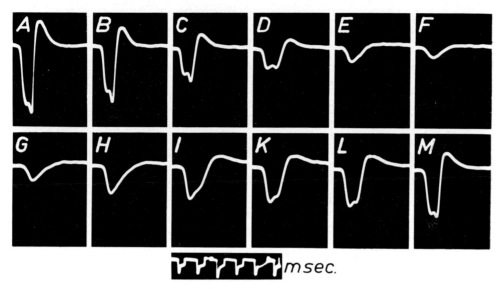

Fig. 2.

the components labelled M, I and P (Fig. 1*D*) originate from different parts of the neuron: component M from the myelinated axon, component I from the initial non-myelinated segment, and component P from the perikaryon proper. The intracellular recordings shown in Fig. 1*E–H* are very similar to the records obtained by antidromic stimulation of motoneurons [5, 6, 41, 11, 12, 13, 14, 3, 2, 17, 18].

Araki and Otani [2] reached the conclusion that the prepotential (the IS spike, [12]), seen on the action potential obtained by intracellular recording from anti- or orthodromically activated motoneurons, originates in the initial non-myelinated segment, which is also the view of Fuortes, Frank and Becker [18] and Eccles [12]. Further, according to the above mentioned authors the subsequent larger component (SD spike [12]) of the potential would be generated by the soma plus dendrites. However, according to Fatt [15, 16] the prepotential seen in intra- and extracellular recordings from motoneurons would be produced by the soma and the subsequent larger potential by the dendrites. As appears from the extracellular records in Fig. 1*A–D*, the M-component follows the repetive stimuli well, whereas the I- and P-components fail at frequencies above 100 c/sec. (frog).

In the course of intermittent stimulation the prepotential of the intracellular recordings (Fig. 1*G–H*) behaves in a similar way as the M-component of the responses obtained by extracellular electrodes. According to my earlier

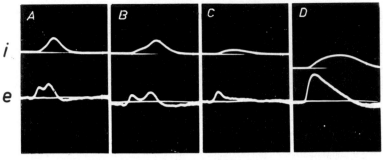

Fig. 3.

interpretation [35] the M-component originates in the myelinated part of the axon.

In the case of extracellular recordings, potentials caused by current flow are measured, whereas, when puncturing a neuron by a microelectrode we are registering the potential across the plasma membrane. Fig. 3 shows recordings from a perikaryon of a dorsal root ganglion cell simultaneously obtained by extra- and intracellular electrodes, in the course of a block developing due to the injury caused by the intracellular electrode. Notice that positivity is upwards in the extracellular recordings in Fig. 3*e*. Recording 3*D*, showing the M-component only, was afterwards registered using higher amplification. It appears also from this experiment that the potentials left over after blocking are the intracellular prepotential (Fig. 3*i*, *C–D*) and the extracellular M-deflection (Fig. 2*e*, *C–D*). Thus, it is obvious that the prepotentials seen in the intra- and extracellular recordings are of the same origin.

In order to illustrate the relation between the courses of the action potentials obtained by intra- and extracellular registrations, subsequently obtained responses from the same perikaryon have photographically been superimposed in Fig. 4. In the recordings shown at the top of this figure, the two intracellular recordings (*i*) have their positive deflections upwards, whereas the extracellular recordings (*e*) have the positive phase upwards at the left and at the right the positive phase downwards. The scale in mV is for the intracellular recording; the amplitude of the extracellular record is about 4 mV. Resting potential 80 mV, overshoot 20 mV. At the bottom of the figure a micrograph of a dorsal root ganglion cell is seen, on which the electrodes for intra- and extracellular recordings have been indicated. It is interesting to notice the similarity between the intra- and extracellular recordings in Fig. 4 and the intracellular responses from a motoneuron and the corresponding electrically differentiated records obtained by Fatt [16]

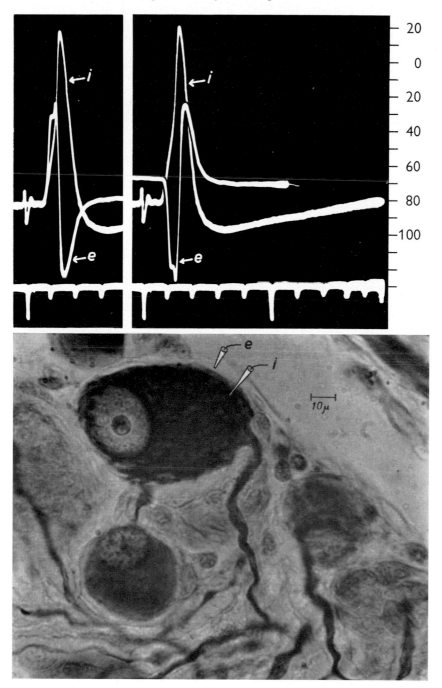

Fig. 4.

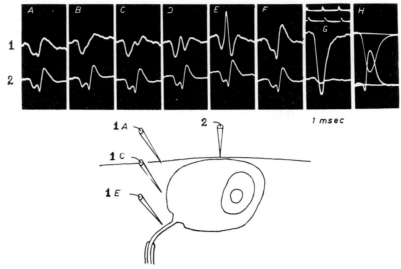

Fig. 5.

The records shown in Fig. 5 are from an experiment in which one extra-cellular electrode, No. 2 (Fig. 5), permanently recorded the activity from the pole opposite to the axon hillock, while another extracellular electrode, No. 1, was inserted into the ganglion. The recordings *A–G* in the upper row (1) were obtained with the electrode No. 1, whereas in the row below (2) the simultaneous recordings *A–G* are shown registered with electrode No. 2. In all recordings negativity is upwards. When the electrode No. 1 was introduced into the ganglion, close to the cell body which was the only one activated in this region of the ganglion (and further the surrounding cells were killed by puncturing them with the electrode), there was no change in the configuration of the recorded potential, except when the electrode was inserted at one certain location which proved to correspond to the region where the axon of the cell was running. In row 1 the subsequently obtained responses are shown when the electrode No. 1 advanced towards the intial segment of the axon. The depth of electrode tip 1*A*, 1*C* and 1*E* is approximately indicated by the letters corresponding to the recordings *A*, *C* and *E* in row 1. The responses at *F* were taken when the electrode was withdrawn to the surface, whereas the records at *G* were obtained when the electrode was inserted anew, the initial segment of the axon now being punctured. The record 1*G* shows the large positive injury potential, and as appears from record 2*G* only the M-component was then more obtainable by recording from the perikaryon pole opposite to the axon hillock with the electrode No. 2.

The record $1E$ was obtained with the tip of the electrode close against the initial non-myelinated segment of the axon. The sequence of the phases of this action potential (positive–negative–positive) shows that the impulse arrives and passes the region close to the tip of the electrode, the negativity corresponding to the depolarization of the initial segment adjacent to the electrode. Comparing the recordings E, 1 and 2 with each other, it appears that the negative phase in the upper record $1E$ corresponds in time with the I-component of the recording which was obtained by the electrode No. 2 placed on the perikaryon pole opposite to the axon hillock. (Notice, on the time scales in Fig. $5G$ the lack of parallelism of the two beams of the oscilloscope tube used.) This finding is in full agreement with the interpretation given [35] that the I-component originates in the initial non-myelinated axon. Further, the recordings in Fig. $5E$ prove that the M-component which corresponds in time to the first positive phase of recording $1E$ in fact arises in more peripheral parts of the axon, possibly in the myelinated axon or the junctional region between the myelinated axon and the intitial segment, and that the P-component (corresponding in time with second positive phase of the recording $1E$) is generated by the perikaryon itself.

Fig. $5H$ shows responses registered from another cell, in which the axon was seen to leave the cell body close to the surface of the ganglion. The I–P complex of the response of this cell was abolished, leaving only the M-component. In the upper record in Fig. $5H$ the M-component is shown recorded with an electrode from the perikaryon proper, whereas the record below was simultaneously obtained with an electrode close to the myelinated axon which after staining was seen in the microscope. The amplification in the recording from the perikaryon is twice that of the recording from the axon. The arrival of the impulse is indicated by the first positive deflection of the record below. It could be suggested that the I-component originates, for instance, in the parts of the perikaryon membrane close to the axon hillock. However, the configuration of the action potential would then undergo changes similar to the ones described in Fig. 5, $1B$–$1E$, independently of where the electrode is inserted into the ganglion close to the active cell body. But this is not the case, as the changes of the action potential were observed only when the electrode was inserted at a definite location where the axon was running. When the electrode was advanced further down at that definite location the initial segment of the axon was hit by the electrode tip (less 1 μ) and a block of the I–P complex was created (Fig. $5G$). Thus, the experiments described above directly prove the correctness of the interpretation given of the origin of the components.

When the microelectrode was inserted into the ganglion a little further away (than in the experiment described in Fig. 5) from the perikaryon in the region where the axon was running, it was sometimes possible to obtain a response showing a configuration similar to the type recorded from the perikaryon pole opposite to the axon hillock (Fig. 5A), but having a reversed polarity. In that case the electrode apparently was situated rather close to both the M- and I-membranes recording the M- and I-components with a negative polarity, while the perikaryon being further away caused a positive P-deflection.

TEMPERATURE BLOCK

It is known that impulse conduction in a peripheral nerve still continues when the temperature is lowered to zero and even below that for a short period of time (e.g. Garten and Schulze, 1913). The recordings in Fig. 6 illustrate this fact and are taken from an experiment in which the monophasic action potential of a frog sciatic nerve was recorded at different temperatures. The amplification was kept constant in the course of the experiment, whereas, the sweep velocity was adjusted in order to keep the length of the action

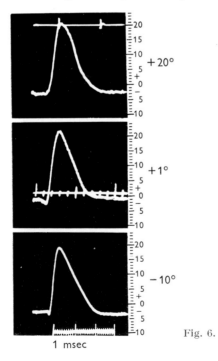

1 msec

Fig. 6.

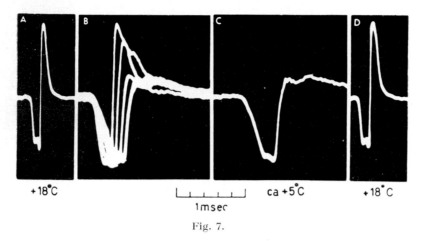

+18°C   ca +5°C   +18°C

1msec

Fig. 7.

potential on the oscilloscope screen approximately unchanged when the duration of the response increased at lower temperatures. The temperature at the
place of the recording was measured with a microtermocouple connected
to a second D.C. amplifier, the temperature being indicated by the level of
the other beam in respect to the simultaneously photographed temperature
scale to the right. This same trace also gives the time in milliseconds. No
major changes in the amplitude or the shape of the action potential occurred
when the nerve for a short period was supercooled to $-10°$, although the
duration of the response was about 20 $\times$ longer at $-10°$ than at $+20°$.

However, the conduction in the perikaryon membrane of the (frog)
spinal ganglion cell is blocked already at $+5°$. Fig. 7 is taken from my
earlier paper [35], and illustrates how such a block in a spinal ganglion cell
was created by means of lowering the temperature from $+18°$ to about $+5°$.
In 7B superimposed sweep tracings of the action potentials are shown,
which were recorded during a period of lowering the temperature. In these
experiments the spinal ganglion was cooled from below, from the side where
the axon emerged from the cell body. Hence it could be assumed that during
the cooling the cell body always had a somewhat higher temperature than
the axonal parts. From the extracellular recordings of the action potential it
appeared that the P-component selectively and reversibly (7D) was blocked
by lowering the temperature to about $+5°$.

Because of the spherical shape of the perikaryon it can be assumed that
the electrical resistance across the interior of the cell from the axon hillock
region to any part of the surface membrane is about equal and comparatively
low. If the propagation in the perikaryon occurs by the aid of local circuits

(like in the axon) it would be expected that all parts of the perikaryon membrane almost simultaneously are depolarized, and that hence the P-component would have the shape of a non-propagated impulse. If the internal resistance is low, then the space constant of the impulse is long, and the propagation fast. Actually, this appears to be the case as was pointed out earlier (1951) [35], and the extracellular negative P-component is considered a recording of the almost instantaneous depolarization of the total perikaryon membrane. In this connection it is worth mentioning some experiments (not reported in 1951) in which recordings were made by the aid of two extracellular electrodes in contact with two asymetrical points on the same perikaryon. Although the recording conditions were optimal (dry surface) and the responses obtained with each electrode separately were of high amplitude (10 mV), no conducted activity along the surface of the perikaryon membrane was detectable if the recording was made differentially between the two electrodes. It was earlier reported [35] that the P-component, before it was completely blocked by lowering the temperature, became diphasic showing a first positive deflection. This positive phase of the P-component was interpreted as indicating activity of the perikaryon membrane near the axon hillock, when the propagation over the cell body was slowed down. (A similar effect was also observed in blocking experiments with cathodal polarization, described below, Fig. 8M.) There is not much reason to believe that when the P-component is blocked, the location of the block would be, say at the equatorial region of the perikaryon membrane, which would mean that the other half sphere of the perikaryon would depolarize and the other one not. Already from this reasoning we can exclude that the I-component could originate in the perikaryon. Thus the only possibility left is to conclude that the temperature block of the P-component occurs at the axon-soma junction, and in this case we possibly can blame the block on the large expansion of the surface membrane to be invaded by the impulse.

According to the view held by Lorente de Nó [29, 30] the conduction in the cell body is particularly slow. In a discussion concerning this matter, he writes ([30], p. 174): "If an invasion is instantaneous, then there is no time delay during invasion; consequently you could not record any spike. The spike is recorded because there is propagation; otherwise there would be no external flow of current."

In recordings with the electrode situated on the perikaryon pole opposite to the axon hillock, the relation (see [26]) between the amplitudes of the negative P-component and the positive I-deflection (P:I relation) was shown to be constant for one and the same cell, independent of the location of the electrode on the surface of the ganglion [35]. This was observed to hold true also when the electrode was inserted into the ganglion close to the perikaryon except in the neighborhood of the region where the axon was running. This P:I relation proved to be astonishingly constant and changed only for a short period when the resting potential across certain parts of the neuronal membranes had been experimentally influenced (for instance by electrical polarization, Fig. 8). On the other hand, large differences in the P:I relation were observed in recordings from different cells. Systematical studies were not done on the P:I relation, but it was noticed that the very large cells which were connected to skin sensory endings showed a comparatively small P-component (the responses from a 90 μ diam. cell body had a P:I $=1:5$ as seen in recording Fig. 3A [35]), and a block was easily created by repetitive stimulation at a comparatively low frequency, while the medium sized cell bodies belonging to muscle receptors regularly showed a P:I relation of about $1:1$ and the block occurred at a higher rate of stimuli. These observations indicate that the P:I relation possibly could depend on the relative dimensions of the perikaryon and the axon, and on some differences in the membrane properties.

If we now assume that the perikaryon is gradually invaded and in consequence thereof that the I- and P-components both originate in the cell body, it would be hard to understand why the I-component in recordings from some types of cells is several times larger than the P-component. In any case the negative P-component must be considered representing the depolarization of the membrane parts adjacent to the electrode, and hence the P-component would be expected to have an amplitude larger than the other components.

The experiments presented above (e.g. in Fig. 5) evidently show that the I-component originates in the initial segment of the axon, and since the P-component is not diphasic but has a monophasic shape like a non-propagated impulse, we are forced to conclude that the total membrane of the perikaryon is depolarized almost simultaneously. Apparently it is possible to record the extracellular P-component due to external current flow between the totally depolarized perikaryon and the axonal membranes. When the perikaryon is depolarized the much smaller axonal membranes are heavily loaded (Fig. 5, 1E) whereas, when the M–I structures depolarize current is drawn from the large perikaryon membrane (Fig. 5, 2E). It appears reasonable to suggest that the P:I relation is determined by the relative dimensions of the perikaryon and the axon and that this relation additionally is influenced by different (e.g. impedance) properties of the I- and P-membranes.

On the basis of the experiments described, it is difficult to determine the location of the M-membrane more accurately than to define it as an axonal structure peripheral to the I-membrane. The M-membrane possibly corresponds to the junctional region between the initial non-myelinated segment and the myelinated axon, a point which functionally might correspond to a "node" possessing a highly excitable membrane. (Notice, the constricted region of the initial segment [8].) Sometimes a deflection with a smaller amplitude than the M-component was isolated [35] which could be supposed to originate in the adjacent node of Ranvier and which deflection possibly corresponds to the diminutive M-component of Eccles [11, 14] which he observed in recordings from antidromically activated motoneurons. The I- and P-components are difficult to block separately (low temperature or weak cathodal polarization of the perikaryon, see below), and being of the same polarity by intracellular recording and in time close together, they are not easily distinguishable from each other in responses obtained intracellularly. The most common and easy type of block to create (at least in spinal ganglion cells), occurs between the M- and I-segment (repetitive stimulation, reduced resting potential across the perikaryon membrane due to, for instance, pressure with the electrode against the cell). The localization of this type of block to the junction between the myelinated and non-myelinated segments is in agreement with the view held by Lorente de Nó [29, 30] concerning antidromic block in motoneurons, and with the interpretation given by myself [35]. This differs, however, from the opinions of Lloyd [28], Eccles [12], Araki and Otani [2] and Frank and Fuortes [17], according to whom the block occurs at the axon-soma junction. Fatt [15, 16] believes that this block occurs at the junction between the cell body and the dendrites.

ELECTRICAL POLARIZATION

By the use of a weak D.C. polarization, applied through a microelectrode in contact with the perikaryon from which the action potential simultaneously was recorded, it was possible to produce a block of different components, depending on the polarity of the current used. The conditions for polarization and recording are shown at the bottom of Fig. 8. The action potentials (negativity upwards) recorded with an extracellular electrode were initiated by electrical stimulation of the peripheral axon or the sensory ending. The record in Fig. 8A was obtained previous to the application of an anodal polarization, and the records B–G represent subsequent recordings obtained during a weak anodal polarization. As appears from B–G the anodal polarization caused a block of the I–P complex, and finally in record G only the

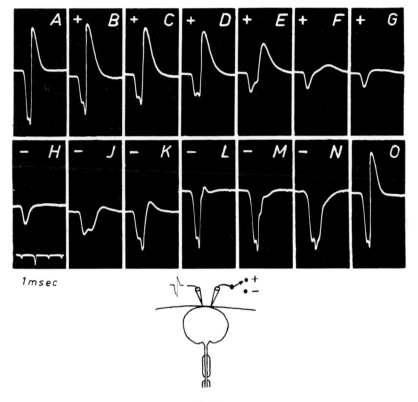

Fig. 8.

M-component remained (cf. Fig. 2). However, as seen in record *B* the first effect of the anodal polarization was an increase of the amplitude of the P-component and a decrease of the M–I deflections. The records *H–N* are subsequent recordings made in the course of a weak cathodal polarization, which was immediately applied after the record *G* was obtained. As seen in *H–N*, cathodal polarization rebuilt the action potential with the exception of the P-component, which proved to be selectively blocked as long as the cathodal current remained on. Notice, that the M- and I-components show a higher amplitude in the responses *M, N* than in the first recording *A*. Record *O* was obtained immediately after releasing the cathodal polarization, the action potential now showing the same configuration as in recording *A*, and displaying a P-component.

On the basis of the interpretation presented above of the origin of the action potential components, an explanation easily is given of the findings obtained in the electrical polarization experiments. The immediate effect after the application of the anodal polarization was an increase of the amplitude of the P-component and a reduction of the M- and I-components (cf. A and B, Fig. 8), apparently due to hyperpolarization of the perikaryon membrane and depolarization of the axonal membranes. Large transient differences in the P:I relation were also described (1951) in connection with repetitive stimulation experiments (see Fig. 1A–C). Such differences must depend on changes of the resting potentials across the corresponding membranes. The internal electrical resistance between any two parts of the perikaryon membrane is low, and hence it is improbable that any larger resting potential differences can exist across two different parts of the same perikaryon membrane. Thus, only the P-component but not the I-component can originate in the perikaryon.

The cathodal polarization recharged the axonal membranes resulting in a hypernormal amplitude of the M- and I-components (Fig. 8I–N). During cathodal polarization inward currents were produced through the perikaryon membranes close to the axon hillock, preventing the conduction spreading from the initial segment into the cell body. Due to the higher resistance of the axon cylinder the density of the inward currents through the initial segment were not large enough to cause inhibition there. If we assume that the cell body is gradually invaded and in consequence thereof that the I- and P-components both originate in the perikaryon, then a positive I-component seen in course of the cathodal polarization would necessarily be followed by a negative P-component originating in the perikaryon pole under the polarizing cathode, since there we have outward currents and no inhibitory effect would be expected. Thus, also the cathodal polarization experiments show that the I-component cannot originate in the perikaryon membrane.

ELECTRICAL STIMULATION

In a series of experiments the spinal ganglion cells were electrically stimulated by a rectangular pulse of current applied through an electrode in contact with the perikaryon pole opposite to the axon hillock. The records in Fig. 9A–D were obtained at a low amplification; the scale is in mV and positivity is recorded upwards. When an anodal pulse was applied, the response started at "on" of the stimulus (9B–C) and at a low stimulus strength, whereas, the cathodal pulse was unsuccessful (9D) or the response appeared at "off" when a stronger stimulus was used. The recordings in 9E were obtained when a cathodal stimulus was used, the neuron responding at "off" of the

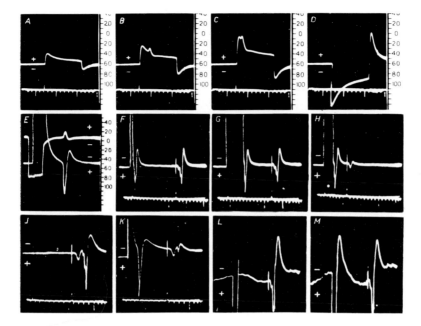

Fig. 9.

stimulus. Both responses seen in 9*E* were registered through the same electrode, a higher amplification being used in the recording with the positive
phase downwards.

In another series of experiments the spinal ganglion cells were, subsequently to each pulse of stimulus, additionally activated from its sensory
axon in order to show the refractory phenomenon (9*F–M*). In the records
F–K the rectangular pulse was cathodal, the response always appearing at
"off" of the stimulus. In the records *L–M* an anodal pulse was used, and the
response came at "on" of the stimulus, in record 7*L* the stimulus being
subthreshold.

The experiments described above show, that when an electrical stimulus
was applied to the perikaryon pole opposite to the axon hillock the action
potential initiated with a prepotential M, the impulse starting at a lower
threshold and at "on" of an anodal stimulus, while response started at "off"
and showed a higher threshold when a cathodal stimulation was used
[36, 37].

Under these experimental conditions it was possible accurately to determine
the positions of the recording and stimulating electrodes in respect to the

neuron. Such particular excitability characteristics seem to be general for vertebrate neurons, since Araki and Otani [2], Fuortes, Frank and Becker [18], and Eccles [12] assumed from experiments on motoneurons, which were directly stimulated through an internal electrode (probably situated in the perikaryon), that the prepotential (NM) of the responses originated in the initial non-myelinated segment of the axon, and that the threshold of the soma membrane was higher than that of the initial non-myelinated segment of the axon.

The perikaryon can be considered a sphere, and since then the internal electrical resistance between any two parts of the membrane is low, it will be difficult by electrical fields of current to produce a large potential difference between two parts of the perikaryon membrane. The same reasoning concerns also the part of the initial non-myelinated axon, which is connected by a low resistance to the interior of the cell body. Efforts by electrical stimulation locally to reduce the resting potential across some part of the perikaryon or the adjacent initial segment will be successfully counteracted by the EMF of the other parts of the membrane. When, for instance, an external stimulating electrode on the perikaryon hyperpolarizes the one half sphere and depolarizes the other one, a considerable strength of current is needed in order to produce a large potential drop across the low resistance interior of the cell body and the adjacent parts of the initial segment, while it is possibly easier to produce a sufficient potential change for initiating a response in the M-region of the axon (see Fig. 14). Notice in this connection, the constriction of the peripheral part of the initial segment [8]. On the basis of such a reasoning the particular electrical excitability characteristics described above, possibly can be explained to depend on geometrical conditions, and then it would be unnecessary to suggest that the membrane properties of the perikaryon and the initial segment fundamentally differs from that of the myelinated axon. However, it cannot be excluded that the M-membrane in addition actually has a lower threshold than the I- and P-membrane.

When an impulse proceeds antidromically towards the cell body, the conditions are somewhat different, since then a wave of membrane breakdown already exists representing a load on the membranes in front of it, and the cell body can possibly easier be invaded. Several of the experiments described above indicate that the conduction into the perikaryon is instantaneous which favors a propagation by the aid of local circuits, for which an electrically excitable membrane is required, while a graded invasion would favor a purely chemical wave of propagation.

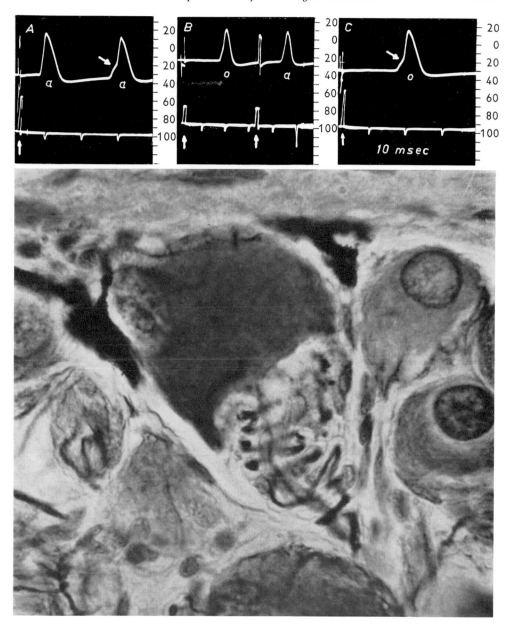

Fig. 10.

SYMPATHETIC GANGLION CELLS

The electrical activity of single neurons of sympathetic vertebral and collateral ganglia of frog was studied by the aid of intracellular microelectrodes. The ganglia are covered by two layers of tough connective tissue sheet, and in order to avoid breaking the electrode tip it was necessary to expose the perikaryon well before inserting the electrode under simultaneous microscopic vision. Isolated ganglia could be kept in Ringer's solution for a considerable time without any obvious deleterious effect. However, after removing the sheets the action potentials diminished rather soon, being abolished in about 20–30 minutes. The sympathetic ganglion cells of frog do not possess dendrites, the synapse probably consisting of a spiral winding of the presynaptic fiber around the initial segment of the axon (see Fig. 10). The largest cells had a diameter of about 40–50 μ.

Typical recordings from sympathetic ganglion cells of frog are shown in Figs. 10 and 11, and they were obtained with a microelectrode inserted into the perikaryon pole opposite to the axon hillock. The scale is in mV and the time is given in 10 msec. The resting potential vas found to be maximally about 60–70 mV, the overshoot 10–15 mV. The action potential showed the same configuration whether evoked anti- or orthodromically ("a" or "o" in the figures). The latency of the orthodromically evoked response was always about 5–10 msec. longer than that of the antidromic one. A single anti- or orthodromic shock often resulted in multiple discharges (Fig. 11). The responses showed a prepotential similar to the one described in recordings from, for instance, motoneurons and spinal ganglion cells. In the course of repetititve stimulation a block easily developed between the prepotential and the subsequent larger component. When the resting potential across the perikaryon membrane was sufficiently reduced, the prepotential solely appeared (Fig. 11C, F). This prepotential was evoked in the same "all or none" fashion by anti- or orthodromic stimulation. In none of the recordings obtained from orthodromically activated neurons was it possible to detect a graded potential component prior to the prepotential described above, which would correspond to the postsynaptic potential (EPSP of Eccles) seen in the recordings from motoneurons and mammalian sympathetic ganglion cells [14].

In analogy with the interpretation given of the components of the intracellular action potential obtained from a spinal ganglion cell, the prepotential seen in the antidromically evoked response of the sympathetic ganglion cell would originate in parts of the axon some distance away from the perikaryon,

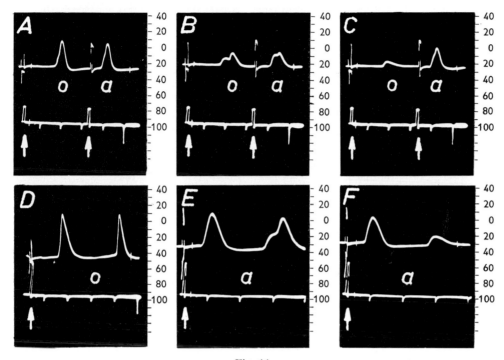

Fig. 11.

whereas, the subsequent larger response would originate in the initial segment (I) of the axon close to the perikaryon and the perikaryon itself (P). The prepotential may still be nominated M, although the neuron is non-myelinated. The prepotentials seen in the anti- or orthodromic responses behaved in identical ways and had the same shape and amplitude, the only difference being that the orthodromic prepotential had a longer latency due to the synaptic delay. This favors the view that both prepotentials have the same origin; the M-segment. Anatomically this type of neuron seems to have only one synaptic contact, the axon-axon synapse. Hence, it seems reasonable to suggest that the M-component of the orthodromic response originates in the part of the axon which is surrounded by the spiral axon, and that the prepotential of the orthodromically evoked response represents the post-synaptic potential. The length of the postsynaptic axon around which the spiral fiber is wound corresponds to a little more than one perikaryon diameter and the M-component probably starts in the peripheral region of that part. The "all or none" behavior of this postsynaptic potential is well compatible with the existence of only one synaptic contact on each

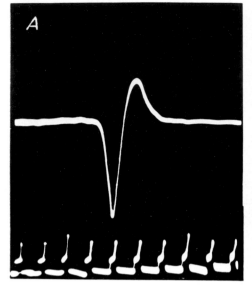 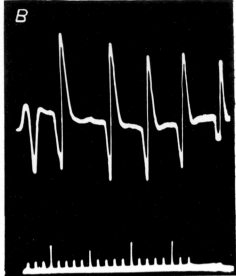

1 msec

Fig. 12.

ganglion cell. Since, then, there is no possibility of gradually changing the synaptic inflow; either one presynaptic impulse arrives or none. In the case of an excitatory synaptic action for instance on a motoneuron, a chemical transmitter substance is assumed to be liberated; the summated effect of several synaptic endings gradually reducing the membrane potential of the dendrites and the perikaryon (Eccles EPSP). This will cause outward current flow through the I- and M-membranes, and if the summated effect is large enough, an impulse is initiated in the M-membrane. In such a case the graded EPSP apparently originates in the dendrites and the perikaryon. The sympathetic (frog) ganglion cell, which only seems to have one synaptic connection located at the M-membrane, has no graded EPSP, since the M-component and the EPSP both represent the "all or none" response of the same M-membrane. The multiple response often seen might be caused by the liberation of a transmitter substance around the M-segment, not only in connection with ortho- but also with the antidromic response; the axon-axon synapse possibly conducts in both directions. Extracellular recordings from single sympathetic ganglion cells were not obtained but would be of interest (see [39]).

In this connection some observations done when studying spinal ganglion cells are worth mentioning. The extracellular action potential recorded from the smallest dorsal root ganglion cells (Fig. 12*A*) did not show the M-component, and it was believed [35] that this could be explained on the basis that these small neurons did belong to non-myelinated axons. This does not seem to be a true explanation, since responses of the non-myelinated sympathetic neurons apparently possess this M-component. Further, in a few experiments performed with the spinal ganglion, veratrine was applied on the exposed surface of the ganglion cells. In that case a single stimulus to some of the neurons caused a repetitive discharge. However, curiously enough, in that firing only the I- and P-components took part. In Fig. 12*B* the first action potential is a M-deflection alone, the second one displays the M–I–P complex, whereas the subsequent four responses only show the I- and P-components. This observation favors a view that some chemical activator is liberated around the I-segment in connection with the "antidromic" propagation of the impulse in the dorsal root ganglion cell.

GENERAL DISCUSSION

A few distinct types of action potentials obtained by extracellular micro-electrode recording from single central nervous neurons have been described: (1) monophasic spikes, negative or positive, (2) diphasic spikes, initially negative or positive, and (3) triphasic spikes, positive–negative–positive. On the rising phase of the diphasic responses often a notch has been observed, in the initially positive responses this seems to be a constant finding. The diphasic initially negative responses generally have an amplitude of maximally a few hundred μV, whereas the initially positive spikes can have amplitudes up to several mV. The elements from which these responses are recorded have not been identified with certainty, since it has not been possible accurately to determine the electrode tip in respect to the nerve cell. The large diphasic spikes have been assumed to originate in the cell bodies. Corresponding types of action potentials have been described, for instance, by: Lloyd [27], Renshaw [32], Kuffler [25], Lorente de Nó [29, 30], Amassian [1], Jung [24], Buser and Albe-Fessard [7], Rose and Mountcastle [23], Tasaki, Polley and Orrego [38], Li [26], Cohen, Landgren, Ström and Zotterman [9], Fatt [15, 16], and Mountcastle, Davies and Berman [31].

Extra- and intracellular recordings of the action potentials from single vertebrate neurons are presented in Fig. 13 in order to show the striking similarity between the anti- or orthodromically evoked responses from different types of nerve cells. The response in 13*A* was recorded with an extra-

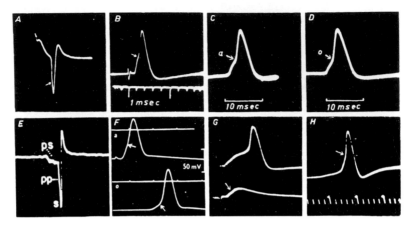

Fig. 13.

cellular electrode from a spinal ganglion cell (frog), which was stimulated by a cathodal pulse of current applied to the perikaryon. The response started at "off" of the stimulus with a M-component, the notch being indicated by an arrow. The record *E* below was obtained with an external electrode from a synaptically activated neuron of the tactile thalmic region of cat (from Rose and Mountcastle [33]). Both responses (*A* and *E*) display the M-, I- and P-components, but additionally the synaptically evoked action potential *E* shows a component (indicated "ps") which was assumed by Rose and Mountcastle to be of presynaptic origin; a part of it might represent an extracellular recording of the EPSP. In the course of repetitive stimulation a block developed between the M-component (indicated "pp") and the subsequent larger response, which is exactly in agreement with the findings on the spinal ganglion cells. Rose and Mountcastle pointed out that the prepotential (M) was constantly observed in every one of a large number of recordings obtained. The large positive component (indicated "s") obviously corresponds to the I-component, the negative component representing the almost instantaneous depolarization of the perikaryon membrane. In analogy with the observations on extracellular action potentials from spinal ganglion cells the response (*E*) of a thalamic neuron (Fig. 13*E*) is interpreted being extracellularly recorded with the microelectrode in contact with the peri-karyon (but not the region adjacent to the axon hillock). The scheme in Fig. 14 has been drawn on the basis of the experiments on spinal ganglion cells (cf. Fig. 5) and *B–D* represents different types of action potentials obtained with an extracellular electrode in different recording positions in respect to the active neuron. The responses *B–D* correspond well to the types of extracellular action potentials described in extracellular recordings from central nervous neurons, and it is suggested that at least a part of them can be interpreted on this basis. The EPSP has not been considered in Fig. 14, the responses merely corresponding to antidromic ones.

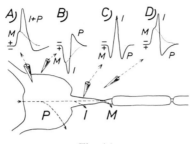

Fig. 14.

The extracellular recordings from individual retinal ganglion cells [21, 40, 20] are of interest in this connection, since the neurons of the ganglion cell layer are regularly oriented with the dendrite towards, the bipolar cells and the axon hillock towards the internal limiting membrane, which makes it possible to determine the position of the electrode tip in respect to the neuron. In most of the recordings the electrode has been situated against the internal limiting membrane, the tip being close to the M- and I-segments of the axon (see the drawing to the left in Fig. 15). According to Gernandt [19], Rushton [34], Kuffler [25] and Barlow [4], the largest and most common type of response recorded from the ganglion cell layer is a diphasic initially negative spike similar to the ones seen to the right in Fig. 15 (reproduced from Kuffler [25], cat retina). The recording conditions for the retinal spikes correspond to those for the response in Fig. 14*D*; hence the retinal spikes are diphasic, initially negative as expected. The components according to the interpretation have been indicated on the drawings to the left in Fig. 15. When synaptically activated a postsynaptic potential (PS) is expected to precede the responses. In the recordings of Kuffler (reproduced in Fig. 15) the repetitive spikes were evoked by a progressive pressure exerted with the electrode tip (diam. 10–15 μ) against the internal limiting membrane. In the course of the experiment a (reversible) block was created between the M- and the I-P components, finally the M-component solely being recorded. Apparently, a retinal ganglion cell when subjected to a progressive pressure behaves in a similar manner as a spinal ganglion cell, the responses in both cases starting in the

M-region (cf. Fig. 2). Further, the action potential of the synaptically activated retinal ganglion cell also starts in the M-trigger region.

The record in Fig. 13B was intracellularly obtained from a dorsal root ganglion cell of frog, whereas C and D represent intracellular recordings obtained from the sympathetic ganglion of frog by anti- and orthodromic activation respectively. The records seen in Fig. 13F are corresponding responses obtained on cat motoneurons (reproduced from Brock, Coombs

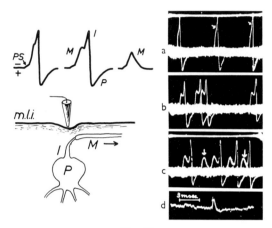

Fig. 15.

and Eccles [5], a antidromic and b orthodromic). The record G is an anti-dromic and H an orthodromic response of toad motoneurons (reproduced from Araki, Otani and Furukawa [3]). It appears very likely that the prepo-tential (arrows, Fig. 13) seen in the recordings from the different types of neurons corresponds to the M-component of the spinal ganglion cell response. Thus, the action potential recorded from the cell body of different neurons always seems to be initiated in the M-segment, whether the nerve cell is activated antidromically, orthodromically, by a pulse of current or mechani-cally by pressure. It appears reasonable to suggest that the M-membrane represents a trigger mechanism on which the summated currents originating in the postsynaptic membranes exert an excitatory or inhibitory action which is a view similar to that expressed by Araki and Otani [2].

In this connection the experiments in which the neurons were mechanically stimulated are of interest, since also in that case the impulse was initiated in the M-membrane. In microscopic vision it was observed that the perikaryon membrane under the electrode tip was deformed locally. The conditions seem to some extent to imitate a synaptic activation; the electrode tip simulating a synaptic ending which in this case mechanically (the synapse chemically) changes the membrane structure and causes a graded reduction of the perikaryon membrane potential (EPSP). This results in a continuous outward current flow through the M-membrane and a repetitive firing. No electrical currents from external sources were used when the nerve cell was mechanically stimulated. Similarly, the synaptic effect on the postsynaptic membranes might be purely chemical, no electrical currents being involved. This is in agreement with Grundfest's (see e.g. [22, 23]) view that the postsynaptic membranes are electrically inexcitable.

All the extracellular diphasic action potentials obtained from different types of vertebrate neurons show very similar configurations. The last action potential component, which apparently corresponds to the P-component of the recordings from the spinal ganglion cells, does not seem to be followed by a (positive) "dendritic component" in the recordings from neurons which possess dendrites. Compare for instance the P-component of the recordings from the thalamic neuron in Fig. 13E and that from the retinal ganglion cell in Fig. 15, with the P-component of the spinal ganglion cell response seen in Fig. 13A. The intracellular recordings from, for instance, motoneurons have a configuration very similar to the responses obtained from spinal ganglion cells and frog sympathetic cells, which have no dendrites. The axonal potential components are easily observed as distinct parts of the response obtained from the cell body by extra- or intracellular electrodes, hence it would be expected that also a conducted spike of the large dendrites would be detected if it exists. These observations support the view that the conducted impulse does not invade the dendrites.

In this connection the old observation is worth mentioning, that the cerebral and cerebellar neurons, which have their dendrites oriented towards the cortical surface, are excitable by an anode and inhibited by a cathode applied on the surface of the cortex; the anode apparently producing outward currents through the M-membrane. This is in good agreement with Grundfest's ([22], p. 135) statement: "The membrane, at least in the apical dendrite portion, is therefore inexcitable by electric stimuli although the soma and the axon of the same cell are excitable and respond with characteristic spikes." If that is true, and the conducted impulse in fact propagates by the aid of local current flow (which requires electrical excitability), then there is no logical reason to expect that the P-component of a neuron would be succeeded by a conducted "dendritic spike component".

SUMMARY

1. The component analysis presented in an earlier paper [35] of the extracellular action potential recorded from single ganglion cells has been confirmed.

2. The relation between the components of the extra- and intracellular recordings has been studied.

3. In agreement with earlier findings it is concluded that the perikaryon membrane is depolarized almost instantaneously.

4. Intracellular recordings from sympathetic ganglion cells of frog are described.

5. On the basis of the component analysis presented a general interpretation is given of extra- and intracellular recordings from single neurons. Since the action potentials recorded with intra- or extracellular electrodes from single neurons have the same general characteristics and corresponding components whether the neuron has dendrites or not, it seems likely that the dendrites do not contribute to the spike potential.

REFERENCES

1. AMASSIAN, V. E., *Electroencephal. Clin. Neurophysiol.* **5**, 415 (1953).
2. ARAKI, T. and OTANI, T., *J. Neurophysiol.* **18**, 472 (1955).
3. ARAKI, T., OTANI, T. and FURUKAWA, T., *Jap. J. Physiol.* **3**, 254 (1953).
4. BARLOW, H. B., *J. Physiol.* **119**, 58 (1953).
5. BROCK, L. G., COOMBS, J. S. and ECCLES, J. C., *J. Physiol.* **117**, 431 (1952).
6. —— *ibid.* **122**, 429 (1953).
7. BUSER, P. and ALBE-FESSARD, D., *Compt. Rend. Acad.* **236**, 1197 (1953).
8. CHU, L. W., *J. Comp. Neurol.* **100**, 381 (1954).
9. COHEN, M. J., LANDGREN, S., STRÖM, L. and ZOTTERMAN, Y., *Acta Physiol. Scand.* **40**, *Suppl.* *135*, 3 (1957).
10. CRAIN, S. M., *J. Comp. Neurol.* **104**, 285 (1956).
11. ECCLES, J. C., *Pflügers Arch. ges. Physiol.* **260**, 385 (1955).
12. —— The Physiology of Nerve Cells. The Johns Hopkins Press, Baltimore, 1957.
13. —— The Neurophysiological Basis of Mind. Oxford, Clarendon Press, 1953.
14. ECCLES, R. M., *J. Physiol.* **130**, 572 (1955).
15. FATT, P., *J. Neurophysiol.* **20**, 27 (1957).
16. —— *ibid.* **20**, 61 (1957).
17. FRANK, K. and FUORTES, M. G. F., *J. Physiol.* **130**, 625 (1955).
18. FUORTES, M. G. F., FRANK, K. and BECKER, M. C., *J. Gen. Physiol.* **40**, 735 (1956).
19. GERNANDT, B., *Acta Physiol. Scand.* **15**, 88 (1948).
20. GRANIT, R., Receptors and Sensory Perception. Yale Univ. Press, 1955.
21. GRANIT, R. and SVAETICHIN, G. *Uppsala Läkareför. Förhandl.* **65**, 161 (1939).
22. GRUNDFEST, H., Physiological Triggers. 1957.
23. —— *Physiol. Rev.* **37**, 337 (1957).
24. JUNG, R., *Third Int. EEG Congr. Symp.*, p. 57 (1953).
25. KUFFLER, S. W., *J. Neurophysiol.* **16**, 37 (1953).
26. LI, C. L., *J. Physiol.* **130**, 96 (1955).

27. Lloyd, D. P. C., J. Neurophysiol. 5, 435 (1942).
28. —— ibid. 6, 143 (1943).
29. Lorente de Nó, R., J. Cellular Comp. Physiol. 29, 207 (1947).
30. —— The Spinal Cord. Ciba Found. Symp., London, 1953.
31. Mountcastle, V. B., Davies, P. W. and Berman, A. L., J. Neurophysiol. 20, 374 (1957).
32. Renshaw, B., J. Neurophysiol. 9, 191 (1946).
33. Rose, J. E. and Mountcastle, V. B., Bull. Johns Hopkins Hosp. 94, 238 (1954).
34. Rushton, W. A. H., Brit. Med. Bull. 9, 68 (1953).
35. Svaetichin, G., Acta Physiol. Scand. 24, Suppl. 86, 23 (1951).
36. —— ibid. 31, Suppl. 114, 52 (1954).
37. —— ibid. 39, Suppl. 134, 19 (1956).
38. Tasaki, I., Polley, E. H. and Orrego, F., J. Neurophysiol. 17, 454 (1954).
39. Therman, P. O., Forbes, A. and Galambos, R., J. Neurophysiol. 3, 191 (1940).
40. Wilska, A., Acta Soc. Med. Fenn. Duodecim. A 22, 50 (1939).
41. Woodbury, W. J. and Patton, H. D., Cold Spring Harbor Symposia Quant. Biol. 17, 185 (1952).

262   *Experimental Cell Research, Suppl.* **5**, *262–271 (1958)*

EXCITATION, INHIBITION AND COORDINATION OF CORTICAL NEURONES

R. JUNG

Abteilung für Klinische Neurophysiologie, University of Freiburg i. Br., Germany

Extracellular recordings of single neurone discharges from the visual and motor cortex in the cat "encéphale isolé" preparation have been used to investigate the coordination of the cortical neuronal system. This report is a summary of the work on inhibition and excitation of cortical neurones, carried out in our laboratory during the last five years mainly by v. Baumgarten, Baumgartner, Creutzfeldt, Grüsser and Akimoto [1–24]. For the discussion of papers from other laboratories the reader is referred to the publications by Jung [18], Jung and Baumgartner [21], Creutzfeldt, Baumgartner and Schoen [9] and Jung, Creutzfeldt and Grüsser [24]. Various patterns of activation and inhibition of cortical neurones after specific afferent stimuli (light on the retina), after non-specific afferent impulses (intralaminar or reticular stimulation) and after direct epicortical electrical stimuli have been found and studied in detail.

The general problem investigated was the control and limitation of excitation to regulate homeostasis of the brain and to determine adequate reactions of the cortex to various stimuli. The results revealed different mechanisms of neuronal coordination that assure the balance of excitation and inhibition in the cortex. The main regulating mechanisms are among others the reciprocal action of antagonistic neurones and the convergence of specific and nonspecific afferent impulses.

Light Stimulation of Visual Cortex

The neurones of the primary visual cortex show five different types of response (*A*, *B*, *C*, *D* and *E*) to light and darkness [20, 18, 4]. Fig. 1 shows a schematic diagram of these neuronal reaction types. In those neurones reacting to light (*B*, *C*, *D*, *E*) pre- and postexcitatory inhibition and reciprocal activity, well-known from other regions of the CNS are observed [21, 5].

Successive inhibition and activation of the same neurones occur after visual stimuli, as well as simultaneous reciprocal activation and inhibition of antagonistic neurones (*B* and *D*). In contrast to these light responsive neurones, *A*-neurones do not react to retinal afferent impulses caused by light on or off. These *A*-neurones may act as a powerful restraining and stabilising system in the cortex, maintaining it at a medium level of excitation [21].

The neurones of the visual cortex are organized as a co-ordinated homeostatic regulation system. A preliminary enumeration [21] of the reaction types of neurones in this system has given the following results. About half of the neurones (*A*) are not responsive to light, the other half is nearly equally

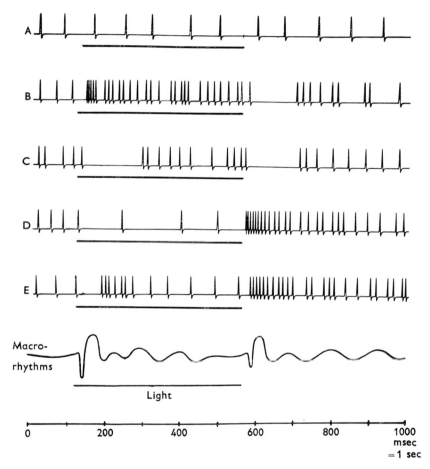

Fig. 1.—*Five types of neuronal responses to light-stimulation in the cats visual cortex* (schematic drawing). *A*-neurones show no response to light. *B*-, *C*-, *D*- and *E*-neurones respond to light-on or -off with activation or inhibition. *B*-neurones: activation by light-on with high frequency initial peak and slower sustained discharge. Inhibition after light-off, late after-activation. *C*-neurones: inhibition after light-on and -off. *D*-neurones: inhibition of spontaneous discharge by light and activation by darkness after light-off. *E*-neurones: short pre-excitatory inhibition by light-on with following activation, stronger activation by light-off. The last line shows the corresponding slow cortical rhythms of surface records.

divided into neurones showing primary activation (*B*) or primary inhibition
(*C, D, E*). Thus even maximal light stimuli are only able to excite a quarter
of the neurones in the visual cortex at the same time, another quarter is simultaneously inhibited and half of the neurones continue to discharge independently of retinal afferents [21, 5].

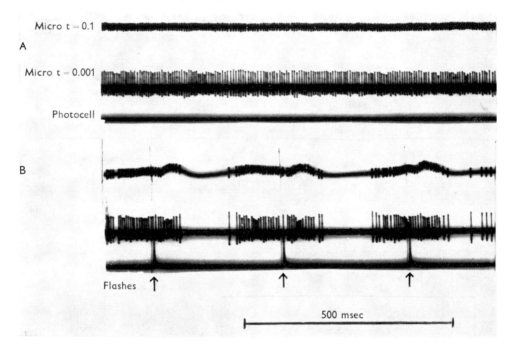

Fig. 2.—*Inhibition of injury discharges of a neurone in the visual cortex* caused by specific
afferent impulses following flash stimulation of the eye. The silent period of injury discharge has
a long latency of 70 msec. This inhibition is preceded by a short activation at 25 msec, when the
evoked potential appears, associated with the specific impulses arriving in the cortex. (*a*) Injury
discharge without illumination, (*b*), with 3 light flashes (cat, MH 21/6).

Inhibition by specific afferents or following electrical stimuli is not only
effective at normally discharging neurones but may also stop abnormal
injury discharges (Fig. 2). This inhibition of injury discharges usually has
a longer latency than the inhibition of normal neurones [9].

Besides the short lasting inhibition periods, showing up as constant
pauses of neuronal discharges following single stimuli, an entirely different
kind of inhibition is demonstrated after flickering light [21].

Rhythmical flicker stimulation by intermittent light or light flashes causes
a maximal discharge in most of the light responsive neurones of the visual

cortex, when the flicker frequency is around 10 per sec [14]. With increasing flicker frequencies from 20 to 50 per sec the mean frequency of neuronal discharges decreases nearly to the level of the resting discharge in darkness (Überlastungshemmung [21]; overload inhibition), see Fig. 3. This inhibition

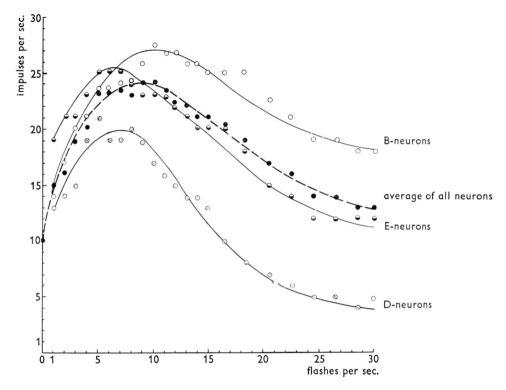

Fig. 3.—*Impulse frequency of the main neuronal reaction types of the visual cortex (B, D, E) at different frequencies of flicker stimulation* (after Grüsser and Rabelo [16]). Flickering light of short flashes (less than 1 msec duration and 12,000 Lux intensity), causes a maximum of neuronal discharge around 10 flashes per sec corresponding to the Brücke–Bartley-effect. Inhibition of overload occurs at higher frequency flashes in all neurones, although the light shed on the retina is 3 times greater at 30 per sec than at 10 per sec. The *D*- and *E*-neurones, activated by light-off show a more marked inhibition at higher frequency flashes than *B*-neurones.

occurs as well with flicker of equal light-dark ratio [13, 14] as with flashing flicker [21, 16], although in the latter instance the amount of light shed on the retina in 50/sec flashes is 5 times greater than in 10/sec. The impulse maximum at medium flicker frequencies and the overload inhibition at higher flicker frequencies can partly be explained by receptor potentials and neuronal mechanisms of the retina [12, 17].

Electrical Stimulation of Nonspecific Afferents to the Cortex

Stimulation of the intralaminar thalamus and of the reticular formation of the midbrain cause various responses in the majority of cortical neurones. These neuronal responses appear mostly together with the surface negative

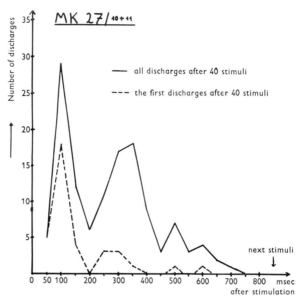

Fig. 4.—*Long latency rhythmic responses of a B-neurone of the visual cortex following stimulation of nonspecific thalamus.* The discharges occur in bursts at 100, 300, 500, 600 msec after the electrical stimulus. Sometimes the first discharge has longer latencies corresponding to the peaks of the rhythmical after-discharge (cat, MK 27/10, 11).

long latency evoked potential and sometimes with shorter latency preceding this wave [6, 8, 1, 2]. Single stimuli cause different types of neuronal responses without relation to the response types to specific stimuli: following thalamo-reticular stimuli one sees activated groups of neuronal discharge or inhibitory pauses of discharge, most commonly periodic groups of rhythmic activation and inhibition (Fig. 4). High frequency stimuli elicit long lasting after-discharges of cortical neurones, sometimes preceded by a short postexcitatory inhibition period. A-neurones, not responsive to light mostly respond to thalamic stimulation.

The interaction of specific and nonspecific afferents on the neurones of the visual cortex is investigated by intralaminar thalamic stimulation on the background of light and darkness and by using thalamic stimuli and light flashes separately and together [7, 8]. Coordinated convergence of the non-specific thalamic afferent system with the specific afferent impulses from the retina after light and dark is shown on neurones of the five types of reaction to light. Both specific and nonspecific afferents act partly on the same neurones with an average result of their excitation and inhibition effects, partly on different neurones. A-neurones, ordinarily not responsive to light,

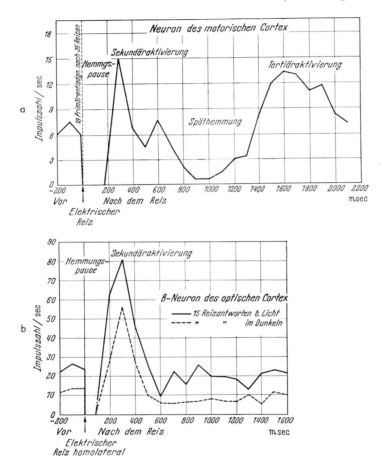

Fig. 5.—*Responses of cortical neurones to electrical stimuli of the motor and visual cortex* (after Creutzfeldt, Baumgartner and Schoen [9]). Average frequency curves from 35 (*a*) and 30 (*b*) stimuli (0.5 msec, 4–6 V). (*a*) The neuron of the motor cortex shows a constant silent period of 200 msec (Hemmungspause) following the stimulus. The primary discharge is inconstant (19 spikes after 35 stimuli). Therefore the silent period cannot be a refractory phase after primary neuronal discharge. Periods of secondary activation, late inhibition and tertiary activation follow in the next two seconds. (*b*) The B-neuron of the visual cortex shows a shorter silent period of 100 msec after electrical stimulation and a stronger secondary activation. Average frequency and activation is higher in light than in darkness.

may show different reactions during light and dark when stimulated from the
nonspecific afferents of the thalamo-reticular system [7, 19, 23]. The *critical
fusion frequency* of some cortical neurones to flickering light can be augmented
by a series of intralaminar stimuli that raise the maximum frequency at
which cortical neurones can follow the flicker [10, 19, 24].

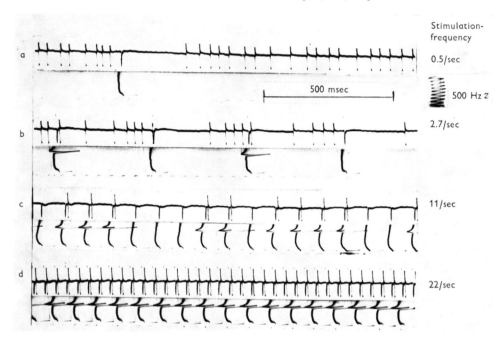

Fig. 6.—*Inhibition of neuronal discharge by low frequency stimulation (a, b). Activation with
primary discharges at higher frequency stimulation (c. d.)* Thyratron stimuli applied to contralateral senso-motor cortex. (*a*, *b*) Low frequency stimulation below 1 per sec causes constant silent
periods of 200 msec duration occurring together with the callosal potential. Inhibition is constant
without primary discharge below 1 per sec stimulation. Few primary discharges with a latency of
13 msec occur between 2 and 3 per sec stimulation. (*c*) At 11 per sec stimulation periods of primary
discharge change with silent periods. (*d*) At 22 per sec activation with regular driving of the
neurone following each stimulus (cat, MH 30/8).

Electrical Stimulation of Cortical Surface

Single or low frequency electrical stimuli of the surface of the sensomotor
cortex (homolateral or symmetrically contralateral) cause constant inhibitory pauses of neuron discharges, preceded or not by an inconstant primary
discharge and followed by a constant secondary post inhibitory discharge
[9, 22]. The inhibitory silent period has 150–400 msec duration in the motor
and 100–200 msec, in the visual cortex (Fig. 5). In the senso-motor cortex

the silent period occurs at the site of stimulation as well as at the symmetrical point of the contralateral hemisphere (Fig. 6). This pause in the discharge cannot be a postexcitatory depression because it occurs whether or not the neurone is discharged in the first msecs after the stimulus. Epicortical test stimuli of the same intensity during the inhibitory pause cause a prolongation of this silent period corresponding to the interval of the two stimuli [23]. Higher frequency stimulation over 5 per sec facilitates the primary discharge and cuts off the inhibitory pause. At higher frequencies, over 10–20 per sec, each stimulus is followed regularly by a primary discharge and inhibitory pauses are no longer observed (Fig. 6 d). When this stimulation is prolonged, it brings the cortex into a preconvulsive condition [23]. These results are explained by assuming two different processes: a slow and easily fatigued inhibitory process and a short facilitative one which is capable of summation [22].

CONCLUSIONS

The neurones of the visual cortex that were most thoroughly investigated show a well coordinated response pattern following light stimulation. These neuronal responses follow the receptor potentials and the excitation and inhibition patterns of the retinal neurones [12, 17, 15]. Compared with the retina, the cortical neurones show a quicker adaptation, a greater variety of modifying influx and especially a more marked tendency to restrain excitation [21, 24]. This neuronal system tends to maintain a medium level of activity and an adequate regulation of cortical function corresponding to the actual situation by four self-regulating control mechanisms:

1. Continuous stabilization of excitation by a regular background discharge of *A*-neurones, not responsive to retinal stimuli.
2. Simultaneous reciprocal activation and inhibition of different antagonistic neurones at light on or off (*B*-neurones versus *D*-neurones).
3. Successive activation and inhibition of all types of neurones reacting to light or darkness (*B*-, *C*-, *D*-, *E*-neurones).
4. Convergence of both specific retino-geniculate and non-specific thalamo-reticular afferents on cortical neurones with facilitation, inhibition or occlusion of discharge.

A coordinated homeostatic regulation system is thus achieved in the cortex because both activation and inhibition in *B*-, *C*-, *D*-, *E*-neurones on one hand,

and the stabilizing basal activity of *A*-neurones on the other, tend to balance each other [21]. Hence the cortex is maintained at a happy medium of activity that prevents synchronous mass discharges of all neurones [5]. Coordination with the nonspecific system allows appropriate adjustment of the cortical neurone activity to changes of afferent influx and assures adaptation to the internal needs of the organism in correspondence with the surrounding milieu.

SUMMARY

Extracellular recordings from single neurones in the visual and motor cortex of the cat after specific and nonspecific afferent stimuli and after electrical stimulation of the cortex are described.

In the visual cortex 5 types of neurones (*A, B, C, D, E*) classified after their responses to light and darkness form a finely coordinated regulatory system to assure a homeostatic balance of reciprocal excitation and inhibition of cortical neurones.

Afferent impulses or electrical stimuli of the cortex may cause neuronal inhibition, appearing as pauses of normal discharges or as stop of abnormal injury discharges with longer latency.

Flickering light induces another phenomenon of overload inhibition: decrease of neuronal discharges at higher flicker frequencies and a maximum of discharge around ten flashes per sec, caused partly by retinal factors.

Convergence of nonspecific thalamic afferents with specific retinal afferents on single cortical neurones is demonstrated in the majority of all 5 types of neurones of the visual cortex. The maximum frequency at which cortical neurones can follow flickering light may be raised by thalamo-reticular stimulation.

Low frequency electrical stimuli at cortical surface cause constant inhibitory pauses of neuronal discharges in motor and visual cortex. High frequency stimulation facilitates neuronal discharges and prevents the inhibitory pause.

Four self-regulating control mechanisms achieve homeostasis of the cortical neuronal systems in the visual cortex:

1. Continuous stabilization of excitation by a regular background discharge of *A*-neurones, not responsive to retinal stimuli.

2. Simultaneous reciprocal activation and inhibition of different antagonistic neurones at light on or off (*B*-neurones versus *D*-neurones).

3. Successive activation and inhibition of all types of neurones reacting to light or darkness (*B*-, *C*-, *D*-, *E*-neurones).

4. Convergence of both specific retino-geniculate and non-specific thalamo-reticular afferents on cortical neurones with facilitation, inhibition or occlusion of discharge.

Regulations 1, 2 and 3 maintain the cortex at a happy medium level of activity. Coordination of specific afferents with the non-specific system (reguation 4) allows appropriate adjustment of the cortical neurone activity to the actual situation.

REFERENCES

1. AKIMOTO, H. and CREUTZFELDT, O., *Klin. Wochschr.* **35**, 199 (1957).
2. —— *Arch. Psychiat. Nervenkrankh.* **196**, 494 (1957/58).
3. BAUMGARTEN, R. v. and JUNG, R., *Rev. neurol.* **87**, 151 (1952).
4. BAUMGARTNER, G., *Pflügers Arch. ges. Physiol.* **261**, 457 (1955).
5. BAUMGARTNER, G. and JUNG, R., *Arch. sci. biol.* **39**, 474 (1955).
6. CREUTZFELDT, O., *XX. Congr. internat. Physiol.*, Bruxelles, 1956, abstr. 202–204.
7. CREUTZFELDT, O. and AKIMOTO, H., *Arch. Psychiat. Nervenkrankh.* **196**, 520 (1957/58).
8. CREUTZFELDT, O., BAUMGARTNER, G. and JUNG, R., *EEG Clin. Neurophysiol.* **8**, 163 (1956).
9. CREUTZFELDT, O., BAUMGARTNER, G. and SCHOEN, L., *Arch. Psychiat. Nervenkrankh.* **194**, 597 (1956).
10. CREUTZFELDT, O. and GRÜSSER, O.-J., *IV. Internatl. EEG-Congr. Bruxelles*, 1957, abstr. p. 148.
11. GRÜSSER, O.-J., *Klin. Wochschr.* **35**, 199 (1957).
12. —— *Naturwissenschaften* **44**, 522 (1957).
13. GRÜSSER, O.-J. and CREUTZFELDT, O., *XX. Congr. internat. Physiol.*, Bruxelles, 1956, abstr. 377–378.
14. —— *Pflügers Arch. ges. Physiol.* **263**, 668 (1957).
15. GRÜSSER, O.-J. and KAPP, H., *Pflügers Arch. ges. Physiol.*, **266**, 111 (1958).
16. GRÜSSER, O.-J. and RABELO, C., *IV. Internatl. EEG-Congr. Bruxelles*, 1957, abstr. p. 153.
17. —— *Pflügers Arch. ges. Physiol.*, **265**, 501 (1957/58).
18. JUNG, R., *EEG Clin. Neurophysiol. Suppl.* **4**, 57 (1953).
19. —— Ford-Symposon on the Reticular Formation, Detroit, March, 1957.
20. JUNG, R., v. BAUMGARTEN, R. and BAUMGARTNER, G., *Arch. Psychiat. Nervenkrankh.* **189**, 521 (1952).
21. JUNG, R. and BAUMGARTNER, G., *Pflügers Arch. ges. Physiol.* **261**, 434 (1955).
22. JUNG, R. and CREUTZFELDT, O., *EEG Clin. Neurophysiol.* **8**, 164 (1956).
23. JUNG, R., CREUTZFELDT, O. and BAUMGARTNER, G., Colloque de Microphysiologie des Systèmes excitables, pp. 411–434. Ed. C.N.R.S. Paris, 1957.
24. JUNG, R., CREUTZFELDT, O. and GRÜSSER, O.-J., *Deut. Med. Wochschr.* **82**, 1050 (1957).

THE SYNAPSES

18 — 583708

Experimental Cell Research, Suppl. **5**, *275–293 (1958)*

THE MORPHOLOGY OF SYNAPSES IN THE CENTRAL NERVOUS SYSTEM

S. L. PALAY

Section on Neurocytology, Laboratory of Neuroanatomical Sciences, National Institute of Neurological Diseases and Blindness, National Institutes of Health, Bethesda, Md., U.S.A.

For the morphologist, the synapse has a particular fascination which is explained by the fact that it is a site of immediate, polarized, specific interaction between independent morphological units or cells. I shall not attempt to review here the long history of the controversy among neuroanatomists concerning the structural independence of neurons. The controversy involved all of the famous personages of classical neuroanatomy—Waldeyer, Golgi, Nissl, Held, His, Kölliker, Boeke, Stöhr, Bielschowsky, Ramón y Cajal, and many others. It has been carefully reviewed by Ramón y Cajal in a monograph originally published in 1934 [24] and recently translated into English [25]. The theory of His and Cajal—the neuron doctrine, as it is called —has been accepted by most neuroanatomists and neurophysiologists for the past 30 years or more, although a few foci of resistance still remain, particularly among certain schools dealing with the innervation of smooth muscle.

The morphological evidence for the neuron doctrine is based principally upon preparations of nervous tissue which have been impregnated with silver salts and which demonstrate the terminals of nerve fibers ending upon the postsynaptic surface. Such preparations provide information regarding the position and shape of the terminals, but nothing regarding their internal structure. Cytological investigations of the large nerve endings in the medulla of various fishes reveal a characteristic collection of mitochondria next to the presynaptic membrane [2, 3, 4, 5]. These mitochondria were noticed by Held in 1897 [16]; he called them "neurosomes". They are concentrated in areas of the brain where nerve endings are particularly numerous such as in the neuropil [30]. They also form a prominent component of the terminal axoplasm at neuromuscular junctions [18, 8]. Although these cytological studies demonstrate some features of the internal structure of the synapse, they cannot provide clear evidence concerning the interface between the terminal and the postsynaptic structures, for this interface is at the limit of resolution of the light microscope and appears as a thin single line. For such detail we must turn to the electron microscope.

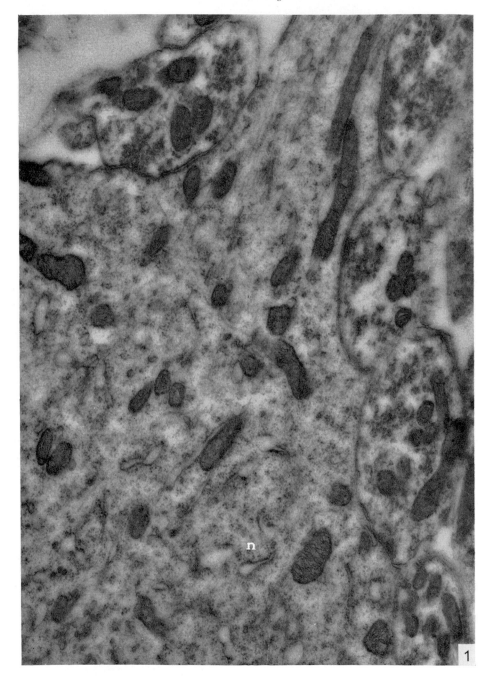

METHODS

The material presented in this paper is taken from the medulla oblongata, cerebellar cortex, and neurohypophysis of the white rat. The tissues were fixed *in situ* in the living, anesthetized animal by injection of chilled, buffered, 2 per cent osmium tetroxide. Fragments were excised, immersed in fresh buffered fixative at about 4°C for 60–90 minutes and then dehydrated rapidly by passage through a graded series of methanol concentrations. The fragments were embedded in a prepolymerized mixture of butyl and methyl methacrylates containing 2 per cent Luperco. Thin sections cut on a Porter–Blum microtome by means of a glass knife were examined in an RCA EMU 2E electron microscope.

OBSERVATIONS

In electron micrographs of sections from the central nervous system, simple nerve endings (end-feet or *boutons terminaux*) appear a small, circumscribed, rounded expansions abutting upon the surfaces of perikarya and dendrites. Recent modifications of silver impregnation techniques [35, 1, 27] have demonstrated in light microscopic preparations the remarkable close-packing of terminals over the surfaces of neurons in the medulla. These observations are confirmed by electron micrographs (Fig. 1) in which it can be seen that the terminals are arrayed one next the other as palisades surrounding the neuron. Each ending is an independent enlargement of a telodendron (Figs. 1 and 5) which expands into a rounded bulb seated in a shallow depression or trough in the postsynaptic surface (Figs. 1 and 2). Processes of glial cells often accompany the telodendra and form caps over the endings (Figs. 4 and 5). Rarely a glial process interposes between the terminal and the postsynaptic surface (Fig. 5), but usually the fit of the terminal into its trough is complete and unobstructed.

The nerve endings in the central nervous system contain two charac-

Fig. 1.—Electron micrograph of a section through a small neuron in the facial colliculus of the rat. The nucleus is not included in the field. The perikaryon occupies most of the figure and the root of a dendrite passes out of its upper margin. The cytoplasm of the perikaryon contains relatively diffuse Nissl substance (*n*) which consists of tubules and cisternae of endoplasmic reticulum and associated fine granules [23]. Small aggregates of Nissl material can be seen within the dendrite as well. Mitochondria are scattered about in the cytoplasm without any characteristic orientation. Thin strands of agranular endoplasmic reticulum also appear in the root of the dendrite, oriented longitudinally. Five rounded *boutons terminaux* form a palisade about the neuron. Each ending fits into a shallow depression in the surface of the neuron or its dendrite. The section includes a bit of the telodendron belonging to the *bouton* at the left of the dendrite. The terminals display the characteristic internal constellation of mitochondria and small vesicles. The synaptic cleft is visible beneath most of the terminals. ×34,000.

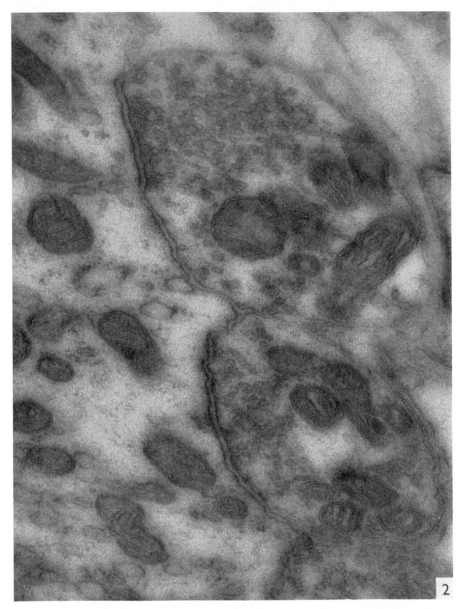

Fig. 2.—Electron micrograph of a section through two *boutons terminaux* on the surface of a
neuron in the abducens nucleus. The upper *bouton* contains five or six mitochondrial profiles
and the lower one contains eight. The remaining area of each ending is almost entirely occupied
by synaptic vesicles of nearly uniform diameters. Notice the concentration of synaptic vesicles
against the more adielectronic portion of the presynaptic membrane. This interrelation together
with the synaptic cleft is designated as a synaptic complex. The figure shows the separation of
the pre- and postsynaptic membranes by the synaptic cleft, which is continuous with the other
intercellular spaces of the central nervous system. ×66,100.

teristic internal components: (1) a cluster of mitochondria, and (2) a throng of small vesicles. The same components are prominent features of the axonal tips in neuromuscular junctions [19, 28, 29]. The fine axon filaments or neurofilaments, which occur elsewhere in the axon and perikaryon, are absent from the terminals in the central nervous system as well as in the neuromuscular junction [7, 10, 29].

The mitochondria exhibit no unusual features; they resemble those in the perikarya in size and shape and in having a noticeable predominance of forms with longitudinally oriented cristae [23]. However, the concentration of mitochondria seems to be greater in the terminals than in the neuronal perikarya. Since the actual number of mitochondria cannot be ascertained from electron micrographs unless a larger number of serial sections is examined, it is necessary to compare the number of independent mitochondrial profiles in nerve endings with the number in areas of comparable dimensions within the perikarya. In the simple *boutons* selected for illustration of this paper, the number of mitochondrial profiles varies from 4–9, and in the larger, more complicated axonal ending of the cerebellar glomerulus (Fig. 6) the number is 26. Such concentrations of mitochondrial profiles have not been encountered either in the perikarya of neurons or in their dendrites and axons (see Fig. 1).

The crowds of small, rounded or oval profiles which fill the remainder of the terminal neuroplasm (Figs. 1–8) have been aptly named "synaptic vesicles" by De Robertis and Bennett [12]. They have been found in the terminals of rod cells in the retina of the guinea pig [32], rabbit [13], and rat [17]; in nerve endings of the sympathetic ganglia of the frog and the neuropil of the nerve cord in the earthworm [12]; in the neuromuscular junction of the rat [19], and the chameleon [29] and in a variety of terminals from the central nervous system of the rat [19, 20, 21]. They have also been noted in terminals about the hair cells of the cochlea [15, 33] and the vestibular organ of the guinea pig [34]. The profiles of these vesicles are from 200 to 650 Å in diameter and are bounded by a smooth, circular or oval, adielectronic line 50 to 70 Å thick. The internum of the profile is slightly denser than the surrounding matrix of the ending. Although the vesicles are usually distributed throughout the terminal they are frequently aggregated toward the presynaptic surface in association with a modification of the surface membrane that will be described below. In some endings there are, in addition to the purely vesicular profiles, a few elongated tubular profiles of the same diameter (Figs. 1, 4, and 5). These appear to be continuations of the delicate, canalicular, membranous structures belonging to the endoplasmic

S. L. Palay

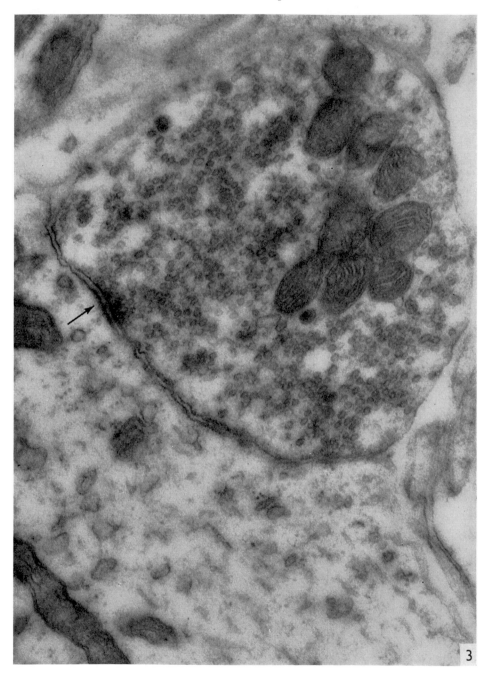

reticulum that can be seen in both dendrites and axons (Figs. 4 and 5). It is probable that the vesicles arise by budding from the ends of these canaliculi.

The presynaptic surface of the terminal is separated from the postsynaptic surface of the perikaryon or dendrite by a thin, uninterrupted cleft approximately 200 Å wide (Figs. 1, 2, 3, 4, 5, 6 and 8). This space, which is included within the synaptolemma of light microscopy [5] is bounded by the independent plasma membranes of the pre- and postsynaptic elements. It represents a complete interruption in the continuity of cytoplasm across the junction. The visualization of this cleft imposes final confirmation of the neuron doctrine.

That the synaptic cleft is a truly extracellular space is indicated by its continuity with the narrow interstitial spaces that can be traced among all the neighboring cellular structures. Rarely, it is enlarged by the intrusion of one or two glial processes (Fig. 5), and this incident only emphasizes its extracellular nature. Usually it is free of any cellular body, glial or otherwise.

Consequently the pre- and postsynaptic surfaces are in immediate apposition, and the characteristics of the plasma membranes at these sites therefore assume increased interest. In electron micrographs of sections the presynaptic membrane appears as a smooth, gently undulating, adielectronic line, approximately 55 Å thick, but it is not of uniform density. In one or more places on each terminal it exhibits increased density and irregularly increased thickness. These spots, 150 to 400 mμ in length, are probably three dimensional in extent, differentiated patches in the synaptic surface of the terminal. Often, but not always, the opposite, postsynaptic membrane is also thickened and denser than it is elsewhere. This occasional, focalized density is the only characteristic differentiation of the postsynaptic surface that has been found thus far.

It is significant that these patches do not occur at sites of glial intrusion into the synaptic cleft and that usually the synaptic vesicles within the terminal are aggregated against the patches of denser plasmalemma (Figs. 2, 3, 4, 5, 6). Hence, the complex of a cluster of synaptic vesicles, associated with a focalized area of dense presynaptic plasmalemma, and the synaptic cleft may be considered as a morphological subunit within the grosser unit comprised by the terminal and synaptolemma. In electron micrographs of the

Fig. 3.—Electron micrograph of a single *bouton* on the surface of a neuron in the abducens nucleus. The ending is filled by eight mitochondrial profiles and a host of synaptic vesicles. The *arrow* indicates a synaptic complex. The synaptic cleft is well shown except in its lower portion where the pre- and postsynaptic membranes overlap in the plane of the section. The cytoplasm of the neuron beneath the postsynaptic membrane displays no characteristic differentiation. × 66,900.

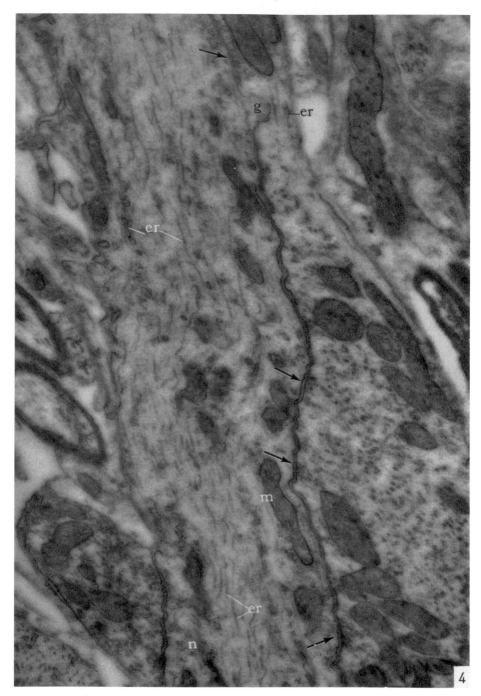

more extensive endings, several such synaptic complexes may be identified. In Fig. 4 which shows a long terminal in contact with a dendrite in the dorsal cochlear nucleus, 4 synaptic complexes are indicated by arrows. In Fig. 6, showing a glomerulus in the granular layer of the cerebellar cortex, 3 synaptic complexes may be seen. If current speculations (see below) on the physiological significance of the synaptic vesicles are correct, then these focal synaptic complexes may represent the actual sites of impulse transmission across the synapse.

Thus far, all terminals examined in the central nervous system of the rat [21] have exhibited the same constellation of structural components. This is true even of those terminals which do not end upon another effector cell, such as the nerve-endings of the hypothalamo-hypophysial tract in the neurohypophysis [22]. In the neurohypophysis of a rat which has been deprived of drinking water or dehydrated by administration of 2.5 per cent saline instead of drinking water, the endings of the nerve fibers in the palisade zone (Fig. 7) appear exactly the same as those elsewhere in the central nervous system, even though in this organ, the nerves end upon a connective tissue basement membrane instead of on another nerve cell. These endings have been depleted of their normal complement of neurosecretory granules, which appear in the endings of the hydrated animal as numerous additional vesicles measuring approximately 100 mμ in diameter and containing a dense homogeneous substance.

With these structural characteristics of the easily identifiable synapses as a basis, it is profitable to examine the more complicated synaptic fields included within the neuropil, that contexture of dendrites, axons, and glia which lies between the perikarya of the gray matter. Throughout the neuropil entangled dendrites and axonal tips can be identified, sometimes in simple pairs, encircled by glial processes, sometimes freely interlaced in a baffling pattern (Fig. 8). The distinguishing features of the axonal tips—their con-

---

Fig. 4.—Electron micrograph of a section through a dendrite and associated nerve endings in the dorsal cochlear nucleus. Numerous membrane-bound tubules of endoplasmic reticulum (*er*) are aligned parallel to the length of the dendrite. Mitochondria (*m*) and bits of Nissl substance (*n*) are scattered about the peripheral cytoplasm of the dendrite. On the right, following the contours of the dendrite, is a long nerve ending of the type classified by Ramón y Cajal [24] as climbing fibers. Probably another portion of the same ending is visible at the lower left border of the dendrite. This elongated terminal contains numerous mitochondrial profiles and a throng of synaptic vesicles, some of which are included in synaptic complexes (*arrows*). Several longitudinal profiles of endoplasmic reticulum (*er*) appear near the upper margin of the picture in a narrow portion of the ending. The continuous synaptic cleft is evident, and a small intrusive glial fiber lies within the cleft at *g*. The portion of the ending on the left is capped by a thin glial sheath. ×30,600.

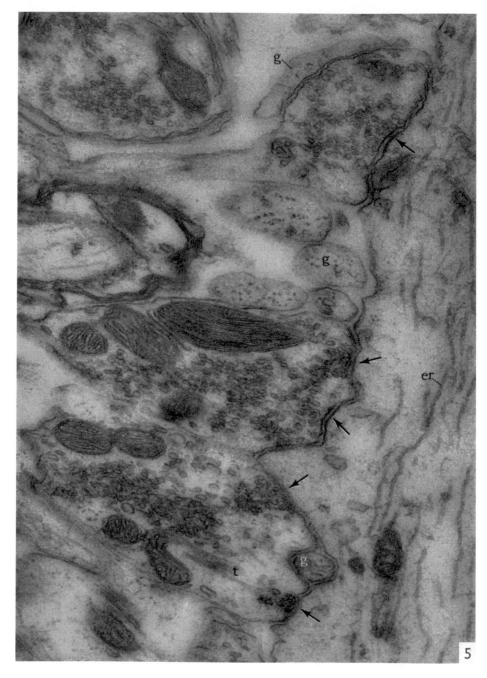

centrated mitochondria and synaptic vesicles—make it possible to pick out the presynaptic terminals with some ease. The dendritic processes are recognizable chiefly by their larger vesicular and canalicular structures [21] and by their smaller complement of mitochondria. Here and there in favorably oriented sections synaptic complexes can be recognized exactly as in the simpler junctions. Thus the architecture of the synapse in all parts of the central nervous system appears to follow the same plan.

DISCUSSION

The electron micrographs that have been presented here demonstrate clearly that the junctions between nerve cells are true contacts or points of apposition where the terminal ramifications of one neuron end freely upon another neuron or its branches. In all of the several types of synapses studied thus far, the terminals of the afferent neuron are separated from the sub-synaptic surface by a narrow cleft which is about 200 Å or less in width and which is continuous with the narrow interstitial spaces between all other components of the nervous tissue. From a morphological point of view, this evidence seems to conclude the prolonged controversy over the neuron doctrine, which states that the nervous system is constructed of independent morphological units, the neurons, connected with one another only by discontinuous contacts. Thus the theory of His and Cajal may be considered validated by direct observation of which the older histological methods were incapable.

These observations show that not only is the connection between nerve cells discontinuous, but also that there is no intervening third element, such as the gliotheca of De Castro [9], between the two neural components of the synapse. The narrow synaptic cleft allows of only a thin layer of extracellular substance, presumably a fluid or thin gel, which has the properties of

Fig. 5.—Electron micrograph of a section through three *boutons terminaux* abutting upon a dendrite in the abducens nucleus. A micrograph of a section serial to this one has been published [21]. The dendrite, lying to the right, has an undulating surface marked with small troughs into which the endings fit. Within the dendrite numerous longitudinally oriented canaliculi of the endoplasmic reticulum (*er*) are shown. The telodendron of the uppermost ending extends from the left margin of the figure toward the dendrite where it enlarges into a rounded terminal, capped by a glial process (*g*). Profiles of other glial processes lie between this ending and the next. All of the endings contain synaptic vesicles and the lower two contain numerous mitochondrial profiles. Synaptic complexes are indicated by arrows. Note the two separate synaptic complexes in each of the two lower terminals. The synaptic cleft of the lowermost terminal includes an intrusive glial process lying between the two synaptic complexes. Tubular membrane-limited profiles (*t*) are also visible within this terminal. × 53,800.

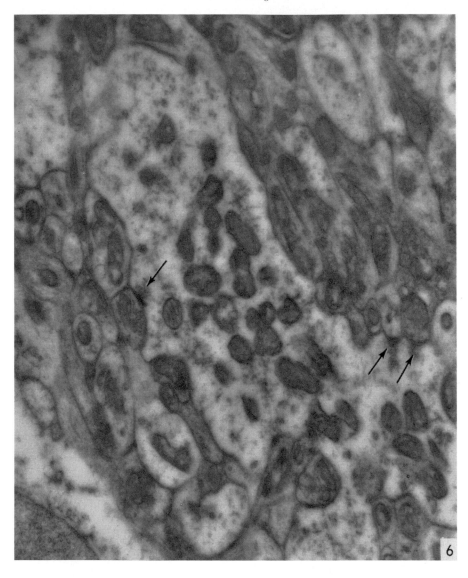

Fig. 6.—Electron micrograph of a section through a glomerulus in the cerebellar cortex. The axonal tip of a branching mossy fiber stretches diagonally across the center of the figure. It contains profiles of numerous mitochondria and clusters of small synaptic vesicles. Arrayed around the margins of the mossy fiber, fitted into bays and troughs in its surface, are the tips of dendritic branches from granule cells. Synaptic vesicles are clustered opposite some of these dendrites to form synaptic complexes (*arrows*). ×25,100.

carrying transmitter substances and ions to the subsynaptic surface. Although glial processes are intimately applied to the outer surfaces of the terminals and of the neurons, the glia cannot be considered as an intrinsic component of the synapse, and their occasional intrusion into the space between the two apposing neural structures may be taken as fortuitous.

In a recent book, J. C. Eccles [14] makes the following simplifying generalizations concerning the synapse (p. 217):

"Essentially the synapse is a device for applying minute amounts of a specific chemical substance to the special receptor area of the subsynaptic membrane, which in turn becomes highly permeable to some or all ions. The resulting electric current flows through the synaptic cleft and so to the remainder of the postsynaptic membrane, including that of the initial segment ... [of the axon]. Thus there are two conflicting requirements in regard to the width of the synaptic cleft: that it should be very narrow, so that the synaptic transmitter is applied as efficiently and as quickly as possible to the subsynaptic membrane; that it should be wide, so that the postsynaptic currents flow as freely as possible."

Eccles calculates that the diffusion time of a transmitter substance like acetylcholine across a synaptic cleft 200 Å wide would be about one microsecond. Therefore, if the dimensions seen in electron micrographs correspond to the order of the dimensions in the living tissue, the synaptic cleft is narrow enough to satisfy the first requirement for efficient action of the transmitter. He also calculates that the resistance in the synaptic cleft over an activated area even 2 μ in diameter would still be low enough to permit free flow of the postsynaptic currents. If, as seems probable, the actual sites of activation under even the large synaptic terminals are only one to four tenths of a micron in diameter, the volume available under the ending for current flow from these centers should provide a tremendous margin of safety. Such considerations assume that the synaptic cleft is really unoccupied by components of the surface membranes that may not have been visualized by the electron microscope. If the apparent cleft is reduced in width by the aliphatic chains of the phospholipides, as in the layers of the myelin sheath, then there would be little or no room for the flow of current as required. Such an interpretation of the morphology would require a careful re-examination of the basic physiological principles involved.

Acetylcholine will diffuse away from a structure as small as an end-bulb so rapidly that its concentration will be negligible in one millisecond after its liberation. However, on the surface of Renshaw cells in the spinal cord, when the cholinesterase has been inactivated, the acetylcholine transmitter action declines at a rate that is thousands of times slower than the calculated

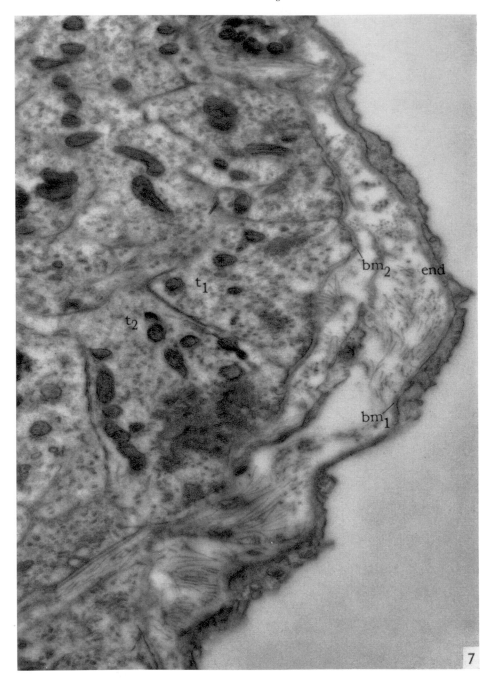

free diffusion rate. This observation has been interpreted to indicate that there is some barrier in or around the synaptic cleft which prevents the free diffusion of the acetylcholine. Thus far, no morphological counterpart for this hypothetical barrier has been found. The synaptic cleft, as mentioned before, is open all round its circumference to the interstitial spaces of the neural tissue. However, there is no reason to expect that the shape of the cleft remains constant; during discharge the terminal may alter in size and shape and may even approach the postsynaptic membrane more closely, effectively sealing off the discharged transmitter in the synaptic cleft. Such a possibility may be tested by observing the synapse during acute activation of the transmitting mechanism.

The internal structure of the presynaptic axonal terminal has already attracted the attention of neurophysiologists and has stimulated certain speculations concerning its possible significance [6, 14]. The most appealing of these possibilities is that the synaptic vesicles—the characteristic components of the terminal—are related to the quantal discharge of a chemical transmitter such as acetylcholine. This transmitter may be free in the lumen of the vesicles or may be bound either to their membrane or to some component of their contents. Presumably the appearance of the nerve impulse at the terminal would result in the instantaneous discharge of a large number of vesicles into the synaptic cleft. The continuous display of miniature postsynaptic potentials would be the reflection of a continuous spontaneous discharge of individual vesicles or small clusters. To date no direct evidence in support of such speculations has been adduced.

De Robertis has carried out two very interesting studies on synapses under different physiological conditions. In the first study [13] he reported that in the rod cell terminals of the retina of the rabbit, the vesicles become smaller and reduced in number when the rabbit is kept in total darkness for a number of days. In the second study [11] he reported that synaptic terminals in the dorsal acoustic nucleus undergo progressive degenerative changes during

---

Fig. 7.—Electron micrograph of a section through the palisade and septal zones in the neurohypophysis of a rat that had been given 2.5 per cent saline to drink for thirteen days. The endothelium (*end*) of a capillary forms an undulating curve along the right margin of the field. Beneath this, to the left, is the connective tissue of the septal zone containing fine collagenous fibers and bounded by two basement membranes, one beneath the endothelium (bm_1) and the other associated with the parenchyma (bm_2). The nerve endings of the hypothalamo-hypophysial tract abut against this second basement membrane. The figure shows four terminals, all containing mitochondria and throngs of fine vesicles. In the two lower endings (t_1 and t_2) many vesicles are crowded against the second basement membrane. Because the neurohypophysis of this animal has been depleted of neurosecretory substance as a result of water deprivation, no neurosecretory granules are visible in this field. × 22,600.

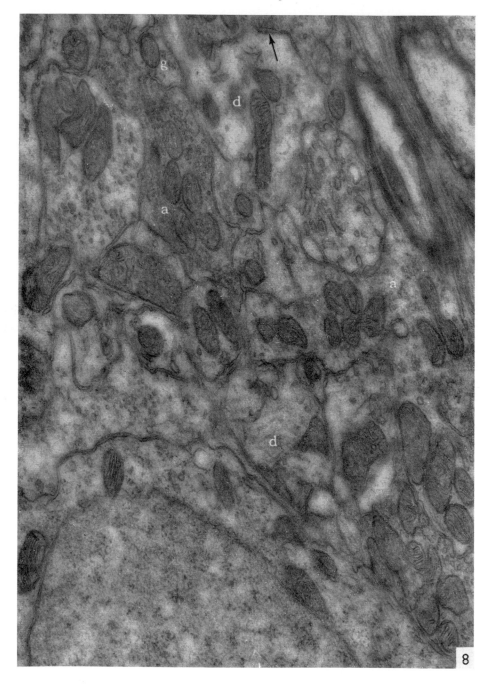

the first 44 hours after destruction of the cochlea. The primary change consists of clustering and lysis of the vesicles so that they rapidly disappear from the terminals, whereas the mitochondria disintegrate at a much slower rate. These changes in the synaptic vesicles may be correlated with the disappearance of transmitter capacity when a nerve is sectioned. An interesting implication of these observations by De Robertis is the dependence of the synaptic vesicles upon continuity with the perikaryon of which they are the farthest outpost. It is not unreasonable to suggest that the vesicles contain substances derived from the synthesizing centers in the perikaryon, perhaps conveyed down the axon via the canaliculi of the endoplasmic reticulum. If this suggestion is borne out by experimental studies, the terminal *boutons* may then be regarded as storehouses for transmitter substances originating some distance away in the nerve cell bodies, in analogy to the neurosecretory pathway of the hypothalamo-neurohypophysial system, which has hitherto been considered quite unusual if not actually heretical [31].

I should not leave the problem of the significance of the synaptic vesicles without alluding to the peculiar situation in certain of the primary receptors, namely, the hair cells of the cochlea and of the vestibular sensory cristae [15, 34]. Here the vesicles occur on the apparently postsynaptic side of the junction between the hair cells and the primary afferent fibers. It is possible that these endings may belong to the tips of efferent fibers which have been described by Rasmussen [26]. If these are not efferents, then this situation seems to be a special case which deserves more thorough study in various species.

The concentration of mitochondria in the presynaptic terminal reflects the high rate of oxidative phosphorylation which is believed to characterize synaptic areas. Whether they are more specifically involved in transmission, particularly in the recovery process, or in synthesis, is completely unknown at present, but the recognized capacity of isolated mitochondrial preparations from liver and kidney for concentrating several ions, among them hydrogen, sodium, and potassium, as well as other small molecules suggests that such a relationship merits serious consideration.

The collection of mitochondria is evidently not a necessary component

Fig. 8.—Electron micrograph of a section through the neuropil of the dorsal cochlear nucleus. A small neuron occupies the lower left corner of the figure. A couple of small myelinated nerve fibers lie in the upper right corner. Between these two landmarks is a tangle of dendritic and axonal tips comprising the neuropil. Axonal terminals (presynaptic) are recognizable by means of their concentrated mitochondria and synaptic vesicles (*a*). The dendrites (*d*) contain few mitochondria and larger tubules and vacuoles. A synaptic complex is indicated by an *arrow*. A few glial processes (*g*) can be identified. ×36,700.

of the presynaptic terminal, for they do not occur in the terminal of the rod cell at its junction with the dendrite of the bipolar cell in the retina [13, 32]. However, even this statement is subject to qualification. The mitochondria are absent from this junction in the rabbit and guinea pig, but in the rat, a single giant mitochondrion is present [17]. Such species variation indicates that our experience should be expanded to include representatives from all the major orders of vertebrates before we make sweeping generalizations.

It is somewhat disappointing that beneath the subsynaptic membrane no specialized organization of cytoplasmic structures is demonstrated by electron microscopy. However, the absence of such specialization may be considered consistent with the hypothesis that propagation of the nerve impulse is essentially a surface phenomenon. If it is necessary to postulate a specialized membrane structure to account for propagation, none is visible in currently available electron micrographs, with the resolutions and methods of preparation now in general use. The application of histochemical methods to electron microscopy is eagerly awaited for leads toward a solution of such problems and for the discovery of the pattern of chemical and enzymatic organization of the structures we can see.

Finally, I think it appropriate to caution against taking too static a view of the synapse and its components. After all, this is not a soldered junction of two hot wires, but a living system. Its morphology as well as its physiology must be considered dynamic. The processes of nerve cells may well be in constant play, flowing and shifting in position and in shape, as they do in tissue culture preparations. The contact points may shift from one position to another by gliding over the postsynaptic surface. At least, we may easily imagine a dynamic "scintillation" of the clustered synaptic vesicles, discharging now at one point, now at another. Such speculations are not fantastic but are merely extensions of current knowledge concerning the dynamic life of the cell as revealed in tissue culture.

SUMMARY

Electron microscopy of the medulla, cerebellar cortex, and neurohypophysis of the rat demonstrates that axonal terminals characteristically contain a collection of mitochondria and small vesicles. Neurofilaments are absent, but a few elements of the endoplasmic reticulum are found. The presynaptic terminal is separated from the postsynaptic surface by a "synaptic cleft" approximately 200 A wide. This cleft is continuous with the narrow interstitial spaces separating all cellular elements in the central nervous system.

Although glial processes occasionally intrude into this cleft nothing comparable to a gliotheca appears. The pre- and postsynaptic membranes display patches of increased thickness and density against which the synaptic vesicles tend to congregate. Some of the physiological implications of these observations are discussed.

REFERENCES

1. ARMSTRONG, J., RICHARDSON, K. C. and YOUNG, J. Z., *Stain Technol.* **31**, 263 (1956).
2. BARTELMEZ, G. W. and HOERR, N. L., *J. Comp. Neurol.* **57**, 401 (1933).
3. BODIAN, D., *ibid.* **68**, 117 (1937).
4. —— *ibid.* **73**, 323 (1940).
5. —— *Physiol. Rev.* **22**, 146 (1942).
6. DEL CASTILLO, J. and KATZ, B., *Progress in Biophysics and Biophysical Chemistry* **6**, 121 (1956).
7. COUTEAUX, R., *Rev. canad. biol.* **6**, 563 (1947).
8. —— *Internatl. Rev. Cytology* **4**, 335 (1955).
9. DE CASTRO, F., *Arch. internatl. physiol.* **59**, 479 (1951).
10. DE ROBERTIS, E., *Acta Neurol. Latinamer.* **1**, 3 (1955).
11. —— *J. Biophys. Biochem. Cytol.* **2**, 503 (1956).
12. DE ROBERTIS, E. and BENNETT, H. S., *ibid.* **1**, 47 (1955).
13. DE ROBERTIS, E. and FRANCHI, C. M., *ibid.* **2**, 307 (1956).
14. ECCLES, J. C., The Physiology of Nerve Cells. Baltimore, The Johns Hopkins Press, 1957.
15. ENGSTRÖM, H. and SJÖSTRAND, F. S., *Acta Oto-Laryngol.* **44**, 490 (1954).
16. HELD, H., *Arch. Anat. u. Physiol. Anat. Abt.*, Suppl. p. 273 (1897).
17. LADMAN, A. J., *Anat. Rec.* **125**, 575 (1956).
18. NOËL, R., *Biol. méd.* **39**, 273 (1950).
19. PALADE, G. E., *Anat. Rec.* **118**, 335 (1954).
20. PALAY, S. L., *Anat. Rec.* **118**, 336 (1954).
21. —— *J. Biophys. Biochem. Cytol.* **2**, Suppl. 193 (1956).
22. —— Progress in Neuro-biology. Vol. II. Ultrastructure and Cellular Chemistry of Neural Tissue. KOREY, S. R. and NURNBERGER, J. I., eds., New York, Hoeber, p. 31. 1957.
23. PALAY, S. L. and PALADE, G. E., *J. Biophys. Biochem. Cytol.* **1**, 69 (1955).
24. RAMÓN Y CAJAL, S., *Trabajos inst. Cajal invest. biol.* **24**, 1 (1934).
25. —— Neuron Theory or Reticular Theory? Objective Evidence of the Anatomical Unity of Nerve Cells. Translated by M. U. PURKISS and C. A. FOX, Madrid, Consejo Superior de Investigaciones Cientifices, 1954.
26. RASMUSSEN, G. L., *J. Comp. Neurol.* **99**, 61 (1953).
27. —— New Research Techniques of Neuroanatomy. W. F. Windle, ed., Springfield, Charles C. Thomas, pp. 27–39, 1957.
28. ROBERTSON, J. D., *Anat. Rec.* **118**, 346 (1954).
29. —— *J. Biophys. Biochem. Cytol.* **2**, 381 (1956).
30. SCHARRER, E., *J. Comp. Neurol.* **83**, 237 (1945).
31. SCHARRER, E. and SCHARRER, B., Handbuch der mikroskopischen Anatomie des Menschen. W. BARGMANN, ed., Berlin, Springer, vol. **VI**/5, pp. 953–1066, 1954.
32. SJÖSTRAND, F. S., *J. Appl. Phys.* **24**, 1422 (1953).
33. SMITH, C. A., *Anat. Rec.* **127**, 483 (1957).
34. WERSÄLL, J., *Acta Oto-laryngol. Suppl. 126*, 1 (1956).
35. WYCKOFF, R. W. G. and YOUNG, J. Z., *Proc. Roy. Soc., Ser. B*, **144**, 440 (1956).

MORPHOLOGICAL AND CYTOCHEMICAL OBSERVATIONS ON THE POST-SYNAPTIC MEMBRANE AT MOTOR END-PLATES AND GANGLIONIC SYNAPSES[1]

R. COUTEAUX

Laboratoire de Biologie animale (P.C.B.), Faculté des Sciences, Université de Paris, Paris, France

THE morphological individuality of the nerve cell and striated muscle fibre is as well-marked at synaptic areas where they are connected with other cells as at any other points of their surfaces.

This fact, that was rendered extremely probable by observations made with the use of the light microscope, was established beyond doubt as soon as the electron microscope was used to examine the motor end-plates and some central synapses. Indeed the electron micrographs show with remarkable precision that plasma membranes limit the nerve cells and muscle fibres at the level of the synaptic zones as they do over all areas of their surfaces.

It is, on the other hand, probable that local interactions which take place during development between the cells closely connected by a junction, determine the origin of the diverse morphological characteristics observed in the vicinity of the apposition zone of the membranes for each of the jointed elements, and which confer on all synaptic regions the obvious character of specialized areas.

One of the unvarying morphological characteristics of the nerve fibre at the level of a synapse is the absence of a myelin sheath. This becomes striking when the continuity of the myelin sheath of a large diameter nerve fibre is interrupted immediately before coming into contact with the post-synaptic element, as is frequently the case with the motor nerve fibres whose activity sets up a muscular response of the twitch type. When the myelination process takes place, the Schwann cells accompanying the terminal nerve branches show no myelogenetic activity: it is as though the junctional sarcoplasm inhibits this activity either directly or indirectly.

The presence, recently demonstrated in the terminal branches of several types of axons (motor endings of the striated muscle, terminal buttons of the central synapses, or pre-synaptic portions of the terminal spherule of

---

[1] Dedicated to Professor Giuseppe Levi on the occasion of his 85th birthday.

the retinal rods) of numerous submicroscopic vesicles, which do not exist, it appears, in other regions of these axons, constitutes another very important characteristic of this specialization.

When compared with the rest of the muscle fibre, the post-synaptic part of the motor end-plate is also found to have certain structural characteristics. The presence in the junctional sarcoplasm of a greater number of nuclei and granules than in other areas of the muscle fibre, has been known for a long time. These nuclei and granules, which for the most part are mitochondria, do not greatly differ from the nuclei and granules which the sarcoplasm presents at the surface of a "sarcoplasm rich" muscle fibre; but it is necessary to emphasize the fact that this abundance of nuclei and mitochondria is constant at the level of a motor end-plate, whereas it is highly variable outside the motor end-plate, where the number of these organelles depends on the type of muscle fibre. In studying their development it is easy to note the direct correlation between the growth of the number of muscular nuclei and mitochondria and that of the number of branches of the nerve endings.

The junctional sarcoplasm has other characteristics of its own with regard to the post-synaptic membrane which covers its surface. The main aim of this paper is to ascertain in which way the morphological and cytochemical characteristics of the plasma membrane which limits the junctional sarcoplasm differ from those of the membrane which limits the sarcoplasm in other areas of the muscle fibre.

As the ganglionic synapses may in certain respects be directly compared with the neuromuscular junctions, especially with regard to the transmission mechanism, the distribution of cholinesterase activities in the autonomic ganglia will also be taken into consideration and compared with cholinesterase activities at the motor end-plate.

MOTOR END-PLATES

Main Structural Features of the End-plate Observed with the Light Microscope

After having lost its myelin sheath, the motor axon branches and connects with the sarcoplasm. Mitochondrial staining reveals in the terminal axoplasm the existence mainly in the axis of the branches of very small granules, the staining affinities of which are those of mitochondria (Text-fig. 1).

Using silver methods one may observe that the "neurofibrils" of the myelinated portion of the motor axon continue into the terminal branches. Whereas the diameter of the terminal nerve branches, in spite of dichotomous branching, is often constant (as may be observed after good fixation), the terminal neurofibrils present in each point of a branch as a bundle tend to be the more slender as the bifurcations have been more numerous.

The nerve branches are joined to teloglia (terminal Schwann cells), and they occupy hollows of widely varying depth, shape and size according to the animal species considered. These "synaptic gutters" or "synaptic troughs" are hollowed out into a flattened-out heap of sarcoplasm rich in nuclei and mitochondria.

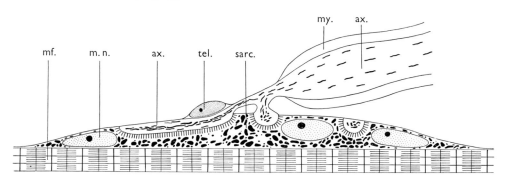

Text-fig. 1.—Schematic drawing of a motor end-plate. *ax.*, axoplasm with its mitochondria; *my.*, myelin sheath; *tel.*, teloglia (terminal Schwann cells); *sarc.*, sarcoplasm with its mitochondria; *m.n.*, muscle nuclei; *mf.*, myofibrils. The terminal nerve branches lie in "synaptic gutters" or "troughs". Immediately under the interface axoplasm–sarcoplasm, the ribbon-shaped subneural lamellae, transversely cut, may be seen as rodlets.

By means of some selective stainings, it is possible with the light microscope to distinguish the "interface" at the level of which axoplasm and sarcoplasm are joined. On a section cut through a motor end-plate this interface appears as a thin line to which are attached on the sarcoplasm side by one of their edges the elongated ribbon-shaped lamellae constituting the subneural apparatus [10, 12]. When they are cut transversally and observed with the light microscope, these subneural lamellae appear as rodlets which are slightly less than a micron in length. They are always perpendicular to the axoplasm and sarcoplasm apposition surface. The juxtaposition of these rodlets which are situated on the deeper face of the nerve terminals results in a picture which resembles that of a palisade or picket-fence.

On a front-view of a motor end-plate the whole appearance of the lamellae of the subneural apparatus which run under the nerve terminals is that of a finger-print. The orientation of these lamellae differs widely according to their position in the subneural apparatus, and they are of unequal lengths. Although more or less equally spaced in the deeper part of the gutter, they are generally more closely packed in the vicinity of the edges.

Among the problems to which the light microscope has given no clear solution, two are particularly important for defining the nature of the relationship of the axoplasm and the sarcoplasm at the end-plate: Is there an interposition of teloglia between the nerve terminals and the sarcoplasm, and are the lamellae of the subneural apparatus exclusively muscular in nature?

As regards the first problem, the neurofibrillar stainings obtained either by means of silver or postvital methods might suggest the idea of a sleeve which completely enfolds the nerve terminals separating them from the sarcoplasm. Examination of sections made through the motor end-plate, after good fixation, by osmio-chromic mixtures, and after staining in different ways, has not confirmed this assumption, but did not make it possible to exclude the hypothesis that a teloglial sheath of submicroscopic thickness is placed between the axoplasm and the sarcoplasm.

Neither the first problem, nor the related second problem set by the subneural lamellae, can be resolved directly with the light microscope alone. As we shall see further on, the electron microscope has provided more precise information of decisive importance on these two points.

Submicroscopic Organization of the Motor End-plate

Recent observations on the end-plate made with the electron microscope after osmium tetroxyde fixation have not only confirmed previous results but they have also filled the gaps in earlier descriptions and provided certain entirely new data concerning the submicroscopic organization of the end-plate.

Amongst the most recently published papers on the ultrastructure of the end-plate, three are preliminary reports (Palade and Palay [47] in the rat, Reger [49] also in the rat and Robertson [52] in the chameleon lizard). Two complete reports were published later [50, 53]. Because of the techniques he used for fixing and preparing the specimens, Reger [50] was limited in his observation and it is from Robertson's paper [53] that most of the data on the ultrastructure of the end-plate will be taken for this review.

After a brief report of recent information supplied by the electron microscope on the inclusions of the terminal axoplasm, the progress of our knowledge on the relationship between the axoplasm and the sarcoplasm will be considered.

Inclusions of the terminal axoplasm and junctional sarcoplasm.—When examined with the electron microscope the small granules observed with the light microscope in the axis of the nerve branches show the characteristic internal structure of mitochondria [45, 46, 56, 57]. This is also the case with the granules of the junctional sarcoplasm (Text-fig. 2).

Apart from the many mitochondria contained in the terminal axoplasm, other much smaller inclusions (300–500 Å) are distributed throughout the thickness of the nerve branches. These "vesicles" have been described

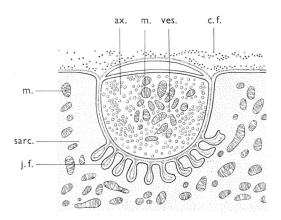

Text-fig. 2.—Schematic drawing of a "synaptic gutter" or "trough", seen in cross-section. *ax.*, axoplasm; *m.*, mitochondria; *ves.*, vesicules; *sarc.*, sarcoplasm; *j.f.*, junctional fold; *c.f.*, collagen fibrils (after Robertson [53], slightly modified).

in the motor nerve endings of the striated muscle by Palade and Palay [47] and by Robertson [53]. It seems probable that these inclusions are homologous to the presynaptic "vesicles" described for some interneuronal synapses.

It is with the discovery of these "vesicles" that a clear qualitative distinction has for the first time been established between the ending and the rest of the motor axon and this suggests a functional specialization of the nerve ending.

It would seem that a correlation may be established between the presence of the "vesicles" and the absence of "neurofilaments" in electron micrographs of nerve endings. If there is a relation of any kind between the neurofibrils observed with the light microscope and the "neurofilaments" shown with the electron microscope, then the filaments cannot be considered as entirely absent from nerve endings, at least with regard to the motor nerve endings of striated muscle, since preparations in which the neurofibrils are selectively stained clearly show the existence of terminal neurofibrils extending the motor axon neurofibrils beyond the preterminal constriction.

In addition to the discovery of the synaptic vesicles, which opens new perspectives regarding the mechanism of synaptic transmission, other progress of great importance has been made concerning the relationship of the axoplasm and the sarcoplasm.

Relationship between axoplasm and sarcoplasm membranes

The first fact established by all the authors who have hitherto studied the ultrastructure of the end-plate is that no teloglia is placed between the axoplasm and the sarcoplasm. These converging results have put an end to the irritating debate promoted by the insufficient resolving power of the light microscope.

A similar problem has been set by all other synapses, and hitherto in every case, when an examination with the electron microscope has been carried out, the conclusion has been the same: that there is no neuroglial interposition between the pre-synaptic and post-synaptic membranes of interneuronal synapses. This fact has been established by Robertson [51] on the axo-axonic synapses of the squid and crayfish, by Palade and Palay [47] and Palay [48] on the central synapses of the rat, and by De Robertis and Bennett [22, 23] on the sympathetic ganglia of frog and the neuropile of the earthworm nerve cord.

In the case of the motor end-plate the teloglia is not present at the precise level of the synapse, that is to say, between the axoplasm and the sarcoplasm, but without penetrating to the interior of the synaptic gutters this teloglia (a satellite of the nerve ending from the first stage in the formation of the motor end-plate [8, 9, 1]) remains attached to the nerve terminals, which justifies the name of "nuclei arborization" given to its nuclei.

Several electron micrographs of Reger [50] show the intimate connections of the teloglia with the nerve terminals.

Robertson has established in the chameleon lizard that above the nerve twig there exists a thin layer of cytoplasm which in appearance differs decidedly from the underlying axoplasm from which it is separated by a double membrane. Though the nature of this superficial layer of cytoplasm has not been established beyond doubt, it seems highly probable that it may be considered as an expansion of the teloglial cell. According to this hypothesis the teloglia close the synaptic gutter as a lid or an operculum and does not, therefore, lie between the axoplasm and the sarcoplasm but between the axoplasm and the extracellular medium.

Further research will show whether this firm closing of the synaptic gutter by the teloglia is the rule, and a constant feature of the end-plate organization. This arrangement of the teloglia as revealed in electron micrographs would then account for the observations made with the light microscope, showing that it always accompanies the terminal nerve twigs.

Another problem left unsolved by light microscopy is that of the nature of the ribbon-shaped lamellae of the subneural apparatus. Being as they are placed at the boundary between axoplasm and sarcoplasm, and sunk in the junctional sarcoplasm, they might be considered as a dependence of the membrane that limits the sarcoplasm, but it was not possible with the light microscopy alone to reject the assumption that the neighbouring cyto-plasms, teloglia and axoplasm, might partly contribute to their constitution. When the interpretation of teloglia at the level of the synaptic interface is disregarded, only the participation of the axoplasm remains as a possibility. The results of Palade and Palay [47] and of Robertson [52, 53] show that the axoplasm does not participate in the constitution of the subneural lamel-lae. These results have shown that the lamellae of the subneural apparatus are formed by narrow infoldings of the sarcoplasm surface membrane to which the axoplasm surface membrane remains completely external.

In consequence of these post-synaptic folds the sarcoplasm surface mem-brane presents two parts at the end-plate. These parts have very different relationships with the axoplasm surface membrane. One is closely joined to the axoplasm surface membrane, whereas the other corresponds to the infoldings, where the membrane limiting the junctional sarcoplasm leaves the one which limits the terminal axoplasm.

Between the infoldings, the surface membranes of the nerve fibre and of the muscle fibre are closely united to each other and their connections are in this respect comparable with those which appear between the pre- and post-synaptic membranes of a central synapse, where there is also an appo-sition of the two membranes. But besides the existence of the junctional folds—nothing comparable to them has hitherto been noted at the interneu-ronal synapses—the structure of the pre- and post-synaptic membranes presents also at the end-plate a structure somewhat different from that of the membranes which form the synaptolemma of the central synapses.

At the point where the two membranes are apposed and form a synaptic compound membrane, it is difficult to determine exactly what belongs to each of the two membranes. But the junctional fold, formed solely by the sarcoplasm surface membrane, offers particularly favourable conditions for the analysis of the latter (Text-fig. 3). Robertson in the chameleon lizard describes three layers: a very dense inner layer, less than 100 Å thick, an outer layer about 200 Å thick which is dense, but less dense than the former, and between these two layers, a light layer about 100 to 200 Å thick.

These three layers may be observed over all areas of the sarcoplasm surface, not only in the interior of the synaptic gutters, but also externally. Proceeding from the junctional folds, one may see their three layers extending into the synaptic compound membrane which results from the appositon of the axoplasm and sarcoplasm surface membranes.

The surface membrane of the axoplasm like that of the sarcoplasm has a very dense inner layer, less than 100 Å thick. It seems probable that the

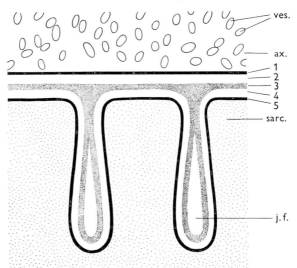

Text-fig. 3.—Schematic drawing of two junctional folds, showing how the sarcoplasm surface membrane joins with the axoplasm surface membrane and forms the synaptic compound membrane. *ax.*, axoplasm; *ves.*, vesicules; *sarc.*, sarcoplasm; *j.f.*, junctional fold (after Robertson [53], slightly modified).

axoplasm surface membrane also involves a light layer and a dense outer layer.

The synaptic membrane complex, about 500 to 700 Å thick resulting from apposition, comprises five layers. The two very dense inner membranes which limit axoplasm and sarcoplasm respectively are separated from each other by three other layers: a dense middle layer and two light layers. One of these light layers obviously corresponds to the light layer of the sarcoplasm surface membrane and the dense middle layer results probably from a fusion of the two dense outer layers of the axoplasm and sarcoplasm membranes.

General Configuration of the Subneural Apparatus

Observations made with the electron microscope have clearly shown that the subneural apparatus is formed by the folding of the sarcoplasm surface membrane within the junctional area. In order to define the shape of the folds and their general arrangement with accuracy, it will be necessary to

make a systematic study of the subneural apparatus with serial ultrathin
sections. By combining electron microscopy data with others obtained with
the light microscope, one may develop several positive conclusions, and
form new assumptions.

The most successful histological methods used for making a topographical
study of the subneural apparatus are naturally those which give a general

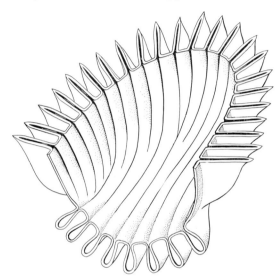

Text-fig. 4.—Schematic three-dimensional
presentation of the subneural apparatus
at the extremity of a "synaptic gutter".
This interpretation is based upon data
hitherto obtained both with the light and
the electron microscope.

view of the junctional folds of the end-plate. This is the case with postvital
staining with Janus green B, methyl violet and dahlia violet, and with or
without ammonium molybdate fixation; this is also the case when histochemical methods are used for localizing cholinesterases, which will be discussed
below.

As a result of these methods it is possible to show that the junctional folds
are not digitate invaginations but long folds differently orientated in relation
to the axis of the gutters containing the terminal nerve twigs (Text-fig. 4).

In the frog the folds are transverse and stretch from edge to edge of the
gutter. This arrangement may be found in reptiles and in mammals, but it is
much less frequent, and is only observed in general, along short gutter segments. In reptiles and in mammals the orientation of the folds often differs
considerably according to whether we are dealing with the deep part of the
gutter or the regions neighbouring the edges. In the deep part of the gutter,
the folds may be orientated in different patterns and often longitudinally.
In this latter case the folds may be as long as the gutters themselves, and the

aspect of the synaptic gutter on a section perpendicular to its axis reminds one of a part of a cog wheel, where the cogs correspond to the folds seen in the cross-section.

In the neighbourhood of the edges of each gutter, the subneural folds have, on the contrary, a constant orientation, which is perpendicular to each edge. The arrangement of folds in these areas explains why the sections cut transversally to the gutter axis have no "cogs" in proximity to edges, except at the gutter extremity.

If the aspect of the transversely cut subneural folds as shown on Robertson's electron micrographs is compared with the above description of the subneural apparatus, one might suppose that the unstained zone which exists in the deepest part of each infolding corresponds to the section of a canaliculus whose length often spreads over a large area of the synaptic gutter.

On the other hand, observations with the light microscope always show on the sides of the synaptic gutter the outcropping of the junctional folds at the surface of the sole. Therefore, if the unstained zone visible in the interior of the folds is really a "free" space, it may be thought probable that the caniculi of the subneural folds open at the end-plate surface by means of slot-shaped openings, placed on either side of each nerve branch.

Distinguishing Characteristics of the Sarcoplasm Surface Membrane within the Synaptic Area

Certain postvital methods used in the staining of striated muscle fibres have already shown that one of the components of what is classically known as the sarcolemma, but without any precise definition, may be selectively stained by these methods [10]; when examined with the light microscope this component appears as a continuous and homogenous membrane which extends under the terminal nerve branches at the motor end-plates. This membrane delimits the synaptic gutters, and it is to the deep face of this membrane that the subneural lamellae are attached. It is probable that the membrane stained by the periodic acid-Schiff method (PAS reaction) at the level of the sarcolemma by MacManus [40] is identical with that stained by postvital methods. These staining methods reveal no important difference between the surface membrane which coats the sarcoplasm within the synaptic area and that which envelops the rest of the muscle fibre.

On the contrary, differences are apparent between the two zones of the sarcoplasm surface membrane when histological methods are used, such as Heidenhain's Azan method, which stains the collagen fibrils of the Perimysium internum or those which, as Laidlaw's silver technique, stain the argyrophil fibrillar network very deeply at the surface of the muscle fibre: none of these methods reveal the existence of any fibrillar structure at the surface of the subneural sarcoplasm. Neither has it been possible to detect collagen fibrils at this level with an electron microscope.

Still further data has resulted from observations made with the electron microscope after osmic fixation. Although the three layers of the subneural sarcoplasm surface membrane and the three corresponding layers of the sarcolemma are continuous, Robertson has observed that the total thickness of these three layers is slightly reduced at the level of the synaptic gutters, and that this reduction is mainly the result of the thinning out of the light middle layer. An interpretation of this fact would at present be premature.

The most effective methods hitherto used for showing the most clearly defined differences between the sarcoplasm membrane located within the synaptic area, and the rest of this membrane, are those histochemical methods which reveal cholinesterase activity. These methods disclose an important and differential concentration of cholinesterase at motor end-plates confined to the post-synaptic membrane. But as results obtained by histochemical methods, especially those concerning the localization of an enzyme, may be vitiated by serious artefacts, the site of a cholinesterase activity at a myoneural synapse can only be firmly established with many converging observations. The most important data which permit us to consider this location as extremely probable are discussed below.

Cholinesterase Activities at the Motor End-plates

It has been established through histochemical methods by several authors, and for the first time by Koelle and Friedenwald [37] on the motor end-plates of different animal species, that a high cholinesterase activity exists at these junctions, which corroborates the earlier results given by manometric determinations [42, 43, 24, 13, 14].

In this localization by histochemical methods of cholinesterase activity at motor end-plates, the pictures obtained by most authors [15, 11, 16, 34, 4, 5, 26, 21, 27, 33, 62, 7, 17] show with great precision that the structures selectively stained, using thiocholine esters or other substances as substrates, are those which have been described previously, on the basis of postvital methods, as the subneural apparatus.

Different pictures obtained with the same methods do, however, have a slightly different appearance, and might even in some cases suggest the idea of a totally different enzymatic distribution at the level of the juxta-synaptic structures.

These divergences reveal the existence of artefacts whose appearance varies according to the manner of using the techniques. Before describing and interpreting histochemical results, it is therefore necessary to define with precision the methods which have been used to obtain them.

Methods

Hitherto the most suitable method devised to localize the cholinesterase activities of striated muscle has been the method of Koelle [35], using as substrates two thiocholine esters.

Let us bear in mind that this method is based upon the enzymatic hydrolysis of thioanalogues of acetyl- and butyrylthiocholine by cholinesterases in a medium obtained by mixing glycine, copper sulfate and the substrate. The liberated thiocholine precipitates as a mercaptide and is replaced subsequently by CuS. Malmgren and Sylvén [41] have shown that Cu-thiocholine precipitates as Cu-thiocholine sulfate.

With acetylthiocholine as substrate it is possible to detect the specific cholinesterases (acetylcholinesterases) as well as the unspecific cholinesterases, whereas with butyrylthiocholine the unspecific cholinesterases are practically the only ones to be revealed.

Apart from this thiocholine method, there are at present many other methods using various substrates, but biochemically less selective than the thiocholine method. Among these some are notably more sensitive than the thiocholine method for the detection of cholinesterases, but in the search for the main sites of enzyme activity, the weak sensitivity of the latter, sharply accentuating the contrasts, has the advantage of facilitating a first survey. It is the only one which will be referred to here.

Modification of the Koelle method.—The results obtained by the thiocholine method differ, often quite considerably, according to different authors. This is due mainly, it would seem, to the conditions of use of these methods, which are often appreciably different from those originally laid down by Koelle.

The conditions under which these methods have been employed here are stated below. These conditions have been the same as in previous research [16]. While we have respected the main steps of the original method as carefully enunciated by Koelle [35, 36], some changes have in fact been adopted, some of which are absolutely indispensable for an accurate localization of cholinesterases.

A first series of changes has been to simplify some of the steps of the thiocholine method. They consist: (1) in omitting certain provisions laid down by Koelle to avoid the diffusion of cholinesterases, such as the addition of Na_2SO_4, at concentrations of 24 and 28 per cent according to the type of esterase, to all the solutions through which the sections must pass, before the ammonium sulfide treatment; (2) in not saturating the incubation and rinse solutions with Cu-thiocholine, this step having been included to prevent diffusion from the enzyme site of the substance produced by the enzymatic hydrolysis of the substrate.

The fact that the cholinesterases have been shown, at least in most cases, to be

very firmly attached to the cellular structures, is sufficient to justify the first modification. The second has resulted from two considerations: the doubtful effect that
saturation of solutions with Cu-thiocholine may have on diffusion artefacts, and the
facility with which it is generally possible to prevent these artefacts through a
suitable choice of incubation pH and buffer [15, 16].

Another modification designed to limit tissue changes has been to fix the tissues
with formaldehyde prior to incubation, neutralized 10 per cent formalin being generally used.

The histochemical detection of a cholinesterase activity has been shown to be
possible in most cases with formaldehyde tissue fixation, but the inactivation rate of
the cholinesterases varies considerably according to the type of enzyme or tissue in
which it is situated [15, 11, 16, 34, 31, 18]. Taxi [61] was able to confirm this histochemical fact through manometric research on homogenates. The inactivation rate
depends, not only on the type of cholinesterase activity, but also on the animal species. Results published by Chessick [3] are in entire agreement with this conclusion.

Therefore, in spite of serious damage to the tissue, in particular to muscle, by
the thiocholine method when it is used without previous fixation, it is essential, in
order to study the distribution of cholinesterase activities in the tissue, to compare
the pictures obtained before and after fixation, and to determine by eliminations
the period of fixation which gives both the best preservation possible and the least
weakening of the enzyme activity.

The systematic comparison of the results obtained after fixation for varying
periods with those obtained on non-fixed pieces shows that at the level of many
tissues the formaldehyde effect on the cholinesterases is sometimes selective. This
action, similar to that of irreversible inhibitor action, provides the basis for a separation in homogenates as well as in histochemical preparations of the cholinesterases
of different types, located in the same organ.

Among the various factors upon which the success of the Koelle method depends,
the pH of the incubation medium is certainly one of the most important. But the
optimum pH for the histochemical detection of cholinesterases is quite different
from the optimum biochemically established pH, for the hydrolysis of acetylthiocholine and butyrylthiocholine in the presence of cholinesterases. At pH 8.0, which
is close to the optimum pH for cholinesterase activity, there is generally no precipitation in the histochemical preparation. When the pH is gradually reduced, the
value at which precipitation occurs is considerably below the biochemical optimum.
At this pH, when the reaction is positive for the first time in the presence of cholinesterases, one may observe during the enzymatic hydrolysis a coarse diffusion of Cu-
thiocholine. The precipitation of this reaction product may occur at relatively considerable distances from the enzyme site and secondarily become attached to a
variety of structures, namely to the nuclear structures of all neighbouring cells,
irrespective of their nature. This diffusion may generally be avoided by choosing a
sufficiently low pH, but the value of the optimum pH, by which coarse diffusion
images are avoided and in particular false nuclear localizations, varies with the
animal species and the type of tissue in which the enzyme is situated. A thorough
search for it must therefore be made in every case. If a tissue contains highly concentrated cholinesterase locations, which requires short incubation periods even
at a low pH, it is often useful, in order to prevent the hydrolysis of the substrate

before the pH has reached a suitable value at the enzyme site, to have, prior to the incubation, a "pre-incubation" in a solution identical to that of the incubation solution, but without substrate. This pre-incubation can last long enough for a fixed tissue, without damage; it assumes special importance in the case of a quantitative study of cholinesterase activities.

As soon as the histochemical optimum pH has been determined, the incubation period remains to be precisely defined. The minimum period of incubation indispens-able to stain the enzyme site distinctly is naturally very variable since, in the first place, it depends on the enzyme concentration at the relevant site. If the duration of incubation is prolonged over this minimum period, there is first of all a darkening of the staining, soon followed by a clogging of the structures with abundant precipita-tion and diffusion leading to the formation of needle-shaped crystals. This means that it is always preferable, in order to find the exact location of the cholinesterases with the Koelle method, to use incubation periods as close as possible to the minimum period length. Thus the optimum period must be found separately for each type of location.

If the enzyme concentration is very weak and significant staining can only be obtained at the cost of long incubation, a more sensitive method, such as the method of Holt [33], using indoxyl derivatives would seem to be indicated.

Main steps of the procedure.—The thiocholine method is usually applied to frozen sections, teased preparations or to very thin organs treated as a whole. Whatever the type of preparation used, the incubation medium reagents only reach an adequate concentration at the enzyme site if it is located at the surface of the preparations, or at the very most at a depth of a few micra. At a much greater depth, and especially with a short incubation period, neither the pH nor the concentration of the substrate have the requisite value. In this connection the end-plates chiefly are suitable material owing to their location at the surface of the muscle fibres and their reduced thickness, that is to say when the end-plate is put into direct contact with the in-cubation medium. This latter condition may be achieved either by immersing teased muscle preparations in the medium, or by immersing whole muscles such as the inter-costal muscles of the mouse and the rat, which on one face at least present numerous and quite superficially placed end-plates. Those preparations in which the muscle fibres remain intact have the advantage of showing the end-plates over their whole extension and as regards the non-fixed muscles, are preferable to the frozen sections in which coarse artefacts are certain to appear as soon as the sections have thawed.

Since fixation of tissues by formaldehyde leads to a more or less rapid inactivation of the cholinesterases, in order to study the distribution of cholinesterases in the tissues, it is necessary to apply the histochemical method to non-fixed and fixed tissues and to compare the results obtained in both cases.

Choice of fixation period depends firstly on the rate at which formaldehyde inactivates the enzyme, and this varies according to the animal species, the nature of the tissue, and the type and concentration of the enzyme at the studied site.

In order to determine the optimum period of fixation, numerous tests are neces-sary in each case: the tissue structures should be stabilized, but a sufficient enzyme activity should be allowed to subsist for detection under satisfactory conditions.

For the study of cholinesterases at the motor end-plates the muscles were fixed by neutralized 10 per cent formalin (4 per cent formaldehyde) at 20°C.

The non-fixed or fixed pieces are immersed in the pre-incubation medium where they remain for 15 minutes. They are then transferred to the incubation medium.

Choice of pH for the pre-incubation and incubation media is of extreme importance in localizing the cholinesterase accurately, for, as has been previously mentioned, it depends on the value of the pH whether diffusion artefacts appear or not.

Another important choice is that of the incubation period. It would be as short as possible to avoid any clogging of the structures where the enzyme is located. If necessary, observation may be made with the phase-contrast microscope which accentuates the staining contrasts.

As for the period of fixation, numerous tests must be made for each site of activity to determine the optimum pH and incubation period.

When very high cholinesterase activities are involved, such as those of the motor end-plates, the pre-incubation and incubation have always been effected at 20°C both for homeotherms and poikilotherms. At this temperature the rate of hydrolysis, notably less than at 38°C, allows us to determine the optimum incubation period with greater accuracy.

The volume of the incubation medium should naturally vary according to the volume of tissue, and it is advisable to renew the medium fairly quickly should the tissue be bulky or possess a very large surface.

When withdrawn from the incubation medium, the tissue fragments are rinsed in distilled water and immersed for some minutes in 2–5 per cent ammonium sulfide.

After washing in distilled water, the non-fixed and fixed fragments were dehydrated and mounted in balsam with or without counterstaining (hemalun). The non-fixed pieces were fixed in 10 per cent formalin before dehydration. It is also possible to mount the preparations in dilute levulose syrup, or to keep them in formaline solution where they remain practically unchanged for some years.

The control preparations were obtained in different ways, by leaving out the substrate from the incubation medium, by treating the preparations with heat for two minutes at 80°C in a hydrated state, and by treatment with numerous chemical compounds which at extremely low concentrations inhibit the cholinesterases.

Inhibition experiments were conducted with a wide series of concentrations for both reversible and irreversible inhibitors, not only with the aim of determining the concentration from which staining is prevented, but eventually to separate by "selective inhibition" the cholinesterase activities of a different nature which can coexist in the same preparation.

Accuracy of the thiocholine method.—What is the biochemical significance to be attributed to the staining provided by the thiocholine method?

The numerous different types of anticholinesterase drugs with greater or lesser differential action, which at present may be used as reversible or irreversible inhibitors, enable an identification of the enzymes responsible for the observed staining to be made under satisfactory conditions.

As the action of the inhibitors often depends to a large extent on the pH, it is necessary when interpreting the results to take into account the pH at which inhibition was effected, that is to say the incubation medium pH as for the reversible inhibitors.

The main body of results hitherto obtained show that the tissues in which cholinesterases have been detected by manometric determinations are all stained by the

Koelle method, with the exception of the erythrocytes in which cholinesterases are probably insufficiently concentrated for the sensitivity of these methods [30], and conversely it is only in a few cases that staining given by the Koelle method is not attributable to a cholinesterase.

As to the value of the localizations, the firmness with which cholinesterases are generally attached to structures justifies some optimism. It is easy to establish in the case of the motor end-plates that after fixation long washing of muscle fibres in saline does not change the distribution of the cholinesterase activity.

On the other hand, the appearance, with certain pH values of the incubation medium of a very important thiocholine diffusion, which results from the hydrolysis of the substrate in the presence of the tissue cholinesterases, calls for great reserve. Each localization must be the subject of a detailed discussion.

Among the procedures which may be used in verifying the validity of a localization may be mentioned the comparison of results obtained by thiocholine methods with those using other substrates.

On the other hand, one may try to limit the risk of a false localization due to diffusion of the hydrolysis products by separating each cellular fragment as much as possible from adjoining structures which may be enzyme-rich and sources of the diffusion. This is possible when the structure that appears to be the enzyme site can be identified with the microscope after grinding of the fixed tissue. In this case the tissue is ground before incubation. A further microscopic examination of the fragments that have been selectively stained under these conditions provides a rigorous control of the histochemical localization carried out on the sections.

Results

By a suitable choice of pH and period of incubation, and using methods which conform to the modification of the Koelle method with acetylthiocholine whose main steps have just been described, it is possible to obtain differential staining of the subneural apparatus, equivalent to that given by certain postvital staining methods.

On the motor end-plates of the mouse, the most differentiated pictures of the subneural apparatus have generally been obtained with incubation at pH 5 or slightly lower and an incubation period of less than 30 minutes at 20°C for the non-fixed muscles, or of 45 to 60 minutes if previously fixed with neutralized 10 per cent formalin (4 per cent formaldehyde) during 24 hours at 20°C. As has been shown by Coërs [4, 5, 7] good results are given on the motor end-plate of man after 8 hours fixation.

Whether for fixed or for non-fixed tissues a treatment by DFP lasting 30 minutes at 38°C has hindered staining at a concentration which is equal to or slightly greater than 2×10^{-7} M. Eserine salicylate used under the previously stated conditions has given the same result at a concentration of 5×10^{-6} M, at 20°C. Also with a concentration at 5×10^{-6} M, at 20°C, prostigmine has prevented the staining of the subneural apparatus.

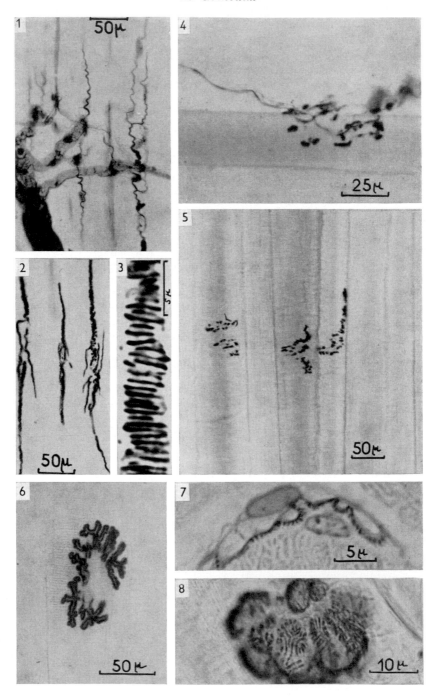

Clear-cut and differentiated pictures of the motor end-plates (end-bushes) of the non-fixed muscles in the frog may be obtained with incubation at pH 5.5 for 30 to 60 minutes at 20°C (Figs. 1, 2, 3). With 10 per cent formalin fixation occupies one hour. An incubation period exceeding one hour is often necessary if there has been a direct contact of the end-bushes with the formalin. Inactivation of the cholinesterases by formaldehyde in the muscles of the frog is too rapid for a longer fixation to be profitable.

A much longer incubation is necessary to reveal the cholinesterase activity of the numerous and small end-plates observed at the surface of each slow muscle fibre when studying the muscles of the frog. These end-plates which correspond to the endings of the "small nerve motor system" described by Kuffler and collaborators are grouped in constellations of widely varying form and size, and are located at different levels in each fibre. In the case of this very special type of ending the subneural apparatus is only represented by a shallow cupule a few micra in diameter, in which lies the small nerve ending and which may be selectively stained by the thiocholine method (Figs. 4, 5).

The end-plates of the lizard require almost the same conditions of incubation as the end-bushes of the frog (Fig. 6).

After staining by the acetylthiocholine method, as after staining with postvital methods, the subneural folds are more or less distinguishable according to the animal species. They are specially distinguishable on the end bushes of the frog. They are also, in general, easily enough perceived on the end-plates of the hedgehog (Fig. 7) and of man (Fig. 8).

Hitherto we have only considered the conditions under which the acetylthiocholine method gives a selective staining of the subneural apparatus.

If on the muscles of mice, fixed by formaldehyde, the pH of the incubation medium is raised, from 5 to 5.5 for instance, after about 15 minutes of incubation at 20°C an intense staining of the terminal nerve branches is generally apparent.

Figs. 1, 2 and 3.—Frog muscle (gastrocnemius). End-bushes (photomicrographs from Couteaux and Taxi [16]). *Fig. 1.* Silver preparation. *Figs. 2 and 3.* Acetylthiocholine method; front view of the subneural apparatus without counterstaining.

Figs. 4 and 5.—Frog muscle (gastrocnemius). Motor end-plates of the "small nerve motor system". *Fig. 4.* Methylene blue method (original photomicrograph from Barets). *Fig. 5.* Acetylthiocholine method without counterstaining.

Fig. 6.—Lizard motor end-plate. Acetylthiocholine method without counterstaining.

Fig. 7.—Hedgehog motor end-plate. Acetylthiocholine method. Cross-section through a motor end-plate, showing synaptic gutters with subneural lamellae; nuclei are stained by hemalun.

Fig. 8.—Motor end-plate of man. Larynx muscle. Acetylthiocholine method without counterstaining; front view of end-plate with focussing on the deeper part of the subneural apparatus.

At a higher pH, other juxta-synaptic structures are also stained: nuclei, various inclusions of the cytoplasm and myofibrils. This staining of the most diverse structures which spreads more and more from the end-plate as the incubation period proceeds, may only be interpreted as a diffusion artefact. As has been previously stated, enzyme diffusion may be considered in this case as practically negligible. These diffusion artefacts therefore prove that thiocholine, a product of enzymatic hydrolysis, may at certain pH levels diffuse through the tissue and be adsorbed by structures bordering on near the enzyme site. Thus, it remains to be established whether the staining of the subneural apparatus by the thiocholine method is not the result of a diffusion from a juxta-synaptic structure.

As staining by diffusion of any structure during a brief incubation period implies vicinity of a cholinesterase site, we may try to escape the risks of a diffusion artefact by separating mechanically the different components of the synaptic region, and then treating them by histochemical methods.

By delaceration or grinding of the "neural" part of a muscle previously fixed by formaldehyde, a pulp is obtained, in which the end-plates are more or less dislocated. From this pulp, a type of homogenate is prepared with the incubation solution. After centrifugation and washing, treatment by ammonium sulfide permits us to observe among muscle fragments some selectively stained strips of membranes on which a few periodically spaced folds of the subneural apparatus are sometimes easily recognizable.

Partial separation has been accomplished with the aid of another technique, less crude than the preceding. It consists of detaching the sarcolemma from the muscle fibre surface and at the same time the subneural apparatus from the underlying myofibrillar bundle. The subneural apparatus, thus completely separated from the myofibrils and from many of the other post-synaptic components of the end-plate, may then be stained in the usual manner. In this rather delicate operation made practicable by a previous formaldehyde fixation, the whole of the nervous part of the end-plate remains attached to the subneural apparatus.

Mechanical separation of the terminal nerve branches from the subneural apparatus appears extremely difficult, and even when using the first technique by dilaceration and grinding, it is not absolutely certain that the post-synaptic membrane and the axoplasmic membrane are indeed disjointed.

The most reliable means of effecting a separation of the terminal nerve branches from the subneural apparatus is to bring about the degeneration of the latter by section of the motor nerve. Histochemical observations have already been made repeatedly on the cholinesterase activity of denervated end-plates. Sawyer, Davenport, and Alexander [55] in a preliminary report and Kupfer [39] indicate for the rat, the guinea pig, and the rabbit, persistence of cholinesterase concentration at the level of motor end-plates after section of motor nerve and degeneration of nerve endings. Formerly Coërs [4, 5, 6], Snell and MacIntyre [58, 59], and Savay and Csillik [54] after a more thorough histochemical study arrived at the same result. These authors have shown that the cholinesterase activity which persists in the denervated end-plate of the rat and of the guinea pig, is in this case also located at the level of the subneural apparatus: the whole appearance of this apparatus generally altered two weeks after the section of the motor nerve, but at this stage, the lamellae may still be seen and stained by histochemical methods.

Appreciable differences are shown between figures hitherto published regarding the time-limit for persistence of cholinesterase activity in the denervated end-plates of the rat and of the guinea pig: three months after the section of a motor nerve, Coërs still found, in the gastrocnemius of the rat, some end-plates which showed a deformed, faintly stained, but well recognizable subneural apparatus; in the same species, and on the same muscle Savay and Csillik observed a residual activity after 4 months and even after 6 months; on the other hand in the guinea pig, Snell and Mac Intyre found no activity after 45 days.

It would seem probable that these differences are mainly due to minor differences in the technique used. With modification of the Koelle technique described above, and checking for the absence of nerve regeneration, Carric (unpublished results) has been able to observe on certain greatly altered motor end-plates of the m. gastrocnemius internus of the rat and of the guinea pig, the persistence of subneural lamellae faintly stained but still well visible six weeks after section of the motor nerve.

In any case, the ensemble of the histochemical results reached today on the cholinesterase activity of the denervated end-plates proves that the staining of the subneural apparatus by means of the thiocholine method is not the result of a diffusion from the terminal nerve branches.

All the above observations have been made using acethylthiocholine as substrate. Butyrylthiocholine gives the same pictures showing that the site of enzymatic activity localized by this substrate is itself also confined to the subneural apparatus. But, as was first shown by Denz (1953) on the diaphragm of the rat, when using this substrate, it is necessary to prolong the incubation period for several hours.

Discussion and conclusions

The existence of a high cholinesterase activity at motor end-plates is now established by numerous histochemical and biochemical data. After the thorough researches conducted by Denz [21] with the aid of several substrates and a number of selective inhibitors of cholinesterases, it would seem that the end-plate contains two cholinesterases, an acetylcholinesterase and an unspecific cholinesterase, the second of these being present in very much smaller quantity than the first.

With thiocholine methods, the subneural apparatus appears as the main site of the cholinesterase activity of the end-plate, when the pH has been appropriately chosen.

The appearance at pH values of important diffusion artefacts, which entails the staining of other structures, challenges the validity of this localization.

It has been stated above that enzyme diffusion may be disregarded and that only the thiocholine diffusion should be taken into account. By mechanical separation of the subneural apparatus from the other juxta-synaptic components before incubation, and by a histochemical study of the cholinesterase activity of the denervated end-plates, it has been possible to establish that selective staining of the subneural apparatus is not the result of a thiocholine diffusion from a neighbouring structure.

Another fact in support of this conclusion, is that histochemical methods for localizing cholinesterases using substrates other than acetylthiocholine and butyrylthiocholine, such as the long-chain fatty acid esters, for example myristoylcholine [21], α-naphthyl acetate [21], indoxyl derivatives [33], and thiolacetic acid [17] also selectively stain the subneural apparatus.

It is also fitting to recall that this conclusion entirely agrees with the biochemical data, and in particular with the results obtained by Couteaux and Nachmansohn [13, 14] on the denervated muscle; these results allowed us to attribute a post-synaptic site to the greater part of the cholinesterase found in the end-plate.

Before electron microscopy enabled us to interpret the subneural apparatus in ultrastructural terms, it was not possible to exclude the possibility that a thin teloglial layer was incorporated in the subneural lamellae, and survived degeneration of the nerve endings after section of the motor nerve.

Neither, therefore, did it seem possible to exclude the possibility that a cholinesterase attached to the subneural apparatus might be located in teloglia.

As a result of electron microscope examination the subneural apparatus may now be considered as formed exclusively by the sarcoplasm surface membrane. We must therefore conclude that the cholinesterase activity observed at the level of the subneural apparatus after denervation of the end-plate is exclusively located at the level of the sarcoplasm surface membrane.

As, at normal end-plates, the terminal axoplasm membrane, that is to say the pre-synaptic membrane, is intimately apposed to the post-synaptic membrane, it is impossible to distinguish one from the other by the use of the light microscope alone when localizing the cholinesterase. Further histochemical research with the electron microscope will therefore be necessary before deciding whether or not a cholinesterase site exists at the level of the pre-synaptic membrane.

In any case, results obtained from the above-mentioned biochemical investigations show that the cholinesterase activity at a possible pre-synaptic site is incomparably smaller than the activity located in the subneural part of the post-synaptic membrane.

GANGLIONIC SYNAPSES

Observations on synaptic transmission at the motor end-plate and the ganglionic synapse revealed some points of similarity between these two synapses regarding the transmission mechanism and the part played by acetylcholine. On the other hand, the possibilities offered by heterogeneous anastomoses experiments of replacing, morphologically at least, the preganglionic fibres by motor fibres of striated muscles (Fig. 9), and vice versa, leads us to suppose that the pre-synaptic parts of these two types of synapses are somewhat related.

Therefore, it might be interesting to investigate whether the cholinesterase location detected at the post-synaptic membrane in the case of the motor end-plate also exists at the post-synaptic membrane of the ganglionic synapse.

Morphological Relationships between Preganglionic Fibres, Ganglion Cells, and Gliocytes

In spite of important investigations on the structure of autonomous ganglia carried out with the aid of the light microscope, such as that of De Castro [20], which extends over a period of more than thirty years and which was carried

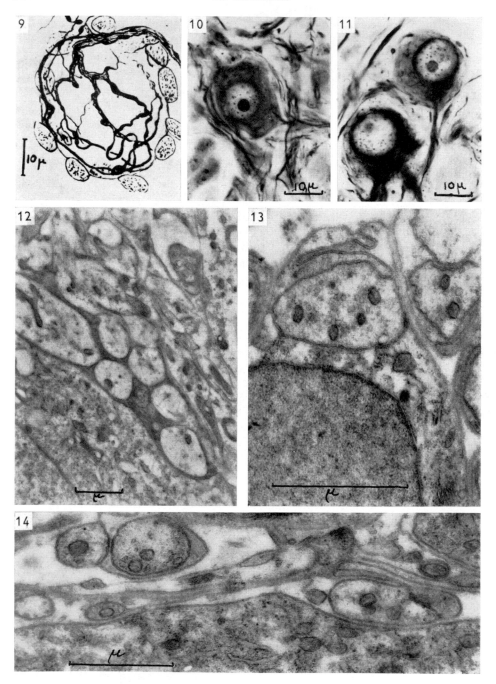

out with the use of silver methods, and that of Hillarp [32] with the methylene
blue method, the relationship between preganglionic fibres, ganglion cells, and
gliocytes are still not clearly defined. When examined with the light microscope (Figs. 10, 11), the structure of the autonomous ganglia appears so
involved and is composed of such small nerve fibres, that only the electron
microscope seems able to give us significant information regarding the
nature of the connections which join the preganglionic fibre endings to
ganglion cells.

De Robertis and Bennett [22, 23] have been able to establish on the frog
with the electron microscope that the ganglionic synapse consists in close
apposition of the membranes of preganglionic fibres and ganglion cells. They
have also shown numerous special vesicles to be present in the presynaptic
terminals.

But even with the electron microscope, it often remains extremely difficult
to interpret the observed aspects. This is evident in Taxi's observations (not
yet published) on the superior cervical ganglion of the rat, a résumé of which
follows.

The electron micrographs (Figs. 12, 13, 14) show that a continuous layer
of varying thickness is formed over the whole surface of the ganglion cells
by the juxtaposition and superposition of gliocytes, and unmyelinated nerve
fibres. When the section passes through their nucleus or its vicinity, the
gliocytes are easily recognizable. It may be established that the cytoplasm
of gliocytes applied to a ganglion cell is only separated from the neuronal
cytoplasm by a "double membrane" about 150 Å thick which results from
the apposition of the two plasma membranes.

Fig. 9.—Superior cervical ganglion. Rat. Phrenic-sympathetic anastomosis. A coarse phrenic
axon formed a pericellular nerve structure round a ganglion cell. Methylene blue method (drawing
from Hillarp [32]).

Figs. 10 and 11.—Superior cervical ganglion. Cajal silver method. Many unmyelinated nerve
fibres surround the ganglion cells on the surface of which button-like endings are sometimes
visible. Note, for instance, a well-distinguishable terminal button at the surface of the upper
neurone of Fig. 11.

Figs. 12, 13 and 14.—Superior cervical ganglion (original electron micrographs from Taxi). Rat.
OsO₄ fixed. *Fig. 12.* In the lower left-hand corner, the nucleus and cytoplasm of a ganglion cell
are partially visible; the ganglion cell surface is covered by numerous nerve and glial processes.
Magnification: ×12,000. *Fig. 13.* An unmyelinated nerve fibre is seen in the interior of the gliocyte the nucleus of which occupies the lower left portion of the field. Note in the upper centre a
typical "mesaxon". Magnification: ×31,000. *Fig. 14.* The lower portion of the field is taken
up with ganglion cell cytoplasm, which is separated by a double membrane from overlying glial
layer. Several processes may be seen in the interior of the glial layer. These processes are connected with the outer surface of the gliocyte by mesaxon-like double membrane. Magnification:
×24,500.

With regard to the processes of gliocytes and the unmyelinated fibres, which form a more or less thick coating around each ganglion cell, a great many of these are also only separated from the neuronal cytoplasm by a "double membrane". But in most cases, it has been impossible to distinguish the terminal unmyelinated part of the nerve fibres from processes of gliocytes by structural difference, particularly by differences between their respective inclusions. The only case in which the nervous nature of a process seems probable is when this process itself is located in the interior of another process, and when the surface membrane of the latter, deeply enfolded, forms a "mesaxon", corresponding to those described by Gasser [25], as existing at the level of unmyelinated fibres. The identification of the nerve fibre and of the glial process is, in this case, due to a particular type of relationship, but whether it is a specific one, remains to be shown. Identification is much more hazardous for all other processes which do not show these special connections: these may be glial processes which contain no nerve fibres, or nerve fibres deprived of a glial sheath at their termination.

Further data on serial sections, and a more thorough study of the varied processes will be necessary in order to establish a marked difference between gliocyte processes and terminal nerve branches. When a clear-cut difference has been defined between these two processes, one problem will remain which appears difficult to solve: How is it possible to distinguish the preganglionic fibres from the processes coming from adjacent ganglion cells which consist of fine dendritic ramifications and collaterals of post-ganglionic fibres? As is shown in the study of sympathetic ganglions after experimental degeneration of the preganglionic fibres, the branches of preganglionic fibres constitute only a part of the numerous unmyelinated nerve fibres which surround ganglion cells.

These initial results of studies on the ultrastructure of an autonomous ganglion shows how premature it would be to come to an immediate decision regarding the nature of the connections which unite the terminal branches of preganglionic fibres to ganglion cells in the mammals.

One important fact however may be stated owing to the electron micrographs. A scrutiny of many sections through the ganglion cells shows that the cytoplasm surface of these neurons is entirely limited by a continuous membrane, and in no way appears to justify the assumption of a structural continuity between the preganglionic fibres and the ganglion cells. Thus, here also, the old controversy concerning the nature of synaptic connections seems practically settled in favour of the neuron theory.

Examination with the electron microscope also reveals that the distances separating the many processes which surround each ganglion cell from the plasma membrane of that cell, are in general too small to be seen with the light microscope.

Distribution of the Cholinesterase Activities at Ganglionic Synapses

As a result of the determinations of Glick [28, 29], and those of Brücke [2], it has long been established that the sympathetic ganglia have a high cholinesterase activity. Koelle and Friedenwald [37], Koelle [35, 36], and Couteaux and Taxi [16] have confirmed these results by histochemical methods.

How is this cholinesterase distributed in the interior of the ganglion?

The rapid decrease of the ganglionic cholinesterase following the section and degeneration of the preganglionic fibres [2, 13, 14, 55] has suggested the assumption that a very important proportion of the cholinesterase is located in the preganglionic fibres.

The first important results obtained by histochemical methods on the distribution of the cholinesterase activity and the autonomous ganglia are those obtained by Koelle in the cat. They corroborate the existence of a site of cholinesterase activity in the preganglionic fibres, and in their intra-ganglionic prolongations. This activity disappears one week after section of the pre-ganglionic fibres. The concentration of the di-iso-propyl-fluorophosphate (DFP) solution necessary to inhibit the cholinesterase in the preganglionic fibres has led Koelle to admit this to be an acetylcholinesterase.

In the stellate ganglion the same enzyme seems to be located in a few nerve fibres leaving the ganglion and in a limited number of ganglion cells. The ganglion cells rich in acetylcholinesterase are still less numerous in the superior cervical ganglion, while in the ciliary ganglion a high concentration of acetylcholinesterase is present in the cytoplasm of nearly all the ganglion cells, and in their processes.

Another cholinesterase activity of autonomous ganglia which Koelle considers as non-specific after inhibition experiments with DFP is almost entirely confined to the capsular and intercapsular glial cells.

From Koelle's observations, it follows that in the autonomous ganglia of the cat there are three main sites of cholinesterase activity: one constant in the preganglionic fibres; a second one, inconstant in the cytoplasm of the ganglion cells and their processes, observed in a small number of the sympathetic ganglion cells and in nearly all the neurons of the ciliary ganglion; finally a third site in the glia of the ganglion.

Koelle does not refer a special enzymatic location at the level of the ganglion cell membrane for any of the types of ganglia studied. In a more recent paper, Szentágothai, Donhoffer, and Rajkovits [60] have applied the acetylthiocholine technique to the experimental study of the ciliary ganglion of birds (*Gallus dom.*), in which the relationships of the preganglionic fibres and ganglion cells are specially suitable morphologically for studying synaptic cholinesterases. The authors have concluded, after a study of this ganglion observed in its normal state, or 6 to 10 days after the section of the preganglionic fibres, that "the specific cholinesterase is mainly localized in the terminal parts of preganglionic fibres, especially in the pre-synaptic articulation surface" and that "smaller cholinesterase activity was found in the post-synaptic surface of the ganglion cells".

Taxi (unpublished observations) in resuming in mammals the histochemical study of the distribution of cholinesterase activity in the autonomous ganglia (superior cervical ganglion of the rat, and the ciliary ganglion of the cat), using acetylthiocholine as substrate, has confirmed the existence of the three main sites of cholinesterase activity described by Koelle, but he has been unable to establish satisfactorily in the mammals studied the existence of a synaptic location similar to that described in the ganglia of birds. In spite of numerous tests carried out on non-fixed and fixed tissues with different periods of fixation and varying pH of the incubation medium, a significant staining has still not been obtained at the level of the neuronal membrane. The only appearances which might indicate a synaptic site have been observed in sections of the ciliary ganglion of the cat, after a treatment of DFP at a concentration of 10^{-8} M which inactivates the greater part of the glial cholinesterase. Unfortunalety, at no pH has it been possible to avoid entirely the staining of the nuclear membrane of certain gliocytes which are closely attached to the ganglion cell surface. By making probable the existence of diffusion artefacts in the near vicinity of the ganglion cell surface the staining of the gliocyte nuclear membrane is a fact which renders the value of the staining noted at the synapse doubtful. If, however, this staining corresponds to differential cholinesterase concentration at the synapse, then it would be difficult, using present methods, to separate in normal ganglions the two sites of synaptic cholinesterase linked respectively to pre- and post-synaptic membranes. Indeed, the electron micrographs of autonomous ganglia show that in the mammals studied the distances separating the pre- and post-synaptic membranes are probably too small for observation with the light microscope.

SUMMARY

As a result of recent findings of electron microscopy the lamellae of the subneural apparatus of the motor end-plate may be interpreted as infoldings of the sarcoplasm surface membrane, that is to say, of the post-synaptic membrane.

Morphological and cytochemical study of this membrane inside and outside the synaptic area has shown its general structural pattern to be the same everywhere but has revealed two distinguishing characteristics of the subneural zone: (*a*) the network of argyrophil fibrils generally observed at the sarcoplasm surface does not exist at the surface of the subneural sarcoplasm; (*b*) the high cholinesterase activity of the motor end-plate is mainly located within the subneural sarcoplasm at the level of the post-synaptic membrane itself.

Concerning ganglionic synapses, the cholinesterase activities may be high in the ganglion cell cytoplasm and in surrounding gliocytes but hitherto in the ganglia of mammals it has not been possible to observe distinctly a special location of cholinesterase at the level of the post-synaptic membrane.

REFERENCES

1. BOEKE, J., *Proc. Koninkl. Ned. Akad. Wetenschap.* **45**, 444 (1942).
2. VON BRÜCKE, F. T., *J. Physiol.* **89**, 429 (1937).
3. CHESSICK, R. D., *J. Histochem. Cytochem.* **2**, 258 (1954).
4. COËRS, C., *Arch. Biol. Liège* **64**, 133 (1953).
5. —— *Rev. belge pathol. et méd. exptl.* **22**, 306 (1953).
6. —— *Bull. acad. roy. Belge. Cl. Sci.* **39**, 447 (1953).
7. —— *Acta Neurol. Psychiat. Belg.* **55**, 741 (1955).
8. COUTEAUX, R., *Compt. rend. soc. biol.* **127**, 218 (1938).
9. —— *Bull. biol. France et Belg.* **75**, 301 (1941).
10. —— *Rev. can. biol.* **6**, 563 (1947).
11. —— *Arch. intern. Physiol.* **59**, 526 (1951).
12. —— *Internatl. Review Cytol.* **4**, 335 (1955).
13. COUTEAUX, R. and NACHMANSOHN, *Proc. Soc. Exptl. Biol. Med.* **43**, 177 (1940).
14. —— *Bull. biol. France et Belg.* **76**, 14 (1942).
15. COUTEAUX, R. and TAXI, J., *Compt. rend. assoc. anat.* **70**, 1030 (1951).
16. —·— *Arch. Anat. microscop. morphol. exptl.* **41**, 352 (1952).
17. CREVIER, M. and BELANGER, L. F., *Science* **122**, 316 (1955).
18. DE ALMEIDA, D. F. and COUCEIRO, A., *An. Acad. brasil. Cienc.* **27**, 41 (1955).
19. DE CASTRO, F., *in* PENFIELD, Cytology and Cellular Pathology of the Nervous System. Vol. I, p. 319. 1932.
20. —— *Arch. internatl. Physiol.* **59**, 474 (1951).
21. DENZ, F. A., *Brit. J. Exptl. Pathol.* **34**, 329 (1953).
22. DE ROBERTIS, E. D. P. and BENNETT, H. S., *Federation Proc.* **13**, 35 (1954).
23. —— *J. Biophys. Biochem. Cytol.* **1**, 47 (1955).
24. FENG, T. P. and TING, Y. C., *Chinese J. Physiol.* **13**, 141 (1938).
25. GASSER, H. S., *J. Gen. Physiol.* **38**, 709 (1955).
26. GEREBTZOFF, M. A., *Acta Anat.* **19**, 366 (1953).

27. GEREBTZOFF, M. A., PHILIPPOT, E. and DALLEMAGNE, M. J., *Acta Anat.* **20**, 234 (1954).
28. GLICK, D., *Nature* **140**, 426 (1937).
29. —— *J. Gen. Physiol.* **21**, 431 (1938).
30. HARRIS, C., COHEN, B. S. and BERGNER, A. D., *J. Histochem, Cytochem.* **1**, 405 (1953).
31. HELLMANN, K., *J. Cellular Comp. Physiol.* **40**, 421 (1952).
32. HILLARP, N. A., *Acta Anat., Suppl.* **IV**, 1 (1946).
33. HOLT, S. J., *Proc. Roy. Soc.* B, **142**, 160 (1954).
34. HOLT, S. J. and WITHERS, R. F. J., *Nature* **170**, 1012 (1952).
35. KOELLE, G. B., *J. Pharmacol. Exptl. Therap.* **100**, 158 (1950).
36. —— *ibid.* **103**, 153 (1951).
37. KOELLE, G. B. and FRIEDENWALD, J. S., *Proc. Soc. Exptl. Biol. Med.* **70**, 617 (1949).
38. KOVAC, M. KRAUPP, O. and LASSMANN, G., *Acta Neuroveg.* **12**, 329 (1955).
39. KUPFER, C., *J. Cellular Comp. Physiol.* **38**, 469 (1951).
40. MACMANUS, J. F. A., *Stain Technol.* **23**, 99 (1948).
41. MALMGREN, H. and SYLVÉN, B., *J. Histochem. Cytochem.* **3**, 441 (1955).
42. MARNAY, A. and NACHMANSOHN, B., *Compt. rend. soc. biol.* **125**, 41 (1937).
43. —— *J. Physiol.* **92**, 37 (1938).
44. NACHMANSOHN, D., ROTHENBERG, M. A. and FELD, E. A., *Arch. Biochem.* **14**, 197 (1947).
45. PALADE, G. E., *Anat. Rec.* **114**, 427 (1952).
46. PALADE, G. E., *J. Histochem. Cytochem.* **1**, 188 (1953).
47. PALADE, G. E. and PALAY, S. L., *Anat. Rec.* **118**, 335 (1954).
48. PALAY, S. L., *J. Biophys. Biochem. Cytol.* **2**, *Suppl.*, 193 (1956).
49. REGER, J. F., *Anat. Rec.* **118**, 344 (1954).
50. —— *ibid.* **122**, 1 (1955).
51. ROBERTSON, J. D., *Proc. Soc. Exptl. Biol. Med.* **62**, 219 (1953).
52. —— *Anat. Rec.* **118**, 346 (1954).
53. —— *J. Biophys. Biochem. Cytol.* **2**, 369 (1956).
54. SAVAY, G. and CSILLIK, B., *Acta Morphol. Acad. Sci. Hung.* **6**, 289 (1956).
55. SAWYER, C. H. and HOLLINSHEAD, W. H., *J. Neurophysiol.* **8**, 137 (1945).
56. SJÖSTRAND, F. S.. *J. Appl. Phys.* **24**, 117 (1953).
57. SJÖSTRAND, F. S. and RHODIN, J., *Exptl. Cell Research* **4**, 426 (1953).
58. SNELL, R. S. and MACINTYRE, N., *Nature* **176**, 884 (1955).
59. —— *Brit. J. Exptl. Pathol.* **37**, 44 (1956).
60. SZENTÁGOTHAI, J., DONHOFFER, A. and RAJKOVITS, K., *Acta Histochem.* **1**, 272 (1954).
61. TAXI, J., *J. Physiol.* **44**, 595 (1952).
62. WOOLF, A. L. and TILL, K., *Proc. Roy. Soc. Med.* **48**, 189 (1955).

Experimental Cell Research, Suppl. **5**, *323–337 (1958)*

PARAMETERS OF INTEGRATIVE ACTION OF THE NERVOUS SYSTEM AT THE NEURONAL LEVEL[1]

T. H. BULLOCK

Department of Zoology, University of California, Los Angeles, Calif., U.S.A.

It is the purpose of this paper to survey and systematize the state of our knowledge on the neuronal basis of the integrative action of the nervous system.

Integration at the unit level can be usefully thought of in terms of the events which determine the firing, that is the output of impulses, of a given neuron and can be defined as a process or set of processes resulting in the output being different from, but some function of the input.

Much has been written which is pertinent to this theme. We may refer here only to a few of the most recent publications: Eccles [6], Grundfest [9, 10], Fessard [7], and Bullock [4]. I will propose two outlines which attempt to summarize the generalized parameters determining neuronal activation and the phenomena which manifest the degrees of freedom with which neurons can integrate their input. Illustrations will be developed for certain of these which have recently been discovered or are less familiar. I am especially indebted in these studies to my associates, D. M. Maynard, S. Hagiwara, C. A. Terzuolo, and T. Otani.

GENERALIZED PARAMETERS DETERMINING NEURONAL ACTIVITY

Sensitivity at any moment

I. Spike excitability as function of preceding activity.
II. Graded-response excitability as function of preceding activity.

Responsiveness at any moment

III. Form of rise and fall of graded response as function of preceding activity.
IV. Form of activity in axonal terminals as function of preceding activity.

It may be of value to point out the generalized parameters which determine neuronal activation. Formulated in one way, a basic distinction would be between those parameters which comprise or are expressive of the sensitivity of the responding mechanisms to graded input and those expressive

[1] The aid of a grant from The National Institutes of Health (B-21) is gratefully acknowledged.

of responsiveness of these systems at the time. This is a distinction which is not recognized by some current pictures of neuronal physiology, but there are many clear-cut facts which indicate that excitability is not always parallel to the magnitude of the response possible at the moment.

Sensitivity is not adequately measured by threshold. In fact it is essential to recognize in dealing with integrative aspects of synaptic activity two different forms of sensitivity. The first might be the more classical form measured by the threshold for spike initiation. This is the critical level of change, necessary to trigger the initiation of an all-or-nothing propagated nerve impulse, which must be imposed by the input at that moment. It will be a function of existing conditions and of preceding activity; here we embrace all those conditions exemplified by milieu, specific and nonspecific chemicals and slow electric fields. This parameter, spike threshold, is of interest only at one limited part of the neuron, namely the locus of origin of the conducted impulse. For some neurons, this may be at or near the base of the axon, in other cases in the cell body or at the bases of dendrites. It is possible that this parameter is also of importance at certain branchings of the axon where the safety factor may be low.

The second form of excitability temporally precedes the first in normal activation and may be called the graded-response excitability. This is not measured by a sharp threshold but by the curve relating amplitude of graded response to amplitude of arriving graded input, a curve which is probably typically highly nonlinear, as well as being labile according to the conditions and the preceding activity. In normal function, this parameter will also refer to something less than the whole neuron but may involve parts of a more extensive fraction of the neuron than the first, presumably the whole region of the surface involved in synapses, therefore commonly both dendrites and soma. Actually, there is considerable evidence now, that the graded response subsumed under the term synaptic potential is a separate process from and may occupy a different part of the neuron than what is often called a local potential, which is subsequent to the synaptic potential. Grundfest [10] has underlined this distinction in proposing that the one is electrically excitable, the other electrically inexcitable. Thus it is really necessary to introduce another stage of graded, labile and probably nonlinear excitability.

Turning now to responsiveness, we know that this may vary from moment to moment *pari passu* with excitability but it may be quite separate. This parameter will concern only graded activity, since spike activity by its nature is quantal or digital and usually exhibits a good safety factor.

The evidence available points to the importance of a set of factors which determine the amplitude and form of the rising phase and also of the falling phase of graded activity e.g. synaptic potentials and local potentials. Here belong the membrane electrical properties and the ion kinetics, specific permeabilities and their dependence on potential. The status of these determinants existing at any moment including for example summation and facilitation may be summed up in the phrase "as function of preceding activity".

The fourth parameter listed has been recognized by those workers ascribing changes in transmission to presynaptic events. The three foregoing are in principle capable of providing for the necessary stages of information processing, transmission and propagation, since they provide means for detecting and converting environmental events of either digital or analog nature first into analog activity in the receptive regions of the neuron, then into the digital code of all-or-none nerve impulses and again back at the next neuron into graded activity which can therefore be integrated. But it is very likely, according to a considerable body of reports, that the nerve impulse does not reach the synapse unmodified in every case. There may be points of low safety factor at the branchings of axonal terminals or these terminal ramifications may behave like dendrites, by acting in a graded manner, the transmitter may be increased or decreased in intensity. If this is true, clearly the form of response in these portions of the neuron as a function of all that has gone before, will be a parallel variable of crucial importance in determining neuronal activity, transmission and integration.

DEGREES OF FREEDOM WITHIN THESE PARAMETERS

Excitation or inhibition.
Facilitation or defacilitation.
After-effect positive, negative or both.
Spontaneity, relaxation-oscillatory or undulatory or none.
Graded-response regions discharged by spike or not.

As a result of variables systematized into the four headings above, many effects or phenomena occur with more than one degree of freedom. Most of the common alternatives are included in this outline. It lists therefore the properties known to be available to junctional regions which in various permutations can provide for neuronal integration at a fairly complex level. The first three rubrics embrace effects imposed by other cells. The last two comprise auto-effects or phenomena mediated entirely within the neuron under consideration. The attempt from there on is to catalog phenomeno-

logically the main alternatives of unit activity which may contribute to determination of output. Treatment at this phenomenological level is necessary
today. It would be desirable to explain the observed diversity of unit activity
in terms of a few already known variables, such as the distribution within the
neuron of different kinds of membrane — e.g. synaptic, non-synaptic locally-
responding and spike-propagating membranes. But the following observed
alternatives cannot with assurance be so explained and must be treated for
the present as basic alternatives.

Excitation or Inhibition

The result of arriving input may be excitation or inhibition. Influx having
opposite effects may arrive simultaneously and result in a complex interaction. Moreover, for different measures of activity, the excitation or inhibition
may be disproportional and indeed can be opposite in sign. As Maynard [12,
14] has documented in the case of inhibition of the cardiac ganglion neurons
of the lobster heart, stimulation of the inhibitory axon slows down the heart
beat by lengthening intervals between bursts of the ganglion and it may
reduce the number of impulses in each burst as well as the duration of the
burst. But these measures may be quite out of proportion to each other and
some measures such as the maximum frequency of the impulses in the burst
may even be increased (Fig. 1). The same point is illustrated further in the

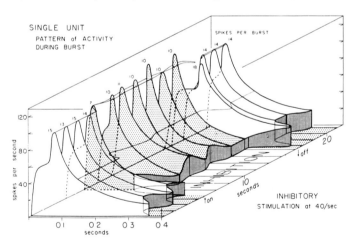

Fig. 1.—The disproportionate effect of inhibition on different measures of unit activity. A single
cell of the several active in the ganglion is plotted showing each burst, representing one heart
beat, as a plane. Note the disproportionate effect of the single inhibitor axon on duration of burst,
spikes per burst, the shoulder on the ascending phase and even a reverse effect on peak frequency.
Adaptation to inhibition and rebound are also shown. (From Maynard [12].)

work of Maynard [12, 14] by the fact that stimulation of the acceleratory axons produces effects which are not mirror images of inhibitor stimulation in many respects.

One of the most interesting discoveries made on this preparation [18], is that the same single inhibitor axon, so called because of its effect upon the

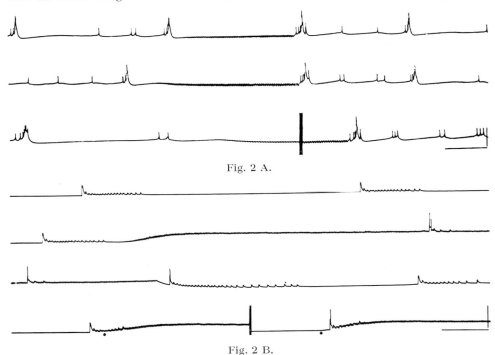

Fig. 2 A.

Fig. 2 B.

Fig. 2.—A single inhibitor axon can inhibit one cell and excite another. (A) A spontaneous cell is hyperpolarized and inhibited. The small ripples are inhibitory postsynaptic potentials which facilitate and summate. The triplets, pairs and single spikes between heart-beat bursts are spontaneously arising in this cell. (B) A non-spontaneous follower cell is depolarized and excited. It fires spikes during inhibition although the synaptic potentials manifesting driving impulses arriving from the pacemaker cell are fewer. No internuncials are involved. Calibrations: 400 ms and 20 mv. (From [18].)

over-all heart beat, actually inhibits only certain cells of the ganglion while others are *directly* excited by it (Fig. 2). In the former cells, an intracellular micro-electrode reveals facilitating and summating inhibitory postsynaptic potentials which accumulate a considerable hyperpolarization, whereas in the latter, facilitating and summating postsynaptic potentials are depolarizing and accumulate to a considerable decrease in the membrane polarization, without intervention of internuncial neurons. This is quite contrary to a "principle" recently restated by Eccles [6] for the mammalian central nervous system.

A curious feature of the hyperpolarizing response which is found in the spontaneous cells of this ganglion, is that it occurs even though the individual inhibitory postsynaptic potentials are more commonly depolarizing than hyperpolarizing. In these cases, with initially depolarizing synaptic potentials, the falling phase of this potential is greater than the rising phase so that the net change which summates is towards increase in membrane polarization, hence inhibition. In a minority of the cells so far encountered, the inhibitory postsynaptic potential is individually hyperpolarizing as well as cumulatively so (Fig. 2).

We cannot as yet correlate these differences with the level of membrane polarization at the start of "inhibitory" input.

Excitatory and inhibitory input need not be in the form of nerve impulses in synaptic pathways. As has been frequently reported, and recently directly measured quantitatively [17, 15], nonspecific fields of fluctuating or steady electric current passing through the tissue can exert strong physiological effects in one direction or the other. The significant feature quantitatively is the extreme weakness of effective fields. The voltage drop in the external medium across the *whole soma* of a neuron can be an order of magnitude smaller than the threshold voltage change that must be applied across the *membrane* of the cell with an internal electrode in order to stimulate. The results seem to demand that the membrane potential across certain regions of the neuron is more critical than that across others, that this region may be extremely sensitive to small fractions of a millivolt and may have an extremely constant threshold, and that the interior of the neuron is significantly non-isopotential. These effects of weak fields are only seen as inhibitory or acceleratory modulation of already existing rhythmic activity. Currents adequate to produce distinct effects are believed to be in the same range as physiologically available currents (brain waves, etc.) within nervous tissue.

Facilitation or Defacilitation

When arriving input is in the form of repetitive nerve impulses the result may be facilitation of successive responses (each increment larger than the last) in the postsynaptic unit or defacilitation (successive responses smaller) or neither. In the last case there may yet be summation, the successive individual responses rising to the same height but occurring each on the falling phase of the preceding one so that a cumulative effect is produced.

Examples of true facilitation wherein successive individual responses are progressively larger, are abundant in the literature.

We will here illustrate only the somewhat less familiar case of defacilitation [11, 5]. Here the first arriving presynaptic impulse elicits a graded excitatory postsynaptic potential which is followed (Fig. 3) by depressed excitability

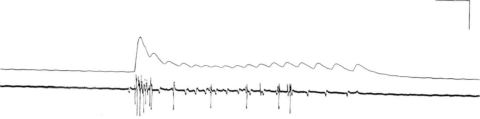

Fig. 3.—Defacilitation occurs at normal frequencies in certain of the synaptic potentials. This cell has suffered some simplification of its burst, representing one heart beat (upper beam). No more spikes and only one sort of synaptic potential, evoked 1:1 by impulses in one of the small cells, the pacemaker, are now occurring. The amplitude is a direct function of the interval since the last. Other forms of synaptic potential, e.g. Fig. 2, do the opposite. Calibrations: 50 ms and 20 mv. (From Otani and Bullock, unpublished.)

or responsiveness (we cannot tell which nor even whether the locus of the effect is in the presynaptic terminals or the postsynaptic membrane). This is in contrast to the usual expectation of enhanced excitability or responsiveness after graded activity. It is as though there were a relative refractoriness following a graded response, such as was seen occasionally in the squid synapse [2]. The range of intervals, from short intervals producing a very great defacilitation or reduced response to long ones, producing nearly completely recovered responses, coincides with the range of intervals normally occurring in the spontaneous activity of the ganglion, so that this parameter very largely determines the amplitude of synaptic potentials following the first (maximal) one in each burst. The same neuron exhibiting this behavior, receives other inputs which elicit facilitating synaptic potentials and may receive in a given experiment, still other inputs, whose synaptic potentials are of constant amplitude in the same range of repetition rate.

Finally, it may be pointed out that, like most other measures of input-output relation in nerve cells, facilitation and defacilitation are at least commonly nonlinear with respect to different frequencies of input.

Positive or Negative After-effects

There may be no appreciable after-effects or there may be a positive or a negative after-effect or both in sequence. A positive after-effect would be represented by after-discharge following the cessation of an excitatory input or after-inhibition following cessation of inhibitory input. Negative after-effect would be represented by rebound inhibition following excitatory, or rebound discharge following inhibitory input.

Fig. 4.—Rebound from inhibition can produce a series of at least two bursts. The first half of the record exhibits synaptic potentials due to impulses arriving in the inhibitor axon; there is neither accumulating depolarization nor hyperpolarization. After the end of stimulation of the inhibitor two rebound bursts in sequence occur. These are due to driving from some pacemaker cell which was released from inhibition. It would be preferable to show the events in this cell but we do not have records from it during this phenomenon. (From Terzuolo and Bullock, unpublished.)

These tendencies may be quite strong and can lead for example to the phenomenon Maynard calls paradoxical driving. If a group of nerve cells which is exhibiting no spontaneity or a very low frequency of spontaneous activity, is intermittently subject to arriving inhibitory input in the form of brief bursts, the release discharge in the pacemakers at the end of each burst will elicit periodic activity in these nerve cells far greater than the activity they were manifesting before. These bursts of activity in the rebound discharge may be themselves strong enough to bring on a compensatory rebound silence and in some cases we have observed three or four well-formed bursts of activity, each burst several tenths of a second in duration and separated from the other bursts by a still longer interval, all following the end of a short period of imposed inhibition through a single axon (Fig. 4).

This is by no means an exhaustive list, but represents the main alternative effects which the built-in mechanisms of the nerve cell provide for and which in turn, through their permutations, permit the output of the neuron to be very different from, although some function of, the input.

Spontaneity

But nerve cells are not purely passive mechanisms waiting for stimulation. At least many exhibit under given circumstances, which are apparently or approximately normal, what we choose to call spontaneous activity. It can of course equally well be regarded as maintained nonadapting response to steady state conditions of the milieu. There are two features of spontaneous activity, which especially deserve notice in this general scheme. The evidence available indicates that the *locus* of generator or pacemaker activity within the neuron may be distinct from that of synaptic activity as well as from that of spike initiation and in fact, there may be more than one locus of pacemaker activity simultaneously active. The resulting output of the cell in terms of nerve impulses can therefore be a complex resultant of graded pacemaker activity in one or more loci, graded synaptic activity in one or several loci

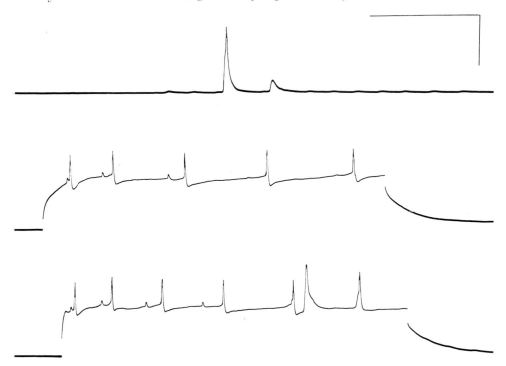

Fig. 5.—Different forms of activity in a cell of the cardiac ganglion of the lobster, *Panulirus*, recorded intracellularly (all figures from this preparation). Upper: The normally recurring heart beat is represented in this cell (type B of Bullock and Terzuolo [5]) by a series of small and two larger *synaptic potentials*, one surmounted by a spike. Middle: A long pulse of current is passed through a second penetrating microelectrode in the same cell. It elicits *pacemaker potentials* in two separate regions with independent rhythms leading to *spikes*, in one case and to smaller, i.e. more distant, spikes or local potentials in the other (we cannot tell which without a record of externally propagated impulses) and to a *local potential* at the ON. Lower: When the normal burst occurs during such a pulse, the synaptic potentials become more effective. Note inconstant spike threshold and amplitude, summation of pacemaker and repolarizing potentials, capacitative artifact and prolonged charging and discharging curve. Calibrations: 100 ms and 10 mv. (From Otani and Bullock, unpublished.)

(and this can be of excitatory or inhibitory, facilitating or defacilitating character), and a labile threshold for spike initiation at still another locus (Fig. 5).

Spontaneous subthreshold activity may take one of two *forms*. The more familiar form is that of a slowly developing depolarization which has been

called a pacemaker potential. This must lead to some new form of activity
introduced at a critical level of depolarization, commonly a complete all-or-
none discharge, in order to complete the cycle and repolarize the membrane again to permit a new slow depolarization to begin. While it is gener-

Fig. 6.—Local potentials can repolarize and complete a relaxation-oscillation cycle in absence of
a spike. This cell, besides being driven during heart-beat bursts (right center) is spontaneous. Its
pacemaker potential leads to a separate, intermediate event, here called a local potential, which
may lead to a spike but failing this can itself "undershoot" to restore the high level of polarization
starting a new pacemaker. Calibrations: 200 ms and 10 mv. (From Terzuolo and Bullock, unpublished.)

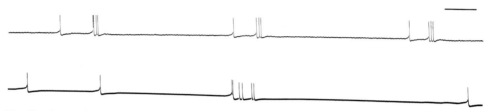

Fig. 7.—A spontaneous cell can fire at high frequency, in bursts though the membrane polarization in the soma does not conduce to this. Type D cells in the crab, *Cancer*, which exhibit 60 mv
spikes but virtually no pacemaker potential in the soma. Calibration: 200 ms. (From Terzuolo
and Bullock, unpublished.)

ally believed that this relaxation-oscillatory form of spontaneous activity
requires a spike discharge to complete the cycle and repolarize the membrane, we have observed in intracellular records of spontaneous ganglion
cells that there is a component of activity separate from the pacemaker
potential but initiated by it at a sufficient degree of depolarization, which is
yet short of a spike and behaves like a local potential in the soma or adjacent
dendritic processes. If this potential is large enough, a spike is initiated and
this usually occurs, but if the spike fails to arise, this local potential is remarkable in being capable of repolarizing the membrane to the high level
permitting another pacemaker potential to begin (Fig. 6). Hence relaxation-
oscillation can take place without spikes being required in each cycle. Fig. 7
illustrates the complexity of recurrent *patterned* firing, apparently arising entirely within one neuron, perhaps by interaction of pacemaker loci.

   But there is another and less commonly seen form of spontaneous subthreshold activity. This occurs as an undulatory almost sinusoidal change of
potential of the membrane and can occur without any new form of activity
to complete the cycle. When new forms of activity occur, for example,

local potentials or spikes, they cluster around the peak of the depolarizing phase of the undulation, but their occurrence may not obviously alter the rate of the slow repolarization which in turn gives way gradually to depolarization, in contrast to the relaxation-oscillation mechanism.

Spike Invasion of Graded Response Regions

There is one further internal mechanism in the neuron which may be of great importance to certain cells in determining their integration. This is some property, perhaps it is a safety factor, which either permits or prevents the graded response regions of the neuron, for example, the soma and dendrites from being invaded by the spike. In most neurons heretofore reported, impulses either originate in or can spread into the soma and the intracellular record shows a complete depolarization or even an overshooting spike which largely or completely wipes out the accumulated prepotentials which determined the initiation of that spike. In the crab and lobster cardiac ganglion, except for a certain type of anatomically localized cells, all cells of hundreds thus far penetrated and remaining apparently normally active for many minutes to several hours, have exhibited spikes which appear in the soma as five to ten occasionally up to 30 millivolt deflections (Figs. 5, 7). These spikes do show the same tendency as spikes elsewhere to be followed by a hyperpolarization but this is small in absolute magnitude and does not succeed in returning the membrane potential to the level before the synaptic potentials began. Since we have independent evidence that these tiny spikes in the soma are manifested in the external record by full-sized propagating nerve impulses, we have interpreted the results to mean that the spikes are initiated at some distance from the soma in a process and are unable to invade the soma. This would seem to be an important property in permitting integration of synaptic input of several sorts, each of which requires some time and repetition to accumulate and control a repetitive output of quite different frequency and pattern.

Another consequence of the same property has great theoretical interest. In many cases we see two or even three sizes of spikes in the same intra-cellular record (Fig. 8). These are associated with separate externally re-corded propagating spikes. It is our interpretation that they occupy separate processes of the cell, travelling in different directions. These two or more distinct impulses in the same neuron can coincide in time or fall at any phase in relation to each other. There must be a corresponding duplication of spike initiating loci and these must be simultaneously influenced by the synaptic potentials and other forms of graded activity, including generator and pacemaker potentials, occurring in the soma and dendrites, but they may be influenced to a different extent and their thresholds for spike initiation may differ. In the anatomical descriptions of Alexandrowicz [1] and Maynard [12], we find a very satisfactory substratum for these effects (Fig. 9).

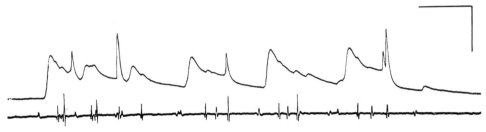

Fig. 8.—Two different spikes of different size may occur in the same neuron. The larger spike propagates an impulse posteriorly to the external monitor electrodes (lower beam); the smaller probably propagates into an anterior process of the cell; it does not produce an impulse in the monitor. Note: inconstant spike threshold; large synaptic potentials due to low frequency firing of the small (upwards) pacemaker spike in the lower beam; rapid repolarization following a spike compared with a synaptic potential of the same height; irrelevance of several of the larger external spikes for the penetrated cell. Calibrations: 50 ms and 5 mv. (From Otani and Bullock, unpublished.)

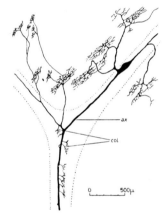

Fig. 9.—A portion of a large ganglion cell in the crab, *Cancer pagurus*. The descending axon can be followed for another 15 mm or more, through the ganglion and into the myocardium, giving off several types of branches. Fibers from other ganglion cells and from extrinsic inhibitor and accelerator nerves make complex connections both near and far from the soma. Pacemaker loci and spike initiating loci could be multiple and far from the soma. From Alexandrowicz [1], with permission.

Attempts to account for nervous integration in theoretical models with purely digital units were supplanted years ago by the recognition of graded activity in evaluating input and leading up to the initiation of the all-or-nothing event. But it would seem necessary now to take notice of the facts that there are several simultaneous and successive, but separate, kinds of graded phenomena in the neuron, each of them likely to be nonlinear and interacting in a complex way to determine output. Our problem now is no more what can be achieved by a model with a simple set of properties ascribed to each unit. Instead we have so many degrees of freedom available that by their combination in even a few of the possible permutations, an unmanageable number of possible outcomes can be realized. We are forced to go back to the living preparation and work still harder to find what limitations are actually present.

These considerations are more than compatible with the recent essays of Fessard [7] and Grundfest [9]. They are merely exemplifications with some interesting special consequences, of the principle that the neuron rather than acting as a unit is a composite of parts, each of which acts in its own characteristic way and interacts in limited ways with the others.

In harmony with this idea and with the notions expressed by a number of authors (e.g. [8, 3]) is the pregnant possibility that even without impulses, one neuron can influence the next. Let me make this explicit. The evidence is not yet, as I see it, direct and unequivocal at the unit level, but indirectly it is very strong even at the unit level and especially at the level of masses of neurons, that we must reckon with communication among nerve cells, not only by digital forms of input and output with conversion to analog forms between, but that even in the absence of spikes as well as in their presence, the graded and low amplitude forms of nonpropagated but decrementally spread activity may directly excite or inhibit closely adjacent dendritic processes. This possibility runs through all of the headings in the outline above and increases, by a large factor, the possibilities for complexity of integrative relations among neurons.

SUMMARY

A classification of the general parameters determining neuronal activity is offered, emphasizing the distinction between sensitivity and responsiveness and, under each of these the forms of graded response as function of milieu and previous history. Spike excitability is a significant parameter only at one locus in the neuron (e.g. initial segment of axon), whereas graded response excitability—not measured by a threshold but labile independently of the former, is significant over a large area (e.g. soma and dendrites, varying among neurons).

A list of "degrees of freedom" within these parameters is offered, that is alternative properties of response, each set of alternatives being apparently independently variable. These are the properties which permit integration at the neuronal level, that is permit output to be some function of input but not one to one with it. The items on the list are illustrated with experiments upon the nine-celled ganglion of the lobster heart, introduced to physiology by Maynard.

1. The result of arriving input may be excitation or inhibition. Simultaneous influx may result in complex interaction; the two effects are not simple opposites or mirror images and may be measured by different aspects of response which themselves do not vary proportionately with input. One and the same presynaptic axon can, without internuncials, cause inhibition of some and excitation of other postsynaptic neurons. Individual inhibitory postsynaptic potentials may have a different equilibrium potential from the cumulative potential from repetitive arriving "inhibitory" impulses.

2. Repetitive input may evoke response which increases by successively larger increments—facilitation, or may evoke successively smaller responses —defacilitation, or may evoke response which shows neither. In any case there may be summation due to slow falling phase of each response. The same neuron may exhibit all these alternatives according to the presynaptic pathway.

3. There may be no appreciable after-effect or there may be a positive or a negative after-effect or both in sequence.

4. There may be spontaneity in a given neuron, or not. Two forms of spontaneity are seen—relaxation oscillations and slow undulations. The former do not require a spike but they do require some new, quasi-threshold process to occur at a critical level of the pacemaker potential; this may be a local process. Pacemaker loci may be a small part of a neuron and separate from synaptic, spike-initiating and other regions, indeed there may be more than one pacemaker region in the same cell at once. The output can therefore be a complex resultant of input, spontaneity, spike threshold and intermediary labile events.

5. Pattern formation can occur intracellulary, that is, besides other possible mechanisms of formulating temporal sequences of non-random and non-rhythmic pattern, pacemaker cells can originate such bursts of impulses without receiving synaptic input.

6. In some neurons the spike invades the graded response regions and wipes out their accumulated graded response; in others the spike apparently never invades these regions, c.g. soma and presumably dendritic regions and the spike potential exerts a trivial effect, permitting accumulating and fluctuating prepotentials and hence more integration.

7. It is suggested, but without direct evidence, that neurons may in some situations influence each other without the mediation of spikes.

These simultaneously variable properties of neurons can, by interacting in permutations, account for a high degree of complexity of integrative nervous action, even in small groups of neurons.

REFERENCES

1. ALEXANDROWICZ, J. S., *Quart. J. Microscop. Sci.* **75**, 185 (1932).
2. BULLOCK, T. H., *J. Neurophysiol.* **11**, 343 (1948).
3. —— *in* G. E. W. WOLSTENHOLME, The Spinal Cord. Ed. Churchill, London, 1953.
4. —— *in* Recent Advances in Invertebrate Physiology. B. T. Scheer, ed. Univ. Oregon Press, Eugeue, 1957.
5. BULLOCK, T. H. and TERZUOLO, C. A., *J. Physiol.* **138**, 341 (1957).
6. ECCLES, J. C., The Physiology of Nerve Cells. Baltimore, Johns Hopkins, 1957.
7. FESSARD, A., *XX Intern. Physiol. Congress, Brussels*, 1956.
8. GERARD, R. W., *in* Mid-Century Psychiatry, R. R. GRINKER, ed. Thomas, Springfield, 1953.
9. GRUNDFEST, H., *in* Physiological Triggers and Discontinuous Rate Processes, T. H. BULLOCK, ed. Amer. Physiol. Soc., Washington, 1957.
10. —— *Physiol. Revs.* **37**, 337 (1957).
11. HAGIWARA, S. and BULLOCK, T. H., *J. Cellular Comp. Physiol.* **50**, 25 (1957).
12. MAYNARD, D. M., Ph.D. thesis. Univ. Calif., Los Angeles, 1954.
13. —— *Biol. Bull.* **109**, 420 (1955).
14. —— in manuscript (1957).
15. MURRAY, R. W., *J. Physiol.* **134**, 408 (1956).
16. OTANI T. and BULLOCK, T. H., *Anat. Rec.* **128**, 599 (1957).
17. TERZUOLO, C. A. and BULLOCK, T. H., *Proc. Natl. Acad. Sci.* **42**, 687 (1956).
18. —— *Arch. Ital. Biol.* (In press.)

SYNAPSES IN THE SUPERIOR CERVICAL GANGLION AND THEIR CHANGES UNDER EXPERIMENTAL CONDITIONS

G. CAUSEY and A. A. BARTON

Department of Anatomy, Royal College of Surgeons of England, London, England

THE word synapse was introduced by Sir Charles Sherrington at the turn of the century to designate the "place of junction between nerve cell and nerve cell". It is, I think, important to remember that in this instance, in contra-distinction to most other structures, the functional entity was named and described prior to the structural entity. In fact, looking at this subject of the synapse in retrospect, one cannot help being impressed by the elegance of thought and technique that has led to the present day explanation of the function of the synapse either on an electrical or chemical, or a combined chemical and electrical basis, and compare this progress with the rather sterile arguments arising from the beautiful histological work that is summarised in such reviews as de Castro [3], Nonidez [9] and Hillarp [8]. The reason is perhaps not far to seek, in that it would appear that the tools available were not adequate to the task. It now appears as though the electron microscope may be able to correct this imbalance and the work of Palay [10] on the central nervous system; de Robertis [4] on the acoustic synapses; de Robertis and Bennett [5] on the frog and earthworm; Robertson [12] on the crayfish and Sjöstrand [13] on the retinal rods, among others, show how keen is the attack.

The present contribution is concerned with the identification of the synaptic regions and the cellular changes in these regions after pre- and post-ganglionic section. This examination involves not only the nerve terminals, but also the Schwann and satellite cells and in this connection one must bear in mind the recent work on the very intimate relation of the Schwann cell and nerve fibre as shown in frog, chick and mammals [6, 7, 2]. The nerve fibre is topographically within the Schwann cell but is separated from the cytoplasm by a membrane and attached to the surface of the Schwann cell by a mesaxon.

MATERIAL AND METHODS

The material used was the superior cervical ganglion of adult rabbits without selection for weight or sex. The ganglion was removed from the anaesthetised animal and fixed immediately in isotonic 1 per cent osmium tetroxide at pH 7.3–7.5 using acetate-veronal buffer. Fixation was for two hours. After embedding in methacrylate, thin sections were cut on a Cook and Perkins microtome and examined in a Metropolitan Vickers EM4 or EM6 microscope.

Preganglionic degeneration was produced by cutting the nerve trunk low in the neck and excising 1 cm. Post-ganglionic section was carried out by cutting the emergent small nerve trunks close to the ganglion. It should be noted that these small trunks were, as far as possible, cut separately so as to minimise damage to the blood supply of the ganglion and greater emphasis was put on the gentle handling of the ganglion and maintenance of its blood supply than on assurance of cutting all post-ganglionic fibres. In a further series of animals the post-ganglionic fibres were first cut and after an interval of 7 days the pre-ganglionic fibres were severed and the ganglia removed after a further 7 days.

RESULTS

The general appearances in a normal superior cervical ganglion are shown in the survey picture (Fig. 1), the nucleus (which is frequently duplicated) of the neurone with its nucleolus and the cytoplasm with its inclusions are shown, but we will not go further with these structures because, although the changes in these structures are of particular significance, they do not immediately concern us in this paper. Surrounding the neurone are the satellite cells and in all the normal material that we have examined the approximation of the cytoplasm of the satellite cell to the neurone is both intimate and continuous. Nuclei of these satellite cells are seen at intervals and within the cytoplasm a number of nerve fibres that will be our major concern later. Between the neurones are a few myelinated fibres and many bundles of small non-myelinated fibres with their associated Schwann cytoplasm and nuclei.

We must return now to the satellite cells and the nerve fibres in immediate relationship to the neurone, for it is here that we will expect the synaptic areas or, as de Castro [3] described them, the "receptor plates" which were defined by him as "areas of connection of the fibres of the spinal cord with the sympathetic neurones". In Fig. 1 there are many small nerve fibres in the satellite cells often in groups associated with the region of the nucleus of the satellite cell. Such groupings are found on the processes in continuity with similar processes of the neurone and while we will confine ourselves here to the axosomatic relationship it must be made clear that there seem to be a larger number of axo-dendritic synapses than of axosomatic synapses. But we have no quantitative data to offer at present and we would stress that, although we hope in the near future to correct this shortcoming, we are only able to discuss this problem qualitatively.

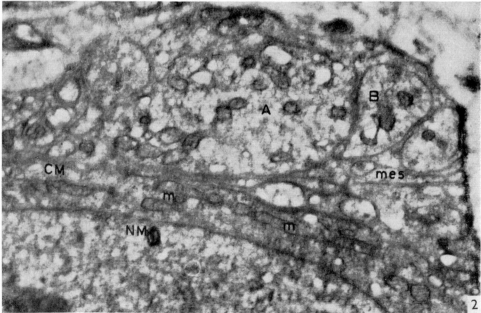

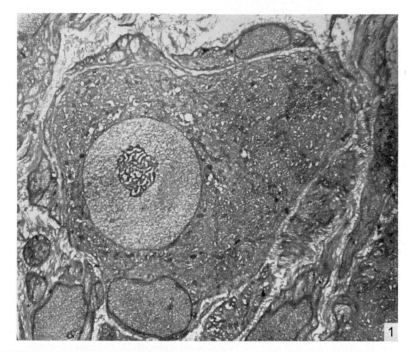

If we view one of these axo-somatic synaptic areas (Fig. 2), we can see the nerve fibres in the satellite cytoplasm and here it is immediately clear that this cell could be equally well called a satellite cell of the neurone or a Schwann cell of the nerve fibres. It will be seen later that this overlap is not only confined to nomenclature, as it seems to us that the behaviour of these cells under experimental conditions is very similar.

Taking the structures in Fig. 2 in a little more detail there is toward the bottom, the nuclear membrane and then in the cytoplasm of the neurone a very elongated mitochondrion and above this the neuronal membrane (CM) and above this the satellite cell and the nerve fibres contained in it, with a long mesaxon at (*mes*). It seems that the whole of this area must be considered from the point of view of transmission from neurone to neurone, although accepting the current idea of a synaptic ending as being a swollen axonal terminal with mitochondria and close approximation between neuronal membrane and axonal membrane probably amounting to 200 Å of which typical examples are shown in Figs. 4 and 5. One must remember when looking back at Fig. 2 that between the nerve fibre marked A and the nerve fibre marked B there is a part of their circumference in which the approximation of the membranes is equally close. It might be that nerve fibre A is a dendrite of the nerve cell shown or, more likely, the dendrite of a neighbouring neurone, whilst B is a preganglionic fibre, then the area of contact indicated would, in fact, be an axo-dendritic synapse occurring in the satellite cell of the neurone shown in Fig. 2. Paton [11] in comparing the action of blocking agents in ganglia and at motor end plates comments that the differences found "may well arise, not from any fundamental difference in transmission processes, but as consequences of the varying anatomy". The clarification of the origin of these closely packed fibres in the satellite cell would be greatly assisted by fibre section and degeneration experiments such as are described later.

A further structural variant to be considered in the synaptic area is shown in Fig. 6. Here we have a small nerve terminal packed with mitochondria and close to the neuronal surface (CM), but instead of the two surface membranes being in close apposition with a cytoplasm to cytoplasm distance of 200 Å units there is a separation by a Schwann cytoplasm of about 0.5 μ.

Fig. 1.—Neurone from the superior cervical ganglion of the rabbit. Showing a neurone; satellite cells with contained nerve fibres; intercellular nerve bundles. × 4000.

Fig. 2.—"Synaptic area" on a superior cervical ganglion neurone. Neuronal membrane (CM), mitochondrion (m), nuclear membrane (NM) and mesaxon (*mes*). × 7000.

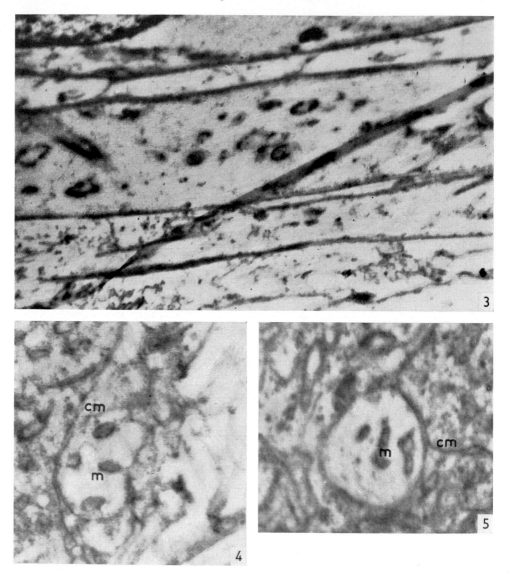

Fig. 3.—14 days degenerated sympathetic trunk. The tubes are all filled with Schwann cell cytoplasm. ×4500.

Fig. 4.—Nerve fibre containing a number of mitochondria (*m*), the cell membrane (*cm*) is in contact with the fibre membrane. ×10,000.

Fig. 5.—A similar ending to the one in Fig. 4. Lettering as for above figure. ×10,000.

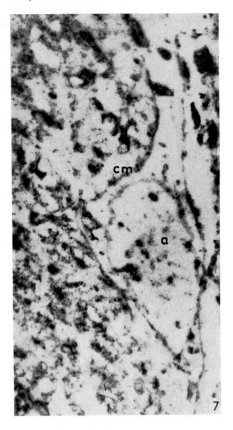

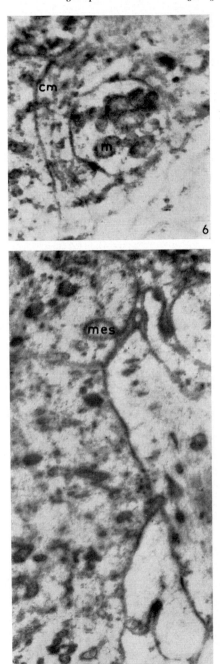

Fig. 6.—Nerve fibre containing a large number of mitochondria (*m*), and separated from the cell membrane (*cm*) by about 1 μ. $\times 10,000$.

Fig. 7.—A single nerve fibre remaining in the satellite cytoplasm 14 days after pre-ganglionic section. Cell membrane (*cm*), nerve fibre (*a*). $\times 8,000$.

Fig. 8.—A portion of the satellite cytoplasm 14 days after pre-ganglionic nerve section showing the freedom from nerve fibres except a possible small mesaxon (*mes*). $\times 22,500$.

It is clear that one of the most promising methods of approach to the further elucidation of the structures described in the normal ganglion is to study the effect of pre- and post-ganglionic section, but it must be remembered that this will not only cause the degeneration of the cut fibres but will also set in motion at once those reactions that lead towards repair.

Gross loss of pre-ganglionic fibres after pre-ganglionic section low down in the neck of the rabbit is not a very early occurrence. At 72 hours after nerve section there are still well formed synapses and synaptic areas, the mesaxons are still clear and there is no gross alteration in the relation of the satellite cell to the nerve terminal. In studies of the acoustic nucleus after destruction of the cochlea De Robertis [4] describes changes in the synaptic vesicles and neuro-protofibrils 22 hours after operation, this type of change we have not studied; but at 44 hours after operation he illustrates advanced degeneration of the synaptic endings which we never saw in the superior cervical ganglion at 72 hours after operation, but did find at 7–14 days after operation (Figs. 7, 8). It would seem that so far as the evidence goes at present the degenerative process is much more rapid in the acoustic nucleus than in the superior cervical ganglion. Hillarp [8] using the methylene blue technique on the superior cervical ganglion found that it was not possible to stain the pericellular network 48 hours after pre-ganglionic section. It seems that the series of chemical changes initiated by interruption of the pre-ganglionic fibres probably affect the ultrastructure of the nerve fibre within 24 hours; affect transmission across the synapse within about 48 hours and lead to the disappearance of the pre-ganglionic terminal in about 7 days.

We have found the maximum changes 12–14 days after pre-ganglionic section, at this time the fibres in the pre-ganglionic trunk are completely disorganised and replaced by tubes filled with Schwann cell cytoplasm (Fig. 3) and in the satellite cells around the neurone there is a marked diminution, but not complete absence of small nerve fibres. Well formed synaptic areas such as that shown in Fig. 2 are conspicuous by their absence. Instead we see either individual normal fibres that may be interneuronal dendrites or in some cases they may possibly be the dendrites of the cell itself. It seems possible that the cytoplasmic changes in these fibres may in the near future lead to more positive identification. Alternatively we see long stretches of satellite cytoplasm as in Fig. 8 and occasionally a configuration such as is shown in that figure at (*mes*) which has the appearance of a shrunken mesaxon and could be the remnant of a degenerating and shrinking pre-ganglionic terminal, or again we see a ghostlike fibre (Fig. 7) which could be a swollen and degenerating pre-ganglionic fibre or an inter-neuronal dendrite.

The bundles of small fibres between the cells are striking in that they certainly do not diminish in number, after preganglionic section, in fact, although we have not yet counted these fibres our impression is that they may actually increase in number. There is no doubt that pre-ganglionic section does cause a marked cytoplasmic change in the neurone [1] and that post-ganglionic sprouting may result. After post-ganglionic section (14 days) apart from the changes in neuronal bundles the most striking feature is the great increase in the inter-neuronal bundles of small non-myelinated fibres produced by the sprouting of the damaged cells and their processes.

The over all picture that we would, therefore, propose at this stage is as follows:—

(1) The pre-ganglionic fibres after some branching to reach different neurones then branch freely in close relation to the individual neurones and are often gathered together within the satellite cells at synaptic areas or receptor plates.

(2) Within a synaptic area these fibres are in a uniform environment of satellite cell cytoplasm with varying degrees of approximation to the neuronal membrane. This approximation is seen at its closest at the synaptic ending where the axo-somatic ending shows as the approximation of two membranes less than 200 Å apart.

(3) The inter-neuronal bundles of fibres are mainly post-ganglionic or inter-neuronal so that pre-ganglionic section does not result in the loss of a large proportion of these fibres but shows a gross change in the immediately peri-neuronal fibres.

(4) In all the experimental combinations we have used there is a marked stimulation of the activity of both Schwann and satellite cell that makes it difficult to see any functional difference between them.

With this hypothetical picture in mind we have done post-ganglionic section and followed it 7 days later by preganglionic section, removing the ganglion 7 days later, and find gross increase in the bundles of inter-neuronal fibres with active Schwann, and probably satellite cells engulfing new fibre sprouts. Neurones with few synaptic endings or synaptic areas and in some cases neurones denuded of their satellite cells that seem to have themselves taken on an active phagocytic role.

SUMMARY

1. An electron microscopic study of the superior cervical ganglion of the rabbit has been made after pre- and post-ganglionic section with particular emphasis of the satellite cells, the nerve fibres within the satellite cells and the inter-neuronal fibres.

2. The satellite cells and Schwann cells show similar reactions to experimental interference.

3. The small fibres invaginated into the satellite cells but connected to the surface of the satellite cells by mesaxons, degenerate after pre-ganglionic section.

4. The fibres between the nerve cells do not show any great loss of number after pre-ganglionic section, but show an increase, presumably by axon sprouting, after post-ganglionic section.

REFERENCES

1. BARTON, A. A. and CAUSEY, G. (in press).
2. CAUSEY, G. and HOFFMAN, H., *J. Anat. Lond.* **90**, 1 (1956).
3. DE CASTRO, F., Cytology and Cellular Pathology of the Nervous System. Ed. W. PENFIELD, New York, Hoeber, 1932.
4. DE ROBERTIS, E., *J. Biophys. Biochem. Cytol.* **2**, 503 (1956).
5. DE ROBERTIS, E. and BENNETT, H. S., *J. Biophys. Biochem. Cytol.* **1**, 47 (1955).
6. GASSER, H. S., *Cold Spring Harbor Symposia Quant. Biol.* **17**, 32 (1952).
7. GEREN, B. B., *Exptl. Cell Research* **7**, 558 (1954).
8. HILLARP, H., *Acta anat.* **2**, Suppl. **4** (1946).
9. NONIDEZ, J. F., *Biol. Rev.* **19**, 30 (1944).
10. PALAY, S. L., *J. Biophys. Biochem. Cytol.* **2**, 193 (1956).
11. PATON, W. D. M., *Pharm. Rev.* **6**, 59 (1954).
12. ROBERTSON, J. D., *Anat. Rec.* **118**, 346 (1954).
13. SJÖSTRAND, F. S., *J. Appl. Physiol.* **24**, 1422 (1953).

Experimental Cell Research, Suppl. **5,** *347–369 (1958)*   347

SUBMICROSCOPIC MORPHOLOGY AND FUNCTION
OF THE SYNAPSE

E. DE ROBERTIS

Instituto de Anatomía general y Embriología, Facultad de Ciencias Médicas,
Buenos Aires, Argentina

THE study of the submicroscopic organization of the synapse is of particular importance in view of the special physiological and chemical properties of this region of the nervous tissue differentiated for the transmission of nerve impulses [24, 31]. While the morphological aspects revealed by the optical microscope gave little background for a satisfactory explanation of the synaptic function [8] it was hoped that the enormous resolving capabilities of the electron microscope would provide more fundamental details of structure. In fact, with the range of resolution that can now be achieved in tissue sections, the macromolecular structures that are revealed are better related to the chemical morphology of molecular complexes and to the intimate physicochemical mechanisms of cell physiology.

Early work done with the electron microscope [53, 57, 24, 25] on different types of synapses settled some of the controversies which in the past derived from the limited resolution of the light microscope and the vagaries of the silver staining technique. These studies and the more recent contributions indicated that at the level of the synaptic junction, there is a direct contact of the cell membranes without interposed cellular material alien to the pre- and postsynaptic components. This invalidates the supposition that the synaptic terminal is surrounded by a continuous glial sheath [12] and confirms and extends to a submicroscopic level the concept of the individuality of the nerve elements implicit in Cajal's neurone doctrine.

Of even greater physiological and biochemical interest was the demonstration of a special vesicular submicroscopic component present in the synapse and designated by De Robertis and Bennett [18] under the heading of "synaptic vesicles". This early report was presented at the Federation Meeting of March 1954[1] and gave some of the essential morphological details of the synaptic vesicles found in synapses of sympathetic ganglia of the frog and in the neuropile of the earthworm. In the abstract the presynaptic location and the intimate relationship of some of this vesicles with the synaptic membrane were particularly stressed. Almost simultaneously, at the March 1954 meeting of the American Association of Anatomists, Palade [48] and Palay [49] reported an agglomeration of small vesicles in the axon endings of several synapses of the central nervous system and in the neuromuscular junction.

---

[1] The first verbal presentation of these findings was made in a Walker-Ames lecture at the University of Washington in November 1953.

The full paper of De Robertis and Bennett [19] submitted for publication in May 1954 described in greater detail the relationship of the membranes with the synaptic vesicles. It was suggested that they may flow toward the presynaptic membrane, perforate it and discharge their content into the intermembranal space and even go across the postsynaptic membrane to become destroyed at the postsynaptic cytoplasm. It was suggested at that time that acetylcholine or other chemical synaptic mediators could be associated with the synaptic vesicles. Since then the presence of a vesicular component has been confirmed in a wide variety of synapses [20, 15, 35, 60, 21, 61, 50, 54, 46].

In this report I shall try to review some research done in our laboratory to obtain information about the physiological significance of the synaptic vesicles. Most of the work has been already published and will only be summarized here [15, 17, 21]. However, some new information regarding the passage of synaptic vesicles through the membranes and the changes occurring under electrical stimulation will be presented.

CHANGES OF THE SYNAPTIC VESICLES AFTER NERVE SECTION

From the beginning of this investigation it was realized that the study of the degenerative changes of the synapse after section of the afferent nerve axon could throw light on the physiological significance of synaptic vesicles. Under the optical microscope the alterations consist primarily of swelling and subsequent fragmentation and granulation of the endings [41, 37, 36, 42, 38]. These degenerative changes can be detected very soon after severance of the axons in some peripheral synapses [56]. In the central nervous system, swelling of the nerve endings has been observed as early as 24 hours after section. It is very interesting that these morphological changes precede the alterations of the nerve in wallerian degeneration. Furthermore in peripheral synapses and particularly in the neuromuscular junction nerve transmission fails before the axon has ceased to conduct [59, 43, 26] and this failure is gradual and not sudden as in the case of nerve conduction

---

LEGENDS.—*cd*, cathecol-containing droplet; *D*, dendrite; *dm*, degenerating mitochondria; *dsv*, degenerating synaptic vesicles; *er*, endoplasmic reticulum; *G*, glial cell; *m*, mitochondria; *nf*, neuroprotofibril; *Psc*, postsynaptic cytoplasm; *Psm*, process of the presynaptic membrane; *Psy*, postsynaptic cell; *sm*, synaptic membrane; *sv*, synaptic vesicles; *SyE*, synaptic ending; *tm*, membrane of the ending.

Fig. 1.—Electromicrograph of a thin section of a normal ventral acoustic ganglion of the guinea-pig. Two synaptic endings (*SyE*) containing mitochondria and numerous synaptic vesicles (*sv*) are found in contact with a dendrite (*D*). The synaptic membrane (*sm*) shows regions of higher electron density (marked with arrows). See further description in the text. × 59,000.

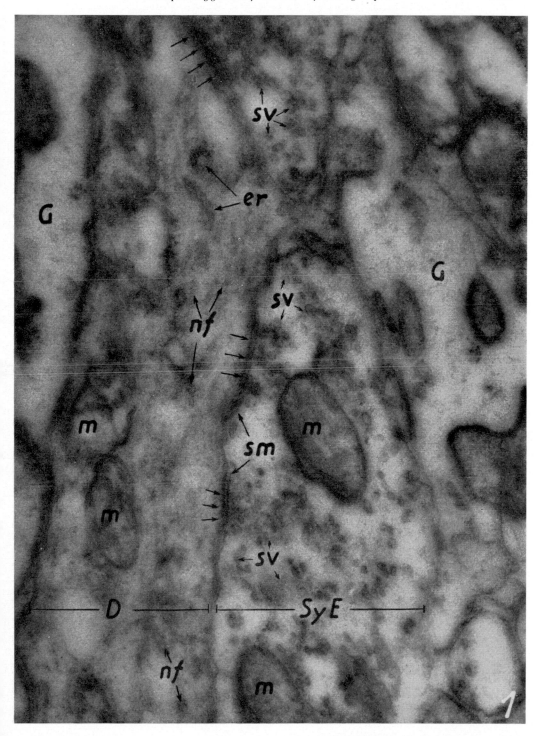

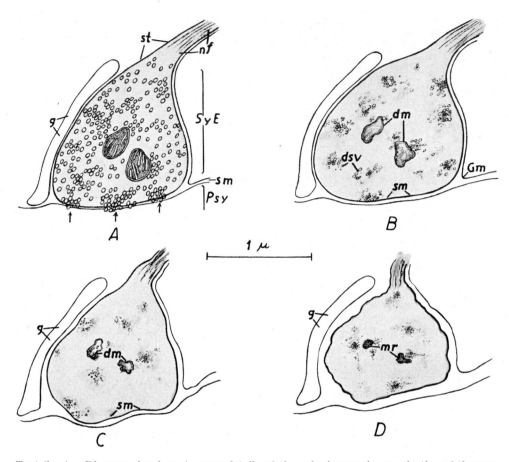

Text-fig. 1.—Diagram showing: *A*, some details of the submicroscopic organization of the synaptic endings in the normal acoustic ganglion. *A*, 22 hours after destruction of the cochlea.
C and *D*, after 44 hours. The sequence *BCD* corresponds to the most common and progressive
process of degeneration observed. *dm*, degenerating mitochondria; *dsv*, degenerating synaptic
vesicles; *g*, glial cell; *gm*, glial membrane; *m*, mitochondria; *mr*, mitochondrial remnant; *nf*,
neuroprotofibril; *Psz*, postsynaptic cell; *Sm*, synaptic membrane; *SyE*, synaptic ending. (Reprinted with modifications from [17].)

Fig. 2.—Similar material as in Fig. 1. A single nerve ending (end foot) in contact with the surface
of a perikarya is shown. The ending contains two mitochondria and numerous synaptic vesicles.
× 63,000.

Fig. 3.—Electron micrograph of a synaptic ending of the ventral acoustic ganglion of a guinea pig
22 hours after destruction of the cochlea. The degenerating ending shows swelling of the matrix,
mitochondria in the process of lysis (*dm*) and reduction in number and size of synaptic vesicles
which are agglutinated into clumps and undergoing dissolution (*dsv*). (Compare with Fig. 2).
× 46,300.

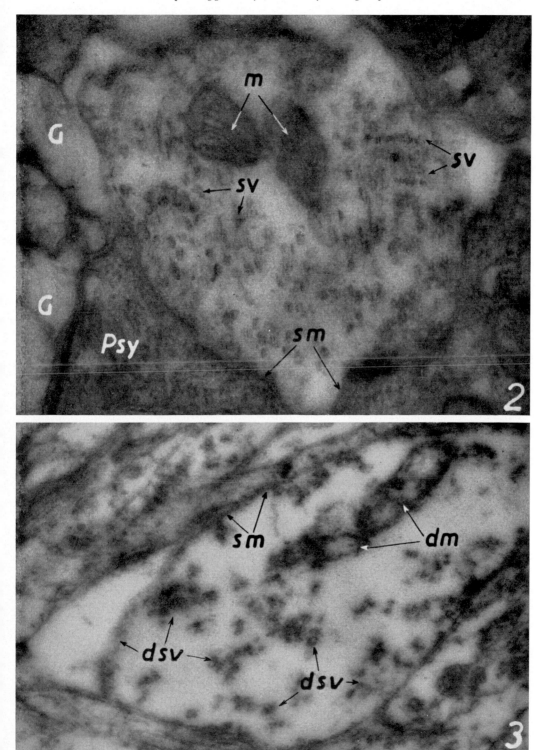

[55]. Similar findings in sympathetic ganglia [11] have been correlated with the progressive decrease in acetylcholine content of the ganglia after section of the preganglionic fiber [47].

Our experimental work was done in the ventral acoustic ganglia of the guinea-pig with destruction of the cochlea on one side; the contralateral remaining as control. The detailed description of the experiments and results has already been published [17] and it will be considered here only in relation to the changes in the synaptic vesicles.

The two types of synapses commonly found in the normal ventral acoustic ganglion—the axodendritic and the axosomatic synapses—are illustrated in Figs. 1 and 2, and represented diagrammatically in Text-fig. 1 A. In Fig. 1 parts of two nerve endings approach and make intimate contact with one side of a dendrite while the other side is related to a glial element. Within the dendrite: mitochondria, vesicular elements of the endoplasmic reticulum and long parallel double edged neuroprotofibrils are observed. The synaptic ending is surrounded by a limiting membrane about 60–70 Å thick that at the junction is in contact with the limiting membrane of the dendrite (Fig. 1) or the perikarya (Fig. 2) and that beyond the junction is in close relationship with the limiting membrane of the neuroglial cell processes. The ending proper lacks the neuroprotofibrils that are found in the axon and dendrites and evidently consists of a specialized expansion of the nerve terminus containing the synaptic vesicles and a few mitochondria embedded in a cytoplasmic matrix of very low electron density.

The *synaptic membrane* results from the apposition or junction of the two limiting membranes of the neurones in contact. One of the membranes can be considered as presynaptic and the other as postsynaptic; the inter-space being of the order of 120 to 140 Å (Text-fig. 4). The synaptic membrane shows regions of increased thickness and electron density (Fig. 1, marked with arrows) in both its pre- and postsynaptic components. At these regions the synaptic vesicles, that fill the endings, come into intimate contact with the presynaptic membrane and they may even fuse with it or penetrate into the intermembranal space (Fig. 1 and Text-fig. 1 A).

The electron microscope observations on degenerating nerve endings confirm the finding of earlier morphological alterations occurring soon after section of the afferent axon [56, 41, 42, 36, 38, 39]. In spite of the fact that the progress of the degeneration is variable in its course for the synapses of different cells, and even for endings coming into contact with a single neuron, the most common sequence of events involves a swelling of the matrix, agglutination and lysis of the synaptic vesicles, lysis and disintegration of mitochondria and finally detachment and breakdown of the membrane at the synaptic junction (see Fig. 3 and Text-fig. 1).

It can be observed that the modifications of the synaptic vesicles are most marked and earliest to develop being followed by the lesions of the mitochondria and membrane. Since these observations concern a synapse of the central nervous system a correlation with physiological results on peripheral synapses might not be warranted. However the physiological [55] and submicroscopical [18, 19, 48] similarities existing between these two types of synapses suggest that the changes described in the synaptic vesicles might be correlated with the early physiological deterioration of synaptic transmission [59, 43, 26, 11] and with the progressive decrease in acetylcholine content found in the peripheral synapse [47].

PHYSIOLOGICAL CHANGES OF SYNAPTIC VESICLES IN SYNAPSES ON THE RETINAL RODS AND CONES

Having demonstrated that the synaptic vesicles undergo early and rapid degenerative changes after destruction of the afferent nerve fiber it was planned to study what modifications occur at the synapse under certain physiological conditions. For this work the synapses of the retina were found particularly fitted since they are localized in two well defined zones, the so-called plexiform layers and have been thoroughly studied with classical microscopical methods [51].

A detailed description of the submicroscopic organization of the rod and cone synapses in the rabbit has been already published [21]. We shall consider here only some of the data related to the changes of the synaptic vesicles and some new information on the structure of the synaptic membrane and its relationship with the vesicles. These observations extend to synapses between two receptors (rod and cone) and the corresponding neurones, the finding of the vesicular submicroscopic component previously described in interneuronal synapses of the central and peripheral nervous system, and the myoneural junction.

One of the striking characteristics of the retinal rods and cones synapses previously observed by Sjöstrand [57] is the fact that the expansions from the bipolar cells penetrate and digitate into the terminal spherule of the rod or into the more enlarged terminus of the cone cell (Figs. 5, 6, 7). This intimate and complex junction appears in the sections showing the very bizarre profiles of a folded synaptic membrane (Fig. 5). Also in this case the synaptic membrane results from the apposition of its pre- and postsynaptic components separated by an intervening space that varies between 80 and 200 Å. An interesting feature of these synapses is the presence of straight dense lines projecting from the profile of the presynaptic membrane (Fig. 5, *Psm*). These projections probably represent blind infoldings of the presynaptic membrane and are generally surrounded by a great number of synaptic vesicles, particularly in the animals maintained in darkness for a few hours (Figs. 4 and 5). Some new high resolution micrographs show that the synaptic membrane may be even more complex since each pre- and postsynaptic component of about 60 Å thick is composed of two denser lateral layers and an inner one of low electron density (see Fig. 6, star marked, and Text-fig. 4).

The characteristic morphology of the synaptic vesicles can be better observed in Fig. 4. They are spherical or oval in shape with a dense limiting membrane 40 to 50 Å thick and a content that is slightly denser than the matrix. Histograms made with animals exposed to light are shown in Text-fig. 2 A. The long diameter varies between 200 and 650 Å with a high peak between 350 and 400 Å, the mean of all measurements being 386 Å.

Other interesting detail of structure is the presence of a few large vacuoles near the connection with the rod or cone fiber (Fig. 4). These vacuoles are frequently interconnected by tubular junctions and resemble the endoplasmic reticulum of Porter. The possibility of a relationship between the endoplasmic reticulum and the synaptic vesicles is suggested by the presence of intermediate forms, but this fact cannot be demonstrated with certainty. Within the homogeneous matrix very fine (less than 50 Å thick) filaments can be observed (Fig. 4).

In order to search for physiological changes in the rod and cone synapses rabbits were maintained in complete darkness for periods of from 24 hours to nine days. The main results found in rod synapses are shown in Text-fig. 2. The histograms show that after 24 hours the change in size of the vesicles is not very conspicuous, although the measurements may indicate a slight increase in diameter, the mean reaching 444 Å (Text-fig. 2 B). The fact that seems more significant, in these dark adapted animals, is the accumulation of a great number of synaptic vesicles around the presynaptic membrane and its processes (Figs. 4 and 5). After 46 hours in darkness there is a definite

---

Fig. 4.—Rod synapse of a rabbit maintained in complete darkness for 24 hours. The synaptic vesicles (marked with arrows) are accumulated in great number near the synaptic membrane (*sm*) and particularly surrounding the process of the synaptic membrane (*Psm*). The endoplasmic reticulum (*er*) is seen at the top end of the spherule. × 61,500.

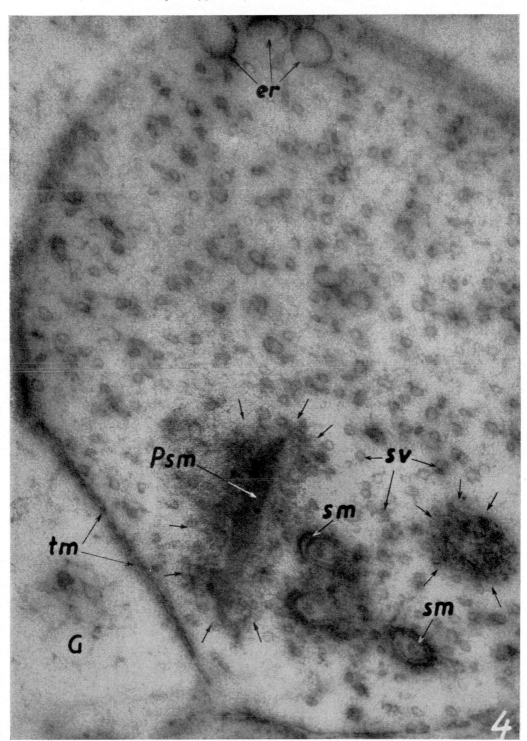

decrease in size of the synaptic vesicles (mean of 281 Å), but the most striking changes occur after 9 days in which the mean is only 195 Å (Text-fig. 2 C and D). Similar changes occur in the cone synapses. These results were tentatively interpreted as being a consequence of the functional disuse of the retina [20].

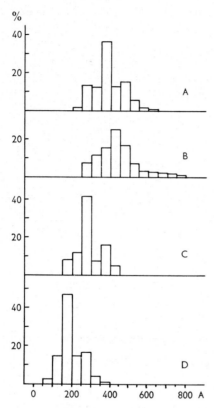

Text-fig. 2.—Histogram showing the distribution of sizes (in percentage) of the synaptic vesicles of the rod synapse. A, rabbit maintained 4 hours under sunlight; B, rabbit in complete darkness for 24 hours; C, rabbit in darkness for 46 hours; D, rabbit in darkness for 9 days. (Reprinted from [21].)

Fig. 5.—Rod synapse of a rabbit dark adapted for a few hours. Note the complex profile of the synaptic membrane with the digitations of the postsynaptic cytoplasm (*Psc*) and the process of the presynaptic membrane (*Psm*). There is a great accumulation of vesicles near the membrane and the *Psm*. × 64,500.

Fig. 6.—Small portion of a cone synapse of a rabbit under intense illumination. Note the attachment of several synaptic vesicles to the presynaptic membrane and some of them (marked with arrows) "passing through" the membrane into the postsynaptic cytoplasm (*Psc*). Marked with a star is a region of a synaptic membrane in which both the pre- and postsynaptic component show a triple layered structure with two dense peripheral an less dense inner layer. Within the *Psc* there are ill defined ghost-like vesicular elements and some fibrous material. × 71,000.

Fig. 7.—Rod synapse of a rabbit under intense illumination. Several vesicles (marked with arrows) are seen in the process of "passing through" the synaptic membrane and inside the *Psc*. (See further description in the text.) × 51,600.

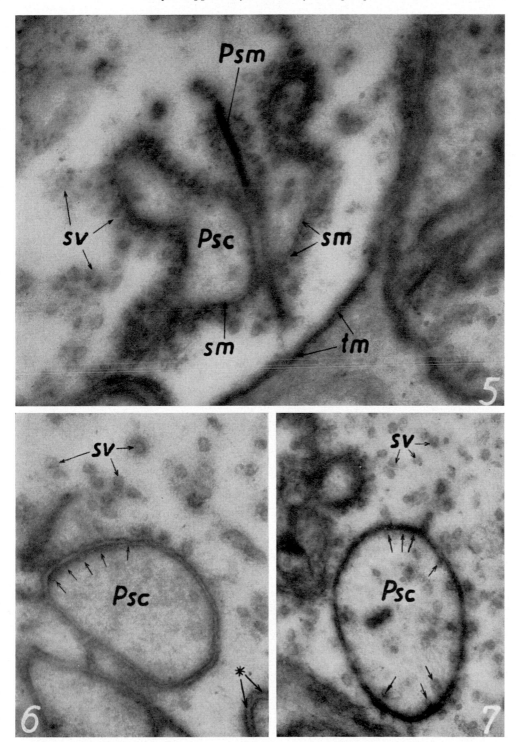

Since our publication some new observations have been made on material from dark adapted animals to compare with rabbits submitted to intense light stimulation.

Some of the findings seem to be of interest for the elucidation of the behavior of the vesicles with respect to the synaptic membrane. Fig. 5 corresponds to a rod synapse of a dark adapted rabbit. The main change seems to be the accumulation of synaptic vesicles near the presynaptic membrane and its processes. In Fig. 6, of a cone synapse submitted to stimulation by light, contact of several vesicles with the presynaptic membrane may be seen, the apparent opening of some of them into the synaptic interspace, and the passage of others beyond the postsynaptic membrane (marked with arrows). In the postsynaptic cytoplasm there are some ill defined ghost-like vesicles and a filamentous material that appears to be related to the disintegration of the vesicles. The passage of vesicles through both membranes is even more evident in the rod synapse of Fig. 7. Several vesicles seem to be in the process of passage and some altered ones are found in the postsynaptic cytoplasm. These observations, which are very similar to those previously described by De Robertis and Bennett [18, 19] in the earthworm, are interpreted diagrammatically in Text-fig. 4. These findings will be considered later in connection with a general interpretation of the physiology of synaptic vesicles.

SUBMICROSCOPIC CHANGES OF THE SYNAPSE AFTER NERVE STIMULATION

Ever since the discovery of the synaptic vesicles it was realized that a more direct approach to this problem was to try to induce changes in the synapse by electrical stimulation. Several tentative attempts made with Prof. Amassian ain 1953, Prof. Luco in 1954 and Prof. Berry in 1956 on synapses of the sympathetic ganglia failed or gave imcomplete results, mainly because of technical difficulties in the preparation of material for the electron microscope and the lack of time to solve them [15].

Fig. 8.—Two nerve endings in the adrenal medulla of a normal rabbit showing mitochondria and numerous synaptic vesicles (106 per μ^2). Some cathecol containing droplets (cd) are seen in the adrenal cells. × 46,600.

Fig. 9.—Nerve endings of a rabbit whose splachnic nerve was supramaximally stimulated with 400 pulses per second for 10 minutes. See the great diminution of the synaptic vesicles (28.2 per μ^2), swelling of the matrix and some deformed and less dense mitochondria. × 43,400.

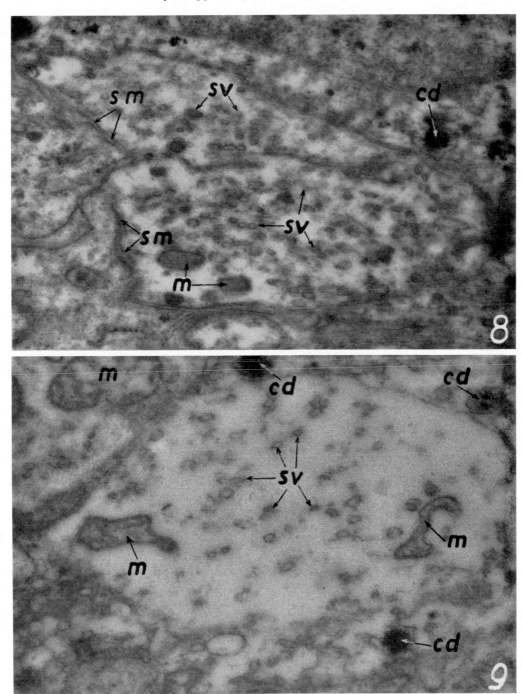

The investigation of this problem had to be postponed and was resumed when we realized that the adrenal medulla was an easier material—from the electron-microscope viewpoint—than the sympathetic ganglia [22]. In fact the nerve supply is very abundant [58] and belongs almost entirely to the

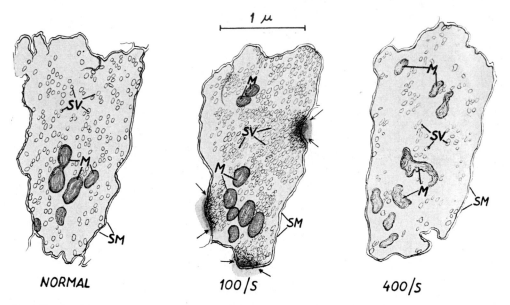

Text-fig. 3.—Diagram showing nerve endings of the adrenal medulla of the normal rabbit, and after stimulation for 10 minutes with supramaximal pulses of 100 and 400 per second. (See description in the text.)

homolateral splachnic nerve which can easily be stimulated. The preganglionic nerve fibers are cholinergic [32, 33] and innervate the chromaffin cells directly without intercalated neurones [58]. This type of junction is generally considered to be of synaptic nature because it has many characteristics akin with other cholinergic neuroeffectors and peripheral synapses

---

Fig. 10.—Electron micrograph of a nerve ending of the adrenal medulla of a rabbit with the nerve stimulated supramaximally for 10 minutes with 100 pulses per second. The large increase in synaptic vesicles is apparent (233.2 per μ^2). Marked with arrows are denser regions of the synaptic membrane where there is an apparent exit and discharge of material from the vesicles (see description in the text). ×50,400.

Fig. 11.—Similar to Fig. 10 but stimulated with 400 pulses per second. There are numerous mitochondria as in the ending of Fig. 10, but the vesicles are considerably diminished (44.5 vesicles per μ^2). ×40,400.

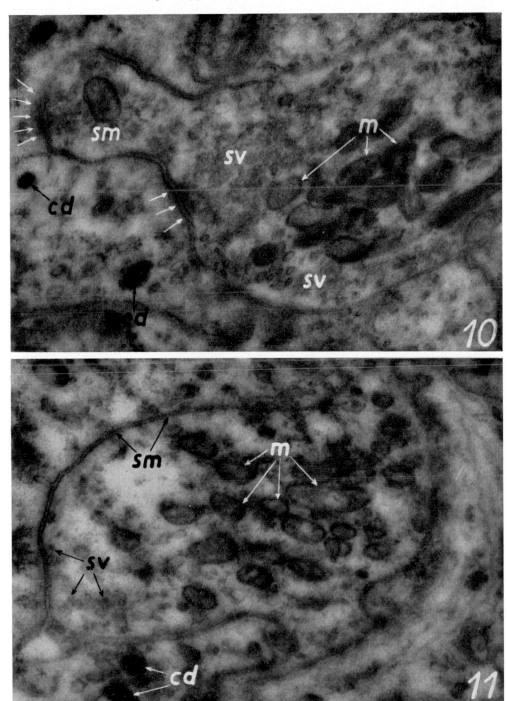

[55]. The signal that can be recorded in this system is the amount of adrenaline, noradrenaline or total catechol secreted into the adrenal vein under electrical stimulation [55, 52] or the analysis of the histochemical and submicroscopic changes of the stimulated adrenal cells with the electron microscope [23].

A preliminary account of our findings is being published and here we want only to emphasize the intense changes that occur in the synaptic vesicles, after prolonged stimulation with electrical pulses of different frequencies. In a number of rabbits under nembutal anesthesia the left splachnic nerve was stimulated with supramaximal pulses of frequencies varying between 8 and 400 per second. Most experiments were done at frequencies of 100 and 400 per second during 10 minutes because Rapela and Covian [52] reported, in the dog, a maximum secretion of catechols at frequencies of 40 to 100 pulses and a considerable diminution at 400 stimuli per second.

Some of our results are illustrated in Figs. 8 to 11 and in Text-fig. 3. In the normal nerve ending a typical vesicular component similar to the synaptic vesicles is observed (Fig. 8). In addition mitochondria, some larger vesicles and, more seldom, neuroprotofibrils are present. Prolonged electrical stimulation of the splachnic nerves induces dramatic changes in the synaptic vesicles. With a stimulus of 100 per second (Fig. 10, Text-fig. 3) there is a definite increase in the number of synaptic vesicles and clusters of them are found near the synaptic membrane, attached to it and apparently liberating their content in the intermembranal space or the immediate vicinity of the synaptic membrane. In the regions marked with arrows in Fig. 10 it can be observed a diffuse increase in electron density and ill defined structures that from the presynaptic side invade the postsynaptic region of the junction. Even more striking are the results observed after stimulation of 400 pulses per second. In this case a considerable depletion of synaptic vesicles takes place and there are some less significant alterations of the matrix and the mitochondria (Fig. 9).

In Table I are presented the results of measurements of the surface in square microns and of the number of vesicles in normal endings, in endings stimulated at 100 per second and at 400 per second. In the control endings there is a mean of 82.6 vesicles per square micron. In those stimulated at 100 pulses per second a significant increase occurs with a mean of 132.7 vesicles per μ^2 and in the synapses stimulated at 400 per second a considerable diminution with a mean of 29.2 μ^2 takes place.

TABLE I. *Number of nerve endings of the adrenal medulla, with different treatments analyzed, the total number of synaptic vesicles measured, and the surface in μ^2 of each ending and the number of vesicles per μ^2.*

Synapse no.	Treatment pulses/s	Total no. vesicles	Surface in μ^2	No. vesicles per μ^2
1	Control	228	2.144	106.0
2	Control	86	1.250	68.8
3	Control	318	2.695	118.1
4	Control	265	2.752	95.9
5	Control	106	1.305	81.1
6	Control	90	2.439	36.9
7	Control	174	2.947	59.0
8	Control	64	0.567	114.0
			Mean:	82.65
9	100/S	581	5.707	101
10	100/S	196	1.744	112.3
11	100/S	628	2.693	233.2
12	100/S	974	8.300	117.3
13	100/S	187	5.550	340.0
14	100/S	230	1.960	117.3
15	100/S	305	2.498	122.4
16	100/S	349	2.540	137.4
			Mean:	132.7
17	400/S	93	3.647	28.2
18	400/S	151	4.863	31.0
19	400/S	111	3.870	28.7
20	400/S	90	4.669	19.2
21	400/S	144	3.231	44.5
22	400/S	80	1.960	40.7
23	400/S	124	4.900	25.3
			Mean:	29.2

DISCUSSION

Synaptic Vesicles and the Physiology of the Synapse

Under the name of *synaptic junctions* are generally recognized the contacts between two neurones or a neurone an another cell type, that are specially differentiated for the transmission of nerve impulses. In a strict sense they embody all the regions "anatomically differentiated and functionally special-ized for the transmission of the liminal excitations from one element to the following in an irreciprocal direction". This is the case of the interneuronal synapse, the contacts between a receptor and a neurone and the neuro-muscular junction. These typical polarized synapses are the great majority in the nervous system of vertebrates and invertebrates.[1] This physiological property supposes the existence of a polarized structural organization at the synaptic junction.

Early workers described a concentration of mitochondria or neurosomes at the end feet [2, 40] and this was later confirmed for several types of syn-apses [3, 4, 7, 8]. This fact led Bodian [8] to suggest the possibility of a re-lationship between mitochondria and the local secretion of acetylcholine and cholinesterase. It was also suggested that mitochondria might be con-cerned with more general metabolic processes which could modify the elec-trical properties of this membrane [8, 5]. This hypothesis now seems doubt-ful in view of present knowledge of the biochemical function of mitochondria. Furthermore there is a considerable variation in the concentration of mito-chondria in different types of synapses and in some cases—as in the rod and cone synapses—they are entirely absent from the ending and are located at considerable distance away from the synapses. This fact precludes that mitochondria have a direct role in synaptic function (see [21]). From purely morphological considerations it seems more justifiable to suggest that the polarization of the synapse is related to the preferential localization of the synaptic vesicles on the presynaptic side of the junction and that this compo-nent might be directly involved in the biochemical phenomena of synaptic transmission.

Any interpretation of the possible physiological role of the synaptic vesicles should take into consideration the important facts that have been recently demonstrated by the use of microelectrodes in the physiology of the neuro-muscular junction. Fatt and Katz [28] found that the end plates of many resting muscles fibers are the seat of spontaneous subthreshold activity consisting of miniatures end plate potentials (e.p.p.), whose amplitude is of the order of one-hundredth of the normal potential in response to a nerve impulse.

Different pharmacological properties of the miniature e.p.p. led the au-thors to postulate that they must be due to the release of acetylcholine

---

[1] This definition would exclude the natural or artificially produced contacts which were designated *ephases* by Arvanitaky [1] and also the contacts with reciprocal transmission found by Bullock [9, 10] in some giant axons of invertebrates and called *quasi-artificial synapse*.

by the endings. Feldberg [3] had already suggested that cholinergic nerve endings, even at rest, continually discharge small amounts of acetylcholine and replace it by chemical synthesis. However the miniature e.p.p. could not be produced by simple molecular diffusion of acetylcholine and Fatt and Katz [28, 29] suggested that the release of the chemical mediator must be in multimolecular or quantal units [14], arising from the synchronous discharge of a large number of acetylcholine ions.

Since the amplitude of the spontaneous potential is only about one hundredth of the functional response to a nerve impulse "it may be concluded that the apparatus for the release of acetylcholine at a junction is subdivided into large number of units (at least 100), each of which is able to operate independently of the rest" [27]. The authors postulate that under the action of driving forces such as their own termal agitation and the electric fields across the membrane these quantal units of acetylcholine are suddenly discharged at localized points of the endings. The electrical excitation occurring at the arrival of the nerve impulse would produce a large synchronized action and thus the simultaneous discharge of many units which determine the end plate potential.

These physiological findings and theoretical considerations find an extraordinary support in the submicroscopic organization of the synapse. The observations made on the structure and relationship of the synaptic vesicles with the membranes and their behavior in different physiological and pathological conditions [15, 16, 17, 21, 22] are all consistent with the concept that the synaptic vesicle may represent the quantal unit of acetylcholine postulated by Fatt, Katz and Del Castillo.

From our first paper [18, 19] we suggested that acetylcholine and other chemical mediators could be associated with particles or vesicles of submicroscopic size. We also postulated that the synaptic vesicles may move toward the presynaptic membrane and discharge their content at the junction. This phenomenon is even better illustrated by the above described observations in rod and cone synapses under stimulation by light (Figs. 5, 6, 7). It is possible to imagine that acetylcholine or other chemical mediators are continuously synthesized and segregated into packets and enclosed by the membrane of the synaptic vesicles. (An entirely similar process takes place in the synthesis of adrenalin and other catechols by the adrenal gland [23]. The vesicles could then flow toward a position adjacent to the synaptic membrane (Text-fig. 4 A). One may postulate that in the resting condition single vesicles may spontaneously and randomly discharge their content at localized spots of the junction originating the miniature end plate potentials

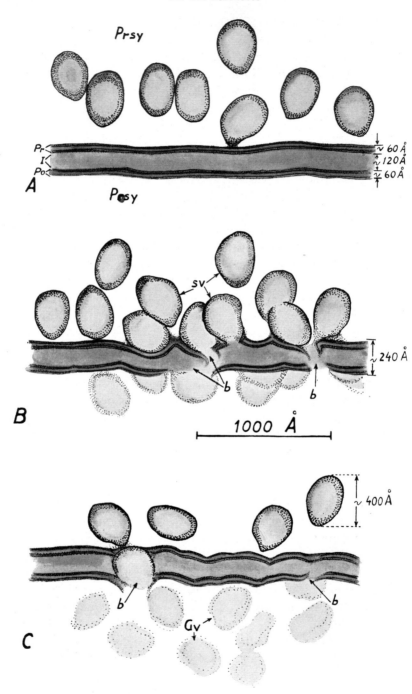

of Fatt and Katz [28]. If the resting condition is prolonged, as in the case of dark adapted animals, an accumulation of vesicles at the presynaptic membrane would occur (Fig. 5). When a propagated electrical disturbance in the form of an action potential reaches the presynaptic membrane many vesicles will synchronously open at the synaptic interspace and liberate its content of acetylcholine and other ions (Text-fig. 4 B). This process may involve the passage and rapid destruction of the vesicles into the postsynaptic cytoplasm (Text-fig. 4 B and C).

These concepts of flow and discharge of the synaptic vesicles are in agreement with those recently postulated by Bennett [6] of membrane vesiculation as a mechanism for active transport and ion pumping. They also involve a dynamical structure for the synaptic membrane with the possibility of local breakdown and restoration during synaptic transmission (Text-fig. 4 B). It is very interesting that this dynamic structural concept of the synapse is in agreement with physiological experiments suggesting that the chemical transmitter short circuits the synaptic membrane [29]. This results in a reduction of the resistance as well as the potential of the membrane and would be indicative of a large increase of permeability to all ions [13].

The finding of changes in the synaptic vesicles under electrical stimulation with different frequencies are also confirmatory of the presumption that the play a physiological role in synaptic transmission. These experiments are suggestive that a balance exists between the process of formation of synaptic vesicles and synthesis of the chemical mediator and that of discharge of the vesicles and release of the transmitter. In the case of the adrenal medulla this balance might be altered in one sense or the other according to the frequency of the stimulus [22].

SUMMARY

A survey of research done in our laboratory to obtain information about the physiological significance of the "synaptic vesicles" described by De Robertis and Bennett (1953–54) is presented.

Text-fig. 4.—Diagram of an interpretation of the ultrastructure of the synaptic membrane and its relationship with the synaptic vesicles: *A*, in resting condition; *B*, during transmission of the nerve impulse; *C*, immediately after transmission of the impulse. The discharge of the vesicles into the intermembranal space and the passage of some of them into the postsynaptic cytoplasm is shown. *b*, breakdowns of the membrane; *Gv*, ghost-like vesicles; *I*, intermembranal space; *Pr*, presynaptic membrane; *Po*, postsynaptic membrane; *Prsy*, presynaptic cell; *Posy*, postsynaptic cell, *sv*, synaptic vesicle. (See further description in the text.)

Degenerative changes of the synapse were observed in the ventral acoustic ganglia as early as 22 hours after destruction of the cochlea. These changes consist in swelling of the matrix of the endings, agglutination and lysis of the synaptic vesicles, lysis and disintegration of mitochondria and finally detachment and breakdown of the membrane at the synaptic junction. The alterations of the synaptic vesicles are the most intense and earliest to develop. The possible correlation of these changes with the early physiological deterioration of synaptic transmission is suggested.

In synapses of the retinal rods and cones with the bipolar cells of rabbits kept in the dark for 2 to 9 days a definite reduction in size of the synaptic vesicles was observed. In dark adapted animals the vesicles accumulate near the synaptic membrane. After stimulation by light the opening of some vesicles into the synaptic interspace and the passage of some of them into the postsynaptic cytoplasm can be observed.

Stimulation of the splanchnic nerve induce intense changes in the synaptic vesicles of the nerve endings in the adrenal medulla. With stimulation of 100 pulses per second for 10 minutes a significant increase of synaptic vesicles per μ^2 was found while with 400 pulses a considerable diminution took place.

The probable significance of the synaptic vesicles in the physiology of the synapse is discussed. Since 1954 we suggested (De Robertis and Bennett, *Federation Proc* **13**, 35 (1954)) that acetylcholine and other chemical mediators could be associated with synaptic vesicles and that they may move to discharge their content at the synaptic junction. The synaptic vesicles may represent the quantal units of chemical mediator postulated by Fatt, Katz and Del Castillo. A mechanism of synthesis within a membrane and of flow and discharge of synaptic vesicles and cathecol containing droplets of the adrenal medulla is postulated.

REFERENCES

1. Arvanitaki, A., *J. Neurophysiol.* **5**, 108 (1942).
2. Auerbach, L., *Neurol. Centr.* **17**, 445 (1898).
3. Bartelmez, G. W., *J. Comp. Neurol.* **25**, 87 (1915).
4. Bartelmez, G. W. and Hoerr, N. L., *J. Comp. Neurol.* **57**, 401 (1933).
5. Bartley, N. and Davis, R. E., *Biochem. J.* **52**, XX (1952).
6. Bennett, H. S., *J. Biophys. Biochem. Cytol.* **2**, Suppl. 99 (1956).
7. Bodian, D., *J. Comp. Neurol.* **68**, 117 (1937).
8. —— *Physiol. Rev.* **22**, 146 (1942).
9. Bullock, T. H., *Cold Spring Harbor Symposia Quant. Biol.* **17**, 267 (1952).
10. —— *J. Comp. Neurol.* **28**, 1 (1953).
11. Coppée, G. and Bacq, Z. M., *Arch. internatl. physiol.* **47**, 312 (1938).
12. de Castro, F., *Trabajos inst. Cajal invest. biol.* **34**, 217 (1942).

13. DEL CASTILLO, J. and KATZ, B., *J. Physiol.* **125**, 546 (1954).
14. —— *ibid.* **128**, 396 (1955).
15. DE ROBERTIS, E., *Acta Neurol. Latinoam.* **1**, 1 (1955).
16. —— *Anat. Rec.* **121**, 284 (1955).
17. —— *J. Biophys. Biochem. Cytol.* **2**, 503 (1956).
18. DE ROBERTIS, E. and BENNETT, H. S. D., *Federation Proc.* **13**, 35 (1954).
19. —— *J. Biophys. Biochem. Cytol.* **1**, 47 (1955).
20. DE ROBERTIS, E. and FRANCHI, C. M., *J. Appl. Phys.* **24**, 1162 (1954).
21. —— *J. Biophys. Biochem. Cytol.* **2**, 307 (1956).
22. DE ROBERTIS, E. and VAZ FERREYRA, A., *J. Biophys. Biochem. Cytol.* **3**, 611 (1957).
23. —— *Exptl. Cell Research* **12**, 568, 575 (1957).
24. ESTABLE, C., REISSIG, M. and DE ROBERTIS, E., *J. Appl. Phys.* **24**, 1421 (1953).
25. —— *Exptl. Cell Research* **6**, 255 (1954).
26. EYZAGUIRRE, C., ESPINDOLA, J. and LUCO, J. U., *Acta Physiol. Latinoam.* **2**, 213 (1952).
27. FATT, P., *Physiol. Rev.* **34**, 674 (1954).
28. FATT, P. and KATZ, B., *J. Physiol.* **117**, 109 (1952).
29. —— *Acta Pysiol. Scand.* **29**, 117 (1953).
30. FELDBERG, W., *Physiol. Rev.* **25**, 596 (1945).
31. —— *Pharm. Rev.* **6**, 85 (1954).
32. FELDBERG, W. and MINZ, B., *Pflügers Arch. ges. Physiol.* **233**, 657 (1933).
33. FELDBERG, W., MINZ, B. and TSUDMIZURA, J., *J. Physiol.* **80**, 15 (1934).
34. —— *ibid.* **81**, 286 (1934).
35. FERNÁNDEZ-MORÁN, H., *Acta VI Cong. Latinoam. Neurocirugia*, p. 599, 1955.
36. FOERSTER, O., GAGEL, O. and SHEEHAN, D., *Z. Anat. Entwicklungsgeschichte* **101**, 553 (1933).
37. GIBSON, N. C., *Arch. Neurol. Psychol.* **38**, 1145 (1937).
38. GLESS, P., MEYER, A. and MEYER, M., *J. Anat.* **80**, 101 (1946).
39. HAGGAR, R. A. and BARR, M. L., *J. Comp. Neurol.* **93**, 17 (1950).
40. HELD, H., *Arch. Anat. u. Physiol. Anat. Abt.* **204**, (1897).
41. HOFF, E. C., *Proc. Roy. Soc. London Ser. B* **111**, 175 (1932).
42. HOFF, E. C. and HOFF, H. E., *Brain* **57**, 454 (1934).
43. LISSAK, K., DEMPSEY, E. W. and ROSENBLUETH, A., *Am. J. Physiol.* **128**, 45 (1939).
44. LUFT, J., *Conference on Tissue Fine Structure*, 1956.
45. —— *J. Biophys. Biochem. Cytol. Suppl.* **2**, 229 (1956).
46. LUSE, S. A., *J. Biophys. Biochem. Cytol.* **2**, 531 (1956).
47. MACINTOSH, F. C., *Arch. Internatl. Physiol.* **47**, 312 (1938).
48. PALADE, G. E., *Anat. Rec.* **121**, 284 (1955).
49. PALAY, S. L., *Anat. Rec.* **118**, 336 (1954).
50. —— *J. Biophys. Biochem. Cytol.* **2**, 193 (1956).
51. POLYAK, S. L., The Retina. The University of Chicago Press, 1941.
52. RAPELA, C. E. and COVIAN, M. R., *Rev. Soc. Arg. Biol.* **30**, 157 (1954).
53. ROBERTSON, J. D., *Proc. Soc. Exptl. Biol. and Med.* **82**, 219 (1953).
54. —— *J. Biophys. Biochem. Cytol.* **2**, 381 (1956).
55. ROSENBLUETH, A., The Transmission of Nerve Impulses. John Wiley & Sons, New York, 1950.
56. SERENI, E. and YOUNG, J. Z., *Pubbl. Staz. Zool. Napoli* **12**, 173 (1932).
57. SJÖSTRAND, F. S., *J. Appl. Phys.* **24**, 1422 (1953).
58. TEITELBAUM, H. A., *Quart. Rev. Biol.* **17**, 135 (1942).
59. TITECA, J., *Arch. Internatl. Physiol.* **41**, 1 (1935).
60. YAMADA, E., *J. Biophys. Biochem. Cytol.* **1**, 445 (1955).
61. WERSÄLL, J., *Acta Oto-Laryngol.*, *Suppl.* *126* (1956).

STUDY OF ADRENERGIC CEREBRAL NEUROHUMORS IN RELATION TO SYNAPTIC TRANSMISSION MECHANISMS

A. S. MARRAZZI

Veterans Administration Research Laboratories in Neuropsychiatry, Veterans Administration Hospital, Leech Farm Road, Pittsburgh, Pa., U.S.A.

POTENTIAL NEUROHUMORS AND A HYPOTHESIS

DIFFUSIBLE substances present in the brain are potential neurohumoral agents. The multitude of such substances identified to date, both liberated and perhaps merely circulating in the brain, includes a number of adrenergic and related compounds. It is the purpose of this presentation to examine their synaptic effects and evaluate their role in transmission in health and disease.

In 1939 [21, 22] the present author developed a logical hypothesis which seemed to merit testing at various synapses including those in the brain. This hypothesis was an extension of the formulation justified by the then available information on neurohumoral function at the neuro-effector junctions. In brief, the data indicated that at all autonomic neuro-effector junctions transmission was regulated and effected by cholinergic and adrenergic mediators; and, in almost all cases, the two influences were reciprocal in direction, so that equilibrium between the two determined the nature and ease of transmission. We asked whether this might not also be true at neuro-neuronal junctions or the synapses of the nervous system.

GANGLIONIC SYNAPSES—CHOLINERGIC INFLUENCES

Our initial experiments concerned themselves with the possible applicability of this hypothesis to transmission across the synapses of autonomic ganglia. Since there were already some indications that acetylcholine was liberated and could operate in the superior cervical ganglion of the cat [14, 15], we first studied acetylcholine and related substances. Previous work had utilized a remote indicator of synaptic function, namely, the nictitating membrane. However, the susceptibility of neuro-effector junctions in the muscle of the nictitating membrane itself presents the possibility of acetylcholine acting on either the junctions or synapses, or both. We therefore resorted to a more localizing technique [21], which consisted of recording the post-synaptic action potential, from the superior cervical or various other autonomic ganglia in the nembutalized cat, in response to a submaximal electrical testing shock applied to the pre-synaptic trunk by fluid electrodes. These stimuli were delivered at the intentionally slow rate

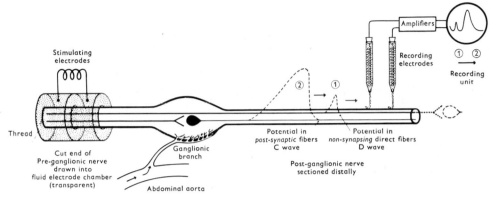

Fig. 1.—Scheme of stimulating and recording set up inferior mesenteric ganglion with intact blood supply.

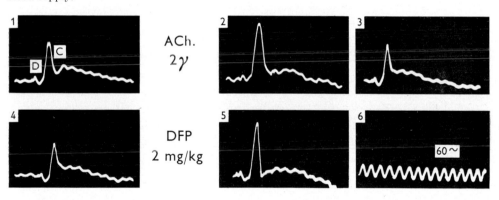

Fig. 2.—Differential effects of drugs on synaptic transmisson (C-wave) and nerve conduction (D-wave) in inferior mesenteric sympathetic ganglion. Acetylcholine and di-isopropylflurophosphate injected intravenously.

of two per second to avoid the spontaneous progressive facilitation we observed at faster rates and reported by Bronk *et al.* [4] (cf. also [2]). The circulation to the ganglion was preserved so that substances could be delivered to the synapses by the normal, physiological route. Fig. 1 also shows the advantage of using the inferior mesenteric ganglion [20] where, because of direct fibers running through the ganglion to synapse later on, transmission, indicated by the post-synaptic C-wave, can be compared simultaneously

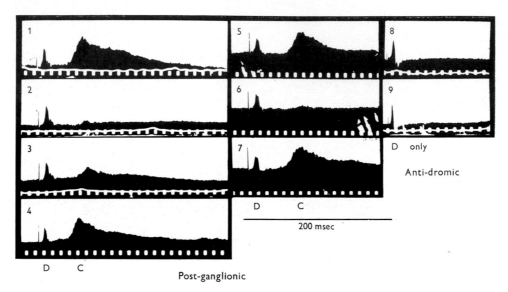

Fig. 3.—Inferior mesenteric ganglion inhibition by adrenaline injected intravenously after line 1.

with conduction, indicated by the D-wave, in the direct, through fibers. In this way we confirmed and expanded the evidence for cholinergic function, showing (Fig. 2) that acetylcholine in microgram doses enhanced synaptic transmission without affecting conduction. The same result (line 2, Fig. 2) was achieved by the use of the anticholinesterase, di-isopropylfluorophosphate (DFP), thus indicating that acetylcholine was preserved at the synapse and must therefore be naturally present and liberated by pre-synaptic impulses. Incidentally, with the advantage of this more discriminating method, we were also able to show that the synaptic effects of acetylcholine in question were also blocked by atropine, as is characteristically the case at the neuro-effector junctions.

GANGLIONIC SYNAPSES—ADRENERGIC INFLUENCES

Turning our attention to possible adrenergic components in chemical regulation of synaptic transmission at this site, Fig. 3 shows a mirror oscillograph record from a similar inferior mesenteric genglion preparation. It is clearly evident from the figure that the adrenaline, given between 1 and 2, 5 and 6, and 8 and 9, inhibited transmission without affecting conduction. The latter is borne out by the lack of effect on D-waves in the first and second columns. This is also seen in the third column, where the D-waves

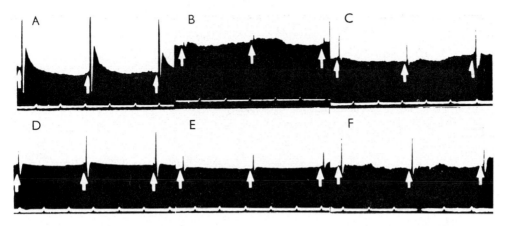

Fig. 4.—Ganglionic inhibition by secretion from the animal's own adrenal. Sympathetic post-ganglionic potentials (cat). Splanchnic stimulation between 1st and 2nd columns. 1st column = controls; 2nd column = maximum action; 3rd column = recovery.

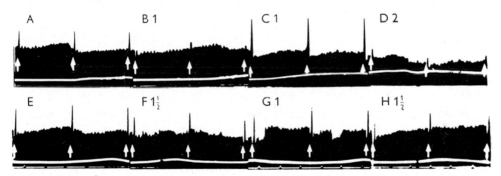

Fig. 5.—Increased stimulus overcoming inhibition of ganglion by adrenaline (*A–D*) or ephedrine (*E–H*). Intravenous injections between 1st and 2nd columns. 1st column = controls; 2nd column = maximum action; 3rd column = increase stimulus; 4th column = original stimulus.

are obtained in isolation by antidromic stimulation with recording from pre-ganglionic electrodes. We have obtained such effects with quantities of physiological significance and in all types of sympathetic ganglia [30] and in the available para-sympathetic ganglia [32] by exogenous adrenaline and by adrenaline liberated from the adrenal medulla [23]. The latter is illustrated in Fig. 4, taken from an experiment in which adrenaline was liberated by stimulation of the splanchnic nerve.

In 1932, Burn showed that ephedrine is dependent upon the presence of adrenergic nerves for its action. We therefore used this in 1939 [23, 24] as a means of testing whether the pre-ganglionic fibers did include adrenergic

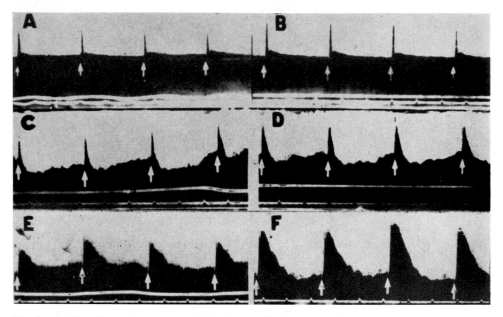

Fig. 6.—Action of anemia on sympathetic postganglionic potentials. *A–B*, rabbit; *C–D* and *E–F*, cats. 1st column before, 2nd column after death. *F* is 10 minutes after death. Sensitivity same as before except *A* and *B* where 1 mm = 20 µV.

nerves. Inhibitory fibers in the pre-ganglionic trunk of the superior cervical sympathetic ganglion of the cat had been postulated by Eccles in 1935 [10, 11]. As recorded in Fig. 5, ephedrine, as indeed all sympathomimetic amines to varying degrees, also manifests a synaptic inhibitory action. It is therefore reasonable to conclude that pre-ganglionic adrenergic inhibitory fibers do exist in these ganglia. Attention is drawn to the confirmation of this by Bülbring in 1944, who collected adrenaline in the effluent from the perfused stimulated superior cervical ganglion of the cat. The synaptic inhibitory effect of adrenaline and of ephedrine is not a secondary one, due to possible sensitization to acetylcholine to the point of converting the latter into an excessive stimulation with resulting paralysis. This follows from the fact that, during the synaptic inhibition (records *B* and *F*) induced by adrenaline and ephedrine respectively, an increase in the pre-synaptic stimulus, thereby presumably increasing the liberated acetylcholine, causes a breakthrough (records *C* and *G*), which would not be the case if the depression of synaptic transmission had been due to sensitization. *D* and *H* of this slide show a return to the inhibitory level when the stimulus is reduced to its original size, indicating that the increased response of the breakthrough was not merely

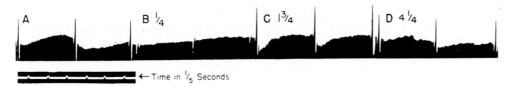

← Time in $\frac{1}{5}$ Seconds

Fig. 7.—Ganglionic inhibition (*B*) followed by facilitation (*C*) and return to norma l(*D*). Sympathetic postganglionic potentials. *A*, control; adrenaline injected intravenously between *A* and *B*. Numbers equal minutes between sections.

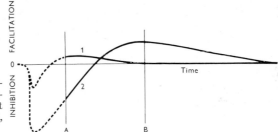

Fig. 8.—Apparent differences in adrenaline effect depending on delay before recording. Dotted line: portion of curve lost due to delay. Curve 1, small dose; curve 2, large dose.

an evidence of the wearing off of the inhibition, which still persisted in the next records *D* and *H*.

Because adrenaline and the other sympathomimetic amines are vasoconstrictors, it is necessary to assure oneself that local ischemia is not the cause of the synaptic inhibition produced by adrenaline within one circulation time. Brown and Feldberg [5] showed that adrenaline does reduce the flow in the perfused superior cervical sympathetic ganglion of the cat. However, as Larrabee *et al.* [19] had shown for the stellate and as we confirmed for the superior cervical, autonomic ganglia are quite resistant to ischemia, so that the immediate effects of complete cessation of circulation in the cat and rabbit superior cervical ganglion are nil, and facilitation often occurs between 5 and 10 minutes after the onset of ischemia (Fig. 6). Only after this does a gradual decline to extinction of response take place in the next 5 minutes. On the other hand, the ganglionic vaso-constriction may contribute something to the picture, as illustrated in Fig. 7, where the recovery from inhibition by adrenaline to the control level passes through a period of facilitation shown at *C*.

If we now draw some excitability curves, Fig. 8, from continuous records (stimulus 2 per second) of the effects of smaller and larger doses (Curves 1 and 2 respectively), it is readily apparent that the sequence of primary specific inhibition followed by secondary non-specific facilitation, due to rebound or vaso-constriction or both, and then recovery, can lead to the wrong impression when mere sampling rather than continuous recording is used. For example, a record taken at Point *A* alone might be interpreted erroneously as a stimulating action of a small dose (reading Curve 1) and a

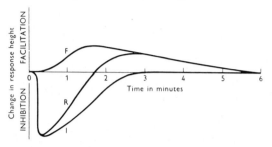

Fig. 9.—Reconstruction from recorded curve of ganglionic inhibition (*R*) of hypothetical curves. *I* = *pure* specific inhibition; *F* = *pure* non-specific facilitation due to ischemia.

depressant action of a larger dose (reading Curve 2). Actually, however, both curves are identical in shape and indicate an identical sequence of events with a time course altered by dosage. Constructing theoretical curves (Fig. 9), we might look upon the actual record (*R*) as the algebraic summation of a primary inhibitory process (*I*) of faster onset and a slower secondary facilitatory process (*F*) due perhaps, in part, to concomitant ischemia.

CEREBRAL SYNAPSES—CHOLINENERGIC AND ADRENERGIC INFLUENCES

Our principal interest in the convenient monosynaptic preparation offered by autonomic ganglia was in the possibility of making use of it as a model to help analyze cerebral synaptic processes. Fig. 10 diagrams the situation suggested by our data in autonomic ganglia, namely, a control of synaptic transmission by a balanced, reciprocating, humoral system consisting of cholinergic excitation and adrenergic inhibition somewhat complicated by possible secondary non-specific effects. Accordingly, leaving out various intermediary steps, we turn our attention now directly to the most nearly analogous situation we have been able to devise in the brain [22].

As described originally by Curtis and Bard [9], there exists a relatively simple transcallosal pathway connecting symmetrical points in the two hemispheres of the cat and monkey brain. Utilizing this system in the lightly nembutalized cat (Fig. 11), we stimulated the lateral or the suprasylvan gyri and recorded from the corresponding points in the contralateral hemisphere. The figure depicts the cat's brain as though transparent and shows the transcallosal pathway as well as the distribution of a "close arterial" injection

into the common carotid artery to the ipsilateral hemisphere. The anastomoses of the circle of Willis do not complicate this situation unless the injection is done too forcefully. The ipsilateral distribution can be readily
demonstrated by the injection of fluorescein and ultraviolet radiation of the
brain, whereupon the ipsilateral hemisphere alone fluoresces. The close

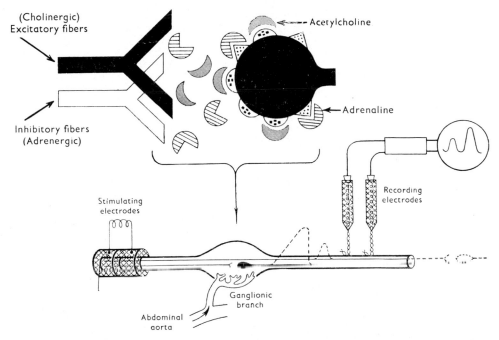

Fig. 10.—Symbolized synaptic findings in ganglionic preparation.

arterial injection enables us to observe central effects uncomplicated by
peripheral ones and the consequent afferent barrage of the central nervous
system thereby initiated. This is so because a small dose will then achieve an
effective concentration in the ipsilateral hemisphere, but on entry into the
general circulation will be so diluted as to prove sub-threshold for peripheral
effects. The insert on the right-hand side of the figure anticipates the neurohumoral mechanisms which will be supported by the data.

A cross-section through the preparation appears in Fig. 12 and indicates
that, by virtue of the volume-conductor properties of the brain, the first
surface-positive wave can be regarded as a record of inflow into the synapse,
which is here defined in its most general terms as encompassing for this
purpose the functionally articulated incoming and outgoing neurons and

the intervening transmission processes. The next or surface-negative wave can be regarded as the outflow from the terminal synapses in the transcallosal pathway. When we obtain changes in surface-negative without corresponding changes in surface-positive waves, we feel justified in postulating a change in output without a change in input, which we define as a synaptic change.

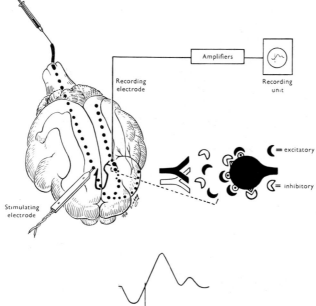

Fig. 11.—Transparent model of brain. Recording from terminal cortical synapses of intercortical transcallosal pathway. Ipsilateral distribution of "close arterial" (common carotid) injection. Synaptic neurohumoral equilibrium symbolized at right.

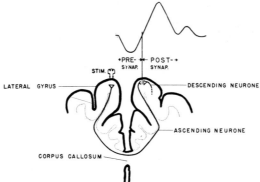

Fig. 12.—Schematic drawing of intercortical transcallosal pathway in the cat. Diagram of evoked potential from optic cortex on stimulating symmetrical point in contralateral cortex, showing pre- and post-synaptic components.

In this way it was possible to demonstrate for the first time (Fig. 13), the effect of small doses of acetylcholine, introduced by a physiological route, on the evoked cortical response. A prolongation of after-discharge had already been recorded by Bonnet and Bremer [3]. It is now seen in *B* of this figure that, without material alteration of the submaximal input, the output has been practically doubled. Then, on dissipation of the acetyl-

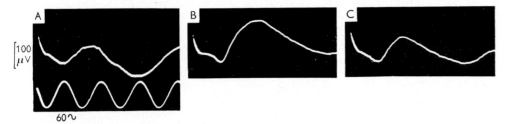

Fig. 13.—Cerebral synaptic action of acetylcholine in a two neurone intercortical (transcallosal) system. Potentials evoked in optic cortex by electrical stimulation of symmetrical point in contralateral cortex. Acetylcholine (1 μg/kg) injected into ipsilateral carotid artery after *A*. *A*, control; *B* enhancement; *C*, recovery.

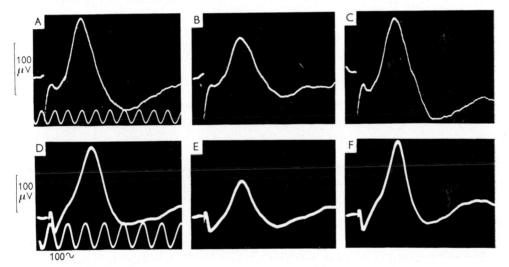

Fig. 14.—Cerebral synaptic action of adrenaline and of nor-adrenaline in a two neurone intercortical (*transcallosal*) system. Potentials evoked in optic cortex by electrical stimulation of symmetrical point in contralateral cortex. Adrenaline (10 μg/kg) injected ipsilateral carotid artery after *A*. Nor-adrenaline (150 μg/kg) injected after *D*. *A*, *D*, controls; *B*, *E*, inhibition; *C*, *F*, recovery.

choline, the response returns to control level (*C*). Maneuvers with anticholinesterases and atropine similar to those described for the ganglion bring similar data and characterize this cholinergic action as qualitatively like that of acetylcholine in the ganglia and elsewhere. We are now ready to consider the cerebral adrenergic and related substances. A list of these will be useful at this point. Vogt [34] has shown that adrenaline and nor-adrenaline are to be found in the brain. The distribution of these has also been described by von Euler [13] and by Amin *et al.* [1], who also find serotonin

380   *A. S. Marrazzi*

and substance *P*. The existence of serotonin as a natural constituent of
brain had been previously described by Erspamer [12] and by Page [31].
Dimethyl-serotonin or bufotenine has been identified in normal human
urine by Bumpus and Page [7], although its site of origin in the body has
not been determined. An action of something like adrenochrome has been
postulated to take place in some schizophrenics by Hoffer, Osmond and
Smythies [17], but adrenochrome has never been demonstrated in the
mammalian body.

Adrenaline and demethylated adrenaline or nor-adrenaline, the two most
studied potential neurohumors, can be demonstrated to have the anticipated
cerebral synaptic inhibitory action (Fig. 14). An important difference is
apparent in that approximately the same effect is achieved by nor-adrenaline
only when the amount is fifteen times that required for adrenaline. In
varying degrees the sympathomimetic amines possess this synaptic inhibitory
action, including ephedrine and amphetamine [27]. The latter two compounds
have as before, additional significance in that their dependence on adrenergic
nerves for the exercise of their actions suggests indirectly that adrenergic
fibers are present at the cerebral synapses under study.

SEROTONIN, CEREBRAL INHIBITORY NEUROHUMOR

More important than these, however, is serotonin, for, as we pointed out
in 1954 [28], this 5-hydroxy-tryptamine, which is an indole relative of
adrenaline and is plentifully found in the brain, is twenty times as potent as
adrenaline as a cerebral synaptic inhibitor. Thus, Fig. 15 presents its action
in a 1-microgram dose (calculated as base). Although this does not exclude
a role for adrenaline and nor-adrenaline, it does make this more potent
synaptic inhibitor potentially of very great, if not of greater, significance. In

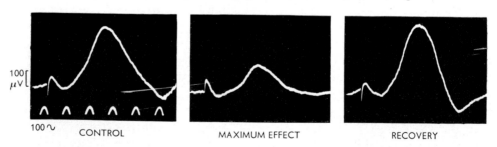

Fig. 15.—Cerebral synaptic action of serotonin in a two neurone intercortical (transcallosal)
system. Potentials evoked in optic cortex of the cat by electrical stimulation of contralateral
cortex every 2 seconds. Serotonin 2 μg/kg injected into ipsilateral carotid artery.

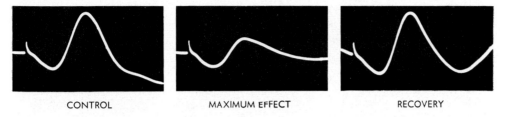

CONTROL   MAXIMUM EFFECT   RECOVERY

Fig. 16.—Cerebral synaptic action of iproniazid in a two neuron intercortical (transcallosal) system. Potentials evoked in optic cortex of the cat by electrical stimulation of contralateral cortex every two seconds. Iproniazid 5 mg/kg injected into ipsilateral carotid artery.

the case of serotonin the data pointing to its natural operation at the synapse is even better than in the case of adrenaline and nor-adrenaline. This is because serotonin is rapidly destroyed by monoamine oxidase which is present in the brain [33], and this enzyme can be specifically inhibited by iproniazid [35]. Accordingly, if an injection of iproniazid duplicates the action of serotonin, as it does in Fig. 16, then it is a fair assumption that the action is due to serotonin naturally liberated at the synapse by nerve impulses and preserved by the inhibitor of monoamine oxidase, its destructive enzyme. This is further borne out by experiments in progress which indicate that at the time iproniazid (an inhibitor of monoamine oxidase introduced into the common carotid artery) is producing a serotonin-like synaptic inhibition, it is differentially inhibiting monoamine oxidase; so that the enzyme titer of the injected side, from which the recording is being taken, is lower than the opposite side at the time synaptic transmission is being inhibited. This would be the case if the inhibition of monoamine oxidase resulted in a failure of rapid destruction and, therefore, an accumulation of serotonin liberated *in situ* at the synapse [16].

The elements seem to us established now of a highly active neurohumoral transmitting and regulating system for synaptic transmission in the cerebrum. The data have been presented for one area but, with varying degrees of completion, we have such data also for other parts of the cortex and subcortex. This leads us to entertain, for further testing, the hypothesis that careful scrutiny, taking into account the complications introduced by lack of anesthesia, etc., will reveal that the synapses are, on the whole, qualitatively alike though with great differences in threshold. Such threshold differences can result in patterns of activity so different that an unjustified assumption of a different synaptic effect is made. For example, synaptic inhibition will decrease activity or, if it inhibits controlling mechanisms, it can release and thereby increase activity of the final neuron [18].

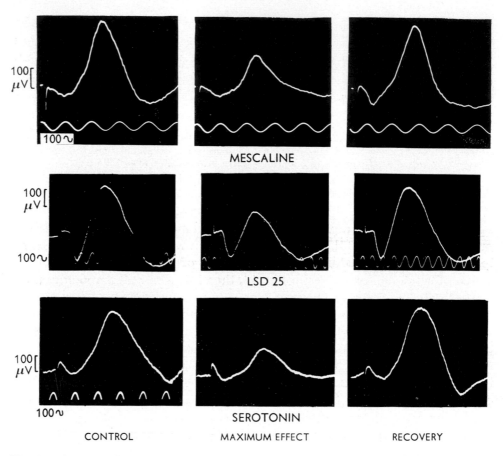

MESCALINE

LSD 25

SEROTONIN

CONTROL   MAXIMUM EFFECT   RECOVERY

Fig. 17.—Approximate equivalent synaptic inhibitory effects of chemical psychotogens.

PSYCHOTOGENS, EXOGENOUS AND ENDOGENOUS

In this connection one cannot forego the opportunity of pointing out that disturbance of the chemical equilibrium regulating synaptic transmission could readily occur due to a multiplicity of factors. The resulting dysfunction could manifest itself, among other things, as mental disturbance. In view of this data and this thinking, it seems no accident that the most potent chemical psychotogens are related to adrenaline and serotonin [28, 26].

These include mescaline, which is closely related to adrenaline, lysergic acid di-ethylamide (LSD-25), related to serotonin which, in turn, is related to adrenaline through adrenochrome, which is a first oxidation product of

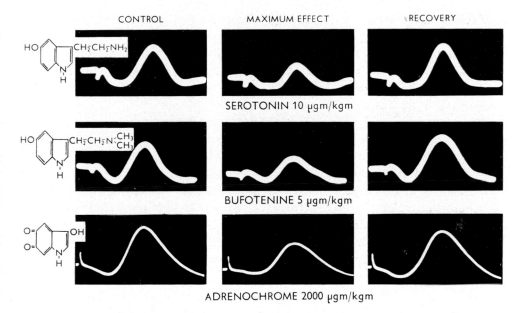

Fig. 18.—Cerebral synaptic inhibition by indoles in a two neurone intercortical (transcallosal) system. Potentials evoked in cerebral cortex of the cat by electrical stimulation of contralateral cortex every 2 seconds. Injections in ipsilataral common carotid artery.

adrenaline, and bufotenine, which is dimethyl-serotonin. All of these could be expected to, and do, produce cerebral synaptic inhibition in a manner identical to that of adrenaline and serotonin. Approximately equivalent synaptic inhibitory effects are presented for these in Fig. 17, where mescaline is effective in milligram quantities, LSD-25 in microgram quantities and serotonin in a quantity of 1 microgram per kilogram.

A comparison of serotonin, bufotenine and adrenochrome (Fig. 18) reveals that bufotenine is twice as active as serotonin, while adrenochrome, though it does possess synaptic inhibitory activity consistent with its structure, manifests only a low potency. Other experiments have determined that serotonin is twenty times as active as adrenaline and that adrenolutin, a hydroxy-derivative of adrenochrome, exhibits a low potency similar to the latter.

If one were looking for candidate chemical substances capable of producing psychoses, one would evidently examine the more active ones. Of these only serotonin and bufotenine are found in the body and only serotonin has actually been found in the brain. We are looking along these lines, not neglecting the possibility that it might be none of these, but perhaps some metabolic intermediary or derivative. We also keep in mind that all mental disturbance need not be accounted for on the basis of an abnormality of synaptic transmission and, furthermore, that it is possible for the synaptic transmission processes to be normal while an altered metabolism of the post-synaptic neurons leads to an abnormal response.

The fact that chemical factors play a role, though not necessarily the only role, in synaptic transmission, is in keeping with the high vulnerability of synapses to many chemical influences. The role of adrenaline and serotonin, which we are grouping together as adrenergic, would well account for the vulnerability of cerebral synapses to the related substances mentioned and to others that might influence the metabolism of adrenergic neurohumors. Work with P substance from Gaddum's laboratory or with the synaptic inhibitor, gamma-aminobutyric acid from Elliott's laboratory suggest that these, as well as other substances little known at present, could well play equally important roles in cerebral function.

SUMMARY

Synaptic transmission mechanisms are studied *in situ* by applying sub-maximal pre-synaptic shocks and recording the evoked action potentials as an index of synaptic activity. The effects of chemicals introduced into the circulation are thereby readily localized and quantitated. The monosynaptic preparation afforded by autonomic ganglia serves as a simple model of the more complicated synaptic situations found operating in the brain. A reciprocal chemical equilibrium between cholinergic and adrenergic neurohumoral influences is demonstrated by this technique to control ganglionic transmission and is equally well demonstrated at cerebral synapses by the analogous technique of transcallosal stimulation of cerebral synapses and recording of cortical evoked potentials. Adrenergic compounds and indoles are thus found to be synaptic inhibitors. The related natural brain constituent, serotonin examined in this way is found to be an inhibitory synaptic neurohumor and the most potent of these yet encountered. Psychotogens, which are related to adrenaline and serotonin, likewise exercise cerebral synaptic inhibition. This suggests that the dysequilibrium of humoral synaptic regulation induced by these exogenous and endogenous psychotogens may account for the resulting mental disturbance.

REFERENCES

1. AMIN, A. H., CRAWFORD, T. B. and GADDUM, J. H., *J. Physiol.* **126**, 596 (1954).
2. BISHOP, G. H., *Cold Spring Harbor Symposium on Qual. Biol.* **44**, 305 (1936).
3. BONNET, V. and BREMER, F., *Compt. rend. soc. biol.* **126**, 1271 (1937).
4. BRONK, D. W., TOWER, S. S., SOLANDT, D. Y. and LARRABEE, M. G., *Am. J. Physiol.* **122**, 1 (1938).
5. BROWN, G. L. and FELDBERG, W., *J. Physiol.* **88**, 265 (1936).
6. BULBRING, E., *J. Physiol.* **103**, 55 (1944).
7. BUMPUS, F. M. and PAGE, I. H., *J. Biol. Chem.* **212**, 111 (1955).
8. BURN, J. H., *J. Pharmacol. Exptl. Therap.* **46**, 75 (1932).
9. CURTIS, A. S. and BARD, P., *Am. J. Physiol.* **126**, 473 (1939).
10. ECCLES, J. C., *J. Physiol.* **85**, 207 (1935).
11. —— *ibid.* **85**, 464 (1935).
12. ERSPAMER, V., *Pharmacol. Rev.* **6**, 425 (1954).
13. VON EULER, U.S., *Pharmacol. Revs.* **6**, 15 (1954).
14. FELDBERG, W. and GADDUM, J. H., *J. Physiol.* **81**, 305 (1934).
15. FELDBERG, W. and VARTIANEN, A., *J. Physiol.* **83**, 103 (1934).
16. GLUCKMAN, M. I., COHN, JR., V. H., HART, E. R. and MARRAZZI, A. S., *Federation Proc.* **16**, 47 (1957).
17. HOFFER, A., OSMOND, H. and SMYTHIES, J., *J. Mental Sci.* **100**, 29 (1954).
18. JACKSON, J. H., Selected Writings. London, Hodder & Stoughton, 1931.
19. LARRABEE, M. G., BRINK, F. and BRONK, D. W., *Proc. Am. Physiol. Soc.* p. 145 (1939).
20. LLOYD, D. P. C., *J. Physiol.* **91**, 296 (1937).
21. MARRAZZI, A. S., *J. Pharmacol. Exptl. Therap.* **65**, 18 (1939).
22. —— *Science* **118**, 367 (1953).
23. —— *Am. J. Physiol.* **127**, 738 (1939).
24. —— *J. Pharmacol. Exptl. Therap.* **67**, 321 (1939).
25. —— *ibid.* **67**, 321 (1939).
26. —— Neuropharmacology, p. 134. Josiah Macy Jr. Found., New York, 1957.
27. MARRAZZI, A. S. and HART, E. R., *Federation Proc.* **10**, 322 (1951).
28. —— *Science* **121**, 365 (1955).
29. —— *J. Nervous Mental Disease* **122**, 453 (1955).
30. MARRAZZI, A. S. and MARRAZZI, R. N., *J. Neurophysiol.* **10**, 167 (1947).
31. PAGE, I. H., *Physiol. Revs.* **34**, 563 (1954).
32. TUM SUDEN, C. and MARRAZZI, A. S., *Federation Proc.* **10**, 138 (1951).
33. UDENFRIEND, S., WEISSBACH, H. and BOGDANSKI, D. F., Pharmacology of Psychotomimetic and Psychotherapeutic Drugs. New York Academy of Sciences, 1957, New York.
34. VOGT, M., *J. Physiol.* **123**, 451 (1954).
35. ZELLER, E. A. and BARSKY, J., *Proc. Soc. Exptl. Biol. Med.* **81**, 459 (1952).

THE RECEPTORS

Experimental Cell Research, Suppl. **5,** *389–410 (1958)*

PHOTOCHEMICAL ASPECTS OF VISUAL EXCITATION

GEORGE WALD[1]

Biological Laboratories of Harvard University, Cambridge, Mass.

FUNCTION depends upon structure to a degree in all cells and cell organelles; but this relationship is particularly intimate in the excitable tissues. Energy conversion is common to all cells; but in the excitable tissues the energy is applied to carry out particular tasks for the whole organism: sensory reception, the conduction of excitation, contraction, secretion—and this demands a special type of *vectorial* performance, which has both magnitude and *direction*.

The unique event in visual systems is excitation by light. What follows after could as well occur anywhere else in the nervous system. A particular type of cellular apparatus is concerned with this excitation process, and as we learn more of its microstructure we see that it presents common elements in all creatures with eyes. In vertebrates these are the outer segments of the rods and cones, the essential microstructure of which was revealed to us in the first instance by Sjöstrand [37]. As is now well known, each outer segment consists of one to several thousand layers or double layers arranged transversely, each layer about 40–160 Å thick, depending upon the animal. In insect eyes the comparable structure is the rhabdomere, running down the length of each retinula cell of the ommatidium. It has lately been shown that the microstructure of the rhabdomere consists, not of layers, but of transverse tubules, so that depending on the orientation of the section one sees the lengths of the tubules as though they were layers, or cuts them in cross section and sees a honeycomb structure [12, 15, 55]. This latter type of structure seems to be common to many invertebrate eyes. It has lately been identified in other classes of arthropods [29, 30]; and we have found it also in the so-called "rods" of the squid retina [52] (Fig. 1).

Every photoreceptor must possess a photosensitive pigment; for the first event in excitation by light is absorption, and to absorb visible light demands a pigment. The basic problem in visual excitation is how the absorption of light by a visual pigment results in nervous excitation. This is only an instance of a much broader problem. We do not yet know the mechanism of any bio-

[1] The investigations from our own laboratory reported in this paper were supported in part with funds from the Rockefeller Foundation and the Office of Naval Research.

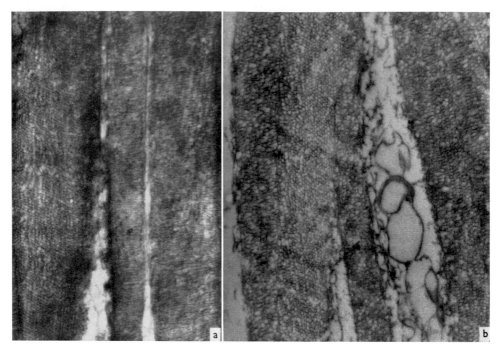

Fig. 1.—Electron micrographs of "rods" of the squid retina (*Loligo pealii*), in longitudinal section. The retinas had been fixed in 1 per cent osmium tetroxide, and embedded in *n*-butyl methacrylate. The rods are built up of a system of transverse tubules, and these appear as cross-striations if cut in long section, or as a honeycomb structure if cut in cross-section. (*A*) ×21,000; (*B*) ×26,200. (From Wald and Philpott [52].)

logical excitation, and can as yet only grope toward a first conceptualization of the processes involved. The grouping can begin with biochemistry; but for anything to come of this, it must eventually be fitted into a machine, the microstructure of the excitatory organelle.

VISUAL CYCLES

The biochemistry of visual systems has come to a very simple position [43, 44, 45]. There are two vitamins A—A_1 and A_2—differing only in that the latter has an extra double bond in its ring. There are the two corresponding vitamin A aldehydes or retinenes, retinene$_1$ and retinene$_2$. We can identify also two families of visual proteins or *opsins*, one found in rod outer segments (rod opsin, or scotopsin), the other in cones (cone opsin, or photopsin). The two retinenes combine with the two opsins to yield the four known pigments of vertebrate vision. Interconversions between the retinenes and vitamins A are catalyzed by the enzyme alcohol dehydrogenase and the coenzyme DPN. All four systems can therefore be formulated in a simple diagram:

$$
\text{Vitamin A}_1 \underset{\text{DPN-H}}{\overset{\text{DPN}^+}{\rightleftarrows}} \text{Retinene}_1
\begin{cases}
+\text{rod opsin} \xrightarrow{\text{light}} \text{rhodopsin} & \lambda_{max.} \text{ (m}\mu\text{)} \quad 500 \\
+\text{cone opsin} \xrightarrow{\text{light}} \text{iodopsin} & 562
\end{cases}
$$

(alcohol dehydrogenase)

$$
\text{Vitamin A}_2 \underset{\text{DPN-H}}{\overset{\text{DPN}^+}{\rightleftarrows}} \text{Retinene}_2
\begin{cases}
+\text{rod opsin} \xrightarrow{\text{light}} \text{porphyropsin} & 522 \\
+\text{cone opsin} \xrightarrow{\text{light}} \text{cyanopsin} & 620
\end{cases}
$$

The invertebrate visual systems that have been examined are all based upon vitamin A_1 and retinene$_1$: those of the squid [40, 1, 22]; certain euphasiid crustacea [25]; the lobster [51]; and the honeybee [14]. They differ from vertebrate systems primarily in the possession of special opsins; and on occasion (e.g., in the squid) in the failure to reduce retinene to vitamin A.

THE SHAPE OF VITAMIN A

An important matter remains to be discussed. It involves an excursion into anatomy; not the relatively gross anatomy revealed by the electron microscope, but anatomy at a much smaller order of dimensions, the anatomy of a molecule.

To synthesize a visual pigment one needs not only vitamin A_1 or A_2, but a particular shape of these molecules. Vitamin A and retinene exist in a variety of geometrical configurations, *cis-trans* isomers of one another. The most stable and hence commonest form is all-*trans;* but this is valueless for making visual pigments. To combine with opsin, a *cis* form of retinene is needed.

Vitamin A possesses four double bonds in the hydrocarbon side-chain, any one of which might be thought to occur in either *cis* or *trans* configuration. There were good reasons to believe however that stable forms of this molecule would have *cis* linkages only at double bonds 9 and 13. A *cis* linkage at double bond 7 or 11 would encounter steric hindrance; the rotation through 180° that ordinarily accompanies the shift from a *trans* to a *cis* linkage could not be completed. Either methyl groups would collide, as at double bond 7; or a methyl group would run into a hydrogen, as at double bond 11. At such *hindered cis* linkages the molecule would not only be bent, as always at a *cis* linkage, but twisted. Since molecular planarity promotes resonance, and

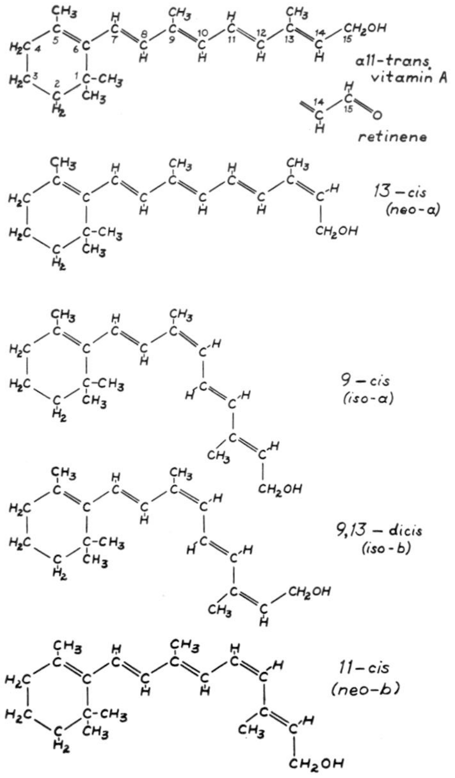

Fig. 2.

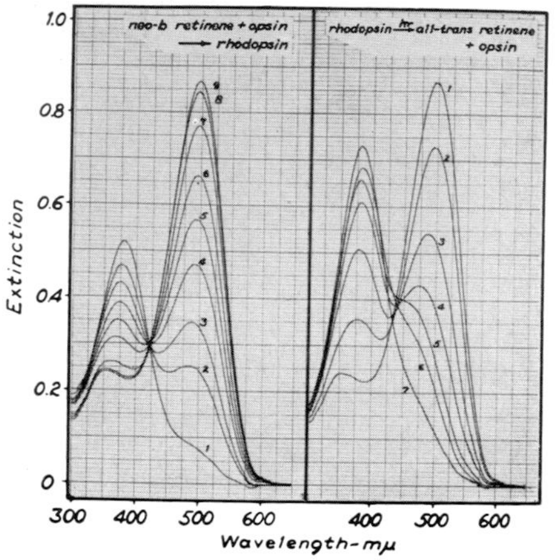

Fig. 3.

Fig. 2.—Geometric isomers of vitamin A and retinene. A similar series of structures, differing only by possessing an extra double bond in the 3,4 position, represents vitamin A_2 and retinene$_2$. The upper four structures represent the unhindered, and hence most probable configurations. The lowermost structure is the hindered *cis* isomer from which all known visual pigments are formed.

Fig. 3.—Synthesis and bleaching of rhodopsin in solution (22.5°C, pH 7.0). *Left:* a mixture of neo-b retinene and cattle opsin incubated in the dark, and absorption spectra recorded periodically, (1) at 0.3 min., (2) at 2.5, (3) 5, (4) 10, (5) 18, (6) 30, (7) 60, (8) 120, and (9) at 180 min. The absorption band of neo-b retinene, at about 380 mμ falls regularly as that of rhodopsin at 498 mμ rises. *Right:* the rhodopsin synthesized at the left (1) is exposed to light for various lengths of time, and spectra recorded. The total irradiations were: (2) 5 sec., (3) 10, (4) 15, (5) 30, and (6) 120 sec. The residue was irradiated an additional 45 sec. with light of shorter wavelengths (7). (From Wald and Brown [47].)

resonance promotes stability, a twisted molecule is expected to be unstable. For this reason one had expected to find only the four unhindered geometric isomers of vitamin A or retinene: all-*trans*, neo-a (13-*cis*), iso-a (9-*cis*), and iso-b (9,13-*dicis*).

It will surprise no biologist to learn that, all of this being well understood, organisms have chosen to base their visual systems upon a fifth isomer, neo-b (11-*cis*), the first natural substance proven to possess a hindered *cis* configuration [23, 32]. All visual pigments yet encountered, rod and cone, whether constructed from vitamin A_1 or A_2, in vertebrates and invertebrates, are synthesized from the neo-b isomer.

Though this bent and twisted isomer of vitamin A or retinene is required to make a visual pigment, the product of bleaching a visual pigment is the inactive, all-*trans* isomer. This must be re-isomerized to the hindered 11-*cis* form before it can go back. A cycle of *cis-trans* isomerization is thus an integral part of every visual system we know.

Fig. 3 shows one passage through this sequence of reactions [47]. At the left rhodopsin is synthesized in solution, and at the right this rhodopsin is bleached. To begin with, a solution of cattle rod opsin was mixed with neo-b retinene, and the absorption spectrum recorded at once (left, curve 1). Though this spectrum was completed within 20 seconds after mixing, it already displays, in addition to the retinene maximum at about 380 mμ, a small hump at about 500 mμ marking the first appearance of rhodopsin. Spectra were recorded periodically thereafter in the dark, at the times shown in the figure legend. Neo-b retinene fell regularly as rhodopsin was synthesized. At the end of 2 hours (curve 9), the neo-b retinene had been completely removed, and replaced by newly synthesized rhodopsin. The small absorption band at about 350 mμ in curve 9 is not the last of the neo-b retinene, but is the β-band of rhodopsin.

At the right of Fig. 3, curve 9 is re-drawn as curve 1. Now the solution is exposed to a short burst of light, and the spectrum recorded again (curve 2). Then it is re-irradiated, and the spectrum again measured (curve 3). The rhodopsin is bleaching, and is reforming retinene. It looks however as though this transaction had created some retinene; for the retinene produced by bleaching has a much larger extinction than that with which the experiment began. Of course no retinene was created; but whereas the experiment began with neo-b retinene, it ends by producing all-*trans* retinene, and the latter has a specific extinction about 1.7 times as high as the neo-b isomer.

With the inclusion of these transformations, the rhodopsin cycle can be formulated as follows:

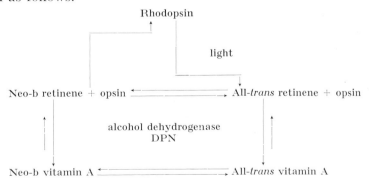

Exactly similar cycles can be written for the porphyropsin, iodopsin and cyanopsin systems, by replacing vitamin A_1 by A_2, or rod opsin by cone opsin.

PHYSIOLOGICAL CORRELATIONS

The function of biochemistry is to provide a molecular basis for physiology. I think it is becoming increasingly clear that fundamental aspects of the physiology of vision have their source in the chemical and physical properties of retinal molecules. I have discussed these relationships in detail elsewhere [43, 44], and there is no need to do more than summarize them here.

The first such relationship involves the correspondence between the absorption spectra of the visual pigments of the rods and cones and the spectral sensitivities of rod and cone vision. We have realized lately that for this comparison it is best to measure the absorption spectra of the pigments in the retina itself or in suspensions of rods or cones, since under these conditions the spectra differ in characteristic ways from those measured in free solution [48, 7]. This is a significant distinction; for it involves the recognition that in the visual receptors the pigments are oriented in highly organized structures that approximate the solid state. It is recognized also that the spectral sensitivity with which we are concerned is that of the naked receptors, undistorted by whatever colored ocular structures may lie in front of or behind them, to screen or reflect back upon them.

When these considerations have been adequately resolved, the spectral sensitivities of the receptors appear to be virtually identical with the absorption spectra of the visual pigments *in situ*. Some of the most satisfactory of such comparisons involve Granit's microelectrode measurements of rod and cone sensitivity in a variety of animals. Examples are shown in Figs. 4 and 5. It is by now clear that all of what Granit has called the vertebrate "dominators" can be matched with the absorption spectra of single visual pigments [43, 45, 18]. By the same token the Purkinje phenomenon—the shift of spectral sensitivity toward the red in going from dim to bright light, from rod to cone vision—involves only the visual transition from dependence upon the absorption spectrum of a rod visual pigment in dim light to dependence on that of a cone visual pigment in bright light.

It should be added that Rushton [35] has lately performed the feat of measuring in the living human fovea the absorption spectra of two cone pigments, apparently those of the "red" and "green" color receptors. They seem to agree closely with the spectral sensitivities derived earlier by Stiles from physiological measurements.

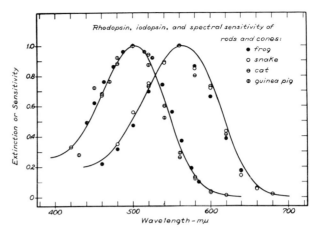

Fig. 4.—The absorption spectra of rhodopsin and iodopsin extracted from the chicken retina (solid lines), compared with Granit's [17] measurements of the scotopic and photopic sensitivities of various animals (points). The spectral sensitivities were measured electrophysiologically and have been quantized. (From Wald, Brown and Smith [50].)

This brings us to a consideration of visual adaptation. For many years it was commonly accepted that the processes of light and dark adaptation reflect physiologically the bleaching and resynthesis of the photosensitive pigments of the rods and cones. This is not the entire basis of visual adaptation; it includes in addition the closing and opening of the pupil, functional changes in the nervous components of the retina and the optic pathways, at times photomechanical changes, and other factors.

There is good reason to believe nevertheless that most of the slower changes —i.e., those that occupy minutes rather than seconds—observed in visual adaptation in vertebrates follow closely the bleaching and resynthesis of the visual pigments. For example, just as in duplex retinas the cones ordinarily dark adapt much more rapidly than the rods, so in extracts from the chicken retina the cone pigment iodopsin is synthesized much more rapidly than the rod pigment rhodopsin [50]. Frog rhodopsin is synthesized in solution relatively slowly, and alligator rhodopsin with great speed; dark adaptation measured in the living animals at the same temperature is found to follow the same time relations [49]. The most extraordinary instance of this parallelism is emerging from the measurements of Rushton and co-workers on the bleaching and synthesis of visual pigments in the living human eye. Just as rod light adaptation in man is completed in about 5 minutes, so this is the time for rhodopsin to bleach in the eye to a steady state value. Similarly, following a high state of light adaptation, rhodopsin is resynthesized in the human retina in something over half an hour, about as long as it takes the human rods to dark adapt [36]; whereas the foveal cone pigments are resynthesized in about 6 minutes, the time required to complete human cone dark adaptation [34].

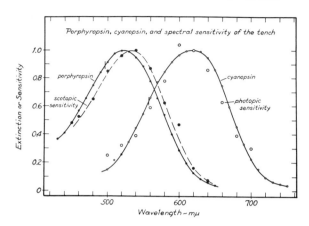

Fig. 5.—Absorption spectra of porphyropsin and cyanopsin (lines, small circles) compared with Granit's [16] electrophysiological measurements of the spectral sensitivities of rod and cone vision in a fresh-water fish, the tench (broken line, large circles). The photopic sensitivity agrees well with the absorption spectrum of cyanopsin, but the scotopic sensitivity is displaced about 10 mμ toward the red from the porphyropsin spectrum (yellow perch). On the other hand this scotopic sensitivity agrees well with the absorption spectrum of tench porphyropsin, as measured by Dartnall [6]. (From Wald [43].)

Whatever other factors may complicate visual adaptation, much of it seems to derive directly from the bleaching and resynthesis of the visual pigments.

The last of the physiological phenomena that we shall discuss involves a special series of relationships. The appearance of vitamin A in the equations of visual excitation links the visual processes with the biochemistry of this vitamin throughout the organism, and with an external factor, its nutritional availability. One consequence of this association is that night-blindness is the first symptom of vitamin A deficiency in man and other animals.

A recent study in our laboratory has attempted to map the entire course of vitamin A deficiency and its cure in white rats [10]. As soon as weanling rats were placed on a vitamin A-deficient diet, the stores of vitamin A in the liver began to decline, and within a few weeks had reached very low values. Up to this point the blood level of vitamin A remained normal; but now it fell precipitately to zero. At this point the rhodopsin content of the retina began to decline, marking the onset of night-blindness. The threshold luminance needed to evoke a perceptible ERG began to rise rapidly, and the ERG at all luminances displayed characteristic changes of size and form. For 2–3 weeks, though the rhodopsin content of the retina was falling, the opsin level remained normal. That is, during this interval the retina contained opsin that could find no vitamin A with which to combine. Then opsin also began to go, and this marked the first appreciable histological deterioration of the retinal tissues.

Here we have another significant intrusion of biochemistry into microanatomy. We have known from some time that the visual pigments, in addition to their more dynamic functions, are important *structural* components of the outer segments of the rods and cones. About 40 per cent of the dry weight of the outer segment of a frog rod is rhodopsin—i.e., opsin—and in the outer segments of mammalian rods and cones this fraction, though usually smaller, is considerable. For this reason we expected that if opsin were to leave the retina, this change should be visible histologically in the deterioration of structure of the outer segments. We have now found that at the point in vitamin A deficiency at which the retinal content of opsin declines, the outer segments of the rods do display a marked degeneration of structure. It must be added, however, that at this time also other retinal tissues, and tissues elsewhere in the body, begin to deteriorate histologically.

When night-blind rats are given vitamin A, preferably by intraperitoneal injection, all these changes are reversed. The level of retinal rhodopsin, and with this the visual threshold, return to normal within 40–60 hours. Simultaneously the ERG retraces in reverse all the changes observed during the development of night-blindness.

ELECTROGENIC SYSTEMS

The parallelisms we have noted between the biochemistry of the retina and visual behavior are encouraging; but they leave untouched the core of the problem, the mechanism by which the initial photochemical events in the rods and cones lead to a nervous excitation. As already said, we do not know the mechanism of any biological excitation, whether in receptor cells, nerve, muscle, or indeed an egg. This is now one of the central problems of physiology.

What is one to look for? The first response in any biological excitation, whatever may follow, is an electrical variation. If a nerve cell, this is followed by conduction; if a muscle, by contraction; if an egg, by the casting of a fertilization membrane, and perhaps division. In all cases, however, the first effect is an electrical variation.

We might therefore ask, how can the attack of light on a visual pigment evoke an electrical viariation? The question, put this simply, is easily answered. We can easily derive electrical variations, for example, from the bleaching of rhodopsin.

We became aware of this in the following way [46]. We wanted of course to learn something of the way in which the chromophore of rhodopsin, retinene, is attached to opsin. A first hint concerning this linkage emerged with the observation that the synthesis of rhodopsin from neo-b retinene and opsin is inhibited completely by very low concentrations of the powerful and specific poison for sulfhydryl groups, *p*-chloromercuribenzoate (PCMB). It was clear that the synthesis of rhodopsin requires the presence of free –SH groups on opsin.

We were anxious to measure these groups, and for this chose the electrometric titration procedure of Kolthoff and Harris [26]. I shall have to describe this procedure, for it bears directly upon our discussion. The arangement consists essentially of a wet battery composed of two half-cells, joined to a galvanometer. A standard mercury–mercuric iodide half-cell is connected through a salt bridge to the experimental half-cell, which contains a solution of ammonium nitrate in which a platinum electrode is rotating.

If one now introduces dilute silver nitrate drop by drop into the experimental half-cell, the silver ions as added take electrons from the platinum electrode, and a current begins to flow, registered by the galvanometer. As one continues to add silver ions, the current rises proportionately. This is therefore in the first instance a device for measuring silver ions.

By the same token it can measure sulfhydryl groups, for such groups remove silver ions from solution by binding them strongly. If one had begun therefore with some unknown quantity of –SH groups in the experimental half-cell, these would remove the first silver ions added, and for a time no current would flow. One could continue to add silver ions until eventually all the –SH groups had been used up. With the addition of the next drop of silver nitrate solution, the first current would be registered by the galvanometer, marking the end of the titration.

One can perform such a titration in dim red light, with a solution of rhodopsin (Fig. 6). As one begins to add silver ions to such a solution, at first no current flows, showing that a few –SH groups are present. Then on further addition of silver nitrate, a current begins to flow, and grows stronger and stronger, until a reasonably large current flow is registered by the galvanometer. At this point if an intense white light is turned on, the rhodopsin bleaches almost instantaneously, and down comes the current. The bleaching of rhodopsin has liberated new sulfhydryl groups, which by binding an equivalent number of silver ions, have produced this electrical variation. It turns out that 2–3 sulfhydryl groups are liberated in this way for each retinene molecule liberated by bleaching. This is true equally of the rhodopsins of cattle, frogs and squid (Fig. 6).

In this arrangement, therefore, we obtain an electrical variation from rhodopsin in free solution in a beaker, under the action of its proper stimulus, light. It will be objected at once that this is a highly unphysiological system, and indeed that is true. The essential point here however does not involve

Fig. 6.—The amperometric silver titration of rhodopsin preparations from cattle, frogs and squid. The titrations were all begun in dim red light. In each case small amounts of silver ion were taken up by –SH groups present initially. Then the current rose proportionately with the addition of further silver ions. In each case, bleaching of the rhodopsin by light caused a fall in the current, as new –SH groups appeared. On adding more silver nitrate, the current rose again. In all these preparations, 2–3 –SH groups were liberated per retinene molecule liberated simultaneously. (From Wald and Brown [46].)

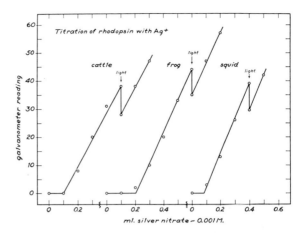

the specific conditions for the electrometric tritration, but the fact that the attack of light on rhodopsin liberates sulfhydryl groups.

The sulfhydryl group is probably the most reactive in biochemistry, and all its special properties are potentially electrogenic. It is weakly acidic, so that under proper circumstances one could measure its appearance in a pH meter. It is a reducing group, so that in another type of system it would produce a change in oxidation-reduction potential. Finally, it strongly binds metal ions, the property we have used in the present experiments. Had we demonstrated in this way the binding of potassium or magnesium rather than silver ions, this would have made a closer physiological model. As already remarked, however, that is not the main point. The liberation of –SH groups when rhodopsin is attacked by light offers variety of opportunities to construct electrogenic systems. All that is needed is to place this reaction within an appropriate physical organization. *In vivo* this would be provided by the microstructure of the rod.

What has been said here of rhodopsin can be assumed to hold for all the other visual pigments so far examined; for in all cases tried as yet their synthesis is poisoned by PCMB, and all therefore seem to be involved in the same type of sulfhydryl relationships.

Since these experiments we have learned of another and independent effect of light on rhodopsin that is equally electrogenic; and this involves a genuinely physiological ion, the hydrogen ion [33]. One brings a solution of cattle rhodopsin at pH about 6 into the cell of a pH meter, and makes the null-point adjustments for measuring its pH. If one now turns a bright light on the rhodopsin in the cup of the meter, the galvanometer needle is immediately dis-

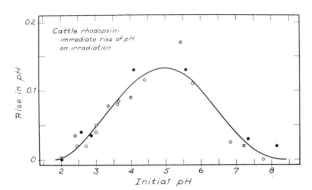

Fig. 7.—Immediate rise of pH on exposure of cattle rhodopsin to light. Measurements made 30 seconds after irradiation, with 3 different rhodopsin preparations. The rise of pH is maximal at pH about 5, and corresponds to the liberation of one acid-binding group per molecule of rhodopsin, with pK about 6.6, close therefore to the pK of the imidazole group of histidine. (From Radding and Wald [33].)

placed. On readjustment, one finds that the pH has risen, in the case of cattle rhodopsin maximally at pH about 5 (Fig. 7). This change is caused by the liberation of one proton-binding group per molecule of rhodopsin, having a pK about 6.6. This pK suggests that we may be dealing with the imidazole group of histidine. In any case this change constitutes another potentially electrogenic response of rhodopsin to light.

I think that such phenomena as this have much to tell us; yet they are not themselves the source of the electrical variations measured ordinarily in the retina. We know this from the fact that a dark adapted rod can be stimulated by the absorption of a single quantum of light [19]. One quantum of light can activate only one molecule of rhodopsin; and this might liberate 2–3 –SH groups and bind one proton. Obviously these changes are by several orders of magnitude too small to account for the electrical variation measured in even a single cell. We must assume that between the attack of light on rhodopsin and the processes responsible for action potentials, physicochemical amplifying devices are interpolated. What can be their nature?

I think of two kinds of answer to this question [42, 44]. One rests on the realization that the transverse membranes which constitute the outer segments of the rods and cones are composed in large part of visual pigments. In that case the attack of light on a molecule of visual pigment might have the immediate effect of knocking a unimolecular hole in a membrane. One can imagine situations in which even so small a hole might have a large effect. If, for example, the membrane were the insulating layer between two conducting layers as in a condenser, its puncture might result in a discharge. Or if the membrane formed part of a voltaic pile—essentially an electric organ—its puncture might result in a change of the generated potential.

The second possibility is that light converts rhodopsin to a catalyst. This is the kind of thing that happens in the photographic plate, in which each grain is made developable by the absorption of one or a few quanta of light [53]. Each absorbed quantum reduces one silver ion in a crystal of silver bromide to an atom of metallic silver; and this serves as a catalyst for the reduction of the entire grain during the process of photographic development.

In the same way we can imagine that an intact visual pigment is an enzyme precursor, a zymogen, activated by the absorption of a quantum of light. Recent work has shown that every instance of zymogen activation we know involves the breaking off from the inactive protein of a small fragment of its structure, one or a few amino acids in length, so exposing the active catalytic center [20, 31]. The process is sometimes called "uncorking". This is what happens when pepsinogen is converted to pepsin, trypsinogen to trypsin, chymotrypsinogen to chymotrypsin. In each case the catalytic center on the zymogen molecule is covered by some small fragment of its structure, and on hydrolyzing this off—"uncorking" it— the enzyme can go to work.

One may imagine this to be the condition of a visual pigment. The intact pigment is "corked" by the attachment of the retinene chromophore to opsin. The absorption of a quantum of light, by opening up this attachment, may expose a catalytic center. That is, the visual pigments may in effect be zymogens, the opsins active enzymes. Such a catalytic center, once exposed, might cause a large and rapid chemical transformation, a first stage of chemical amplification. Indeed the product of this action might itself be an enzyme, catalyzing a further process; and this would mean a second stage of amplification [42].

If opsin is indeed a catalyst, what process does it catalyze? If we only knew what we would like to achieve in this regard, we might begin to look for it. Unfortunately we do not as yet know what is needed for an excitation, and hence where to begin to look.

If either of these suggestions is relevant—whether the knocking of a hole in a membrane or the activation of an enzyme—we have the assurance that either effect will persist for a time. The hole, if one is made, will stay open; the enzyme will have a little time in which to act. For the retinene split from opsin by light cannot go back directly. It comes off as an inactive isomer; and must be isomerized to or exchanged for the active, neo-b isomer, before it can recombine with opsin, bringing the action to an end. This may be the point of the isomerization cycle in vision.

ROLE OF THE PIGMENT EPITHELIUM

Pigment epithelium and sheath of Schwann

It would be a mistake to consider the role of the rods and cones in visual excitation apart from a tissue with which they maintain the most intimate anatomical contact and physiological relations. This is the pigment epithelium. Franz Boll [2], in the paper that announced the discovery of rhodopsin, said, "Meine anatomische Überzeugung ist die, dass die physiologischen Einheiten ... sehr complizierte Wesen sind, zu deren Bildung einerseits die Elemente der Stäbchenschicht, andrerseits die Epithelien des retinalen Pigmentes zusammentreten und die also histologisch als Doppelzellen oder Zwillingszellen anzusehen sind. ..." All that we have learned since has strengthened this view.

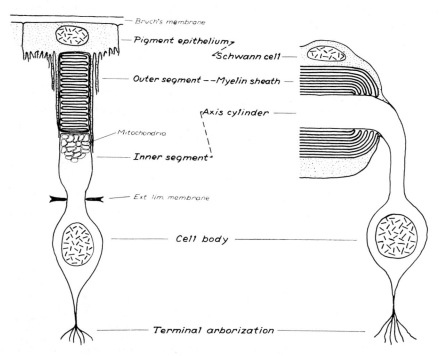

Fig. 8.—Structural relations between a retinal rod and a peripheral nerve cell. The pigment epithelium of the retina, with its long protoplasmic processes in which the outer segments of the visual receptors are embedded, bears much the same intimate relation to the outer segment of a rod, as does the Schwann cell to a nerve axon. Both tissues are neuroglial. The outer segment is comparable in structure with the myelin sheath, both being composed of double layers. The inner segment of the rod is comparable with the axis cylinder of nerve. Both cells possess comparable cell bodies with nuclei; and both end in arborizations which make synaptic contact with other nerve cells.

The pigment epithelium is a single layer of flat, roughly hexagonal cells. At its outer border, lying between it and the highly vascular choroid, is the *lamina vitrea* (glassy or Bruch's membrane), formed in part by the pigment epithelium (Fig. 8). From the inner surfaces of the epithelial cells, long, fine protoplasmic filaments project among the rods and cones, reaching down to the external limiting membrane, so that both the inner and outer segments of the visual cells are embedded in these filaments.

Embryologically the pigment epithelium is a true retinal layer, though non-nervous, and connected only by intimate contact with the neural retina. In the embryo, the out-pocketing of the brain that forms the optic cup encloses a space, an inlet from the ventricle of the brain, lined, as is the ventricle, by ependymal cells. Those that line the distal inner wall of this space become the rods and cones; those that form its proximal boundary become the pigment epithelium. The mature pigment epithelium and the layer of rods and cones meet and interdigitate as two more or less modified ependyma, meeting across a collapsed ventricle.

The relationship between the pigment epithelium and the rods and cones in the eye seems to me homologous with that between the sheath of Schwann (neurilemma) and the nerve fibers of the peripheral nervous system. I believe this to be a significant homology, and that like all good homologies it goes beyond embryological and anatomical considerations to include close physiological correspondences.

To pursue this comparison a little further: the layered microstructure of the outer segments of the rods and cones resembles the layered structure of a myelin sheath. If with a micro cork borer one bored out a little radial plug from a myelin sheath, this would bear a strong resemblance to the outer segment of a rod or cone. I think that close parallels can be drawn between the following pairs of tissues (Fig. 8):

Retina	*Peripheral nerve*
Pigment epithelium	Schwann cells
Outer segment of rod or cone	Myelin sheath
Inner segment	Axis cylinder
Rod or cone body	Cell body

We understand as yet only fragments of the physiological interaction between the pigment epithelium and the rods and cones. I think it highly probable, however, that this interaction has much to do with the mechanism of visual excitation; and that much of the progress in the years ahead will be concerned with it. For this reason I should like to review briefly what is known of this relationship.

Exchanges of materials

In general only mammals possess a retinal circulation [24]; even in mammals this is sparse and confined to the inner layers of the retina. In some cases, as in the human fovea, it is entirely lacking. Probably even when such a retinal circulation is present, the inner and outer segments of the rods and cones depend principally upon the highly vascular choroid layer for their exchanges with the blood [54]. All such exchanges pass through the pigment epithelium. They involve not only oxygen and energy metabolites, but such special substances as vitamin A. The retina must obtain its vitamin A initially from the blood circulation through the pigment epithelium; and there is good evidence that most of the vitamin A released during light adaptation by the bleaching of the visual pigments diffuses out of the retina into the pigment epithelium. Some of this may also find its way back into the blood.

Metabolic relationships

Kühne [28] was convinced that intimate contact with the pigment epithelium is necessary for rhodopsin to be synthesized in the rods. He reported, as is well known, that a frog retina taken out of the eye can no longer regenerate rhodopsin, and that it regains this capacity if laid back smoothly upon the pigment epithelium. He said that for this to occur the retina may be dead, but that the pigment epithelium must be alive.

We know also that a portion of human retina which has come away from its contact with the pigment epithelium, in so-called retinal detachment, is blind; and that an operation which reestablishes this contact may restore vision. It is therefore clear that the pigment epithelium makes an active contribution to the visual processes, and seems to have some special relation to the synthesis of rhodopsin in the rods.

What is the nature of this dependence? It very likely includes all the exchanges of material mentioned above. In addition the pigment epithelium, at least in some eyes, seems to have much to do with completing the isomerization cycle described earlier in this paper. The bleaching of the visual pigments yields primarily all-*trans* vitamin A, and this must be isomerized to the neo-b configuration. The only mechanism we have found for this process, though we feel reasonably certain that other mechanisms exist, involves the action of an enzyme called retinene isomerase [21]. In the frog eye this seems

Fig. 9.—Electron micrograph of the cross section of the outer segment of a rod in the leopard frog (*Rana pipiens*). $\times 22,000$. The outer segment, 5–7 μ in diameter, is furrowed throughout its length by 20–25 deep "incisions". A delicate membrane (*M*) encloses the whole outer segment. (From Wald and Philpott [52].)

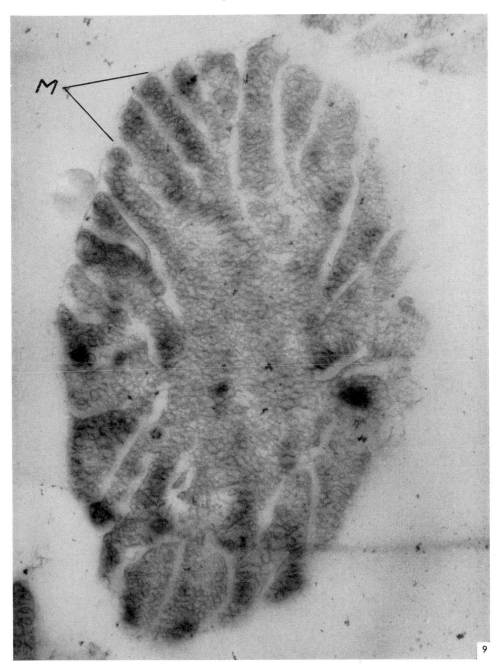

to be primarily concentrated in the pigment epithelium; whereas in the cattle eye it seems to occur primarily in the retina. It is possible that the distribution of this enzyme in frog eyes may account in part for Kühne's observations.

The vitamin A liberated by the bleaching of visual pigments is also rapidly esterified in the eye [27]. The enzymatic system concerned with this process has been isolated in part, and seems to be present in the pigment epithelium as well as in the retina.

All that we can say as yet is that the pigment epithelium takes part in a variety of such processes which have a place in the visual cycle. I think that all of this is very meagre, and that almost surely the main aspects of this relationship still elude us.

One feature of rod microstructure seems to be related directly to the need for such metabolic interchanges as we have discussed. A few years ago Sjö-strand [37] showed that the outer segment of a perch or guinea pig rod has a deep furrow or "incision" running down its entire length.[1] A perch rod is about 1.4 μ in diameter, a guinea pig rod considerably thicker, about 2.2 μ in diameter. Fernández-Morán [11] found that the thin platelets into which one can fragment the outer segments of frog rods, and which are about 6 μ in diameter, contain a large number of such furrows or "incisions". Fig. 9 shows a cross section of the outer segment of a rod of the frog, *Rana pipiens*. Such rods possess 20–25 incisions. Fig. 10 shows part of a similar cross-section of the outer segment of a rod of the urodele, *Necturus. Necturus* outer segments are 8–10 μ in diameter, and have about thirty such incisions.

Such a complex system of fissures is the common device for achieving *surface*. We see in this short series of rod outer segments, that the greater the diameter of the rod, the larger the number of incisions. That is, thicker rods appear to develop commensurately greater surface by having more incisions, which cut their structure into a constellation of relatively narrow columns. Why is *surface* important to a rod? The answer may be that it promotes diffusion and other interactions between the rod and the protoplasmic filaments from the pigment epithelium.

Development and regeneration

It has lately been shown that the myelin sheath of peripheral nerve is formed by the Schwann cells; indeed the myelin sheath is the Schwann cell

---

[1] The relationship suggested here is intended to be no more than approximate and statistical. De Robertis [8] reports that the outer segment of a rabbit rod is about 1 micron in diameter and possesses one longitudinal incision. Such a single incision may perhaps have some quite different significance from the throwing of the entire surface of the outer segment into folds, encountered in the larger rods of amphibia.

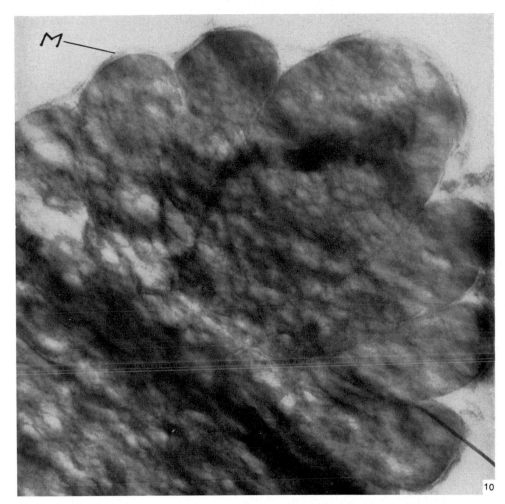

Fig. 10 —Electron micrograph of crosss ection of the outer segment of a rod of the salamander *Necturus* (the mud-puppy). ×40,070. The outer segment, 8–10 μ in diameter, is cut into a cluster of narrow columns by about 30 deep longitudinal incisions. A delicate double membrane (*M*) surrounds the whole structure. (From Brown and Philpott [47].)

membrane wrapped in a spiral around and around the axoplasm [13]. The parallelisms discussed above between the structures of peripheral nerve and of the retina suggest that similarly the pigment epithelium may form the transverse layers of the outer segments of the rods and cones.

The work of de Robertis [8, 9] has given strong support to the old notion that the outer segments of the rods and cones are derived embryonically

from cilia, such as ordinarily are associated with ependymal cells. The outer
segment seems to begin as a cilium, and its proximal portion remains undifferentiated in the adult receptor as the "connecting cilium". In the later development of the rod, de Robertis observed that the apical portion of the primitive cilium bulges, and acquires sacs which eventually flatten and reorient
to compose the transverse layers of the adult outer segment [9]. He expresses
some doubt concerning the mechanism of this process, and the source of
the material of which the layers are made. His observations do not exclude,
nor are they incompatible with, the possibility that the pigment epithelium
contributes to the formation of the outer segments.

Whatever its role in this process, the pigment epithelium does on occasion
display a remarkable capacity for generating retinal structure. When an eye
is removed from an adult salamander, and replaced in the eye socket, the
entire neural retina degenerates, and an entire functional retina is regenerated
from the pigment epithelium [38]. The neural retina itself in the adult salamander has no capacity for regeneration; but portions of the pigment epithelium, as soon as they are removed from contact with the neural retina, by
degeneration of the latter or by dissection, promptly begin active mitosis
followed by the differentiation of daughter cells into the tissues of a new neural
retina [39].

Electrical activity

Attempts have recently been made to locate accurately the source of the
vertebrate electroretinogram, by carefully controlled penetration of the retina
with a microelectrode. Brindley [3] concluded from one such study in the frog
that the external limiting membrane probably represents the critical high
resistance barrier across which the principal potential changes of the ERG
are established. More recently Brown and Wiesel [5], working with the unopened eye of the cat, have come to a somewhat different conclusion. From
their experiments it appears that the b-wave of the ERG may originate in
the outer plexiform layer or the inner margin of the outer nuclear layer; but
the a-wave and c-wave seem to originate close to the inner margin of Bruch's
membrane, possibly therefore in the basal portions of the cells of the pigment
epithelium. Whatever the eventual outcome of such experiments, it must be
conceded that the outer segments of the rods and cones are about as intimately
related to contiguous cells of the pigment epithelium as to their own inner
segments; and they could about as well communicate an excitation to the
one as to the other. 'Communicate an excitation' is perhaps the wrong expression here. The outer segments of the rods and cones may be principally

confirmed with *modulating potentials,* for example by changes of resistance, between two highly metabolic structures: the pigment epithelium and the inner segments.

REFERENCES

1. Bliss, A. F., *J. Biol Chem.* **176**, 563 (1948).
2. Boll, F., *Arch. Anat. u. Physiol., Physiol. Abt.*, **4** (1877).
3. Brindley, G. S., *J. Physiol. (London)* **134**, 360 (1956).
4. Brown, P. K. and Philpott, D. E., unpublished observations.
5. Brown, K. T. and Wiesel, T. N., Intraretinal recording with micropipette electrodes in the unopened cat eye, *in* Fuortes, M. G. F. (ed.), *Symposium on Electrophysiology of the Visual System*, Natl. Inst. Health, Bethesda, Jan. 16–17, 1958.
6. Dartnall, H. J. A., *J. Physiol. (London)* **116**, 257 (1952).
7. Denton, E. J., Light absorption by the intact retina, in *Proc. Natl. Phys. Lab. U.K.*, Symp. No. 8 (Visual Problems of Colour). H.M. Stationery Office, London, 1958.
8. de Robertis, E., *J. Biophys. Biochem. Cyt.* **2**, 319 (1956).
9. —— *ibid.* **2**, Suppl. 209 (1956).
10. Dowling, J. and Wald, G., *Proc. Natl. Acad. Sci. U.S.* **44** (1958), in press.
11. Fernández-Morán, H., *Progr. Biophys. and Biophys. Chem.* **4**, 112 (1954).
12. —— *Nature* **177**, 742 (1956).
13. Geren, B. B., *Exptl. Cell Research* **7**, 558 (1954).
14. Goldsmith, T. H., *Proc. Natl. Acad. Sci. U.S.* **44**, 123 (1958).
15. Goldsmith, T. H. and Philpott, D. E., *J. Biophys. Biochem. Cyt.* **3**, 429 (1957).
16. Granit, R., *Acta Physiol. Scand.* **2**, 334 (1941).
17. —— *Acta Physiol. Scand.* **3**, 137, 318 (1942); **5**, 108, 219 (1943).
18. —— *Studium Generale* **10**, 244 (1957).
19. Hecht, S., Shlaer, S. and Pirenne, M. H., *J. Gen. Physiol.* **25**, 819 (1941–42).
20. Herriott, R. M., Essential chemical structures of chymotrypsin and pepsin, *in* The Mechanism of Enzyme Action (W. D. McElroy and B. Glass, ed.), p. 24. Johns Hopkins Press, Baltimore, 1954.
21. Hubbard, R., *J. Gen. Physiol.* **39**, 935 (1955–56).
22. Hubbard, R. and St. George, R. C. C., *J. Gen. Physiol.* **41**, 501 (1957–58).
23. Hubbard, R. and Wald, G., *J. Gen. Physiol.* **36**, 269 (1952–53).
24. Hyrtl, *Sitzber. d. k. Akad. Wien* **43**, Abt. 1, 207 (1861).
25. Kampa, E. M., *Nature* **175**, 996 (1955).
26. Kolthoff, I. M. and Harris, W. E., *Ind. Eng. Chem. Anal. Ed.* **18**, 161 (1946).
27. Krinsky, N. I., *Federation Proc.* **14**, 88 (1955).
28. Kühne, W., Chemische Vorgänge in der Netzhaut, *in* L. Hermann, Handbuch der Physiologie, vol. 3, part 1, p. 312. Leipzig, F. C. W. Vogel, 1879.
29. Miller, W. H., *J. Biophys. Biochem. Cyt.* **3**, 421 (1957).
30. —— *Science* **126**, 1233 (1957).
31. Neurath, H., Gladner, J. and Davie, E., The activation of chymotrypsinogen and trypsinogen as viewed by enzymatic end-group analysis, *in* The Mechanism of Enzyme Action (W. D. McElroy and B. Glass, ed.), p. 50. Johns Hopkins Press, Baltimore, 1954.
32. Oroshnik, W., Brown, P. K., Hubbard, R. and Wald, G., *Proc. Natl. Acad. Sci. U.S.* **42**, 578 (1956).
33. Radding, C. M. and Wald, G., *J. Gen. Physiol.* **39**, 909 (1955–56).
34. Rushton, W. A. H., *Nature* **179**, 571 (1957).
35. Rushton, W. A. H., Human cone pigments, in *Proc. Natl. Phys. Lab. U.K.*, Symp. No. 8 (Visual Problems of Colour). H.M. Stationery Office, 1958.
36. Rushton, W. A. H., Campbell, F. W., Hagins, W. A. and Brindley, G. S., *Optica Acta* **1**, 183 (1955).
37. Sjöstrand, F. S., *J. Cellular Comp. Physiol.* **42**, 15 (1953).
38. Stone, L. S., *Anat. Record* **106**, 89 (1950).
39. —— *J. Exptl. Zool.* **113**, 9 (1950).

40. WALD, G., *Am. J. Physiol.* **133**, 479 (1941).
41. —— The molecular organization of visual processes, *Colloid Chem.* **5**, 753 (1944).
42. —— Mechanism of vision, *in* NACHMANSOHN, D. (ed.), Nerve Impulse, Transactions of 4th conference. Josiah Macy, Jr. Foundation, New York, pp. 11–57, 1959.
43. —— *Am. J. Ophthalmol.* **40**, 18 (1955).
44. —— The biochemistry of visual excitation, *in* Henry Ford Hospital International Symposium, on Enzymes: Units of Biological Structure and Function (O. H. GAEBLER, ed.), p. 355. Academic Press, New York, 1956.
45. —— Retinal chemistry and the physiology of vision, *in Proc. Natl. Phys. Lab. U.K.*, Symp. No. 8 (Visual Problems of Colour). H.M. Stationery Office, 1958.
46. WALD, G. and BROWN, P. K., *J. Gen. Physiol.* **35**, 797 (1951–52).
47. —— *Nature* **177**, 174 (1956).
48. —— *Science* **127**, 222 (1958).
49. WALD, G., BROWN, P. K. and KENNEDY, D., *J. Gen. Physiol.* **40**, 703 (1956–57).
50. WALD, G., BROWN, P. K. and SMITH, P. H., *J. Gen. Physiol.* **38**, 623 (1954–55).
51. WALD, G. and HUBBARD, R., *Nature* **180**, 278 (1957).
52. WALD, G. and PHILPOTT, D. E., unpublished observations.
53. WEBB, J. H., *J. Opt. Soc. Amer.* **28**, 309 (1949).
54. WEISS, O., Physiologie der Ernährung und der Zirkulation des Auges, *in* Kurzes Handbuch der Ophth. II, 1 (1932).
55. WOLKEN, J. J., CAPENOS, J. and TURANO, A., *J. Biophys. Biochem. Cyt.* **3**, 441 (1957).

Experimental Cell Research, Suppl. **5**, *411–425 (1958)*

SUBTHRESHOLD EXCITATORY PROCESSES IN THE EYE OF *LIMULUS*[1]

E. F. MacNICHOL, Jr.

Departments of Biophysics, Johns Hopkins University, Baltimore, Md., and IVNIC, Carácas, Venezuela

Sɪɴᴄᴇ Hartline found that it was particularly easy to get single unit recordings from the eye of *Limulus* it has been intensively studied by quite a few workers and a great deal is known of its properties [2, 5]. It is a coarsely facted compound eye containing about 1000 sensory units or ommatidia. Each ommatidium is attached to a transparent projection from the cornea which serves to conduct the light. Fig. 1 shows a stained section of several

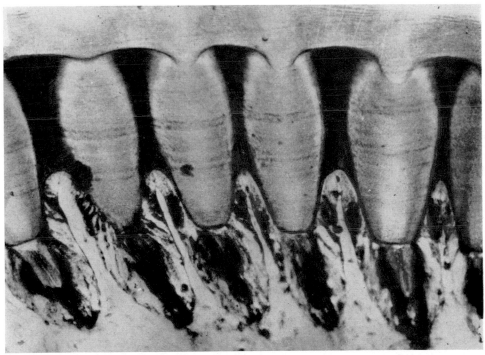

Fig. 1.—Stained section through *Limulus* eye showing cornea at top with transparent projections to which the ommatidia adhere. The perikaryon and distal process of the eccentric cell can be seen in the ommatidium at the far left. (Photograph by courtesy of Dr. W. H. Miller.)

[1] This investigation was supported by Grant G-922 to the Johns Hopkins University from the National Science Foundation and by an equipment Loan Contract between the Office of Naval Research and the Johns Hopkins University.

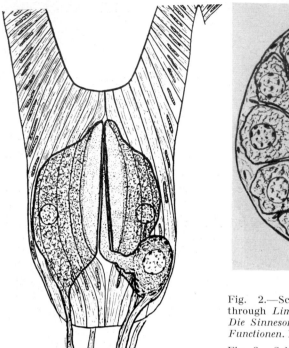

Fig. 2.

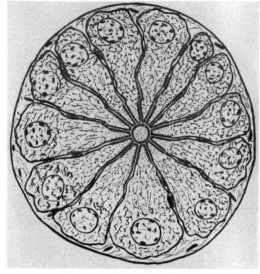

Fig. 3.

Fig. 2.—Schematic drawing of sagital section through *Limulus* ommatidium. (From R. Demoll, *Die Sinnesorgane der Arthropoden, ihr Bau und ihre Functionen.* E. Vieweg & Sohn, Braunschweig, 1917.)

Fig. 3.—Schematic drawing of transverse section through *Limulus* eye. (Same source as Fig. 2.)

of these ommatidia. Each consists of about a dozen large cells shaped and grouped like the segments of an orange around the distal process or dendrite of a large neuron known as the eccentric cell. Fig. 2 is a drawing by the German histologist, Demoll, of a longitudinal section of an ommatidium showing at the top the transparent projection of the cornea, the retinula cells, and the eccentric cell with its distal process passing up between them. Fig. 3 is another of Demoll's drawings of a cross section of an ommatidium showing the retinula cells surrounding the distal process of the eccentric cell. The light sensitive portions or rhabdomeres in this eye are fused into a finned ring surrounding the distal process of the eccentric cell. The fine structure of these rhabdomeres is most interesting, and has been described by Miller [6]. Fig. 4 shows some optical sections of three ommatidia made by Dr. Miller showing the densely pigmented retinula cells, the eccentric cell with its distal process and axon and the rhabdomeres like septa between the retinula cells. Wagner and I have shown by impalement of the cells with micropipette electrodes under visual control that the eccentric cell, which

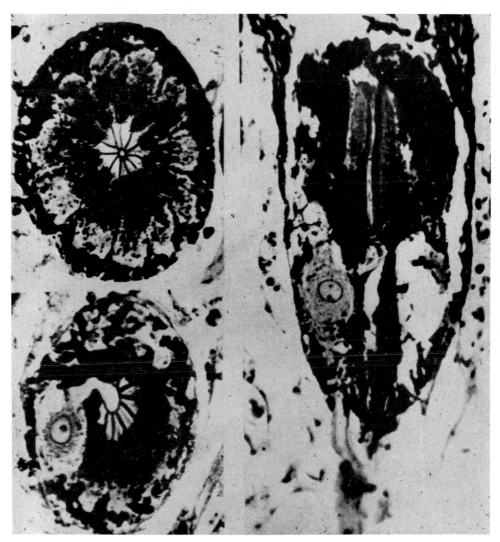

Fig. 4.—Photographs of sections through single ommatidia. The transverse section in the upper left-hand photograph shows the rhabdomeres surrounding the distal process of the eccentric cell. The oblique section in the lower left-hand photograph shows the body of the eccentric cell and the lower part of the distal process where it becomes enveloped by the rhabdomeres. The right-hand photograph shows the body of the eccentric cell, its axon and the distal process passing between the rhabdomeres. (By courtesy of Dr. W. H. Miller.)

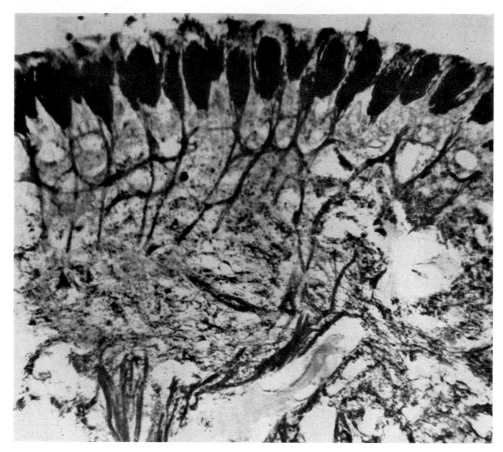

Fig. 5.—Section through a *Limulus* eye showing the optic nerve fibers. The cross connections between the fibers are believed to mediate the lateral inhibitory effect described by Hartline and Ratliff. (Silver stained section, by courtesy of Dr. W. H. Miller.)

has a large axon, is responsible for the repetitive discharge observed in the optic nerve. The retinula cells also have axons but appear to be electrically silent, except for a 50 mv resting potential. What this function is we do not yet know: perhaps it is only to secrete the rhabdomeres.

The axons of the eccentric cell and retinula cells of each ommatidium form bundles which converge to form the optic nerve as shown in Fig. 5, which is a silver stained section of the eye. Between the nerve bundles are cross connections which are believed to mediate the lateral inhibitory effect which has been extensively studied by Hartline, Wagner and Ratliff [4].

When an ommatidium is impaled by a microelectrode, three types of

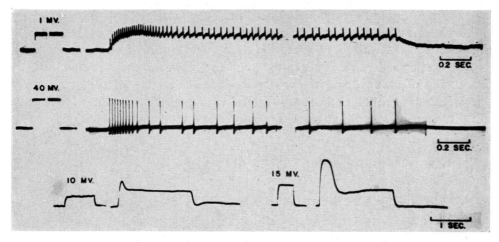

Fig. 6.—Typical responses from *Limulus* ommatidia using saline filled micropipettes for recording. The large spike discharge shown in the middle record has been definitely found to come from the body of the eccentric cell. The origin of the types of response shown in the other two records is still uncertain. Upward deflection indicates positivity in all records. D.C. amplification used throughout.

response to light are normally found, as shown in Fig. 6: large positive slow potentials which may be as great as 30 mv, a discharge of large positive spikes which may be as great as 40 mv, and mixtures of small spikes and slow potentials. Because of the very dense black pigment in the ommatidium it is difficult to say which structures give rise to these three types of response. We have definite information only in the case of the large spikes because we have obtained them regularly from the body of the eccentric cell in ommatidia that have been torn open when the eye was sectioned in making the preparation. The bodies of the retinula cells give a large resting potential but do not appear to give more than a millivolt of slow potential change. Sometimes we can get small spikes from them, but since these are less than a millivolt it is likely that they are merely conducted passively from elsewhere. The large slow potentials apparently arise in the rhabdomeres or the distal process of the eccentric cell, since they are usually found when the electrode penetrates somewhere along the mid line and in the distal half of the ommatidium. One of the graduate students in our laboratory, Mr. Stephen Yeandle, has several records of large slow potentials and large spikes occurring together, which only adds to our confusion on the question of localization.

Whatever their site of origin the slow potentials bear a definite relation to the intensity of the illumination and to the frequency of spike discharge. Fig. 7 shows the amplitude of the slow potential plotted as a function of the logarithm of light intensity during the third second of prolonged illumination. There is clearly an approximately linear relationship over a light intensity range of 4.75 L.U., or a 60,000 fold change in illumination.

Fig. 8 shows the relationship between the slow potential change and the frequency of spike discharge taken from the same set of records (one of those instances in which both spikes and slow potentials could be picked up simultaneously). Again there is an approximately linear relationship.

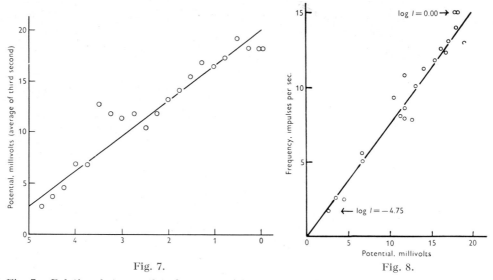

Fig. 7.   Fig. 8.

Fig. 7.—Relation between the slow potential recorded during the third second of prolonged illumination by a micropipette electrode inserted into a *Limulus* ommatidium. Data obtained by measurement of records of the type shown in the top trace of Fig. 6.

Fig. 8.—Relation between the slow potential recorded in the same experiment as Fig. 6 and the frequency of the spike discharge.

From these results it is tempting to postulate that the slow potential is a generator potential which is instrumental in causing the discharge, that is, the action of the stimulus on some portion of the receptor causes an electrical depolarization in some part of the structure and then the electric currents generated thereby excite a specialized region of the neuron into repetitive activity. This is an old idea and has been invoked in other systems, for example by Katz [4] in the case of the stretch receptor of the frog and by Eyzaguirre and Kuffler [1] in the crayfish. However, the evidence is not conclusive in the present case. It can always be argued that the slow depolarization is just the sign of some underlying process and that the discharge is produced directly by a chemical transmitter or in some unknown way.

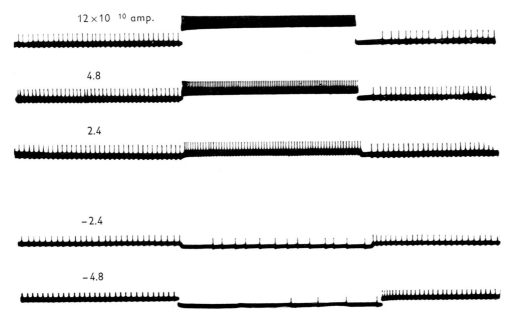

Fig. 9.—Effect of passing electric current through the recording micropipette upon the frequency of spike discharge recorded from the body of an eccentric cell in the eye of *Limulus*. A variable potential was applied to the micropipette through a 10,000 megohm resistor. D.C. amplification was used for recording (positive deflection upward). The amplitude of the spikes was approximately 40 mv and the pipette resistance was approximately 20 megohms.

The fact that the receptor can produce a repetitive discharge in response to current flow gives us a little more evidence in support of the generator theory. Fig. 9 shows a series of records taken during an experiment in which repetitive discharge could be produced or inhibited by passing a current into or out of the eccentric cell through the same pipette that was used to record the activity. This was done by applying potentials through a 10,000 megohm resistance connected to the grid of our amplifier. The preparation was initially discharging spontaneously at a slow rate due to injury of the cell by the pipette. Currents applied in the positive direction, that is, tending to reduce the resting potential, increased the frequency of discharge. Currents in such a direction as to increase the polarization of the cell membrane inhibited the discharge, as might be expected. In fact, on some occasions we have been able to restore badly injured cells in which the resting potential was very small and which were discharging at a high rate to a condition in which spontaneous activity was completely suppressed and response to light was normal. Fig. 10 is a plot of the frequency change as a function of current.

These results give more confidence that the slow depolarization may be the causal agent in repetitive activity. However, they are still not conclusive. It would be more convincing if it could be shown that the slow depolarization could be detected at light intensities too small to produce a spike discharge. It appears that it can be, and this is the only new result to be described in this presentation.

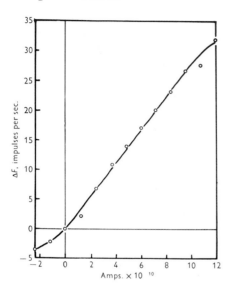

Fig. 10.—Relation between the change in frequency of discharge of the photoreceptor cell from which the recordings of Fig. 9 were taken and the intensity of the current passed through the cell. The cell was discharging spontaneously in the absence of current so that it was possible to inhibit this discharge by making the micropipette more negative.

EXPERIMENTAL RESULTS

The effect at first became evident in experiments on the electrotonic spread of the slow potential into the axon of the eccentric cell. When a bundle of optic nerve fibers showing unitary activity was placed between non-polarizable electrodes connected to a high-gain DC amplifier the spikes discharge was found to be superimposed upon a slow potential that was identical in form to the slow potentials recorded by micropipettes, this is shown in the top trace of Fig. 11. The gain of the amplifier was increased until the spikes were much larger than the oscilloscope screen. The slow potential could be detected with light intensities below the dark adapted threshold of the preparation as shown in the other 4 traces. Each trace was taken at a light intensity of 0.1 L.U. greater than the one above it. It is evident that there is a definite response to the flash in each record though the amplitude at the lowest intensity was less than 50 μV. In the bottom trace a spike

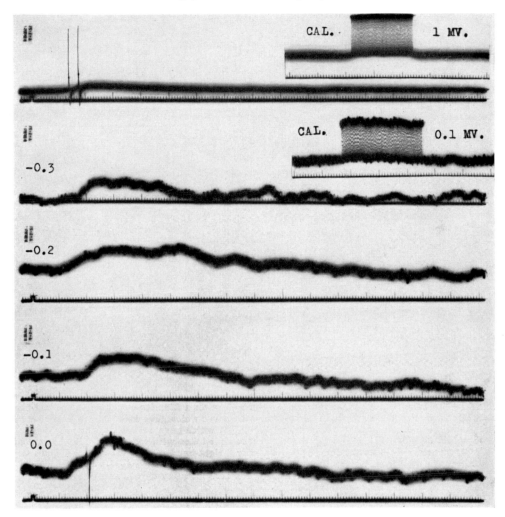

CAL. 1 MV.

CAL. 0.1 MV.

−0.3

−0.2

−0.1

0.0

Fig. 11.—Subliminal slow potentials recorded from *Limulus* optic nerve fibers. The top record shows the amplitude of spikes and accompanying slow potentials in response of a flash of light of intensity well above threshold. The lower four records were recorded with 10 times the amplifier gain used in making the top record. The middle three records indicate subliminal responses. The bottom record shows a threshold response for the discharge of a single spike. The lower trace in each record indicates 0.1 and 0.1 seconds. The brief upward deflection in each time trace shows the duration of the stimulating 0.01 flash of light (0.01 sec).

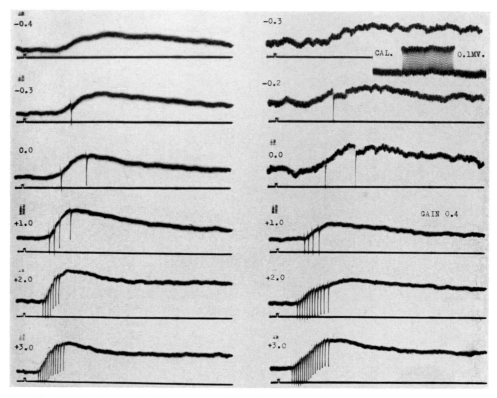

Fig. 12.—Effect of changing the pattern of illumination on a *Limulus* eye upon the size of the slow electrical responses recorded in a bundle of optic nerve which gave a unitary spike discharge. Left-hand set of records taken with annular diaphragm which gave a shadow on the region that gave minimum spike threshold. Right-hand set of records taken with small spot of light focussed on region which gave lowest spike threshold. Upper 3 right-hand records taken at 2.5 times the amplifier gain used in obtaining the other records. Figures at the left edge of each record give the logarithm of the intensity of the test flash. The zero intensity for each set of records corresponds to the threshold for two impulses.

is present and it does not wipe out the slow potential which decays the same time course as if the spike had not occurred. This experiment appeared to demonstrate the subliminal effect for which we were looking. However, the situation is more complicated. When the diaphragm that focussed the spot of light on the eye was moved, it was noticed that when it was in some positions the magnitude of the slow potential at threshold intensity for a spike response was much larger than when the spot was focussed for minimum threshold. The effect was not due to the interference of the ERG since differential recording was used with the nerve suspended between two wick electrodes both of which were out of solution.

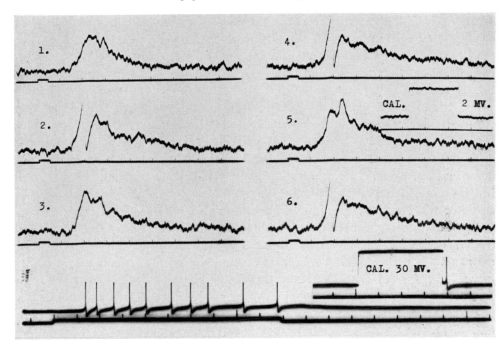

Fig. 13.—Threshold and subliminal responses recorded from a micropipette electrode inserted into a *Limulus* photoreceptor cell. To make the upper six records the stimulating flash of light was adjusted to give a spike response 50 per cent of the time. A section of record was selected in which there were spike responses to alternate flashes. The bottom record shows a typical response to prolonged illumination recorded with one-tenth the amplifier gain. Flash duration 0.01 sec. Time marks 0.01 and 0.1 sec. in upper 6 traces, 0.1 sec. in bottom trace.

Fig. 12 shows the effect. The right hand series of records was taken with a small spot adjusted to give minimum spike threshold. The left-hand set of records was taken with the active ommatidium in the shadow of an annular diaphragm. The relative light intensities are corrected so that the intensity marked zero is the threshold for 2 impulses in both cases. The upper three right-hand records were taken at 2.5 times the amplifier gain of the other records as is indicated by the increased noise. Clearly (except for the bottom records in which so much intensity was used that the slow potential reached saturation) increased light on surrounding areas of the eye gave an increased slow potential even though the recording was supposed to be from one ommatitdium.

I do not know how to interpret this. What we call a single fiber is in fact not anatomically single but only functionally so as far as the spike discharge is concerned. It may be that the bundle often includes fibers from other ommatidia which are damaged so that they cannot propagate spikes but still can conduct electrotonically. Perhaps the potential is a sign of the inhibitory effect. However, an inhibitory potential would be expected to be in the direction of hyperpolarization of the neuron, whereas in these experiments the potential was positive, that is, in the direction of depolarization.

Further experiments in which recordings were made with intracellular electrodes clearly show a subthreshold potential that could not have been provided by surrounding units. This is shown in Fig. 13. The bottom trace shows a typical discharge recorded by an internal micropipette in response to prolonged illumination. Spikes having an amplitude of 25 mV were found to be superimposed on a small slow potential. When the amplifier gain was increased by a factor of about 15, the spikes were deflected off the screen and the slow potential was shown more clearly. When the records shown in the figure were taken, the light intensity was adjusted to threshold. A series in which response took place to alternate flashes was selected for reproduction. Notice the slow potential is of the same amplitude regardless of whether or not a spike is discharged and that a spike does not wipe it out. There are often small spikes, larger than noise, which resemble those Bullock described (see pp. 323–337). We do not understand their meaning. They are clearly not ordinary spikes that have been blocked somewhere, because they are frequently seen in very rapid succession partially fused together. If they were axon or cell body spikes, there would have to be a refractory period between them. Perhaps they are subthreshold responses of the type described by Katz.

DISCUSSION

Apart from its support of the theory of electrical excitation of impulse discharge, the subthreshold electrical response also helps to explain the subliminal facilitation experiments of Hartline and Wagner [2]. Using the classic double shock, only in this case double flash technique, they were able to outline the time course of facilitation following a subliminal flash of light. The method is shown schematically in Fig. 14. Each flash is followed by prolonged excitation which builds up and decays. When the total excitation reaches a magnitude determined by the distance between the horizontal lines, a discharge is produced. In their experiment, the results of which are shown in Fig. 15, the conditioning flash shown on the lower line was set to 70 per cent of normal threshold and the test flash adjusted just to give a response. The magnitude of the test flash was then compared with the magnitude of a control flash of threshold intensity. The process was repeated with various time intervals between the conditioning and test flashes. The function (1-*F* test)/(*F* control) was taken as a measure of facilitation. The resulting curve of facilitation agrees roughly with the time course of our slow potential.

Thus there are two ways of showing that subliminal processes exist: a method of showing residual facilitation, and an electrical method. One ob-

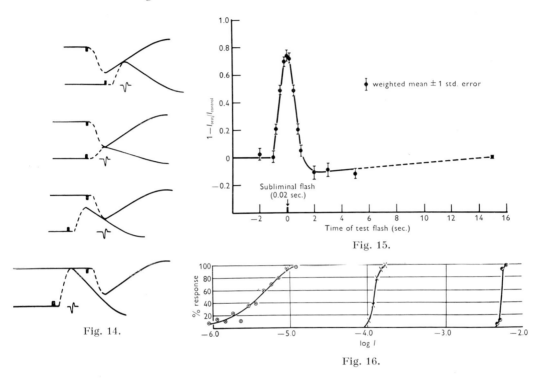

Fig. 14.

Fig. 15.

Fig. 16.

Fig. 14.—Schematic diagram of the double flash method of measuring subliminal excitatory processes. The upper curve represents the excitation due to the conditioning flash (plotted downward). The lower curve represents the excitation due to the test flash (plotted upward). The distance between the horizontal lines indicates the magnitude of the excitation required to give a threshold response. For any position of the test flash the response must be just large enough to touch the response to the conditioning flash to produce a spike. (From Wagner and Hartline, as yet unpublished. Figure by courtesy of Dr. H. K. Hartline.)

Fig. 15.—Results of double flash experiment used to indicate the time course of subliminal excitation). (Excitation of photoreceptor produced by a short flash of subliminal intensity.) (From Wagner and Hartline, unpublished. Figure by courtesy of Dr. H. K. Hartline.)

Fig. 16.—Determination of the number of quanta required to produce a spike response in a single optic nerve fiber in the eye of *Limulus*. The sets of points represent the per centage of responses to various flash intensities plotted as the logarithm of the flash intensity. The three groups of points were taken at different states of light adaptation. A Possion curve for *N* or more events has been fitted to each set of points. The left-hand curve represents the dark adapted state and indicates that six quanta are needed. (Figure by courtesy of Dr. H. K. Hartline.)

vious question to be settled is whether or not these processes are quantised. Wagman, Hartline and Milne [7] have shown by Hecht's method using Poisson statistics that apparently only a few quanta are required to excite the limulus receptors when they are dark adapted. Fig. 16, taken from their experiments, shows the effect of light adaptation on the apparent number of quantat required at threshold. The left-hand curve showing the dark adapted case is the one of interest to us and represents 6 quanta. I believe Hartline has found values as low as 2 or 3. If this is really true, the subliminal potential cannot vary continuously with light intensity but only in discrete jumps since you cannot have fractional quanta in a single flash; this assumes, of course, that a single quantum absorbed gives a fixed increment in electrical response. In other words the gain of the biological amplifying mechanism is constant. The facilitation experiment would not be expected to show discrete jumps, since the method depends upon determining threshold by repeated trials. The curves will be smoothed out and appear to be continuous even though sometimes N and sometimes $N + 1$ quanta are required to give a threshold response.

Although in principle the subthreshold electrical response can test the validity of the quantum hypothesis, the experiments so far carried out cannot do so because of the noise in the recording system which does not permit a sufficiently accurate measurement of the magnitude of the response. An improvement in signal to noise ratio is required to settle this question, but this awaits further improvements in our apparatus, perhaps by the introduction of an integrating technique which measures the total response instead of its time course. Such a method should produce an effective decrease in bandwidth and a consequent improvement in the signal to noise ratio.

SUMMARY

Slow electric potentials arising in single receptors of the eye of *Limulus* have been recorded by electrotonic spread into the optic nerve fibers and by direct intracellular recording using micropipette electrodes. These potentials could be elicited by flashes of light of intensities below that required to trigger a spike response.

The time course of these potentials parallels that of subliminal facilitation following a flash of light. It is believed the potentials arise in an early step in the excitatory process.

Note added in proof: Mr. Stephen Yeandle, a graduate student in our laboratory at Johns Hopkins, has recently shown that the subliminal potentials are quantised. He has found that in response to flashes of very low intensity discrete "bumps" of potential appear. The frequency of appearance of these bumps is related to the light intensity by the Poisson distribution characteristic of a single quantum. (S. Yeandle, doctoral thesis, unpublished.)

REFERENCES

1. EYZAGUIRRE, C. and KUFFLER, S., *J. Gen. Physiol.* **39**, 87 (1955).
2. HARTLINE, H. K., MacNICHOL, E. F. and WAGNER, H. C., *Cold Spring Harbor Symposia Quant. Biol.* **17**, 125 (1952).
3. HARTLINE, H. K., WAGNER, H. G., and RATLIFF, F., *J. Gen. Physiol.* **39**, 651 (1956).
4. KATZ, B., *J. Physiol.* **III**, 261 (1950).
5. MacNICHOL, E. F., AIBS Publication No. 1. Molecular Structure and Functional Activity of Nerve Cells, pp. 34–62. American Institute of Biological Sciences, Washington D.C., 1956.
6. MILLER, W. H., *J. Biophys. Biochem. Cytol.* **3**, 421 (1957).
7. WAGMAN, J. H., HARTLINE, H. K. and MILINE, L. J., *Federation Proc.* **8**, 159 (1949) (abstr.).

ELECTROPHYSIOLOGICAL ANALYSIS OF THE VISUAL
SYSTEMS IN INSECTS

H. AUTRUM

Department of Zoology, University of München, Germany

PHYSIOLOGICAL analysis of living systems has a threefold purpose: (1) Investigation of the working of the single elements constituting the system; (2) investigation of the manner in which these elements co-operate; (3) investigation of the influence which the operation of the system exercises on animal behaviour.

In analyzing the single elements one will choose as simple a system as possible, one in which the dependence of the response on the conditions of the experiment can be subjected to pure study. Primarily through Hartline's fine investigations, the retinal cells of *Limulus* have provided important insight into processes in the element of the "receptor-cell". But even in the lateral eye of *Limulus* the sensory elements exert an influence upon one another [13, 15]. They are therefore not entirely independent. They can be isolated experimentally, however, and the properties of the single sense cell examined. Hartline and his collaborators [14] were able to introduce micro-electrodes into single sense cells of *Limulus*, thereby establishing unequivocally that in the retinal cell there exists a resting potential. Upon illumination the retinal cell is depolarized. For low intensities of illumination the depolarization reaches a plateau which is maintained during the period of illumination. This directly proves that illumination creates an action potential in the retinal cells. With extracellular leads the distal corneal end of the retinal cell becomes upon illumination more negative with respect to the proximal end. Inversely we may presume that, at least in the eyes of the arthropods, negative potentials take their origins from depolarization of the retinal cells. Simple negative potentials of approximetely the same type as those of *Limulus* are also found upon illumination of the compound eyes in many insects (grasshoppers, *Dytiscus*, *Periplaneta;* also crayfish, *Cambarus* [11]). They originate in the layer of retinal cells in the compound eye [6]; ganglionic components have no share in it. The electrical response of this type of eye is a cornea-negative monophasic wave; it increases with increasing intensity of the stimulating light. The magnitude of this monophasic potential is markedly affected by light- and dark-adaptation (Figs. 1, 2).

Eyes in other insects (*Apis, Vespa, Bombus, Cynomyia, Calliphora*) furnish quite different electrical responses to stimulating light: at the beginning of the stimulus a great positive on-effect occurs, whereas during the period of illumination the potential disappears or is negative; the end of the stimulus is followed by a negative off-effect (Fig. 1 c, d) [21, 1].

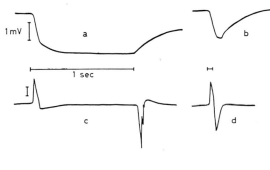

Fig. 1.—Action potentials from the eye of the grasshopper *Tachycines* (*a* and *b*) and the fly *Calliphora* (*c* and *d*). Duration of illumination in *a* and *c* 1 sec, in *b* and *d* 50 msec. Cornea-negative deflection plotted downward. DC-amplifier.

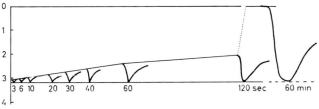

Fig. 2.—*Tachycines* (grasshopper). Course of dark-adaptation in the eye. Light-adaptation for 1 min on a stimulating area of 10 mm diameter at a distance of 185 mm from the eye and a luminous emittance of 8.5 HK/cm² precedes the record. Test flashes of 20 msec duration 3, 6, 10, 20, 30, 40, 60, 120 sec and 60 min after the end of light-adaptation. The negative summit of the deflections in all cases has the same value, the individual responses are superimposed on a slowly vanishing DC-response.

Fig. 3.—Beginning of the action potential of the eye of *Calliphora* with slow recording and low amplification. *Right*, The delineated part of left trace with swift recording and higher amplification. The positive on-effect is preceded by a small negative deflection.

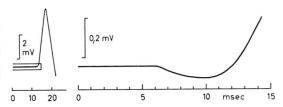

Under certain conditions (in *Calliphora*, for instance, upon green or blue light) the positive on-effect is preceded by a small, highly transient, negative wave (Fig. 3). This negative wave, originating from the retinal cells, triggers the positive on-effect, which originates in cells of the ganglionic layers of the eye [3].

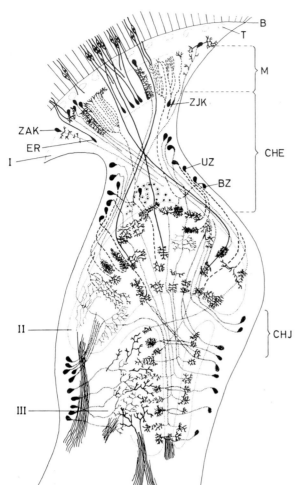

Fig. 4.—Scheme of the structure of the
optic lobes of *Calliphora* as revealed
by the method of Golgi. I, II, III, the
3 optic ganglia. *B*, membrana limitans
of the retinula. *BZ*, bipolar nerve cells
in the chiasma externum (*CHE*). *CHI*,
chiasma internum. *ER*, ends of nerve
fibres of the retinula cells. *UZ*, unipo-
lar nerve cells in the chiasma externum. *ZIK*, centifugal nerve cells [8].

    It can be proved that, even in these complex polyphasic responses of the
eye, the retinal cells proper react with a simple negative potential. In *Calliphora* in particular, the optic ganglia are very close to the retinal cells (Fig. 4),
which can be removed operatively; from the isolated retinal cells we then
obtain the same monophasic negative waves as in *Limulus* or *Dytiscus*, or
other insects of monophasic potentials (Fig. 5). Thus the retinal cells react
in all cases with monophasic potentials [3]. In diphasic potentials another
component is added, which apparently does not proceed from the retinal
cells.

ORIGIN OF THE COMPONENTS OF THE INSECT ERG

In order to elucidate the origins of those components of the ERG, which besides the negative ones from the retinal cells make up the ERG, the optic ganglia are successively removed by operation. The result is the striking positive component which invariably appears immediately after the negative wave sets in, and, probably, in essential connection with it, disappears from the retinogram only after the removal of the thin layer of ganglionic cells immediately adjoining the retina (Fig. 5). This layer contains cells peculiar from the histological point of view, which, though looking like ganglionic cells, extend their continuations only to the periphery, towards the nerve fibres of the retinal cells. Therefore they can only affect the nerve fibres of the retinal cells and consequently the retinal cells themselves. In *Calliphora*, Cajal and Sanchez [8] described them as "células centrífugas cortas en forma de pincel" (Fig. 6). As long as these short centrifugal cells endure, the positive component appears in the ERG [3].

We have also demonstrated the dependence of the positive component

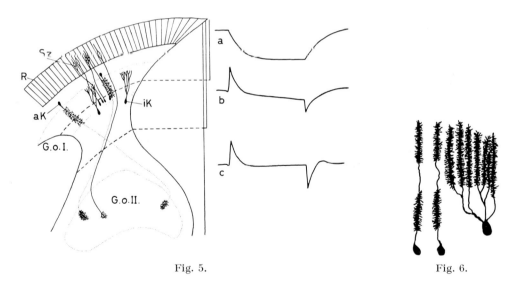

Fig. 5.   Fig. 6.

Fig. 5.—Scheme of the structure of the optic lobes of *Calliphora*, reduced to the retinula nerve fibres, centripetal (*AK*) and centrifugal (*IK*) nerve cells of ganglion opticum 1. *R*, retinula with the receptor cells (*SZ*). *Right*, action potentials (*a*) from the isolated retinula after eliminating the layer of the centrifugal cells; (*b*) from the retinula plus intact Ganglion I; (*c*) from the whole optic system including retinula and optic lobes.

Fig. 6.—*Calliphora*; short centrifugal cells in the ganglion opticum I [7].

upon the negative wave in another way. Poisoning the eye by picrotoxin[1] or nicotine alters the diphasic potential in a similar sense; after poisoning, the illumination potential of *Calliphora* begins with a negative wave, the positive on-effect is reduced or disappears. As for the resting negative wave, a re-

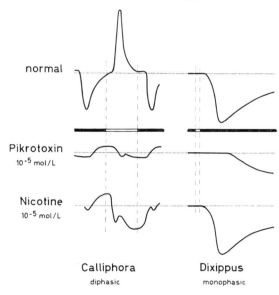

normal

Pikrotoxin
10^{-5} mol/L

Nicotine
10^{-5} mol/L

Calliphora
diphasic

Dixippus
monophasic

Fig. 7.—Effects of picrotoxin and nicotine on the illumination potential of *Calliphora* and *Dixippus*. Stimulation: In *Calliphora* flickering light of 10 flashes/sec; in *Dixippus* single flash of 8 msec. Cornea negative deflection recorded downward. (Autrum and Hoffmann, unpublished.)

markable difference is observed between the actions of picrotoxin and nicotine. With picrotoxin the intial rise of the resting negative wave is less steep and its magnitude is much smaller than with nicotine (Fig. 7). The fusion frequency is lowered.

In comparison, while picrotoxin alters the monophasic potential of *Dixippus*, nicotine does not. Picrotoxin reduces the magnitude of the negative potential; its latency is lengthened, its shape is smoothed, and the fusion frequency becomes less. Nicotine has no effect at all upon monophasic potentials (Fig. 7).

In insects nicotine blocks the synapsis [17, 19, 16]. It stops the synaptic transmission of the negative retinal cell potential, and consequently the positive potential can no longer be triggered by the unaltered negative wave. Hence, with nicotine the positive potential disappears because of the failure of synaptic transmission. As synapse poison, nicotine elicits no effect upon the monophasic potential itself. This also proves that the negative potential originates in the retinal cells without synaptic interaction.

---

[1] E 605 (Diaethyl-*p*-nitrophenylmonothiophosphate) has the same effect as picrotoxin.

The effects of poisoning the monophasic potentials by picrotoxin prove that picrotoxin acts on the sense cells themselves, for it reduces the sense cell potential and lengthens its latency. Finally, it can no longer elicit a positive potential in spite of normal functioning of synaptic transmission.

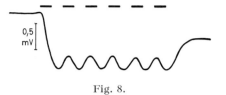

Fig. 8.

Fig. 8.—*Tachycines;* flickering response. Stimulus, upper traces (6 flashes/sec). Fusion frequency about 20.

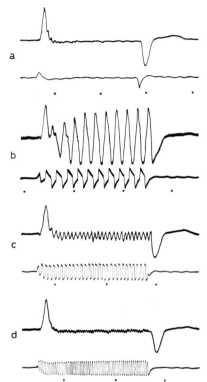

Fig. 9.—*Calliphora;* flickering response to intermittant light of various flash frequencies. Upper trace ERG, lower trace light stimulus (upward trace means light on, downward trace light off). Time trace (points) 0.1 sec. Flash frequencies: (*a*) constant stimulus of about 0.2 sec, (*b*) 47/sec, (*c*) 133/sec, (*d*) 246/sec. (Small high frequency rhythmic potentials from the optic ganglion are superposed upon the ERG.)

Fig. 9.

These experiments support the view that the negative wave is a presynaptic phenomenon of the sense cells and that the positive wave is a postsynaptic response to it.

So far the observations have not been very surprising. They become very remarkable, however, once we undertake to examine in greater detail the differences between eyes of monophasic and polyphasic potentials.

The fusion frequency for stimulation by flickering light is quite different in both types of insect eyes. Eyes of monophasic potentials have a low fusion frequency, ranging from about 10 to 20 flashes/sec (Fig. 8). In the compound eye of *Calliphora* (Fig. 9) the fusion frequency approximates 250/sec, in *Apis* even 300/sec [1, 2, 4]. But if the optic ganglia in *Calliphora* are removed, the monophasic potential has an equally low fusion frequency of about 10 to 20/sec as in eyes of monophasic potentials [3]. The fusion frequency is a measure for the inertia of the visual system. The eye in grasshoppers, beetles and other insects, and in *Limulus* is slow; the eye in flies, bees, wasps etc. is fast. These differences are of fundamental importance for pattern vision among insects.

THE TEMPORAL RESOLVING POWER OF THE COMPOUND EYE

The question naturally arises whether the retinal action potentials have a correspondence in actual visual performance. Are these animals really able to see 200 or even 300 flashes/sec? There are two arguments in favour of this.

(1) Comparing the ERG in man with the subjective fusion frequency, we find that the subjective one is greater than the electrical (cf. [9]).

(2) Behavioral experiments show that such high fusion frequencies play a part in the reactions of the intact animal, and that bees, flies and wasps are indeed able to distinguish such frequent flashes [4].

Insects of fast or slow eye types placed in a rotating cylinder, painted with alternating vertical black and white stripes, respond by turning or moving their antennae as long as the moving stripes are recognizable to them. At excessive speed of the cylinder, the reactions to the rotating pattern of stripes cease and the animal can no longer discriminate the individual stripes; these are fused. In this way it can be shown that eyes of slow type are able to discriminate a maximum of 10 to 20, and eyes of fast type a maximum of 200 to 300 stripes/sec. The results of behaviour experiments are in accord with physiological observations.

The resolving power of the resting insect eye is very poor in comparison with the human eye. The acuity of the picture is limited by the visual angle of the single ommatidium. The visual aperture of the single ommatidium in the bee is about $1.6°$. This means about $\frac{1}{80}$ of the visual acuity in man. Accordingly the amount of information which a bee receives through the eye while sitting still is small. In motion (in flight), however, the amount is substantially increased through the high temporal resolving power of the eye. Pattern discrimination by flying insects is achieved by changing a spatial display of light and dark shapes into a temporal sequence of stimuli. Hence, information supplied by the eyes of flying insects to the central nervous system is spatially poor, but temporally rich. It can be demonstrated that stroboscopic vision, too, requires considerably shorter periods of time than in man or slow type eyes [5]. If we were to show bees a film providing the same illusion of motion as in human beings without flickering, we should have to project about 300 pictures/sec. It might well be for technical reasons, then, that there is no cinema in bee-colonies.

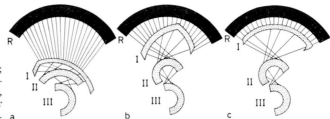

Fig. 10.—*Aeschna* (dragonfly); position of retina (*R*) in relation to the optic lobes I, II, III in young larvae (*a*), older larvae (*b*) and imago (*c*) [18, 3].

INTERACTION: THE EYE OF THE AESCHNA LARVA

A fascinating problem from the neurophysiological point of view is the interaction between the optic lobe and the retinal cells. I have pointed out the result of a successive removal of the optic ganglia as far as the lamina ganglionaris: the ERG becomes increasingly negative, until finally it equals the monophasic potential in *Limulus*, *Tachycines*, or *Dytiscus*, and until the fast response has turned to slow. The influence of the optic lobe is, in an inverted sense, evident from the larval development of *Aeschna cyanea* (a dragon fly). The optic ganglion I (Fig. 10) in young larvae, at first lying at a considerable distance from the retina, approaches it in the course of development, until it finally comes to be very close to the retinal cells [18]. These morphological transformations are parallelled by changes in the electrical response of the eye; the ERG in young larvae is monophasic, the fusion frequency being low; the ERG in older larvae becomes diphasic, with increasing fusion frequency. Destruction of the optic lobe in the imago renders the ERG monophasic again, fusion frequency growing low [3].

SLOW AND FAST REGENERATION OF VISUAL SUBSTANCES

Thus we are in the fortunate position to attribute, in *Calliphora* and a series of other insects, certain reactions to certain elements of the optic apparatus. Our next task will be to draw conclusions from these reactions with regard to the basic processes underlying them. To start with, let us examine the properties of the isolated retinal cell itself. Upon illumination its sensitivity decreases (light-adaptation); in the dark its sensitivity increases (dark-adaptation), because, as is generally assumed, the photosensitive substance, put out of action by illumination, is being regenerated. This regeneration, measured in terms of increasing illumination potentials after preceding light adaptation, and for constant conditions of stimulation, procedes with relative inertia; it requires periods of time varying with the duration and intensity of preceding illumination from some minutes to some hours (Fig. 2).

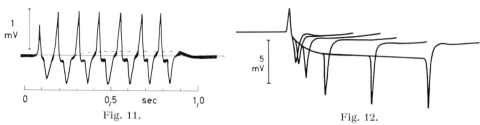

Fig. 11.   Fig. 12.

Fig. 11.—*Calliphora;* flickering response to 8.5 flashes/sec. The second and following responses are of equal magnitude. The dark adaptation, even after strong stimuli, is completely finished in fractions of a second.

Fig. 12. *Calliphora;* off-effects after light stimulus of various duration (20, 50, 100, 250, 500, 900 msec).

However, watching the same process of regeneration in the intact bee or fly eye, that is under co-operation of the "células centrífugas" in the optic ganglia, we may note complete regeneration after fractions of a second, and this even with strong stimuli (Fig. 11). Besides, this rapid regeneration appears to begin only at the moment when stimulation ceases, and not during the actual period of illumination.

This conclusion is founded on the following observations. Subsequent to the cessation of light stimulation the retinogram of *Calliphora* shows a vigorous negative wave, the off-effect, the magnitude of which increases with increasing intensity and duration of stimulation. A graph (Fig. 12), which registers the off-effects for common intensity but varying periods of stimulation (20, 50, 100, 250, 500, 900 msec) provides an envelop which resembles the pure negative illumination potential of the retinal cells themselves. From this we may infer that the negative component of the complex retinogram in the bee and fly appears in the off-effect. As long as regenerative processes in the retinal cells do not commence, we may expect the magnitude of the off-effect to depend solely on the quantity of photosensitive substance changed by absorption of light. (This does not mean that the ERG is proportional to the quantity of absorbed light.) This quantity of light-sensitive substance transformed by light absorption again, is proportional to the product Jt, J designating the intensity of illumination, and t the period of stimulation. In this connection it is of interest to note that upon illumination of the retinal cells of the slow type the response is small; it is, however, imposed on a slow DC-potential, so that the ultimate magnitude remains the same (Fig. 2).

We shall then have to measure which quantities to choose for t under proportional reduction of J, without diminishing the off-effect. As long as their magnitudes remain constant for all values of Jt, regeneration cannot

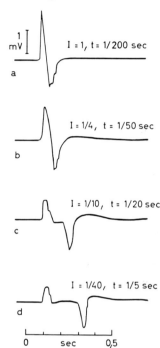

1 mV — $I = 1, t = 1/200$ sec

a

$I = 1/4, t = 1/50$ sec

b

$I = 1/10, t = 1/20$ sec

c

$I = 1/40, t = 1/5$ sec

d

0   sec   0,5

Fig. 13. *Calliphora;* constancy of off-effects to light stimuli of constant energy $I \times t$. The on-effect decreases with decreasing light intensity I.

have set in. As a matter of fact, the off-effect remains constant within a range from $t = 2$ to $t = 500$ msec, provided Jt remains constant (Fig. 13). Consequently it is certain that up to half a second of illumination no retrograde process takes place in fast reacting eyes. After the stimulating light and the positive potential of the centrifugal cells are gone, the negative potential, present in the off-effect, returns to 0 in 10 to 30 msec. The photosensitive structure now regenerates extremely fast.

By contrast the Bunsen-Roscoe law ($Jt =$ const. elicits effects of equal magnitude) for the monophasic potentials is only valid for periods of time shorter than 30 to 60 msec [12, 1]. After this period of time regeneration of the primary structures has a remarkable value, but it lasts for a long time, nearly one hour. Regeneration of the exposed photosensitive substance seems to be inhibited in eyes of high fusion frequencies during the period of illumination, but proceeds afterwards much more vigorously than usual. Since this inhibition is accompanied by the appearance of very high electrical potentials—the positive potentials from the centrifugal cells—it may be suggested that these centrifugal cell potentials are the cause of inhibition.

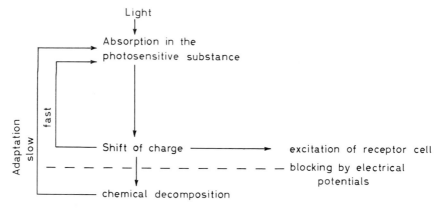

Scheme of primary processes in receptor cells.

Fig. 14.—Scheme of primary processes in visual cells.

The fact that retinal cells in all insects (in *Dytiscus* under normal conditions, in the fly after the destruction of the optic ganglia) react in the same inert way as in the animal kingdom in general, permits us to conclude that the photochemical primary action is of the same kind in all cases. While this is the case it has also to be of such a nature that it will allow for the inventive physical genius of bees and flies, first to prevent by electrical forces immediate reconstruction of exposed visual substance during the period of illumination, and, second, to effect this reconstruction after illumination has ended in a matter of msec.

DISCUSSION

It is altogether too early to develop exact conceptions of the physico-chemical mechanism which promotes this phenomenon. What is presented here is a hypothetical framework which might prove fruitful in the quest for models. The tranformation in the complex of photosensitive substances following the absorption of light while it is initially of little moment—a shift of charge or ionisation—nevertheless leads through some intermediates still unknown to the stimulation of the retinal cell. It is possible to maintain the visual structure in this condition in spite of further illumination, that is, to prevent secondary reactions, by bringing electrical fields or currents to act on it. If the destruction of the electrical field coincides with the end of illumination, the stimulated substance is still present in a concentration corresponding to the quantity of stimulation Jt, and makes an instantaneous appearance in a correspondingly high potential (off-effect); since it has not been changed profoundly, and since no secondary reactions have occurred, it reverts to its original condition in the course of a few msec, and as a result the retinal cell is again fully sensitive. In the absence of the stabilizing electrical field, on the other hand, more profound changes, perhaps of a chemical nature, take place, such as desintegration of the substance. Very soon, however, restitution commences, which partly proceeds immediately from the stimulated condition (as a rapid process), and partly (as a slow process) from ensuing chemical products (for instance, by way of re-synthesis). Hence the chemical changes which the substances undergo, are not a link in the chain of actions leading from absorption to stimulation; although they do lower the sensitivity in the retinal cell appreciably for a long time, thus being responsible for slow adaptation.

We thus assume that primary actions immediately following the absorption of light in the photosensitive substance can be influenced by electrical action. The effects of potentials of the "células centrífugas cortas" are by no means those of an electric interaction which quickly destroys depolarisation of the retinal cells, but these potentials act upon the primary process in the retinal cells. It is not the whole truth when we describe the interaction between *Lamina ganglionaris* and receptor cells as electrotonic feedback mechanism. In my opinion the ganglion cells exert some control upon the primary mechanism within the receptor cells; they influence the photosensitive structure itself. This is possible if the photosensitive substance is arranged in a highly specific morphological structure. Since the electronmicroscopic analysis of the ultrastructure of the visual cells of vertebrates by Sjöstrand, and of insects by Fernández-Morán, there can be no doubt about the occurrence of such a morphological arrangement in molecular dimensions of visual receptor cells. In this connection we should also note that the electric potentials in the eye of the fly are of relatively considerable magnitude. When using extracellular Ag-AgCl-electrodes we obtain potentials from the retina of frog of about 1 mV. From the isolated retina of *Dytiscus* or *Calliphora* we get potentials of roughly the same magnitude. In the presence of the optic ganglia, however, we very easily obtain from the visual system in the fly potentials as high as 20 mV. Clearly, in these structures much stronger electric forces are at work than those familiar to us from other central nervous structures. This forms an important argument for regarding the electric phenomena as being of particular significance in the visual system of the insects. Admittedly, this is only speculation, and as yet nothing more than a hypothesis.

SUMMARY

In the compound eyes of insects two physiological types may be distinguished: The electrical response of the eyes of grasshoppers, beetles, cockroaches is a cornea-negative monophasic wave; the magnitude of the potential is markedly affected by light- and dark-adaptation. The fusion frequency is low (20–30/sec). In the eyes of other insects (bees, wasps, flies) occurs a di- or polyphasic potential with a positive on- and a negative off-effect. The response is not affected by light- or dark-adaptation. The fusion frequency is high (approximately 300/sec).

After the destruction of the optic ganglia the isolated retinal cells of this type respond with a monophasic negative wave in the same manner as the type-I-eye. The negative wave is a presynaptic phenomenon, originating in the retinal cells; this negative wave triggers the positive component, which is a postsynaptic phenomenon and originates in short neurons in the optic ganglion. These neurons have only centrifugal dendrites. It is assumed that the primary actions immediately following the absorption of light in the photosensitive structure of the retina cells can be influenced by an electrical action exerted by the short centrifugal cells. The primary mechanism within the receptor cells is controlled by the centrifugal action of secondary neurons.

ADDENDUM

Burtt and Catton [7] inserted small electrodes (about 10 μ in diameter with a free tip of 5–10 μ) into the eyes of various insects (*Locusta, Calliphora, Aeschna* larvae). Locating the electrode tip at, or near, the surface of the eye, they obtained a negative on-wave and a positive off-wave in all insects. With progressively deeper penetration of the electrode into the optic lobes there was a reversal of sign at a critical depth. This reversal is related to the first synaptic layer which contains the giant monopolar (centripetal) cells. They conclude that this layer of cells is the source of a major part of the illumination potential.

These findings are not in agreement with the conclusive experiments of Hartline and collaborators in *Limulus*. These authors definitely showed that the negative wave of the ERG originates in the receptor cells themselves. Bernhard [6] came to the same conclusion using the eye of *Dytiscus*, and Hartline, Wagner and MacNichol [14] confirmed the results of Autrum and Gallwitz [3] in the housefly.

Among electrophysiologists it is a well known fact that the sign of potentials depends on the resistances between the potential source and the pick up electrodes (cf. [21]). Electrodes do not terminate with the end of their silver wire or glass tube; they are continued by the electrolytes and damaged tissues with which they are in contact. Thus, by the methods of Burtt and Catton [7], it is impossible to determine the real origin of the illumination potential. All that can be concluded from their experiments is that the *physical* properties of the preparation cause a reversal of sign at certain levels of the ganglionic layers.

Burtt and Catton did not succeed in finding a positive component, attributed by Autrum to the first synaptic layer. We obtained similar results, if the preparation had been injured. Burtt and Catton admit stretching and distortion by the electrode ([7], p. 79), and therefore they only observed the negative component from the receptor cells. The fundamental differences between the eyes of grasshoppers and *Calliphora* have been demonstrated by us using contact electrodes too ([1], pp. 210–211), and not only by inserting electrodes into the eye.

REFERENCES

1. AUTRUM, H., *Z. vergl. Physiol.* **32**, 176 (1950).
2. —— *Naturwissenschaften* **39**, 290 (1952).
3. AUTRUM, H. and GALLWITZ, U., *Z. vergl. Physiol.* **33**, 407 (1951).
4. AUTRUM, H. and STÖCKER, M., *Z. Naturforsch.* **5 b**, 38 (1950).
5. —— *Biol. Zentr.* **71**, 129 (1952).
6. BERNHARD, C. G., *J. Neurophysiol.* **5**, 32 (1942).
7. BURTT, E. T. and CATTON, W. T., *J. Physiol.* **133**, 68 (1956).
8. CAJAL, S. R. and SÁNCHEZ, D., *Trab. lab. invest. biol. Madrid* **13**, 1 (1915).
9. DODT, E., *Graefe's Arch. Ophthalmol.* **151**, 672 (1952).
10. FERNÁNDEZ-MORÁN, H., *Nature* **177**, 742 (1956).
11. HANOAKA, T., *J. Physiol. Soc. Jap.* **12**, 192 (1950).
12. HARTLINE, H. K., *Am. J. Physiol.* **83**, 466 (1928).
13. —— *Federation Proc.* **8**, 69 (1949).
14. HARTLINE, H. K., WAGNER, H. G. and MacNICHOL JR., E. F., *Cold Spring Harbor Symposia Quant. Biol.* **17**, 125 (1952).
15. HARTLINE, H. K., WAGNER, H. G. ank RATLIFF, F., *J. Gen. Physiol.* **39**, 651 (1956).
16. KRUPP, H., LENDLE, H. und STAPENHORST, K., *Arzneimittelforschung* **2**, 258 (1952).
17. PRINGLE, J. W. S., *J. Exptl. Biol.* **16**, 220 (1939).
18. VIALLANES, H., *Ann. sci. nat. Zool.* (Paris) **18** (1884).
19. WIERSMA, C. A. G. and SCHALLECK, W., *J. Neurophysiol.* **11**, 491 (1948).
20. WIERSMA, C. A. G. and WRIGHT, E. B., *J. Exptl. Biol.* **23**, 205 (1947).
21. WULFF, V. J. and JAHN, T. L., *J. N.Y. Entomol. Soc.* **55**, 65 (1947).

Experimental Cell Research, Suppl. **5**, *440–450 (1958)*

ELECTRICAL STUDIES OF COLOR VISION IN THE TURTLE

A. FORBES and HELEN WENDLER DEANE

The Biological Laboratories, Harvard University, Cambridge, Mass., U.S.A.

A previous paper [2] reported for the retina of either the frog or the fresh-water turtle that a quick shift of illumination from one color to another evoked an electric response; this response could not be abolished by any balancing of intensities. In the frog, the shift response was small compared with the on-effect *b*-wave and was further reduced by light adaptation. These facts suggested that it was partly due to the difference in spectral sensitivity of rods and cones.

The turtle retina, having so few rods as to provide an almost all-cone receptor field, proved a much better subject for the study of this effect. The shift responses were much larger than those of the frog, sometimes almost as large as the on-effect *b*-wave. The fact that these shift responses could not be abolished seemed to signify distinct types of cones, differing in their sensitivity to different colors. The shift response appeared to be a composite of the off-effect of one type of receptor and the on-effect of another.

Two ways were readily available for seeking evidence as to the number of types of cones and the regions of the spectrum to which they are most sensitive. One was to determine the spectral sensitivity of the turtle eye by measuring the on-effect *b*-wave over a wide range of intensities of illumination at closely-spaced intervals across the visible spectrum [1]. Shoulders on the spectral sensitivity curves might indicate peak sensitivites of different elements. The other way, suggested by Dr. Jeffries Wyman, was to record the sizes of the shift responses at many degrees of color difference across the spectrum. If, as the difference in wave length between a fixed color and the variable color increased, the shift responses increased in a series of well-defined steps, the curve of response plotted against wave length should show the regions of maximum sensitivity of each type of receptor. A preliminary report on the early results with this latter method was published last year [3].

METHODS

For both approaches to this problem, fresh-water turtles (terrapins) of the family *Emydidae* were used, mostly *Pseudemys scripta elegans*. The animal was placed in the dark for at least two hours, then it was decapitated and an eye was excised under dim light. The outer half of the eye, including the lens, was removed. The inner half of the eye was placed in a lucite moist chamber with wicks soaked in saline solution leading from the surface of the retina and from the sclera. These leads were connected through electrodes of chlorided silver wire with the input of an amplifier. Recording was done either with a string galvanometer powered by a Grass capacity-coupled amplifier or with a Grass model 5 Polygraph driven by a direct-coupled amplifier.

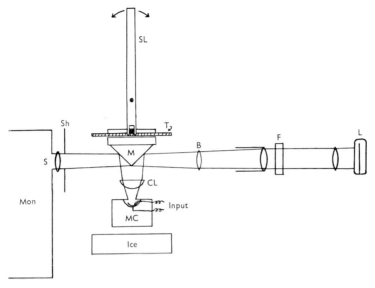

Fig. 1.—Diagram of the optical system, which permits shifting from a fixed-color source (right) to a variable-color source (left) with minimum flicker. *B*, collimating lens for filter source; *CL*, plano-convex cylindrical lens; *F*, filter; *L*, tungsten ribbon lamp; *M*, double mirror; *MC*, moist chamber for eye preparation; *MON*, monochromator; *S*, exit slit of monochromator; *Sh*, shutter; *SL*, shift lever; *T*, track for mirror support.

A rectangular "pupil", 3×4 mm, in a card on the cover glass of the moist chamber admitted a patch of uniform illumination to the retina. A shielded wooden cover enclosing the moist chamber kept out stray light and, with the aid of a pan of ice under the moist chamber, kept the temperature between $16°$ and $18°C$ throughout the course of an experiment.

Spectral sensitivity

For relating electric response to stimulus energy at a number of wavelengths in the visible spectrum, a Perkin-Elmer model 83 glass prism monochromator was arranged with a 500 Watt tungsten lamp as a source, appropriate lenses, and a mirror to throw a beam of light vertically into the retina (see left-hand portion of Fig. 1). A Zeiss shutter controlled the duration of the flash, generally 0.2 second. The intensity of the light was regulated in part by the width of the entrance and exit slits, geared together, in the path of the light. An Eastman Kodak circular neutral wedge provided additional control of intensity. The energy of each test flash was measured by placing a calibrated Weston barrier-layer photronic cell in the same position as the retina and recording with a galvanometer the current produced at each wavelength at each slit and wedge setting employed. The calculated relative energy was converted to relative number of quanta.

This system sufficed for extensive recording of electroretinograms at intervals of 10 or 15 mμ across the spectrum from 430 to 750 mμ at seven intensities, from near threshold to about 10 foot candles, a range of more than 1000-fold in most parts of the spectrum. Measurements of the height of the b-wave (from the trough of the a-wave) on a large number of retinas provided data for plotting sensitivity curves based on the reciprocals of the relative numbers of quanta required for equal responses at all wavelengths. For comparing different experiments or different stages of a long experiment, we recorded at frequent intervals the b-wave evoked by a flash of standard brightness at λ 640 mμ (200 μ slit, 0 wedge; relative number of quanta, 12.7). With this response considered 100 per cent, the responses to all other flashes were calculated as percentages of this value.

Shift response

The second approach, viz., a quantitative study of the shift response, requires a more intricate optical arrangement. It was necessary to provide a beam from a fixed color source and a method of quickly shifting the illumination of the retina from this light to the variable color from the monochromator. The fixed color was provided by a Baird interference filter supplemented by combinations of Wratten, Corning and Jena filters to provide single, narrow bands. In different experiments four filters with different transmission peaks were used for the fixed color: 675, 570, 540 and 510 mμ. The source of light was a tungsten ribbon lamp controlled by a Variac.

The arrangement for effecting a rapid shift from the fixed to the variable color was to project the two beams horizontally in opposite directions along the same path (Fig. 1). Into this path was introduced a wedge with silvered surfaces both at 45° from the vertical. This double mirror was mounted on a track above the retina, and by means of a hand lever it could be moved quickly toward either beam, its position determining which beam was reflected downward into the retina. By careful adjustment of the collimating lenses in the two beams, it was possible to reduce the flicker during transition to an insignificant amount, as shown by the fact that when the two beams were of equal intensity and wavelength, the response to flicker in the electroretinogram amounted to less than 5 per cent of the height of the on-effect *b*-wave. The shifts from one beam to the other were made at nearly equal time intervals of about 2.5 seconds.

For quantitative evaluation of the shift responses in relation to difference of color between the two beams, we adjusted their intensities to give *b*-waves of equal height. In most experiments, we kept this magnitude at a constant percentage of the standard on-effect to a flash at 640 mμ (see above) throughout a series of tests as the wavelengths diverged. The range covered was from 510 to 675 mμ at intervals of 10 mμ. To represent the results graphically, the heights of the shift responses for each value of the variable wavelength, both from long-to-short and short-to-long wavelengths, were measured. The average was converted to percentage of the height of the on-effect *b*-wave; the results were plotted as ordinates against wave lengths as abscissae.

RESULTS AND INTERPRETATION

Spectral sensitivity

The on-effect to moderate or strong light in the fresh, healthy, dark-adapted turtle eye begins with a small negative *a*-wave, followed by a large positive *b*-wave (Fig. 2). With red or orange light, the *b*-wave displays a quick, sharply peaked deflection and a slower shoulder. As the wavelength of the test flash is decreased, the *b*-wave becomes more rounded until, at about

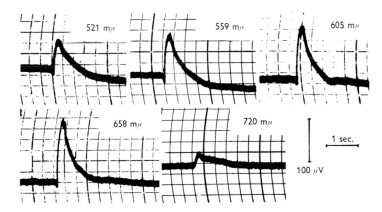

Fig. 2.—Electroretinograms of *Pseudemys* retina produced at five different wavelengths, all to the same relative number of quanta, 10. Flashes 0.2 second in duration. Recorded with the Grass Polygraph, with the driver-amplifier filter set for half-amplitude frequency at 60 cycles/second.

580 mμ, the initial peak disappears. With decreasing wavelength, the a-wave becomes larger, reaching its maximum between 570 and 520 mμ; in the blue and violet the a-wave again becomes smaller. In contrast with the frog retina, the b-wave at most intensities is largest in the red and shrinks as the wavelength is decreased until, with blue light, only small responses occur.

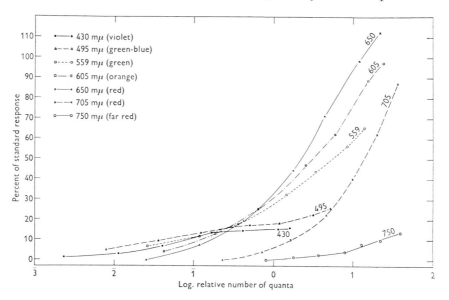

Fig. 3.—Curves showing the average proportionate responsiveness of the turtle eye at seven selected wavelengths, plotted against the logarithms of the relative numbers of quanta. Each point represents the responses recorded in 6 to 10 different eyes. From Deane *et al.* [1].

Occasionally in the winter and early spring a turtle was found in which both eyes yielded atypical responses, the on-effect consisting of a large a-wave and little or no b-wave. These animals were usually in obviously poor condition. Such responses were deemed abnormal and were not used in compiling our data.

Using weak stimuli, close to threshold, we found maximum sensitivity in the blue and green parts of the spectrum; with strong stimuli the greater sensitivity in the red and orange was very striking (Fig. 3). Noteworthy is the fact that the curves relating height of response to stimulus intensity are not parallel: those for blue and blue-green have gentle slopes, whereas those for orange and red have a more sigmoid form; they rise steeply and cross those for the shorter wavelengths. The existence of these two classes of curves points to the activity of two different types of receptors, rods and cones.

From many measurements at a wide range of intensities, we have selected two levels of responsiveness to portray the spectral sensitivity of the terrapin eye with moderate and strong stimulation. Fig. 4 shows graphs in which the ordinates represent the reciprocals of the relative numbers of quanta required to give on-effect *b*-waves of two sizes, 90 per cent and 55 per cent of the

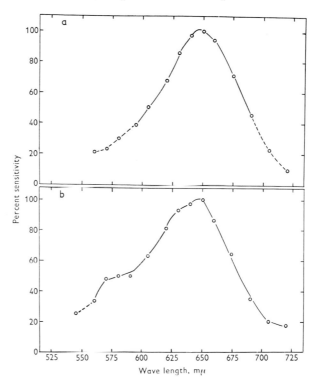

Fig. 4.—Spectral sensitivity of the turtle's eye to (*a*) bright lights evoking responses 90 per cent as high as the standard response and (*b*) moderate lights evoking responses 55 per cent of standard. To construct the curves, the reciprocal of the relative number of quanta necessary to produce the response at 650 mμ was considered 100, and the other reciprocals were expressed as percentages of this. Dotted lines signify that the values were extrapolated from the data. From Deane *et al.* [1].

response to our standard stimulus at 640 mμ. It will be seen that both curves show maximum responsiveness at about 645 mμ. With the higher level of response, the curve is nearly symmetrical; with the lower, the left descending limb of the curve shows two fairly distinct shoulders, one between 640 and 605 mμ, the other between 590 and 560 mμ.

The pronounced maximum in the red and the two shoulders are presumptive evidence of three types of color receptors whose peak sensitivities lie in these color ranges, red, orange and yellow-green. Parenthetically it should be noted that, with very low intensities, the peak lies somewhere in the blue or green, but our data do not permit its exact localization. This peak presumably represents the activity of the few rods present in the turtle retina.

Shift response

Most of our experiments were done with the filter for the fixed color giving peak transmission in the deep red (675 mμ). After testing balance with the monochromator set at the same wavelengths, we tested the shift responses at progressively shorter wavelengths, with the intensities adjusted to give a

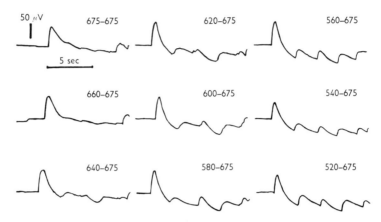

Fig. 5.—Representative records of the shift response with filter 675 as the fixed color. In each instance the initial response represents the on-effect to the monochromatic beam, which was set to produce a *b*-wave 30 per cent as high as the standard. (Variability in its height reflects the changing sensitivity of the excised eye.) Thereafter the source was shifted to the filter beam and back to the monochromator beam twice, and then the shutter was closed. *Pseudemys;* Grass Polygraph, with filter set for half-amplitude frequency at 15 cycles/second.

constant proportionate magnitude in the height of the on-effect *b*-wave with each beam. A typical series of records from such an experiment is shown in Fig. 5. It is evident that in a given test the heights of the shift responses from short-to-long wavelength and the reverse are not always equal (cf. [2]). For purposes of plotting, the average of these two was used. The resulting curve from an experiment with filter 675 is shown in Fig. 6 *a*. Clearly the increase in shift response does not proceed at a uniform rate. A marked steepening of the curve occurs at the transition from red to orange, another from orange to yellow, and a third from yellow-green to blue-green. Between these upward inflections of the curve there are relatively flat regions where the rise is more gradual. The plateaus extend usually from 625 to 610 mμ and from 580 to 550 mμ. It appears, then, that the discrimination between red and orange begins to be significant at about 640 mμ and that the orange receptor reaches its peak sensitivity in the vicinity of 620 mμ. Excitation of the yellow-green receptor begins to increase the shift responses about

610 mμ, and its peak of sensitivity appears to lie near 570 mμ. The fourth receptor (rod) becomes sensitive at about 540 mμ and shows its peak near 520 or 510 mμ.

The significance of these observations was supported by similar experiments in which the fixed color was supplied by one of the other filters. The

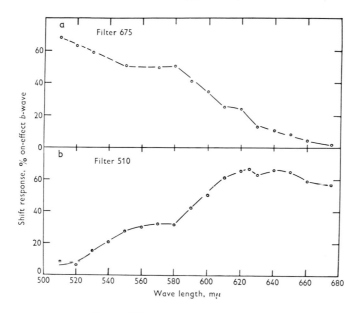

Fig. 6.—(*a*) Plot of the proportionate shift response against wave length with filter 675 providing the fixed color. The points to the right of 560 mμ are averages of two runs, one in which the height of the on-effect *b*-wave was 50 per cent of standard and the other in which it was 80 per cent. For the points to the left of 560 mμ (dotted line), the height was 40 per cent of standard. (*b*) The proportionate shift response with filter 510. Average of two runs; height of the on-effect 30 per cent of standard.

blue-green filter (510 mμ) is near the probable peak of rod sensitivity and well away from the peaks of all the cones. The yellow-green filter (570 mμ) is close to the wavelength that appears to be at peak sensitivity for the cones farthest from the red. The green filter (540 mμ) lies about half way between them.

The experiments with the blue-green filter gave the best complementary data to those with the red filter. The results of such an experiment are illustrated in Fig. 6*b*. As the variable wavelength is moved progressively toward the red, the shift responses again increase in stepwise fashion. The inflections and the relatively flat regions correspond so closely with those regions in

Fig. 6 a as to leave little doubt that they signify, respectively, approaches to peak sensitivities of the several receptors and the actual peaks.

Fig. 7 shows the results of one typical experiment with each of the other two filters, with peak transmissions at 540 and 570 mμ. In each case, the shift response falls to about zero when the monochromator is set for the same

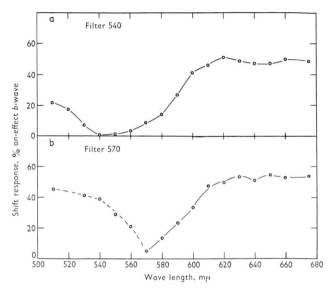

Fig. 7.—(a) The proportionate shift response with filter 540. Average of two runs, height of the on-effect 35 per cent of standard. (b) The proportionate shift response with filter 570. To the right of 570 mμ, average of two runs with height of on-effect set at 40 and at 65 per cent of standard; to the left, height 40 per cent of standard.

wavelength as the filter; the curves rise on both sides of this minimum. As in Fig. 6, these curves show maxima in the orange and in the red (610–630 and 640–660 mμ).

In Fig. 7 a, with the fixed color at 540 mμ, the initial rise to the right of the minimum is gradual, suggesting that this beam stimulates both the rods and the yellow-green receptors; therefore no plateau is evident in the yellow-green. The curve becomes steep between 580 and 600 mμ, indicating the increasing effect of the orange receptor, which shows its peak here at 620 mμ. In the experiment illustrated in Fig. 7 b, the fixed color, 570 mμ, probably stimulates dominantly the yellow-green receptor. The steep rise to the right, beginning immediately, suggests that the effect of the orange receptor increases rapidly between 570 and 610 mμ. Both curves in Fig. 7 show fairly rapid increases in shift response to the left of the minimum, where the variable color changes from green toward the blue. This seems to relate to the shifting between cone and rod activity.

It is noteworthy that in successive experiments with different filters for the fixed color, and even in those with the same filter, we find that the inflections and peaks in the curves appear at slightly different points, varying as much as 20 mμ. To explain the lack of uniformity in this respect, we should note that the shift responses are presumably composites of on-effects and off-effects of two or more receptors. It is a common finding that the relative sizes of on- and off–effect with any given light are variable. This relation varies somewhat between different retinas under the same experimental conditions. On prolongation of the exposure to light, even for a few seconds, the off-effect increases considerably, due to light adaptation. With aging of the excised retina, the off-effect tends to increase. It is impossible to explore the entire spectral range under exactly equal conditions in two successive experiments. Therefore it is not surprising that the locus of inflections and peaks in these curves varies somewhat.

CONCLUSIONS

The data obtained by plotting spectral sensitivity and by measuring shift responses both indicate that the cone system of turtles has three types of receptors, with peak sensitivities approximately at 645, 620 and 575 mμ. It is interesting to note that in the turtle retina each cone possesses a brightly colored red, orange or yellow oil droplet. These colors agree quite well with the maxima noted above, but whether these "filters" contribute to the sensitivities of the different types of cones remains to be demonstrated. The few rods in the turtle retina account for the sensitivity to blue and green recorded with weak illumination and the shift responses when the shorter wave beam is in the blue-green region.

SUMMARY

In the nearly all-cone retina of the fresh-water turtle, recording the on-effect to monochromatic lights at several intensities across the spectrum furnished spectral sensitivity curves plotted as reciprocals of relative quanta which evoke b-waves of equal size at all wavelengths. At moderate intensities these curves suggest three types of cones with maximum sensitivities at 575, 620, and 645 mμ (Fig. 4 b).

Responses to sudden shift of illumination from one color to another confirmed this inference. In each experiment an interference filter furnished a fixed color, and a monochromator a variable color. Four filters, 510, 540, 570, 675 mμ, were used in different experiments. The stepwise increase in shift response as the difference in wavelength between the beams increased, also indicated receptors with peak sensitivities at about 575, 620 and 645 mμ (Figs. 6 and 7). These wavelengths correspond closely with the colors of the oil droplets in the cones of these turtles.

These studies were supported in part by grant number B-536 from the National Institute of Neurological Diseases and Blindness of the National Institutes of Health, U.S. Public Health Service.

We wish to express our indebtedness to Dr. Christina Enroth-Cugell, Marjorie Neyland and Mary Susan Gongaware, who participated in the early experiments on spectral sensitivity and quantitative shift response of the turtle eye.

REFERENCES

1. DEANE, H. W., ENROTH-CUGELL, C., GONGAWARE, M. S., NEYLAND, M. and FORBES, A., *J. Neurophysiol.*, in press (1958).
2. FORBES, A., BURLEIGH, S. and NEYLAND, M., *J. Neurophysiol.* **18**, 517 (1955).
3. FORBES, A., ENROTH, C., NEYLAND, M., GONGAWARE, M. S. and DEANE, H. W., *Federation Proc.* **15**, 65 (1956).

Experimental Cell Research, Suppl. 5, 451–469 (1958)

THE SLOW ELECTRICAL RESPONSE OF THE OLFACTORY END ORGANS

D. OTTOSON

Department of Physiology, Karolinska Institutet, Stockholm, Sweden

ONE reason why so little is known about the processes involved in the excitation of the chemoreceptors in the nasal mucosa is the difficulty of recording the afferent discharge from the olfactory organ. Recently, however, it has been shown that olfactory stimulation leads to the appearance of a slow potential change in the sensory epithelium of the nose [12, 13]. The fact that this potential can be obtained in gross recordings from the surface of the mucosa has provided a simple method for studying what happens when molecules of odorous compounds are brought in contact with the olfactory end organs. The results of experimental analysis of the source of the response suggest that the potential comes from the olfactory receptors and therefore has to be regarded as being of a similar nature as the slow generator potentials [11] which have long been known to be evoked by stimulation of whole sense organs (see, e.g. [3, 18, 5]). As will be discussed below there is a striking similarity between the electroretinogram of certain invertebrate eyes and the response of the olfactory sense organ. Because of this resemblance it has been suggested that the olfactory response should be called the electro-olfactogram.

Most of the experiments which will be referred to in the following discussion have been carried out on frogs. The frog was selected for the study of the function of the olfactory sense organ because its nasal cavities have a relatively simple structure. The entire olfactory receptor area can therefore be easily exposed and explored with the recording electrodes. The recordings have been made with a direct coupled amplifier. The moistened cotton wool on which the preparation was placed formed the indifferent electrode while the recording electrode was in contact with the surface of the olfactory epithelium. Olfactory stimulation was brought about by blowing a small amount of odorous air against the nasal mucosa. The air was first filtered through activated carbon and then passed over a solution of the stimulating substance. In most experiments water was used as solvent.

FUNCTIONAL PROPERTIES OF THE OLFACTORY RECEPTORS AS REVEALED BY STUDIES OF THE ELECTRO-OLFACTOGRAM

The response of the olfactory epithelium to a puff of odorous air is a slow negative monophasic potential which is characterized by a rapid rising phase and a relatively slow fall (Fig. 1). The amplitude of the potential de-

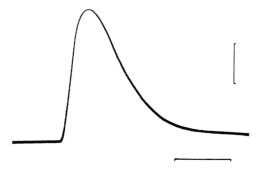

Fig. 1.—The olfactory receptor potential. Response obtained from the frog's nasal mucosa to stimulation with butanol vapour. Vertical line 1 mV. Time bar 2 sec. [13].

pends on the stimulus strength and increases approximately logarithmically with increasing stimulus intensity. The response can be obtained only from those regions of the mucosa where sensory cells are found. Within this area the magnitude of the potential varies from one site to another. These variations seem to be related to differences in the development and distribution of the olfactory receptors in different regions in the mucosa. Recordings of the response at different depths within the epithelium reveal that the potential comes from the outermost layer of the mucosa, i.e. the layer of sensory hairs. These extremely thin filaments, which are the true olfactory receptors, seem to share many of the properties characteristic of dendrites [16]. For example their activity is not blocked by antidromic electrical stimulation of the olfactory nerves; furthermore the olfactory receptors do not seem to be electrically excitable, as shown by the fact that the slow receptor potential cannot be produced by electrical stimulation of the sensory epithelium.

The study of the electro-olfactogram recorded under various experimental conditions has provided a means for direct analysis of the functional properties of the olfactory end organs. These investigations have disclosed that the olfactory receptors are extremely sensitive to changes in their ionic environment but surprisingly resistent to oxygen deficiency. When exposed to the action of ether or chloroform vapour they rapidly loose their excitability. On the other hand, they are still able to react to stimulation after treatment with local anaesthetics. This observation lends further support to the notion that the response is a receptor potential.

In theories on odour discrimination the assumption has often been made that there exist different types of olfactory receptors with specific sensitivities to different odours. Due to the difficulties encountered in studies of this problem it has hitherto not been possible to obtain any unequivocal experimental data which prove or disprove this concept. Investigations on the responses after selective adaptation of the olfactory epithelium to different odours have made the sensitivity of the olfactory end organs amenable to direct examination. The results obtained from these experiments strongly suggest that there actually exist different types of receptors with specific sensitivities to different odours. No evidence has, however, been found for the existence of a limited number of primary odours.

The view is widely held that the olfactory receptors are rapidly adapting end organs. Adrian's observation [1] that the afferent inflow to the olfactory bulb in the rabbit does not cease during prolonged olfactory stimulation shows, however, that this concept has to be revised. Direct evidence showing that the olfactory end organs adapt comparatively slowly has been obtained in studies on the electrical response evoked in the nasal mucosa by a continuous flow of odorous air. In these experiments it was found that the olfactory potential was maintained at an almost constant level throughout the duration of the stimulation.

The investigations on the electro-olfactogram have further revealed an interesting resemblance between the chemoreceptors in the nasal mucosa and the photoreceptors in the eyes of certain invertebrates. This similarity is illustrated by the records in Fig. 2. The upper record shows the electro-retinogram of the water beetle [3]. The duration of the light stimulus is about 6 sec. The lower record shows the response of the olfactory epithelium of the frog when a continuous stream of butanol vapour is blown into the nasal cavities for about 15 sec. The similarity between the electrical responses of these two types of sense organs provides a reason for believing that the mechanisms which are involved in the excitation of the olfactory receptors are similar to those which lead to the excitation of the photoreceptors by light.

The chemoreceptors in the nasal mucosa and the visual receptors are also similar in so far as both contain a pigment. The chemical constitution and exact location of the olfactory pigment is not known. According to Gerebtzoff and Schkapenko [10] it is a lipoid soluble substance which is partly located in the peripheral extensions of the sensory cells and partly in the cells of Bowman's glands. It has been suggested by several authors that the olfactory

pigment has a function akin to that of the visual pigment. According to a
theory recently advanced by Wright, Reid and Evans [17] the olfactory pigment is supposed to act as an energy acceptor in the processes which lead
to the excitation of the end organs. If the yellow pigment in the olfactory
mucosa has the suggested functional significance which is similar to that of

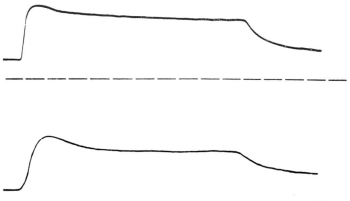

Fig. 2.—*Top:* Electroretinogram of *Dytiscus*. Time marking: $\frac{1}{5}$ sec. [3]. *Bottom:* Electro-olfactogram of frog. Response to stimulation with a continuous flow of odorized air. Stimulus duration:
15 sec. Time bar: 3 sec. [13].

the photochemical substance in the visual cells, olfactory stimulation might
be expected to produce a bleaching of the sensory epithelium. No appreciable
discoloration can, however, be observed either in the frog or in the rabbit or
cat when odorous air is blown into their nasal cavities.

THE RELATIONSHIP BETWEEN THE PROPERTIES OF ODOROUS COMPOUNDS AND THEIR OLFACTORY STIMULATIVE EFFICIENCY

The connection between the olfactory stimulative power of different
odorous substances and their physical and chemical properties has long been
a matter of dispute. The problem has been studied in numerous investigations, but we are still ignorant of what properties are shared by odorous compounds or in what respects they differ from odorless substances. The paucity
of knowledge on the mechanisms of olfactory stimulation is clearly revealed
by the fact that we cannot predict from the chemical constitution or physical
constants of a substance whether or not it smells, or how it smells.

To obtain information on the relationship between the properties of
odorous compounds and their ability to excite the olfactory end organs the
comparative stimulating efficiency of a great number of substances has been

examined. In these experiments the magnitude of the electro-olfactogram was taken as an index of the stimulative power of the substances.

No evidence was found to indicate a direct correlation between the chemical constitution and the olfactory effect evoked by different odorous compounds. It has to be mentioned, however, that in some cases the olfactory stimulative

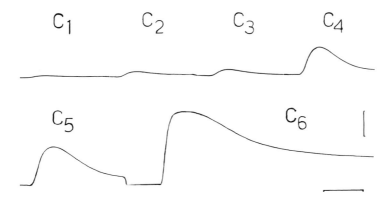

Fig. 3.—Responses evoked by homologous aliphatic alcohols (C_1 to C_6) of equimolar concentration.

efficiency could be related to certain chemical properties, e.g. the degree of unsaturation, but it was evident that this connection was not causal.

In studies on the relation between the physical properties and the stimulative power homologous substances were generally used as stimuli. The advantage of using such substances lies in the fact that the physical properties of members of homologous series change in an orderly manner as the series is ascended. A great number of substances belonging to different series was tested, but the present report will be confined to those experiments in which aliphatic alcohols were used. It was found that on ascending the series of primary alcohols their stimulative power gradually increased. This is illustrated by the records in Fig. 3 showing the responses to stimulation with the vapours of equimolar solutions of the first six members in the series. The increase in amplitude of the responses with increasing number of carbon atoms in the chain of the substances was found to extend to octanol. Because of their low water solubility alcohols longer than octanol could not be tested in water solutions. To compare their efficiency with that of the lower members of the series, the alcohols from propanol to dodecanol were dissolved in mineral oil. It was then found that the response evoked by the higher members became gradually lower as the chain length increased.

The maximum response was, however, not evoked by octanol but by heptanol. Besides this shift, which obviously is to be ascribed to the difference in action of the two solvents on the test substances, it was also found that the mutual differences in stimulative power between the lower alcohols were smaller when oil was used as solvent. In this connection it has to be mentioned that

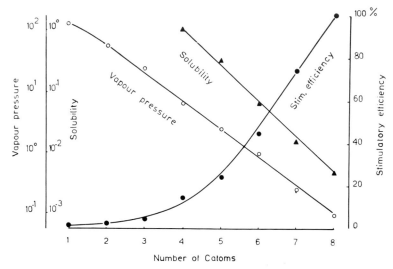

Fig. 4.—Relation between olfactory stimulative power (● — ● — ●) and physical properties of primary aliphatic alcohols. Vapour pressure: O—O—O. Water solubility: ▲—▲—▲ [14].

it has been shown in studies on human taste thresholds [6] that heptanol has a lower threshold than octanol when dissolved in oil.

The increase in olfactory stimulative power with increasing length of the carbon chain of the lower alcohols was first observed by Passy [15] and has since been described by several authors. Backman [2] showed that a similar gradual change in olfactory effect also occurs on ascending many other series of homologous compounds. Since in most of them there is a decrease in water solubility with increasing chain length, he drew the conclusion that the olfactory stimulative efficiency of odorous compounds is determined by their solubility properties. As mentioned above there is in most homologous series an orderly change of the physical properties as the series is ascended. An example of this is shown by the curves for water solubility and vapour pressure of the first eight alcohols (Fig. 4). The water solubility as well as the vapour pressure decreases gradually as the number of carbon atoms increases, while the stimulative efficiency at the same time increases. The connection between the vapour pressure and the ability of the alcohols to evoke an olfactory response is further illustrated in Fig. 5. In this case the saturated vapour pressures have been plotted against the partial pressures of alcohols of equal stimulating power. It will be seen that the partial pressures for the alcohols from butanol to octanol increase linearly with the saturated vapour pressures. This is of interest in view of the fact that the

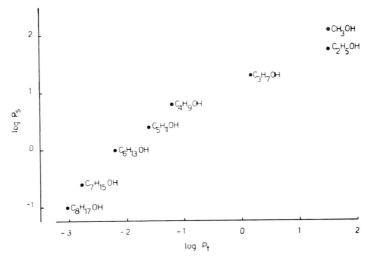

Fig. 5.—Relation between partial vapour pressure (P_t) and saturated vapour pressure (P_s) of alcohols of equal stimulating efficiency [14].

relation between partial pressure of a substance and its saturated vapour pressure can be regarded as an expression of its thermodynamic activity. The thermodynamic activity represents the partial molal free energy and is for a substance in the vapour phase numerically equal to its relative pressure. For a substance in solution and of low solubility the thermodynamic activity can be put equal to the relation between its mole fraction in the solution and its solubility. When a substance is distributed in equilibrium between different phases its thermodynamic activity is the same in all of them. In order to know the activity of a substance at its actual site of action in a biological structure it is therefore sufficient to know its activity in the external medium provided that an equilibrium is reached.

Thermodynamic activities have been applied by many authors (see e.g. [9, 4]) in investigations on the comparative effectiveness of narcotics. Since many substances have been found to be active at the same thermodynamic activities, the assumption has been made that substances of equal thermodynamic activities exert equal effect. The thermodynamic scale has also been used by some few authors in studies of the stimulative power of odorous compounds. Thus it has been shown by Dethier and Yost [7] that many homologous hydrocarbons are rejected by insects at almost equal thermo-dynamic activities.

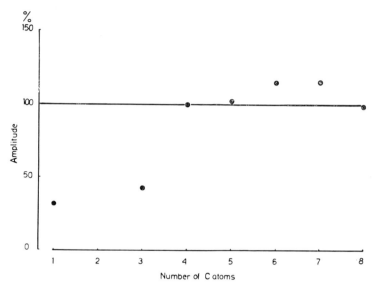

Fig. 6.—The olfactory stimulative efficiency of homologous aliphatic alcohols of equal thermo-dynamic activities [14].

Fig. 6 shows the stimulative efficiency of the first eight primary alco-hols, the thermodynamic activities of these having been adjusted to equal that of 0.01 *M* butanol. The amplitude of the response to stimulation with the vapour of butanol of this concentration was taken as 100 per cent. It will be seen that the tested alcohols fall into two groups with respect to their stimulative power. The first group includes the first three members which evoke comparatively small responses. The second group includes the members from butanol to octanol which have approximately equal stimula-tive efficiency. A possible interpretation of the difference in effect on the olfactory epithelium between the two groups is that the processes involved in the excitation of the olfactory receptors do not represent an equilibrium, and that consequently physical laws for such states cannot be applied on olfactory processes. In the search for an answer to the question of which properties determine the olfactory stimulative efficiency of odorous com-pounds, the thermodynamic scale may nevertheless prove to be of great value.

SUMMARY

Electrophysiological studies of the olfactory epithelium in the frog have shown that a slow response is generated in the sensory layer when odorous air is blown towards the mucosa. By investigations on the responses evoked under various experimental conditions the functional properties of the olfactory end organs have been amenable to direct analysis. The similarity of the electrical reaction of the olfactory organ to odorous stimuli and the potential elicited in the evertebrate eye by light is discussed. The relationship between the olfactory stimulative effectiveness and the physico-chemical properties of the stimulating agent has been examined by using different homologous substances for stimulation. It was found that certain substances of equal thermodynamic activities have equal stimulatory effect.

The author wishes to thank Dr. Charles Edwards for his assistance in the preparation of the manuscript.

REFERENCES

1. ADRIAN, E. D., *EEG. Clin. Neurophysiol.* **2**, 377 (1950).
2. BACKMAN, E. L., *Upsala Läkareför. Förhandl.* **22**, 319 (1917).
3. BERNHARD, C. G., *J. Neurophysiol.* **5**, 32 (1942).
4. BRINK, F. and POSTERNAK, J. M., *J. Cellular Comp. Physiol.* **32**, 211 (1948).
5. DAVIS, H., TASAKI, I. and GOLDSTEIN, R., *Cold Spring Harbor Symposia Quant. Biol.* **27**, 143 (1952).
6. DETHIER, V. G., *Federation Proc.* **11**, 34 (1952).
7. DETHIER, V. G. and YOST, M. T., *J. Gen. Physiol.* **35**, 823 (1952).
8. FERGUSON, J., *Proc. Roy. Soc. Ser. B* **127**, 387 (1939).
9. FERGUSON, J. and PIRIE, H., *Ann. Appl. Biol.* **35**, 532 (1948).
10. GEREBTZOFF, M. A. and SCHKAPENKO, G., *Compt. rend assoc. anat.* **68**, 511 (1952).
11. GRANIT, R., Sensory Mechanisms of the Retina. Oxford University Press, London, 1947.
12. OTTOSON, D., *Acta Physiol. Scand.* **32**, 384 (1954).
13. —— *ibid.* **35**, Suppl. 122 (1956).
14. —— to be published (1957).
15. PASSY, J., *Compt. rend. soc. biol.* **44**, 447 (1892).
16. PURPURA, P. D. and GRUNDFEST, H., *J. Neurophysiol.* **19**, 573 (1956).
17. WRIGHT, R. H., REID, C. and EVANS, H. G. V., *Chemistry and Industry* p. 973 (1956).
18. ZOTTERMAN, Y., *J. Physiol.* **102**, 313 (1943).

Experimental Cell Research, Suppl. **5**, *460–492 (1958)*

THE ULTRASTRUCTURAL ORGANIZATION OF THE ORGAN OF CORTI AND OF THE VESTIBULAR SENSORY[1] EPITHELIA

H. ENGSTRÖM and J. WERSÄLL

Department of Otology, University of Göteborg and Department of Histology, Karolinska Institutet, Stockholm, Sweden

EVEN in rather primitive animals a system of sensory cells is found, usually provided with hairs on their upper surfaces, cells which are of importance for the animals in their localization in space. These sensory cells are found accumulated in simple sensory organs such as the sideline organ and the statocyst.

In higher animals the corresponding sensory organs are transformed into a complicated system of ducts, the semicircular canals and the sac-like utricle and saccule. The sensory epithelia are here delimited to certain sensory areas, the maculae of the utricle and saccule and the ampullar cristae in the ampullae of the semicircular canals.

Part of this organ, specially adapted to respond to vibratory stimuli, is in mammals developed into a highly differentiated hair cell receptor organ, the organ of Corti in the cochlea. Whilst the transformation of primitive vestibular hair cells into cochlear sound receptors was followed by a pronounced structural differentaition, the vestibular sensory epithelium seems in many ways to retain a general resemblance in structure within the different vestibular sensory regions.

In the vestibular, as well as in the cochlear sensory epithelia, different types of sensory elements are found, surrounded by supporting cells. The general arrangement of these cells is a well-known fact where the pioneering work of Retzius, Held, Kolmer et al. [44–48, 20–22, 24–26] must be emphasized.

[1] This report has been supported by grants from the Swedish Medical Research Council.

Fig. 1.—Light microscopic picture of the organ of Corti from the basal coil of a dog showing the general arrangement of the cellular components, especially those mentioned in this paper. *TM*, tectorial membrane; *IHC*, inner hair cell; *OHC*, outer hair cell; *CT*, tunnel of Corti; *OP*, outer pillar; *N*, myelinated nerve fibres; N_1, spirally running nerve fibres (cross sectioned); *BM*, basilar membrane; *BC*, Boettcher's cells.

Fig. 4.—Upper part of an inner hair cell from the guinea-pig cochlea. *H*, hairs; *Cu*, cuticle; *F*, filamentous protrusions from supporting cell; *B*, border to the reticular membrane; B_1, border between supporting cell and hair cell; *M*, mitochondria; *G*, intracellular granulations; *R*, cytoplasmic structures.

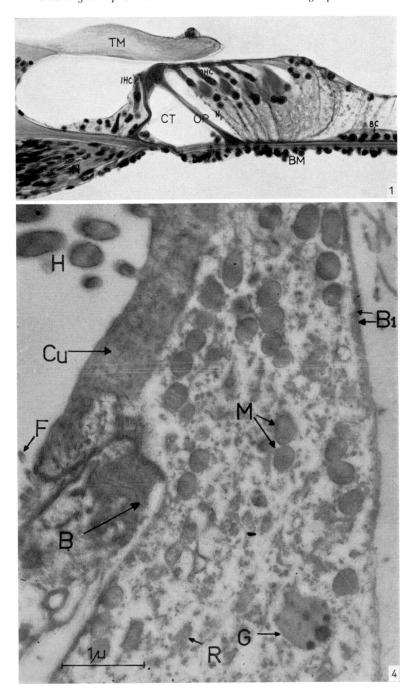

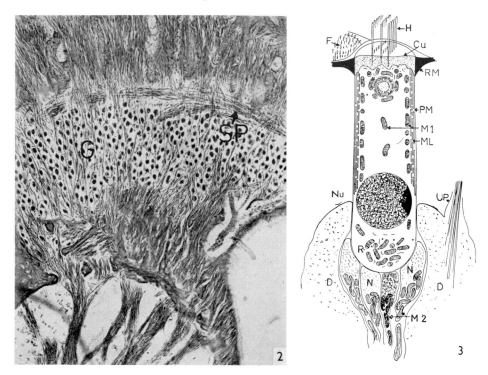

Fig. 2.—Light microscopic picture of the nerve fibers in a guinea-pig cochlea, showing the course of the spiral bundle (*SP*) and the ganglion cells (*G*).

Fig. 3.—Schematic drawing of an outer hair cell with nerve endings (*N*), containing mitochondria (*M*). *H*, hairs; *Cu*, cuticle; *RM*, reticular membrane, *PM*, plasma membrane; M_1, mitochondria; *ML*, membranous layer; *Nu*, nucleus; *D*, Deiters' cell; *UP*, upper falang; and *F*, filiform processes.

The ultrastructural organization of the organ of Corti has been discussed in a series of papers by Engström and Wersäll [14–17] as well as by Engström, Sjöstrand and Wersäll [12–13] and recently by Spoendlin [55] and the structure of the sensory epithelium of the ampullar crests in a recent monograph by Wersäll [57]. The submicroscopic organization of the macular sensory epithelia has been described by Wersäll, Engström and Hjort [59], by C. Smith [54] and recently by Engström [9, 10] and by Wersäll [58]. This paper will give a resumé of our results in the study of the inner ear made during the years 1951–1957.

Fig. 5.—Cross sectioned hairs on an outer hair cell from a guinea-pig cochlea. The hairs form three rows of hairs above the cuticle.

Fig. 6.—Supranuclear portion of an outer hair cell. In this case the cochlea has been exposed to sound for 24 hours (2000 cps at 105 db). A series of "Hensen bodies" are seen, forming a rich system of laminated bodies.

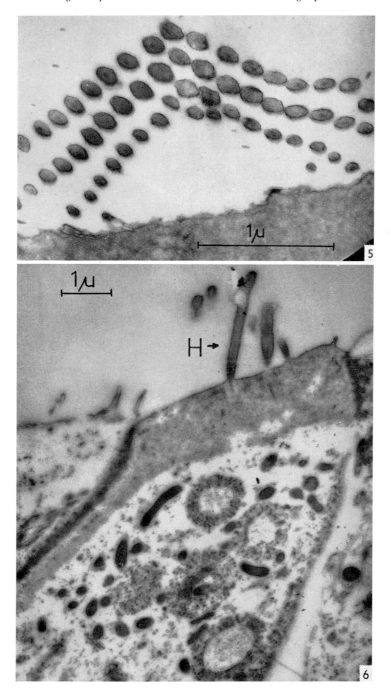

ULTRASTRUCTURAL ORGANIZATION OF THE ORGAN OF CORTI.

Sensory Cells

At the present time it is generally accepted that the outer and inner hair cells in the organ of Corti form the most important sensory elements. Both these types of cells are surrounded by supporting structures of a very complicated nature. Among these cells the pillars, the phalangeal cells and the Hensen cells are of the greatest interest (Fig. 1).

Outer Hair Cells

The outer hair cells are formed as elongated cylinders with a rounded lower end and a flat upper surface, enclosed in the reticular membrane. Even by means of light microscopy the round cellular nucleus, situated in the lower part of the cell, is easily recognized. At the upper cellular surface the cell is bordered by a distinct and rather thick cuticle, from which a varying number of very slender and probably rather stiff hairs protrude. These hairs reach from the cellular surface to the tectorial membrane. In that region found below the cuticle a rather dense formation, the Hensen body, has been described. Hensen and Retzius have ascribed a spiral organization to this structure. By light microscopy it is possible to distinguish a number of small mitochondria in the region between the nucleus and the cuticle. Covell has described how these mitochondria may change under the influence of quinine and other agents. In the lower parts of the hair cells light microscopy reveals a number of small granules forming the Retzius body. The electron microscopic examination permits a detailed description of the structures mentioned above.

The cuticle has a relatively even upper surface, but its lower side is irregular with ridges and protrusions into the cellular cytoplasm. The cuticle is rather opaque and very finely granulated. From the upper surface of the cuticle a number (60–70) of hairs emerge and each hair consists of an intracellular and an extracellular part. The intracellular portion or the hair root is considerably thinner than the extracellular part. The hair root is slightly thicker near the surface but tapers down towards the deeper parts of the cuticle,

Fig. 7.—Part of a ganglion cell from the spiral ganglion of a guinea-pig. Outside the nucleus (*N*) there is seen a rich system of granulated membranes (*IM*) and around these in the cytoplasm of the cell clustered, rosette-like agglomerations of opaque granules. The cell also contains a large number of mitochondria (*M*) with inner double membranes, and a Golgi comples (*GB*). The cell has a distinct outer myelin sheath (*My*).

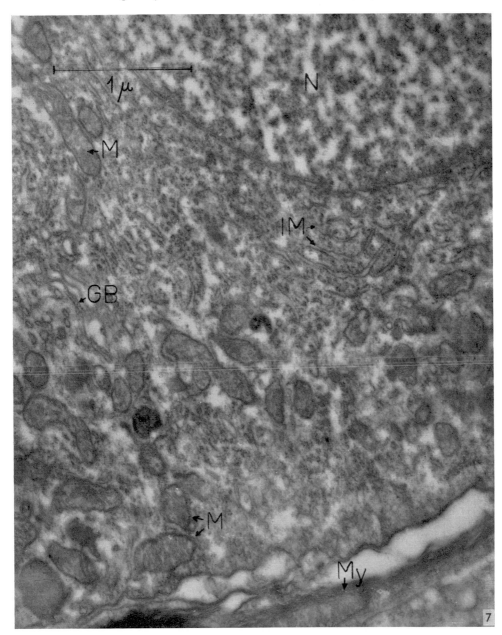

where it sometimes reaches the border to the cytoplasm. The extracellular part of the hair, the hair proper, consists of an axial fibril, continuous with the hair root, thicker near the cuticle and thinner higher up, and outside this fibril of a protoplasmic sheath, forming the major part of the hair substance. This protoplasmic sheath has a distinct surface membrane continuous with the uppermost layer of the cuticle. In the guinea-pig the hairs comprise 3 or 4 rows of hairs often arranged in the form of a U or V. (Figs. 5 and 6.)

It has long been debated how the top of the hairs finish and if there is any continuity between the hairs and the fibrous structures found in the tectorial membrane [2, 55]. It is almost impossible to ascertain if the ultrathin sections, prepared for electron microscopic examination, represent the outer ends of the hairs. On no occasion have we seen pictures showing a continuation of hair fibrils into the tectorial membrane. In electron microscopic studies carried out by Wersäll on the development of the organ of Corti it has been possible to study early stages of development where the tectorial membrane has been preserved in close contact with the hairs. In none of his micrographs showing rows of distinct and well developed hairs has he been able to observe a transition from the hairs to the tectorial membrane. In the vestibular part of the inner ear Wersäll has been the first to show that the sensory cells on their cuticle in addition to cilia of the above mentioned type are supplied with one single flagellum, showing a complete correspondence in structure with that of ordinary kinocilia. We have not yet observed such cilia in the organ of Corti, although, judging from light microscopic studies, it is possible that the cochlear hair cells also are provided with such flagellae. That part of the hair cell found below the cuticle is bordered by a very thin and distinct outer plasma membrane. This membrane shows, in the fixed specimens, very small irregularities, not found by us on other cells treated in the same ways. It is convenient for the description of the hair cells to consider them as consisting of one supranuclear and one infranuclear part, showing considerable structural differences. Even if quite large differences can be found between hair cells from the various cochlear coils, there seem to be in principle the same general differences between the supra- and infranuclear parts in all the hair cells (Fig. 3).

Figs. 8 and 9.—These two micrographs are taken from the spiral osseous lamina at that point where the myelinated fibres shed their myelin sheath. It can clearly be seen how the number of myelinated lamellae diminish and how each opaque layer divides into two thinner lines near the axoplasm (*Ax*). The axoplasm has a distinct margin, the axolemma (*Axl*). In high resolution pictures the intermediate opaque line between the coarser opaque lamellae can be followed to the neighborhood of the axolemma. The arrangement is of a helical nature and the myelin coating gets thinner and thinner as described by Engström and Wersäll and by Usman and Geren.

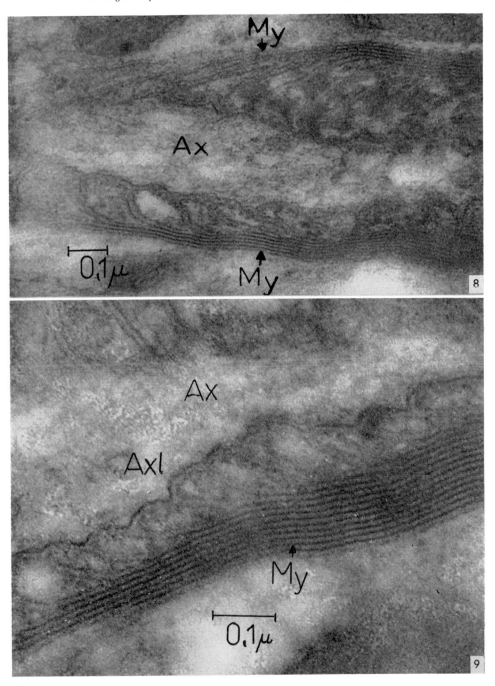

Within the supranuclear part we find inside the "vertical" surfaces of the cells a more or less pronounced membranous arrangement. In some cells it is possible to distinguish up to 6 or 7 layers of membranes with a thickness of around 300 Å. They each have an outer, rather opaque coating, and a slightly opaque centre. The membranes are not continuous all around the cell, but contain openings or gaps, and they have therefore been described as layers of discontinuous membranes (cf. [8]). The plasma membrane and the discontinuous layers surround the central cytoplasmic portion of the supranuclear part of the outer hair cells. Spoendlin [55] has recently described these membranes without finding any discontinuity. He believes that they consist of 6–12 separated opaque membranes with a thickness of 70 Å and an interspacing of 100–150 Å. He maintains that the discontinuity found in our specimen depends on fixation failure and gives an interesting description of how the discontinuity arises. However, in the description of this phenomenon his drawings show a systematic arrangement in membranes with discontinuity along certain definite lines and not haphazardly ([55], Fig. 10). Thus it is probable that even according to Spoendlin's figures there exists a system of thicker lamellae and that these lamellae have a thickness of around 250–300 Å. (According to Spoendlins [55] measurements 2×70 Å $+100$ or 150 Å.) The major part of the cytoplasm is rather homogeneous, slightly opaque and contains only very fine granulations. However, a layer of mitochondria is invariably found inside the discontinuous membranes. These mitochondria are often rather long and show an inner lamellar organization as seen in other mitochondria [50, 51, 49]. In addition to these peripheral mitochondria there is also an axial group of mitochondria in the supranuclear part. Immediately below the cuticle, corresponding to the Hensen body, many outer hair cells contain one or a few rounded bodies surrounded by oblong mitochondria. This Hensen body is sometimes composed of concentric membranous layers, showing a striking resemblance to the above described lamellar layers. In other cells the Hensen body seems to contain lamellar structures greatly resembling an ordinary Golgi network. It seems probable that the Hensen body is a specialized or modified Golgi apparatus.

The infranuclear part of the hair cells is bordered by a distinct plasma

---

Fig. 10.—Base of an outer hair cell (*HC*), surrounded by granulated nerve endings (*Ne*) with small vesicles and mitochondria (*M*).

Fig. 11.—Unmyelinated nerve fibres (*N*), surrounded by the first row of Deiters' cells (*DC*). The nerve fibres (*N*) are found to contain mitochondria (*M*). At one point (*Div*) it can be seen how a nerve fibre branches.

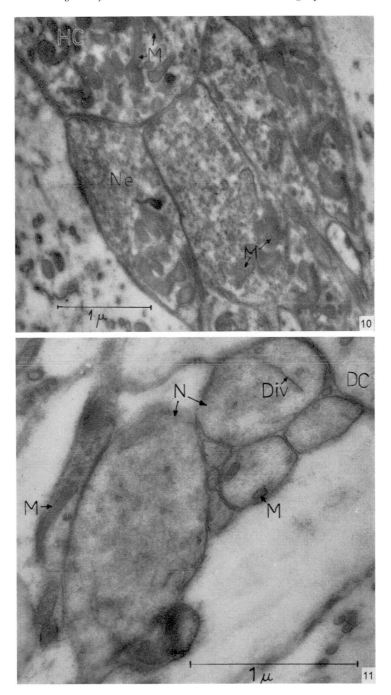

membrane which shows no continuity with surrounding cells or nerve endings. In no case have we been able to observe the corresponding well developed, discontinuous membranes as in the supranuclear part. Odd membranes
can, however, exist. The outer wall will therefore seem considerably thinner
in the infranuclear part than in the supranuclear. The cytoplasm inside the
plasma membrane contains partly very small rounded granules and partly
a large number of relatively small mitochondria. These mitochondria are
the equivalent of those granula described earlier as the Retzius body. The
nucleus of the hair cell is rich in chromatin, is finely structured, and has,
generally speaking, the same characteristics as are found in ordinary nuclei.
The infranuclear part of the hair cells is surrounded, partly by the Deiters
cell, partly by the complicated nerve ending system which is found between
the Deiters cell and the hair cell outside the base of the latter.

The Inner Hair Cells

As is known from light microscopic investigations, the number of inner
hair cells is smaller than that of the outer hair cells. Even in inner hair cells
the upper, relatively flat surface is enclosed in the reticular membrane. The
cells often appear to have a somewhat bent upper neck and an irregular, oval
lower part containing the nucleus. It is possible to discern an upper cuticle
which is rather thick from which a smaller number of hairs protrude. Largely
the cuticle has the same characteristics as the surface of the outer hair cells.
The hairs on the cells generally appear in two rows. They are slightly coarser
than those found on the outer hair cells. They consist partly of an intracellular
part or root, and partly of an extracellular portion which forms the actual
hair. Inside the hairs the same structure prevails as in the outer hair cells
(Fig. 4). The nucleus which is finely granulated and often has the shape of
a regular oval, is situated in the lower part of the cell. It is in general larger
than the nucleus of the outer hair cells.

The supranuclear part of the inner hair cell has a finely granulated
cytoplasm. In the cytoplasm quite a large number of rounded or oval mitochondria and granules are to be found. We have not been able to discover
any distinct accumulation of mitochondria inside the "vertical" sides of
the cells. However, there is invariably a large number of mitochondria in

Fig. 12.—Cross-sectioned outer pillar in their slender portion, containing around 1500–1600
fibres (F). The fibres begin to form smaller groups of fibres.

Fig. 13.—Light microscopic picture of the utricular macula in a guinea-pig.

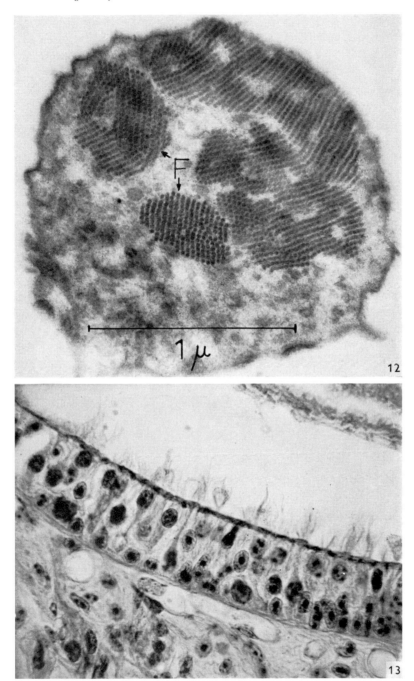

the area under the surface cuticle. The mitochondria contain regular, inner membrane formations of the kind described above. We have not discovered any distinct Hensen body in the inner hair cells. In the supranuclear part a number of granules are sometimes found which are slightly larger than the mitochondria. These granules are sometimes less opaque than the surrounding cytoplasm. There are also very opaque granules containing parts of varying density. The "vertical" sides of the inner hair cells are bordered, on the outside, by a thin distinct plasma membrane under which scattered membrane-like formations can be discerned. In the inner hair cells studied by us there were never any definite, well developed fenestrated membranes of the kind found in the outer hair cells. In the infranuclear part of the inner hair cells, directly under and near the nucleus of the cell, a small number of α-cytocisternae are found which are cleft-like spaces in the cytoplasm, each space being surrounded by a granulated membrane. Similar membranes have earlier been described in the sensory cells of the vestibulary apparatus by Wersäll [57], Smith [54] and Engström [9] and will be further discussed on page 487. Below these membranes there are, in the infranuclear part, rounded or slightly oval mitochondria somewhat irregularly distributed in the finely granulated cytoplasm. The lower part of the cells is generally not so evenly rounded and regular as in the outer hair cells. Instead it appears many times in our sections to have a slightly irregular surface and outside the plasma membrane there are bulb-like granulated and agranulated endings. It appears to us as if the construction of the inner hair cells in principle bears a resemblance to that of the vestibular sensory cells.

The Supporting Cells of the Organ of Corti

The most important cells in the supporting part of the organ of Corti are the pillar cells, the Deiters cells and the Hensen cells.

The Pillar Cells

The inner pillar cells are, as a rule, shorter than the outer ones and their number in man is in the literature estimated at 5600 inner pillars and 3850 outer. In principle both kinds of pillars are, by and large, similarly constructed. They consist of a base, a narrower middle part or stem and a head. In both light microscopic and electron microscopic studies it has been seen how the pillar cells with their lower base stand on the basilar membrane, but are distinctly divided from this by a cell membrane (Fig. 1). We have never been able to observe any continuity between the fibres of the basilar membrane and the inner structure of the pillar. This is, as pointed out earlier [17] a very important fact, as a continuation of the basilar membrane fibres into pillar fibres would indicate a similarity in structure. In the lower part, nearest to the basilar membrane there is a very finely granulated and homogeneous structure in which the supporting fibres of the pillar, the tonofibrillae, are attached. From this basal part or foot plate, a large number of thin fibrillae with a diameter of about 130–140 Å arise. Their arrangement can be seen in Fig. 12. Most likely they are continuous through the whole length of the pillar up to the top or head. In a less dense area of the foot of the pillar, free from fibres, the cell nucleus is located. In the guinea-pig cochlea the head part of the pillar contains a very finely granulated, electron dense material into which the fibrillae radiate. The fibres here show a very typical arrangement forming arches and are very likely arranged according to mechanical principles, forming together a functionally favorable supporting structure. The number of fibres in the pillars is difficult to define, but in some pillars from the second coil from the top we have managed to count the number at around 1600. The cytoplasm of the pillar consists of a fairly finely structured matter, where a small number of cytoplasmic granules and mitochondria can be found.

The cytoplasm of the pillar is bordered on the outside by a distinct plasma membrane and inside the middle part or stem, the different pillars run quite separate from each other. But within the bottom and top parts, nearly-lying cells border directly on to each other. In this basal region there are cell borders with a distinct cellular membrane of ordinary appearance. In the head region, where the opaque matter described above can be found, this matter almost reaches to the plasma membrane and the cell border, but outside it there is an extremely thin layer of cytoplasm, and the nearby pillar tops are bordered towards each other by a thin membranous structure (cf. [55]). The major part of the cytoplasm of the pillars is collected in the basal and head regions.

The Deiters Cells

In comparison to the pillar cells the Deiters cells are considerably richer in protoplasm. They consist of a cytoplasm bordered outwards by a distinct plasma membrane and contain fine fibres, granules and mitochondria. In the inner part of the Deiters cells there are a small number of tonofibrillae which have approximately the same thickness as those tonofibrillae found in the pillar cells. The Deiters cells, like the pillar cells, are situated directly on to the basilar membrane, but are distinctly separate from this. In the very basal part there is a somewhat irregular thin layer of extremely finely granulated or homogeneous, rather opaque matter into which the tonofibrillae emerge as a rule from a larger area. They then join up in the inner part of the cell to an eccentric fibrillar bundle which is often situated near the surface. From this fibre bundle tonofibrillae reach out, some of them up towards the asymmetrical cup-like part enclosing the base of the hair cells,

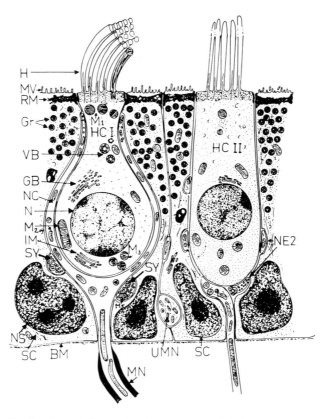

Fig. 14.—Schematic drawing of the vestibular sensory epithelium. *H*, hairs; *MV*, microvilli; *RM*, reticular membrane; *GR*, granules in a supporting cell (*SC*); *VB*, vesiculated bodies; *GB*, Golgi complex; *NC*, nerve chalice; *N*, nucleus; M_1, subcuticular mitochondria; M_2, mitochondria in the nerve chalice; M_3, subnuclear mitochondria; M_4, mitochondria around the nucleus; *IM*, intracellular granulated membranes; *SY*, granulated synapse; *NS*, nucleus of a supporting cell; *BM*, basilar membrane; *MN*, myelinated nerve; *UMN*, unmyelinated nerve; *HC I*, hair cell of type I; *HC II*, hair cell of type II; NE_2, granulated nerve ending at the base of a hair cell of type II.

Fig. 15.—Sensory cell of Type I in the crista epithelium, surrounded by nerve chalice (*NC*) and outside the nerve chalice by granulated supporting cells (*GR*). *GB*, Golgi body, *IM*, intracellular membranes, *M*, mitochondria. 12,000 ×.

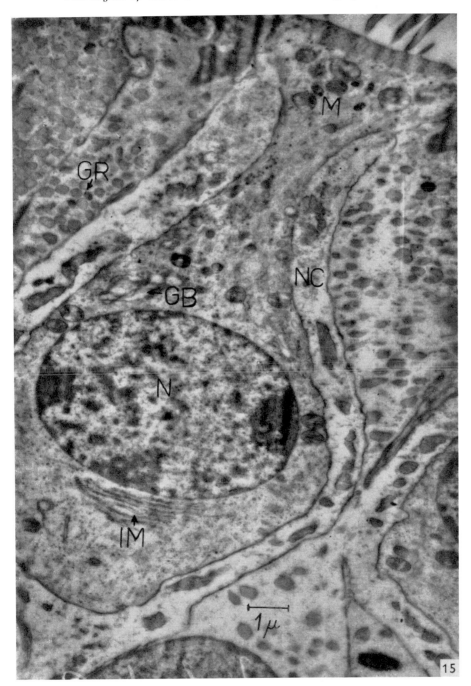

and a smaller number towards the upper phalanx which reaches the surface of the organ of Corti. In the vicinity of this surface the protoplasm in the phalanges increases and forms a fairly large protoplasmic formation, the phalanx, which contributes to the formation of the surface of the organ of Corti. These phalanges are enclosed by the reticular membrane. In the upper part of the phalanx the tonofibrillae radiate and are anchored partly in the opaque matter which forms the reticular membrane. The number of rows of Deiters cells usually corresponds with the number of rows of hair cells. The outer row of Deiters cells shows an extraordinary course. Here again, as described earlier, there is a basal part which reaches up to the hair cells and a narrow tapering phalanx which reaches up to the reticular membrane. This cellular process, however, runs along the outside of the outer tunnel directly inside the Hensen cells. In a horizontal section through the organ of Corti these narrow processes are found outside the outer wall of the outer tunnel where their outer surface lies along the Hensen cells, while the sides facing the tunnel are free, isolated from each other. On the surface of the Deiters cell phalanges on the side forming the upper surface of the organ of Corti, there is, as Engström and Wersäll have shown [14], a great number of very narrow, finger-like processes, microvilli, the importance of which is not yet clear. Corresponding microvilli are found in large amounts on that part of the organ of Corti which is formed by the Hensen cells. However, no similar processes can be seen on the free surfaces in the inner part of the organ of Corti.

The Hensen Cells

These cells comprise the outer part of the organ of Corti. They consist of cells with an extremely high water content. They are bordered on the outside by a distinct plasma membrane. This plasma membrane has, as mentioned above, a very great number of long (0.2–0.3 μ) finger-like protrusions on the free surface of the organ of Corti. These processes give that part of the organ of Corti which is formed by the Hensen cells, a surface slightly resembling that of the striated border in the intestines and kidneys. The importance of these small processes has not yet been established, but it is possible that they are of importance as resorptive elements (cf. [14, 40, 55]). The Hensen cells in the guinea pig cochlea are rich in large osmiophilic granules in the two upper coils which can easily be seen in both the light microscope and the electron microscope.

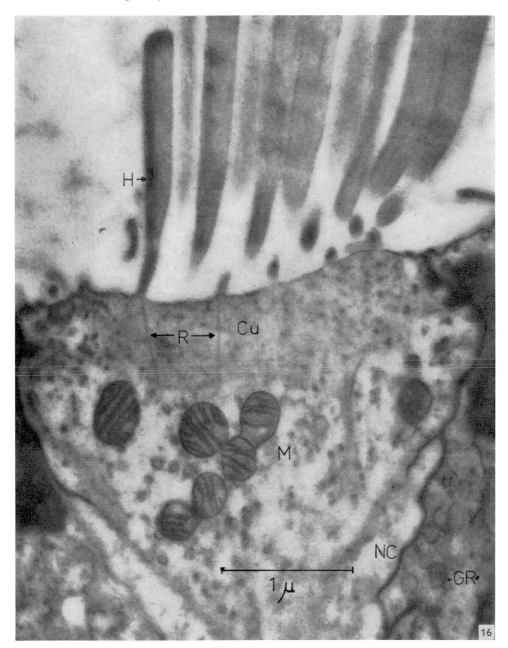

Fig. 16.—Cell surface of the sensory cell of Type I from the utricular macula in a guinea-pig. On the surface a number of hairs (*H*) with small rootlets (*R*) and mitochondria (*M*) are seen below the cuticle (*Cu*).

The Basilar Membrane

The construction of the basilar membrane in the cochlea has been the subject of careful anatomical and physiological studies (cf. [10]). Investigation by the electron microscope makes possible a very good analysis of the construction of the basilar membrane. The membrane is generally described as having two different zones, the arcuate and the pectinate zone. At least on sections through the second coil in the cochlea of the guinea-pig it is seen how the basilar membrane projects from limbus spiralis which is its medial attachment. Within the area from limbus spiralis to the base of the outer pillar, the actual basilar membrane consists of a coarse, irregular mass of minute fibres, radially arranged. These fibres are surrounded on the tympanic side by a homogeneous matter and the cells of the tympanic covering layer. The division from the actual organ of Corti itself is very distinct and sharp with no continuity. The bordering layer consists of a distinct double membrane. In thin sections through the fibre structures in this inner zone of the basilar membrane it has been discovered that these coarse fibres are each comprised of a very large number of minute fibrillae. The fibres are arranged mainly radially. Under the base of the outer pillar cells the basilar membrane undergoes a radical change. The single layer of fibres of the inner zone is divided here into two distinct layers, separated by a remarkably homogeneous structure-free layer. In this area odd nuclei occur, generally lying very near the upper layer. When the basilar membrane has been divided into two layers at the outer pillars these two layers usually take on a different appearance. The lower layer consists mainly of radiating, comparatively coarse and quite compact bundles of fibrils. These fibres anastomize to a certain extent and thin slender fibril bundles are seen running over, between the coarser strings in some places. The top layer which lies immediately under the cell borders of the organ of Corti consists of an almost homogeneous, very thin network of fine fibril structures on which the organ of Corti rests. In surface sections through this layer the construction of the layer and the structure of the small fibrillae also contained therein can be studied in detail. As the basilar membrane approaches the spiral ligament there is a reunion between the upper and lower layers, and also between the fibrillae which form these layers. Under the influence of intense sound important structural changes can be seen in the basilar membrane with oedema and scattering of the small fibre units.

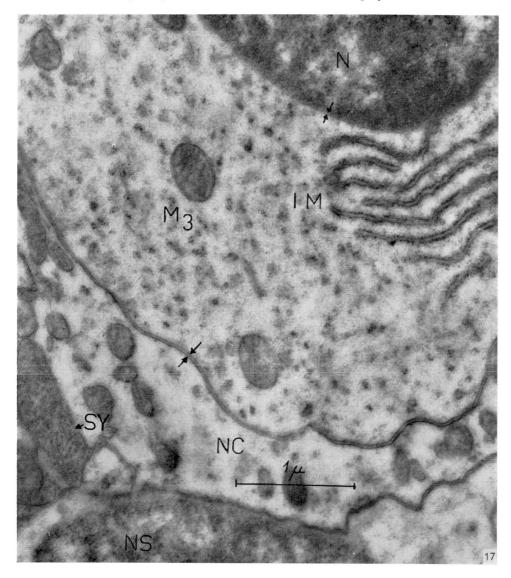

Fig. 17.—Lower part of a hair cell Type I from the sensory epithelium in the macula saccul of guinea-pig. *N*, nucleus, *IM*, intracellular membranes or α-cytocisternae. M_3 mitochondria in the infranuclear group of mitochondria. *NC*, nerve chalice, *Sy*, granulated synaptic nerve ending in contact with the nerve chalice. *NS*, supporting cell nucleus.

The Innervation of the Hair Cells (Figs. 7–11)

Through a long series of studies chiefly by Retzius [44–48], Lorente de Nó [31–33] and Rasmussen [43], but also later by Fernandez [18] and Portman jr [41–42] and others, it is evident that the organ of Corti is innervated by two different kinds of nerve fibres, afferent fibres with the ganglion cells collected in ganglion spirale Corti, and efferent fibres which come from the contralateral superior olivary complex. These latter fibres run a helical course and are of a smaller caliber than the afferent nerve fibres within the modiolus and the spiral ganglion. Regarding the extreme endings of the various nerve fibres there is, as yet, no definite information, but Rasmussen [43] and Portman jr [41–42] have made it evident that they are efferent fibres and the latter [41] maintains that he has been able to follow their course to the inner hair cells. Fernandez [8], on the other hand, who also regards them as efferent, suggests that the fibres do not only innervate the inner hair cells, but that branches also go to the outer hair cells. In our earlier studies we did not examine the course of each of the two kinds of nerve fibre. The most important feature of our studies has been determining the way in which the contact between the nervous elements and the hair cells is made, and the appearance of these areas. In more extensive present studies we have tried to damage or influence these nerve endings and we hope eventually to be able to reach a conclusion about the changes arising in the nerve endings on stimulation of the hair cells. Both the afferent and the efferent fibres within the canalis Rosenmülleri in the modiolus. Inside the outer part of the spiral osseous lamina the fibres lose their myelin sheath and are bordered only by a thin membrane without any definite myelin lamellae. The fibres pass through the medial attachment of the basilar membrane to the upper side of the basilar membrane. Some of the nerve fibres run into the inner spiral bundle, while some go more or less directly to the inner hair cells, and others run between the inner pillar cells and out through the tunnel of Corti between the outer pillars and arrive at the outer wall of the space of Nuel. On the border of the first, second, third

---

Fig. 18 *a.*—Cross-sectioned hairs on the surface of a vestibular sensory cell (*ampullar crest*) containing one kinocilium (*KC*). *b*, Longitudinal section through a kinocilium from the same region.

Fig. 19.—Granulated nerve fibres going between the nerve chalice *NC* and a supporting cell (*SC*) near a hair cell Type II in the sensory epithelium of the utricular macula. *M*, mitochondria. *Sy*, synaptic membrane.

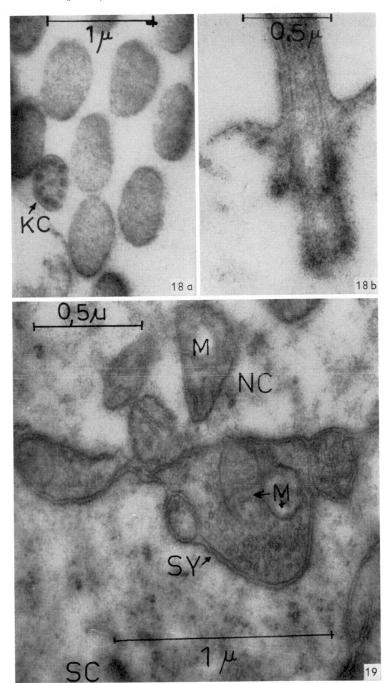

and fourth rows of Deiters cells respectively, a large number of nerve fibres turn at right angles and continue as spironeurons along the organ of Corti. The main features of their course are well known through the work of Retzius [44–48] and Lorente de Nó [31–33], and through observations made by Held, Kolmer and others [20–22, 24–26] we have some knowledge of the way in which the nerve fibres make contact with the sensory cells. It is beautifully shown by the electron microsocpe how these nerve fibres running a spiral course, attach themselves to the medial surface of the Deiters cells where they continue their course distinctly separate from the Deiters cells in furrows or sometimes completely enveloped by folds from the Deiters cells. The neurons, running in a spiral can be followed right into the organ of Corti (compare Lorente de Nó [33], Fernandes [18] and Fig. 11). From the spiral nerve fibres there are branches to the hair cells. With electron micro- scopy it can be seen how slender branches leave almost at right angles from the coarse, spiral fibres. Almost immediately after these branches have left the main fibre, curved very electron-dense mitochondrial structures appear in their centre, in the neuroplasm of which they are comprised. When the branch, after a short course, approaches the hair cells it starts to swell and ends in bulb-like formations under and round the base of the hair cells. These bud-like nerve endings are completely intercellular, located in a cleft-like space between the Deiters cells and the hair cells. Beneath the base of every hair cell there is a number of nerve endings, often varying in size in the different rows of hair cells. The nerve endings are closely adhering to the thin plasma membrane of the hair cell, but at the same time they are separated from the membrane by their own plasma membranes. Every such bulb-like formation is bordered outwardly by a thin "synapto- lemma" and inside there is a great number of mitochondria, closely packed together, especially in the first row of the hair cells. Along the outer rows of the hair cells they lie more isolated and seldom reach the same size as in the first row of hair cells. At the first row of hair cells the nerve termina- tions form very large nerve end bodies (Fig. 10), while the nerve endings in the other row of hair cells are comparatively small. With the electron microscope it is clearly seen that the different nerve endings under the same hair cell are different in structure. It has thus frequently been observed how the most central bulb-like ending contains remarkably opaque and closely packed collections of mitochondria, but the terminations located on the outside are less electron dense. In studies of a large number of electron microscope preparations from the guinea-pig cochlea we have seen how a medium sized nerve fibre, rich in protoplasm, and a slender, more opaque

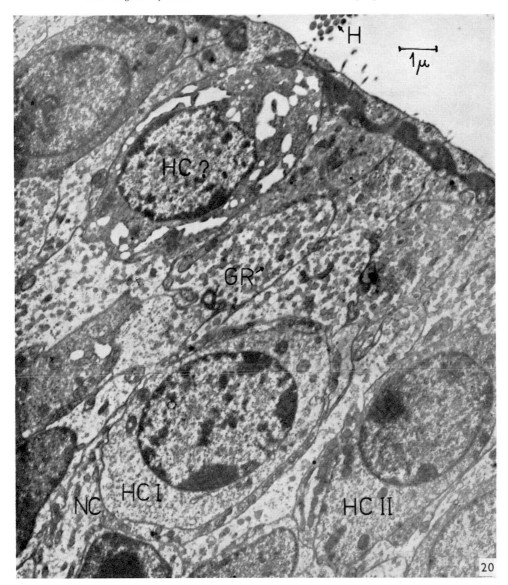

Fig. 20.—Hair cells of Type I (*HC I*) and of Type II (*HC II*) in the utricular macula. Nerve chalice, *NC*. Granules in the supporting cells. *HC* refers to a sensory cell of the atypical form sometimes observed in the macular epithelia. *H*, sensory hairs.

kind of fibre run towards the outer hair cell. Whether it is a question of two different kinds of nerve fibres is not clear, neither is it known whether these two fibres have the same kind of nerve endings or not. This question, which is of the utmost importance for the understanding of the physiology of the cochlea, will be further discussed in more detail. On account of the great difficulties encountered because of the complicated course of the fibres, we have not yet managed definitely to ascertain whether or not the organ of Corti is innervated by two kinds of nerve fibres, different in structure.

This problem is now subject to a careful analysis by Engström.

The Tectorial Membrane

The structure of the tectorial membrane has been described by a number of scientists. An electron microscopic description has recently been given by Spoendlin. In recent years we have on several occasions isolated the tectorial membrane and studied it in the electron microscope. As yet, however, we have not been able to explain the fine structure of the membrane. In phase contrast microscopy and in light microscopic investigations the tectorial membrane shows a very distinct, comparatively coarse fibrillar structure, but observations made with the electron microscope have not on any occasion fully verified those made with the light microscope. With the aid of electron microscopy and after fixation with osmic acid, acrylate embedding and sectioning, a fibrous mass is obtained containing extraordinarily fine fibrils (approx. 40 Å). These fibrils appear considerably thinner in the electron microscope than in the light microscope and are similar to fibres found in a fixed gel. In some areas the fibrillar structures are packed more closely. Observations by Belanger [1] and Ringertz [19] have shown that the tectorial membrane, like the gel in the otolith membrane over saccular and utricular maculae and the cupula of the semicircular canals incorporate radioactive sulfate (S^{35}). Research as to the nature of the tectorial membrane is still going on, but electron microscopic investigations point to the possibility of its consisting of a jelly-like formation with very slender micellar structures interspaced by substances disolved during the preparation.

The cells of the labium vestibulare to which the tectorial membrane is attached have a very high grade of differentiation with a well developed Golgi complex and a rich cytoplasmic mitochondrial system.

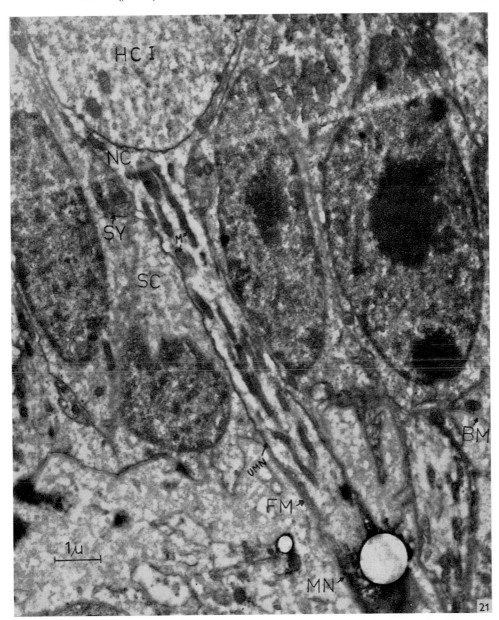

Fig. 21.—Myelinated nerve (*MN*) on its way from the nerve chalice (*NC*) around a hair cell of Type I (*HC I*). In the unmyelinated part a large number of long mitochondria. Surrounding the lower part of the nerve chalice granulated nerve endings (*SY*) are seen. At *FM* folded myelin membranes (cf. Fig. 8–9).

THE ULTRASTRUCTURE OF THE VESTIBULAR SENSORY EPITHELIA

In the guinea-pig the vestibular apparatus consists of three semicircular canals, the utricle and the saccule. Each semicircular canal contains, in the ampullar portion, the ampullar crest, covered by sensory epithelium. The sensory epithelium comprises a large number of sensory cells with sensory hairs on their free surface. Above this epithelium a jelly-like substance, the cupula is found. It is generally regarded as being of prime importance for the excitation of the sensory cells.

The utricular and saccular sensory epithelium is located in the maculae. The sensory cells of these maculae are, as will be shown below, also provided with sensory hairs protruding from the surface. They are covered by a jelly-like material containing large numbers of light-reflecting calcite crystals, the statoconiae. A description will be given below of the different vestibular sensory regions.

The Structures of the Ampullar Crests

This subject has recently been carefully studied by Wersäll [57] and a comprehensive review of the literature is given in his paper.

As stated above each ampullar crest is covered by sensory epithelium and the general appearance of the crest is often referred to as saddle-shaped. The sensory cell region is surrounded by high cylindrical cells forming the planum semilunatum, much discussed in connection with the formation of endolymph. Outside the semilunar region large quantities of pigment occur in the labyrinthine wall.

According to Wersäll's observations, the sensory epithelium on the ampullar crest consists of sensory cells and supporting elements. The sensory cells appear as two distincts kinds of hair cells described by Wersäll as Type I and Type II (Fig. 14).

Hair Cells of Type I (according to Wersäll)

These cells are bottle-shaped with a short neck and rounded base and each cell is surrounded by a very large nerve chalice. Outside these nerve chalices the supporting cells are to be found (Fig. 15).

Each hair cell is bordered by a distinct plasma membrane and is completely separated from surrounding cells and nerve endings by thin intercellular spaces.

Each cell contains one nucleus and a cytoplasm with different kinds of cytoplasmic components. Every cell has a cuticle at the surface of the sensory epithelium. From the cuticle a large number (60–80) of hairs protrude and Wersäll [57] showed that the main part of these hairs consisted of a type generally described as stereocilia, while one single hair showd an inner structure in every way consistent with the general features of motile flagellae or kinocilia.

The hairs protrude from the cuticle of the hair cell. This cuticle consists of an extremely finely granulated substance of relatively high opacity. Although the stereocilia which protrude from these hair cells are considerably longer (around 40 μ), they show a striking resemblance to the hairs described in the organ of Corti. As in the organ of Corti the hair proper, outside the cell, has an inner axial structure with a length of around 4 μ. At that distance the central fibre vanishes. We are convinced that the basal portion, containing the core, has a higher rigidity than the outer part of the hair. Thus the proximal part stands out rigidly from the surface while the distal part seems to be more flexible.

The hairs of the kinocilium type bear a very close resemblance to other kinocilia. Thus they consist of an outer fibrillated portion and a basal corpuscle. We have not been able to ascertain if there are any basal rootlets. The function of these kinocilia-like structures is not known but it is most interesting to see how corresponding elements are found in the olfactory, as well as in the retinal sensory epithelia (Figs. 18 *a* and 18 *b*).

The cytoplasm contains a number of organelles, among them intracellular membranous systems and mitochondria which we are going to discuss here.

There are two systems of cisternae, the α-cytocisternae and the γ-cytocisternae or the Golgi body.

The α-cytocisternae form 1 to 8 flat, parallel, cleft-like spaces in the infranuclear part of the cell. Each space is bordered by a membrane with a thickness of 40–60 Å. On the outside these membranes are provided with large amounts of small granules, or groups of granules, where each granule has a diameter of about 150–200 Å. Similar cytoplasmic differentiations are found in several other cells and have been characterized by Palade [36–37] as cisternae and by Sjöstrand as α-cytomembranes [51].

The γ-cytocisternae are bordered by agranulated, smooth membranes forming a complicated system. These cisternae are generally found in the supranuclear part rather near the nucleus and are the equivalent of the Golgi body.

The mitochondria of the hair cells of Type I have a certain tendency to accumulate in three different cellular regions. Consequently, there is generally a group of almost round mitochondria found directly below the cuticle. These mitochondria are almost spherical with a diameter of appr. 0.3–0.4 μ. Another group of mitochondria is found near the Golgi body. These mitochondria have a length of up to 0.8 μ. A third group of mitochondria is found in the infranuclear part of the cell.

As mitochondria often occur in regions with a high metabolic rate the occurrence of mitochondria in certain regions of the sensory cells suggests a certain spatial functional differentiation.

The hair cells of Type I are enclosed in a very large nerve ending forming a goblet-shaped nerve chalice. The demarcation between hair cell and nerve ending is quite distinct. The enclosure of the hair cell is not complete but only the uppermost portion of the hair cell is free. The general appearance of the hair cell and its relation to the nerve chalice can be found in Figs. 15, 17, 21. There is a minute lighter space (150–250 Å) separating the hair cell from the nerve chalice. This space is bordered by an inner membrane (around 50 Å) belonging to the hair cell and an outer membrane (around 50 Å) belonging to the nerve chalice. The latter is continuous with the outer demarcation of the nerve chalice. This membrane is also continuous with the axolemmal membrane of the nerve fibre (Fig. 17).

The nerve chalice neuroplasm is very slightly opaque and contains a number of small mitochondria which, further down in the axon, are replaced by extremely long and slender mitochondria (Fig. 21). The neuroplasm of the chalice contains in its most distal part a small number of round granular or vesicular structures, in many ways resembling the synaptic granules earlier described by several authors in the presynaptic neuroplasms. The density of these granules is not of the same magnitude as that of the granules of the synaptic terminations which will be discussed later. Scattered granules may also be found further down in the nerve chalice and also in the axon of the nerve. Fibrillar structures, regularly observed in the axon are not so frequent in the nerve chalice. Outside the nerve chalice a system of highly granulated nerve endings, discussed below, can be observed. The supporting cells surround the nerve chalice and the granulated terminations. In that region of the axon where myelin lamellae occur the general appearance in the myelin sheath organization, discussed later can be observed.

Hair Cells of Type II

Compared with the hair cells of Type I the hair cells of Type II are much more cylindric with a rather flat cuticular surface and a rounded or pointed infranuclear region. Their length varies in different parts of the crests, and cells with a long and slender, as well as short and stocky cell body, can be observed.

The cytoplasm contains a large number of evenly distributed particles with a moderate opacity giving the cell a rather dense appearance when compared with hair cells of Type I. There are very few α-cytocisternae in these cells, but agranulated membranes, forming the Golgi body are regularly observed in the supranuclear part. The agglomeration of the mitochondria in certain regions as described in hair cells of Type I is less obvious in these sensory cells.

The cuticle and the hairs on the cell surface have the same general appearance as those described above.

The most striking feature of the hair cell of Type II as compared with Type I is the difference in innervation. While the latter had one large nerve chalice the hair cells of Type II are provided with a number of bud-shaped nerve endings among which Wersäll [57] observed some containing large amounts of synaptic granules and others with few, or completely lacking such granules. Both these types of nerve endings are found in direct contact with the plasma membrane of the sensory cell. The nerve endings are regularly located at the basal part of the hair cell.

The Supporting Cells

The supporting cells occupy the spaces between the sensory elements. Their diameter varies in different epithelial levels and their nuclei are generally located at the basal part of the cell. The nuclei have very distinct nucleoli and very dense chromatin. They reach from the basal membrane to the surface of the epithelium and contain large amounts of cytoplasmic granules. We have not observed any system of sustentacular fibres corresponding to the well developed supporting fibres of the organ of Corti. The cytoplasm contains a well developed Golgi body, mitochondria and highly osmiophilic inclusions, which sometimes reach a considerable size.

On the epithelial surface of the crests the supporting cells are provided with a large number of thin walled microvilli.

The epithelium of the crests has a well developed reticular membrane and a distinct basement membrane.

The Structure of Utricular and Saccular Maculae

The utricular and saccular sensory epithelium shows in many ways a striking resemblance to the crista epithelium (Figs. 17, 20, 21).

Thus hair cells of Type I and Type II are found surrounded by supporting cells. The two kinds of hair cells have a pronounced correspondence in
structure and type of innervation with those described in the crests. We therefore refer to that chapter or to the publications by Wersäll, Engström and
Hjorth [59], Smith [54], Engström [9], Wersäll [58] and to the discussion in
this paper.

While the crista epithelium on its surface has a distinct cupula, the macular
surface is covered by a jelly-like substance containing a large number of
light reflecting crystals, the statoconia. These crystals have been studied
by Carlström, Engström and Hjorth [4] with the aid of electron microscopy
and X-ray diffraction and found to be composed of calcite in man and the
guinea-pig.

DISCUSSION

Both the sensory cells of the organ of Corti and those of the vestibular
sensory epithelia have a characteristic appearance. They are provided with
sensory hairs on their surface and have a well developed nerve ending
apparatus around the lower part of the cell body.

Within the organ of Corti there is a considerable difference between the
inner and outer hair cells, structural differences which are so pronounced that
they indicate a distinct difference in their functional behavior.

There has been a long discussion about the afferent and the efferent inerva-
tion of the cohlea. Rasmussen, Fernandez and Portman have discussed the
problem in a series of papers without having reached any definite conclusion
as to the final course of the efferent cochlear bundle.

The vestibular sensory epithelium contains two distinct types of hair cells.
These were first described by Wersäll in the ampullar crest and were later
found in the utricular as well as in the saccular maculae [54, 9, 10, 58].
Of these, Type I has a rounded cell body and is enclosed by a large nerve
chalice. Type II has small bud-shaped nerve-endings around the lower
part of the cylindrical cell body. Regarding the vestibular apparatus much
discussion has also arisen around the possibility of an afferent and an efferent
innervation (cf. [29, 30]). Hitherto not much has been known about these
nerve fibres. Studies by Wersäll [57] have clearly shown how granulated and
agranulated nerve endings appear at the base of one type of hair cells. In the
vestibular epithelia Engström has shown [9] that the agranulated nerve
chalices have a system of distinctly granulated nerve endings on their surface
(Fig. 19). These bear a close resemblance to the presynaptic neural terminations described by Palay, Palade and others [38]. Engström [10] has assumed

that these nerve endings may have an inhibitory function and that they represent a typical synapse between an afferent neural system leading impulses from the nerve chalice to the central vestibular ganglia and an efferent inhibitory system. He supposes that they form an important regulatory "feed back" system.

As the vestibular sensory cells of Type II also have a distinct differentiation in agranulated and granulated nerve endings, the question arises as to whether the granulated endings which also greatly resemble ordinary presynaptic nerve terminations, have an efferent function of whether there is a functional difference of some other kind between these two types. If we ascribe a presynaptic function to all granulated nerve endings this would mean that at least the outer cochlear hair cells have a very large system of efferent nerve endings at their base. Further information and experiments are here necessary (*c.f.* Engström [9, 10]).

Of great importance in this connection is the question of whether granulated nerve endings everywhere have the same functional significance and mode of function as granulated nerve endings around sensory cells.

SUMMARY

This paper contains a survey of the structural organization of the organ of Corti and of the vestibular sensory epithelia.

The outer and inner hair cells are described and the general principles of their innervation discussed.

There is a complicated sustentacular system around the hair cells, and the general structure of this system and of the tectorial membrane is reported.

A report is given on the ultrastructural organization of the vestibular sensory epithelia.

The problem of the afferent and efferent innervation of the inner ear sensory regions is discussed.

REFERENCES

1. BELANGER, L. F., *Science* **118**, 520 (1953).
2. BORGHESAN, E., Fisiopatologia del canale cochleare. Scuola Tip, Palermo, 1954.
3. —— *J. Franç. O.R.L. Chir. Maxillo-Faciale* **3**, 213 (1954).
4. CARLSTRÖM, D., ENGSTRÖM, H. and HJORT, S., *Laryngoscope* **63**, 1052 (1953).
5. COVELL, *Arch. oto-laryngol.* **23**, 633 (1936).
6. ENGSTRÖM, H., *Acta oto-laryngol.* **39**, 364 (1951).
7. —— *ibid.* **40**, 5 (1951).
8. —— *Rev. laryngol.* **II**, 808 (1955).
9. —— *Arch. Hals-, Nasen- u. Kehlkopfheilk.*, in press (1957).
10. —— *Acta. oto-laryng.*, in press (1958).

11. ENGSTRÖM, H. and HJORTH, S., *Acta oto-laryngol.*, *Suppl.* **XCV**, 149 (1950).
12. ENGSTRÖM, H., SJÖSTRAND, F. S. and WERSÄLL, J., *Förhandl. Svensk Otolaryngol. För.* **1**, 1 (1952).
13. —— *Proceedings of the fifth internatl. congr. of Otorhinolaryngol.*, p. 563 (1953).
14. ENGSTRÖM, H. and WERSÄLL, J., *Ann. Otol. Rhinol. & Laryngol.* **61**, 1027 (1952).
15. —— *Acta oto-laryngol.* **43**, 1 (1953).
16. —— *ibid.* **43**, 323 (1953).
17. —— *Ann. Otol. Rhinol. & Laryngol.* **52**, 507 (1953).
18. FERNANDEZ, C., *Laryngoscope* **61**, 1152 (1951).
19. FRIBERG, U. and RINGERTZ, N. JR., *J. Embryol. Exptl. Morphol.* **4**, 313 (1956).
20. HELD, H., *Abhandl. sächs. Akad. Wiss. Leipzig Math.-naturw. Kl.* **28**, 1 (1902).
21. —— *ibid.* **31**, 193 (1909).
22. —— *Handbuch der Normalen und Pathologischen Physiologie*, **XI**, p. 467. Berlin, 1926.
23. HENSEN, V., *Wiss. Zoöl.* **13**, 481 (1863).
24. KOLMER, W., *Zentr. Physiol.* **18**, 620 (1904).
25. —— *Ergeb. Physiol.* **11**, 372 (1911).
26. —— in ALEXANDER u. MARBURG, *Handbuch der Neurologie des Ohres*. **1**, 101 (1923–1924).
27. KOLMER, W., in MÖLLENDORFF, *Handbuch der mikroskopischen Anatomie des Menschen*, **III**, 250 (1927).
28. —— in JAFFE, Anatomie und Pathologie der Spontanerkrankungen der kleinen Versuchtiere, p. 473. Berlin, 1931.
29. LOEWENSTEIN, O., *Z. vergleich. Physiol.* **17**, 806 (1932).
30. —— *Brit. med. Bull.* **12**, 110 (1956).
31. LORENTE, DE NÓ, R., *Trab. Inst. Cajal invest. biol. Madrid* **24**, 53 (1926).
32. —— *Laryngoscope* **43**, 327 (1933).
33. —— *ibid.* **47**, 373 (1937).
34. PALADE, G. E., *Anat. Record* **114**, 427 (1952).
35. —— *J. Histochem Cytochem.* **1**, 118 (1953).
36. —— *J. Biophys. Biochem. Cytol.* **1**, 59 (1955).
37. —— *ibid.* **1**, 69 (1955).
38. PALAY, S. L., Progress in Neurobiology. Neurochemistry. Chapt. VI, p. 64, 1956.
39. PALAY, S. L. and PALADE, G. E., *Anat. Record* **118**, 335 (1954).
40. PLOTZ, E. and PERLMAN, H. B., *Laryngoscope* **65**, 291 (1955).
41. PORTMAN, M., Les fibres nerveuses efférentes cochléaires. Thèse, Bordeaux, 1952.
42. —— *Acta oto-laryngol.* **46**, 352 (1956).
43. RASMUSSEN, G. L., *J. Comp. Neurol.* **84**, 141 (1946).
44. RETZIUS, G., Über die peripherische Endigungsweise des Gehörnerven. Biologische Untersuchungen. I:3, p. 51. Stockholm, 1881.
45. —— Das Gehörorgan der Virbeltiere. Das Gehörorgan der Fische und Amphibien. Stockholm, 1881.
46. —— Das Gehörorgan der Vögel und der Säugetiere. Stockholm, 1884.
47. —— Die Endungsweise des Gehörnerven. Biologische Untersuchungen. N.F. III, 29. Stockholm, 1892.
48. —— Über die Endigungsweise des Gehörnerven in den Maculae und Cristae acusticae im Gehörlabyrinth der Wirbeltiere. Eine historisch-kritische Übersicht. Biologische Untersuchungen. N.F. **XII**, p. 21, 1905.
49. RHODIN, J., Correlation of Ultrastructural Organization and Function in Normal and Experimentally Changed Proximal Convoluted Tubuli Cells of the Mouse Kidney. Stockholm, 1954.
50. SJÖSTRAND, F. S., *J. Cellular Comp. Physiol.* **42**, 15 (1953).
51. SJÖSTRAND, F. S. and RHODIN, J., *Exptl. Cell Research* **4**, 426 (1953).
52. SMITH, C. A., *Ann. Otol. Rhinol. & Laryngol.* **63**, 435 (1954).
53. —— *Anat. Rec.* **121**, 451 (1955).
54. —— *Ann. Otol. Rhinol. Laryngol.* **65**, 450 (1956).
55. SPOENDLIN, H., *Pract. oto-rhino-laryngol.* **19**, 192 (1957).
56. WERSÄLL, J., *Acta oto-laryngol.* **44**, 359 (1954).
57. —— *ibid.*, *Suppl.* **126** (1956).
58. —— *Arch. Zool.*, in print (1957).
59. WERSÄLL, J., ENGSTRÖM, H. and HJORTH, S., *Acta oto-laryngol.*, *Suppl.* **116**, 298 (1954).

Experimental Cell Research, Suppl. **5**, *493–519 (1958)*

SYNAPTIC INHIBITORY MECHANISMS. PROPERTIES OF DENTRITES AND PROBLEMS OF EXCITATION IN ISOLATED SENSORY NERVE CELLS[1]

STEPHEN W. KUFFLER

Wilmer Institute, The Johns Hopkins Hospital and University, Baltimore, Maryland, U.S.A.

THE nerve cells in stretch receptor organs of different crustacea, discovered by Alexandrowicz [2], have presented physiologists with unique opportunities. The sensory neuron, with the cell body located in the periphery, can be activated by passive stretch [45] similarly to other deformation sensitive neurons. In addition there exists a neural motor control of the fine muscle bundle into which the dendrites of the sensory cell insert. Contraction set up by motor nerves in the receptor muscle can cause discharges in the sensory neuron even in the absence of passive stretch [35]. This dual regulation is analogous to that found in the vertebrate muscle spindle in which the small-nerve motor fibers modulate or govern the spindle afferent discharge [40, 37]. In addition to these similarities between vertebrates and crustacea in the design of nervous control, the stretch receptor nerve cell of crayfish and lobster possesses a direct inhibitory innervation which can promptly suppress the sensory discharge in the presence of continued excitation by stretch [36]. Fig. 1 presents schematically the organization of a single crustacean stretch receptor.

More interesting, at least for the present discussion, is the relative ease with which some basic cell properties can be investigated in the receptor cell in complete isolation. Axon and cell body can be studied under direct observation, and even the dendrites are accessible in some of the cells. The dendrites clearly show specific properties in respect to impulse propagation and excitation by stretch deformation. Further, inhibitory synapses are located on them. In lobster receptors an additional efferent neuron of small diameter, (dotted line Fig. 1, named thin accessory neuron by Alexandrowicz [3]) physiologically not yet identified, makes contact with the dendrites.[2]

---

[1] Supported by a research grant from the National Institutes of Health, United States Public Health Service.

[2] The function of this neuron has recently been established in lobster receptors. It also has an inhibitory role but to be effective it has to be stimulated at a higher frequency than the large inhibitory neuron which is discussed in this paper. Sensory nerve cells of lobster thus can possess a dual inhibitory regulation by (i) a 'fast' inhibitory axon of relatively large diameter and (ii) a 'slow' inhibitory neuron of smaller diameter (Burgen and Kuffler, *Nature* **180**, 1490 (1957).

494   S. W. Kuffler

The stretch receptor 'organ' with its few elements thus possesses many features which are found in vertebrates. In all respects so far explored the similarities in behavior and in the mechanisms between this crustacean neuron and mammalian nerve cells, especially the spinal motoneurons, have been surprisingly close. Further detailed work, however, will undoubtedly bring out the differences as well. Therefore, it seems clear that although

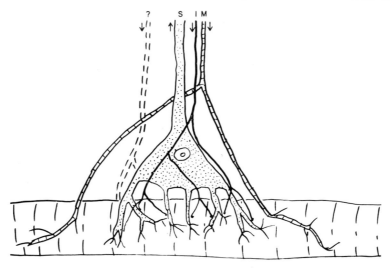

Fig. 1.—Schema of functional organization of crustacean stretch receptor. Sensory neuron (S) has its cell body near receptor muscle strand. Peripheral portions of dendrites are embedded in muscle strand. Inhibitory axon (I) forms synapses on dendrites. Motor nerve(s) (M) supply muscle strand which also has inhibitory innervation (not drawn). Dotted line represents neuron of unknown function (see footnote #2), supplying nerve cell [2, 3, 23].

certain properties may be established clearly in the receptor cell, they should not be automatically transferred to other cells in other species. A full account of the physiological properties of the receptor organs can be found in a series of recent publications [35, 19, 20, 36]. Electron microscope studies, only recently started, may further help in explaining some of the puzzling phenomena of this cell system.

Definition of Nerve Cell Constituents

The more recent attempts to analyze physiologically conditions of excitation and conduction as well as pharmacological properties in different parts of cells have somewhat strained the existing nomenclature. This applies especially to the terms 'dendrite' and 'soma' (perikaryon, cell body). Few workers will regard the peripheral vertebrate sensory nerve fibers as dendrites merely because they conduct impulses toward the cell body. Nor is a distinction between cell body and axon difficult, although the transitional region, the axon hillock area, is somewhat indeterminate. 'Soma' according to some includes all the cell processes (except axon), not just the region around the nucleus. Distinctive terms will be retained in this study, i.e. 'dendrites' for the nonaxonal processes emerging from a central area surrounding the nucleus, which will be called cell body. Physiologically, this distinction is still inadequate because in the present sensory cell the proximal portion of the dendrites seems to have properties regarding conduction which resemble those of the cell body. In the distal part of the dendrites, however, different behavior has been found.

Processes of Excitation

Normally stretch-deformation is the adequate stimulus for the sensory cell. The specific sensitivity is confined to the distal regions of the dendrites which insert into a fine muscle strand. The base of the dendrites and the cell body itself are relatively stretch insensitive, similar to peripheral axons.

The Graded Generator Action

If a receptor cell is held in an unstretched state, its resting potential is about 70 mV and no discharges are set up. In the recent studies most measurements were made with an intracellular lead inserted into the cell body. If stretch is applied in a finely graded manner, there occurs a graded reduction of the resting potential. The graded subthreshold action occurs at the site of stretch deformation where the distal dendrite portions make contact with the muscle strand into which they are embedded. This process in the dendrites has been called the generator process and the potential accordingly is the generator potential. In Fig. 2A light stretch was applied; the change in membrane potential reflects the time course and, up to the threshold level, the intensity of stretch-deformation. The generator potential is analogous to the slow graded potentials in receptor regions of many sense organs, like the eye, the muscle spindle, the Pacinian corpuscle, the nasal epithelium, etc. [34, 28, 4, 26, 41].

Conducted impulses are set up at a critical level of depolarization which is near 10 mV in slowly adapting cells and near 20 mV in fast adapting neurons. An example is shown in Fig. 2B in a 'slow' cell in which the cell's firing level was near 12 mV. This remained constant (broken line), although the initial near-threshold stretch was further increased (2nd arrow), increasing the frequency of discharges up to 14/sec. In Fig. 2C the threshold firing level

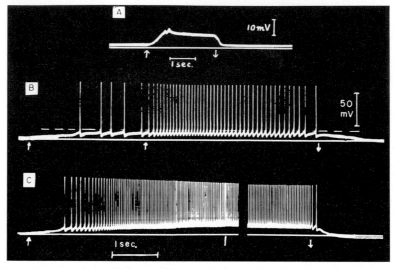

Fig. 2.—Potentials recorded with intracellular leads from the cell body of sensory neurons. *A*, Generator potential during subthreshold stretch is graded according to intensity of stretch-deformation. Stretch and relaxation marked by arrows. *B*, At a critical level of depolarization by the generator action, low frequency conducted impulses are set up. At second arrow, additional stretch increased the discharge rate to about 14/sec without appreciably affecting the firing level (dotted line). *C*, Same cell, stretch gradually increased between first arrow and straight line and then held constant. Note rise in firing level as the frequency of sensory discharge increases (over 30/sec). Several seconds of rhythmic discharge not shown (dark gap). Relaxation is followed by small transient hyperpolarization (after Eyzaguirre and Kuffler [19]).

was similar but with further steadily increasing stretch and discharge frequency (30/sec.), the firing level rose appreciably.

From an estimate of the magnitude of the generator potential at its site of origin, one can deduce readily the essential difference between properties of the dendrites and the rest of the cell. If, for instance, the generator potential recorded at the cell body reaches a firing level of 20 mV, one can conclude that at some distance from the recording electrode the potential must have been larger. The generator potential is electrotonically conducted along the tapering dendrites over distances which in some cells may be only 0.1 mm, in others 1.0 mm. The space constant of dendrites is not known, but one may assume that in many instances an attenuation to at least one half must have occurred. Graded activity up to 40 mV should therefore occur in the distal dendrite portion, certainly well beyond the "firing level" of a normal axon. In other terms, it means that at least parts of dendrites have a very high threshold. This agrees with the conclusion that normal all-or-none conduction does not penetrate to the distal ends of the dendrites. Among other evidence for this view is the finding that part of the generator potential persists during antidromic invasion of the nerve cell [20]. *The distal dendrite portions, therefore, may be regarded as differentiated tissue specialized for local graded activity.* Other distinct properties can be uncovered by specific drug action on dendrites and by an analysis of synaptic transmission (cf. later).

Graded activity in cortical dendrites of cats has been found by Clare and Bishop [13] and recently Purpura and Grundfest [42] have obtained much new evidence on the distinctive properties of dendrites in different parts of the cortex. For an extensive treatment of graded activity in different cells, Bishop's [7] interesting and imaginative review should be consulted.

Site of Initiation of Conducted Impulses

From a comparative physiological point of view, the sensory cell presents a very suggestive model for events which have long been postulated for cells in the central nervous system. The sensory cell possesses in the generator process a physiological mechanism by which the state of the neuron can be altered and 'set' over long periods. Thus, by graded subthreshold stretch of the dendrites the cell can be depolarized and its excitability, or readiness to discharge, can be adjusted over a considerable range. It can be brought, for instance, right to the verge of discharging and in such a state the slightest additional stimulus will trip off an afferent impulse.

Present evidence indicates that conduction starts somewhere centrally of the small diameter dendrite region, depending on various conditions. The slowly adapting receptor has relatively long dendrites, and a low threshold generator potential of 8–12 mV is recorded at the cell body (Fig. 2 *B*, *C*). In such cells it was occasionally seen that the cell body firing level was actually 20–25 mV as measured by partially blocked antidromic impulses. If this soma threshold applies for normal activity in 'slow' receptor cells the following alternatives must be considered (i) the impulse starts in the relatively high threshold dendrites, but since the site is some distance from the recording lead the firing level will appear diminished due to electrotonic decrement. This was assumed in the previous studies of Eyzaguirre and Kuffler [19] (ii) conduction is initiated in the relatively low threshold initial axon segment near the axon hillock, as concluded by Eccles and coworkers [16] and by Fuortes, Frank and Becker [25] in the spinal motoneuron.[1] The

[1] In a recent study Case, Edwards, Gesteland and Ottoson (*Biol. Bull.* **113**, 360 (1957)) have shown that in slow receptor cells in lobster, even during moderate stretch, the site of origin of conducted impulses is in the initial axonal region. From there the impulses propagate centrally along the axon and also back into the soma-dendrite system. Potential changes were recorded with NaCl filled micropipettes (about 0.5 μ opening) touching the cell surface simultaneously at two points. This method is more selective for localizing activity than intracellular leads which record changes from a relatively large area. The second alternative, therefore, seems to be the correct one.

fast adapting neuron has shorter dendrites and a larger threshold generator
potential of around 20 mV. Its threshold, however, as measured by partial
antidromic impulse block at the soma-axon junction was also near 20–25 mV,
indicating that in this cell the site of impulse initiation is in or near the cell
body. As stretch is progressively increased in both neuron types, the site of
origin of the impulses clearly occurs out in the axon. During some phases
of strong stretch, impulses are seen which 'grow up' in the axon to their
normal size as they conduct away from the cell body region. At the same
time, andidromic impulses diminish in size as they approach the cell and
with sufficiently strong stretch-depolarization all orthodromic or antidromic
conduction ceases near the soma-axon boundary region (Fig. 9, [19]). Another instance of conducted impulses reaching their full size somewhere in
the axon occurs during grouped high frequency activity. Intracellular leads in
the cell body may record a minute 'local' potential only, while electrodes on
the axon at a distance show the usual large impulses. The role of dendrites
in causing these impulses is clear but the mechanism is hypothetical (see
Fig. 16 [20]).

The present views of impulse initiation may be summarized as follows:
Stretch deformation sets up the generator potential in the peripheral portion
of dendrites. By electrotonic spread other cell regions are excited and all-or-
none conduction generally starts more centrally in the larger portion of dendrites, in the cell body or in the initial axon stretch. The generator potential
persists for the duration of the stretch, its magnitude depending on the
amount of stretch deformation. This in turn controls the frequency of
sensory discharge. The actual site of origin of propagated impulses has been
shown to fluctuate according to intensity of depolarization. While the distal
dendrite portions are clearly specialized for graded activity, the proximal parts
of the dendrites, the cell body and the axon carry fully conducted impulses.

Configuration of Cells and the Role of the Cell Body in Conduction

Several years ago it was thought that the cell body always constituted some
sort of peripheral integrating system for activity in the dendrites which
converge on it [18]. The cell body or the nearby axon region would then be
the sole site for the initiation of conducted impulses. Although this seems to
be true for some stretch receptors and for those motoneurons which have
been studied, such a rigid assumption should not be accepted for the nervous
system as a whole in both vertebrate and invertebrate systems. The diversity
of dendrite configuration has been found to be very great. Fig. 3 is reproduced
from the study of Florey and Florey [23] in crayfish and similar observations

were made by Alexandrowicz [2]. In many instances a cell body, conventionally presented as a near-spherical structure containing the nucleus, actually does not exist. In some cells which we have observed, the axon approaching the receptor muscle simply becomes thicker and divisions of differing diameters leave this thickened extended portion of the neuron, subsequently dividing into multiple further branches of varying length. The

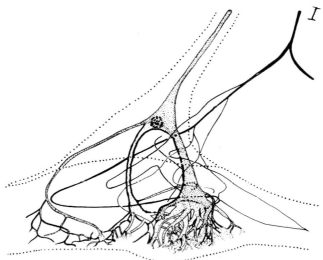

Fig. 3.—Drawing of silver stained fast adapting receptor cell in crayfish by Florey and Florey [23]. Inhibitory nerve (*1*). The cell configurations may vary a great deal.

position of the nucleus in such an elongated "cell body" may be variable. It may be seen in a part of the cell which otherwise would perhaps be identified as a large dendrite. Of special interest for physiological studies may be the occasional long dendrites which enter the neuron somewhat centrally of the cell body in relative isolation in or beyond the axon-hillock region. Cutting such a dendrite in its periphery has been seen to set up afferent discharges from the cell. These comments, referring to cell shapes unlike the prevalent model receptor cells, are made in order to avoid premature rigid standardization which later may become linked with physiological properties. No attempt has so far been made to correlate a particular soma-dendrite configuration with physiological discharge behavior. It is surprising on the whole that so much structural diversity should give the relatively uniform physiological patterns which have been seen. This, presumably, merely reflects the insensitivity of our intracellular recording method in differentiating local details of activity within individual cells.[1]

In the receptor cells of crayfish evidence shows that the cell body does

---

[1] See Case, Edwards, Gesteland and Ottoson (*Biol. Bull.* **113**, 360 (1957)).

carry all-or-none impulses. Apparently in the present preparation that part
of the cell which contains the nucleus and the tissue surrounding it is
essential for the long range integrity and survival of the neuron, but does not
necessarily determine or greatly influence the mode of conduction in that
region. Specific geometrical configuration, however, should have effects, as
yet undetermined, on conditions of current spread and distribution, and
therefore on impulse initiation and conduction. If the threshold in the cell
body is higher than in the axon, it may give rise to 'steps' or delays in the
orthodromic or antidromic action potential and will influence the site of
impulse initiation. Direct threshold measurements by passing current across
the cell membrane have not yet been made.

The question may be raised how a regular rhythmic discharge series comes
about if, for instance, impulses should arise in several of the dendrites or in
some of the distinct (see Fig. 3) dendritic centers or subcenters. Presumably
the problem is similar to that existing in other systems containing neural
arborizations such as in the sensory axon arising in the muscle spindle,
where multiple filaments converge finally into a single axon. Once a properly
conducted impulse arises in one portion of the dendrite system it will spread
over the whole cell and into the other dendrites, unless they carry an impulse
of their own at that time. In any event, only one impulse can leave through
the axon since any independently arising impulses in the larger dendrite
portions will be extinguished by 'collison'. After the first discharge, the
subsequent impulse will arise from the dendrite which has the quickest
recovery. Thus, if one dendrite with its own terminal subdivisions is excited
more than the others, due to a peculiar distribution of forces set up by stretch,
it should become the pacemaker for the cell. The pacemaker may shift to
another portion of the system as the excitatory influence is altered. All these
questions have to be studied in each cell system because variations are quite
likely to occur, especially since the anatomical configuration of cells shows
such a diversity. The pacemaker region in the sinus of the frog heart is electrically similar to that portion of the dendrites where the generator potential
arises (Fig. 11). A shift in the pacemaker site and of the pacemaker potential
maximum was observed occasionally by Hutter and Trautwein [33] in the
frog following inhibition.

Transferring of conclusions regarding the details of the excitation processes
in sensory cells to other cells, particularly to the mammalian central nervous
system must be done with caution. Some of the analogies, however, pointed
out by Bishop [7] and reported by Purpura and Grundfest [42] make broad
generalizations tempting.

Processes of Inhibition

The analysis of the mechanisms underlying inhibitory action at the cellular level has largely been made possible by the use of intracellular electrodes. So far the neuromuscular junction of crustacea has been studied by Fatt and Katz [21], the spinal motoneurone by Eccles and coworkers (recently reviewed [16]) and heart inhibition by Burgen and Terroux [9]; Hutter and Trautwein [33]; Harris and Hutter [30]. The single cell inhibitory synapse in lobster and crayfish has also been a suitable preparation during the past few years [36]. The main progress in this field has been towards an understanding of ionic movements during inhibitory activity. The controlling influences behind the ionic fluxes, however, are not known. The current investigation of the effect of substances which initiate inhibitory action, i.e. tend to repolarize (or hyperpolarize) is another analytical tool. Further, we now know that the inhibitory transmitter can modulate activity not only at synapses, thus acting at the place of initiation of impulses, but it can also inhibit conduction of propagating impulses (see below).

Effect of Inhibition at Different States of Cell Activity

The drawing in Fig. 4 illustrates one of the simplest methods of stimulating the inhibitory axon to a sensory nerve cell through an axon reflex. If a cell is discharging, due to maintained stretch, it can be promptly stopped by inhibitory impulses. This also is illustrated in Fig. 4 where stimuli at 34/sec

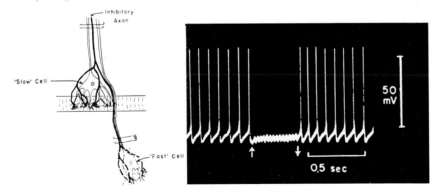

Fig. 4 (*left*).—Schema for stimulating the inhibitory (*I*) axon to the slowly adapting cell in the stretch receptor organ of the eighth thoracic segment of crayfish. The *I* fiber (black solid line) branches and innervates both receptor cells. The *I* impulse spreads by "axon reflex" into the slow cell and its appearance is correlated with inhibition of afferent discharges. (*Right*) Intracellular recording from a slowly adapting receptor cell at 24°C. The regular train of afferent discharges (11/sec) set up by maintained stretch is interrupted by stimulation of the *I* axon, between arrows, at 34/sec. Small deflections are inhibitory potentials [36].

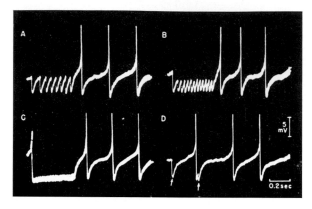

Fig. 5.—Intracellular records from a 'slow' cell in the second abdominal segment (24 °C). Recording at high amplification, only lower portions of orthodromic impulses are seen. A and B. Maintained afferent impulses are inhibited by I stimulation at 21 and 34/sec. Each I impulse causes a rapid transient repolarization of the prepotential (generator potential). C, I stimuli at 150/sec. cause a maintained repolarization. After cessation of stimulation, a prepotential redevelops at an accelerated rate and leads to prompt resumption of discharges. D, two I impulses (arrows). I_1 impulse arrives when the prepotential is large and it causes a large repolarization potential, while I_2, arriving as the prepotential starts to develop, causes a small change. All I potentials reach similar levels [36].

(between arrows) suppress the orthodromic impulses while stretch is maintained. The recordings are made with intracellular leads. Details of the inhibitory action can be seen at higher amplification with different frequencies of stimulation. Each inhibitory [I] impulse in Fig. 5 A at 21/sec has a distinct effect. It causes a transient repolarization towards the resting potential level. If stimuli are much more frequent, 150/sec as in Fig. 4 C, the potential can be virtually held at a fixed level. At this frequency, the inhibitory repolarizing actions of impulses follow each other so rapidly that there is little time for individual potentials to return to their starting levels. It is this 'holding' or 'clamping' action, although produced by transient discrete inhibitory processes, which is behind effective inhibition. The cell membrane is prevented from reaching the firing level and cannot go through the cycle of impulse generation and conduction. From Fig. 5 A and B it can be seen that if I impulses arrive when the membrane potential is depolarized (when the generator potential is near the firing level), their repolarizing action will be relatively great. Accordingly in Fig. 4 D two identical I impulses (arrows) cause quite different effects. The first one repolarizes the membrane, which was near the firing level, by about 4 mV, while the second one has little effect because the cell membrane is nearer to its 'resting' level immediately following an orthodromic discharge (see below Fig. 12).

Experiments as those in Fig. 5 when *I* stimuli were given during the afferent action potential have also shown that in receptor cells inhibitory action does not interfere appreciably with an impulse once it has been set up (see, however, Fig. 7). It acts on the graded generator potential, preventing it from reaching the threshold for discharging the cell. This is in agreement with the finding that the generator action set up by stretch-deformation is located in the dendrites, which also is the area where the synaptic inhibitory junctions are located [23].

Inhibitory Equilibrium Level

At present it seems reasonable to view the process of inhibitory action in the following way: The inhibitory nerve impulse produces a transmitter which initiates in the postsynaptic cell membrane a specific reaction. As a rule the process in the postsynaptic region carries the cell towards its resting potential, i.e. toward the membrane potential which is found when the cell is fully relaxed. The repolarization level which is achieved during inhibition, however, need not be identical with the full resting potential. An example is shown in Fig. 6. An impaled receptor cell was stimulated by periodic bursts of *I* impulses during relaxation and during varying degrees of stretch. During a train of six stimuli at 30/sec, each *I* impulse caused a *de*polarization of about 4 mV (first two arrows) while the cell was almost fully relaxed. As stretch was applied (third arrow), the resting potential was reduced by about 20 mV until a train of conducted impulses was set up. After the third afferent impulse, this activity was halted by another series of inhibitory impulses. Instead of a depolarization as before, each impulse *re*polarized (hyperpolarized) the cell by about 9 mV. In Fig. 6*B*, under somewhat greater stretch, the repolarizations of individual inhibitory actions are 12 mV. In Fig. 6*C* the cell was relaxed again and the inhibitory *de*polarization returned once more (last two arrows). It should be noted that the inhibitory repolarization, as well as the depolarization, carried the cell to a potential of about 6 mV above the resting potential, i.e. the full resting potential reduced by 6 mV. At this membrane potential the *I* impulses caused little or no effects and above or below this level they reversed the direction of their electrogenic action. *This reversal point of inhibitory potentials has been called the equilibrium level of the inhibitory process.* A perhaps clearer example is presented later in Fig. 12. There the resting potential of a 'fast' cell was reduced by approximately 16 mV without setting up impulses. An *I* impulse repolarized the cell by about 10 mV (Fig. 12, -58 mV). At the smaller initial depolarization levels of 63, 65 and 67 mV, the same inhibitory impulses repolarized by 5,3 and 1.5

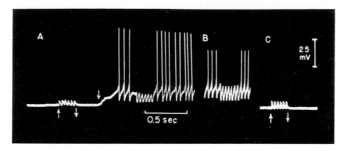

Fig. 6.—Inhibitory effects at different membrane potentials. Fast cell from third abdominal segment, intracellular records. *A*, receptor almost completely relaxed, six *I* impulses at 30/sec cause depolarization potentials (arrows). At third arrow stretch causes about 20 mV depolarization and three discharges, followed by *I* train setting up repolarization potentials. Further continued increasing stretch results in afferent impulses which gradually decline in height. At gap 10 sec. of record cut out. In *B*, same *I* train inhibits, the repolarization potentials reaching 12 mv. *C*, during complete relaxation of cell, 6.5 mv. *I* depolarization peaks are seen [36].

mV. When the cell was brought within about 6 mV of its unstretched membrane potential (70 mV), the inhibitory potentials were beginning to be reversed. Thus, the equilibrium level of the inhibitory process is just below 70 mV in this cell. By stimulating at higher frequencies, no greater potential change can be achieved than the ceiling set by the equilibrium level. The *I* equilibrium levels vary in different cells and in fact it is thought that they are nearer to the resting potential in most fresh preparations.

An interesting aspect of the inhibitory action in relation to cell excitation is that the sign of the electrical potential change is not the primary factor (later). The inhibitory process tends to keep the membrane at the equilibrium level and will prevent deviations in either direction. On the whole the greater the deviation from the equilibrium level (e.g. 6 mV in Fig. 6) the greater the inhibitory potential. Thus, although an inhibitory impulse may depolarize a cell this will not lead to excitation but to inhibition as long as the *I* equilibrium level remains below the firing level (e.g. Fig. 6 or 8 *A*).

Ionic Mechanisms during Inhibition

The first direct evidence of a change in membrane properties during inhibition was obtained by Fatt and Katz [22] in crustacean muscle fibers. The acceleration of the decay in the e.p.p.'s during inhibition was attributed to a decrease in membrane resistance. In the crustacean receptor cell a similar mechanism suggests itself. The evidence is derived from interaction experiments between *I* impulses and antidromic impulses. In some experiments antidromic impulses were decreased in size by several mV if they

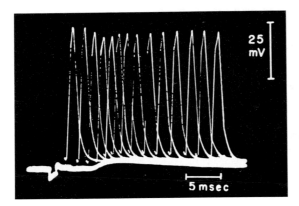

Fig. 7.—Interaction between *I* potentials and antidromic impulses. Slow cell, intracellular record-ing. Sweeps recurring at 10/sec. are superimposed. *I* impulses set up inhibitory depolarization. Antidromic impulses placed at different times during *I* potential are reduced. Impulse peaks reduced maximally (2 mV) during initial phase of *I* potential. Resting potential 70 mv. Control size of antidromic potentials is given by the two impulses at the beginning of sweep before *I* potential rise [36].

propagated into the cell body during the inhibitory potential. The effect was greatest during the rising phase and the peak of inhibitory action de-clined over 15 msec or more. This is seen in Fig. 7 where the decrease in impulse peaks occurs during the *entire* time course of the inhibitory potential. A more striking demonstration of a similar event is given in Fig. 8. In this cell antidromic invasion of the cell body was blocked or incomplete. The antidromic potentials were further decreased if they arrived during inhibitory stimulation or a short period (10–20 msec) afterward. It is significant that the effects were independent of the electrical signs of the inhibitory potentials which depolarized in Fig. 8 *A, b, c* repolarized in Fig. 8 *C, b, c* and caused little change in potential in Fig. 8 *B, b, c.* All of them, however, reduced further the already incomplete antidromic invasion of the cell body. The extent of the effect, especially its duration which outlasted the inhibitory potentials, depended on the frequency of the preceding stimulation. These results are explained if one assumes that inhibition decreases the membrane resistance in the dendrites. Thereby much of the current which was caused to flow by the blocked impulses and which was divided between cell body and dendrites, will be diverted through the newly created low resistance dendritic path. Thus the depolarizing action of the antidromic impulses, as measured in the cell body, will be diminished (for details the original paper, Kuffler and Eyzaguirre [36] should be consulted). An essentially similar phenomenon has been seen by Coombs, Eccles and Fatt [14] in spinal moto-

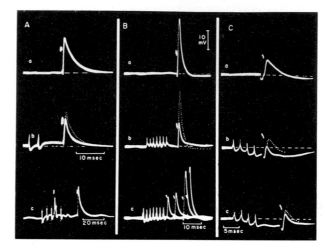

Fig. 8.—Effect of inhibition on blocked antidromic (A) impulses. Fast cell, second abdominal segment, 21°C. Resting potential 70 mv (unstretched). Intracellular electrodes, filled with 0.6 M K₂SO₄. Aa, A impulse alone (17 mv), blocked at the axon-soma boundary region. Ab, two I impulses set up depolarization in relaxed cell and subsequent A is reduced and its time course accelerated. Dotted line indicates control. Ac, two A impulses. A_1 during inhibitory train more reduced than A_2 after cessation of I stimulation (note slower sweep). Ba and Bb, Preparation lightly stretched. A impulse again greatly reduced by preceding train of seven I impulses at 500/sec. No appreciable potential change was set up by I train alone. Bc, A impulses placed at different times after I train, reveal time course of I effect. Ca and Cb, Cell stretched, I impulses repolarize (b) and again reduce A. Cc, A moved later, is less affected. Voltage calibration same for all records. Large dots preceding A's are artefacts [36].

neurons. More direct evidence for an increased conductance during inhibition, but in the presence of acetylcholine in a different tissue, was recently obtained in strips of auricles of the frog by Trautwein, Kuffler and Edwards [44]. The time constants and space constants of the fibers were reduced with applied concentrations of about 10^{-5} M/L ACh. An increased K⁺ flux under such conditions has since been obtained by Harris and Hutter [30] and the increased conductance was actually measured with intracellular leads by Trautwein and Dudel. Pflügers Archiv ges. Physiol. (1958) (in press).

Increased conductance during inhibition indicates increased ionic movement. At present only few of the known ions can be held responsible for the effects. In the first place, the ionic movement which leads to inhibition must be quite selective, i.e. specific. An indiscriminate breakdown of barriers to the passage of all ions as occurs during the transmitter action at the neuromuscular junction (for a detailed discussion see del Castillo and Katz [12]) leads to near-complete depolarization. Selective Na⁺ movement, as during the nerve impulse, makes the cell interior positive relative to the outside [32].

The equilibrium potential for Cl^- and K^+ ions, however, is near the resting potential level and increased mobility of these ions across the membrane could explain the observed repolarization or hyperpolarization. Such considerations presumably led Fatt and Katz [22] to suggest a specific Cl^- and/or K^+ conductance increase during the inhibitory synaptic action in crustacea. The hypothesis was tested and well supported in experiments on spinal cord motoneurons by the injection of various ions [14]. Parallel with an increased intracellular Cl^- concentration the inhibitory hyperpolarization was first reduced and then turned into a depolarization. By increasing the internal Cl^- concentration and changing the inside-outside ratio, the Cl^- equilibrium potential was shifted nearer to the zero level. As a consequence the membrane potential during inhibition either decreased or reversed in sign, depending on the direction of the net Cl^- movement. If the Cl^- equilibrium went beyond the firing level, inhibitory stimuli led to excitation. A depletion of intracellular K^+ in motoneurons acted in the same manner, although the evidence was more circumstantial. Much other evidence, however, assigns a role to K^+ during inhibition (see later).

In the receptor cell the same problem was approached by changing the extracellular ionic environment. If K^+ is removed from the solution the resting potential of the cell increases and at the same time the *I* potential hyperpolarization becomes greater (Edwards, Hagiwara and Kuffler, unpublished). At near zero outside K^+ the resting potential is farther removed from the K^+ equilibrium potential than in normal saline [32]. The increase in *I* potential therefore is likely to be due to an increased K^+ conductance. Attempts to replace Cl^- in the extracellular fluid by anions like NO_3 proved inconclusive because the effects were multiple, such as an increase of the resting potential coupled with complex changes in the *I* potential.

According to present views, therefore, the inhibitory transmitter opens the 'channels' for K^+ and presumably Cl^- movements. The equilibrium level for the inhibitory process may be expected to be in between the equilibrium potential of K^+ and Cl^- (see also Discussion).

Activation of an Inhibitory Mechanism by Gamma Aminobutyric Acid

The present study of gamma aminobutyric acid (GAB) [17] was started after a brief preliminary report by Hayashi and Nagai [31] appeared describing the effectiveness of this compound in inhibiting cortical activity in mammals. Since then Bazemore, Elliott and Florey [5] have found GAB to be a potent component of Florey's 'inhibitory factor' [24]. It presumably plays a role in the glutamic acid metabolism of the mammalian brain [6, 43] from

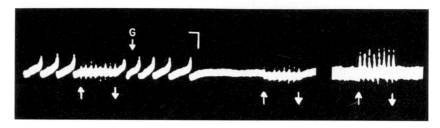

Fig. 9.—Effect of Gamma aminobutyric acid (GAB) on membrane potential and on I potentials. Discharges of slowly adapting cell inhibited by I stimuli at 20/sec (first two arrows). Note, only lower portions of action potentials seen. At G drop of 10^{-5} M/L GAB added to solution surrounding the cell. Discharge is inhibited and the membrane potential is held somewhat below the firing level. I stimuli (4th and 5th arrow) set up slight repolarization. During gap the GAB concentration was increased to 10^{-4} M/L. I stimulation repeated (last two arrows), now does not cause appreciable potential shift. Amplification doubled in the last record; the sharp deflections are artefacts. Calibration 0.2 mV and 0.1 sec. (for details see Kuffler and Edwards, $J.$ $Neurophysiol.$ (1958) in press.)

which it can be extracted. It is also a constituent of crustacean nervous tissue (unpublished).

The main point of interest for the present discussion is the specific action of GAB in stopping discharges of the sensory cell by a mechanism which in many essential aspects resembles neural inhibition. Rather than inhibiting by depolarizing (e.g. excess K^+) it can also hyperpolarize and move the depolarized membrane toward its resting state. In concentrations used at present (10^{-4} to 10^{-5} M/L) its effect is largely, but not exclusively, confined to the dendrites where the inhibitory synapses are located and where stretch-deformation acts.

In these experiments potentials were recorded near the cell body with a D.C. amplifier using extracellular electrodes. They can be compared with those obtained with intracellular leads. In Fig. 9 a 'slow' cell discharges under moderate stretch. Only the lower portions of the action potentials are seen, showing the slowly rising generator potential and the afterpositivity (undershoot). A train of I impulses (first two arrows) at 20/sec inhibits, repolarizing the membrane to the afterpositivity level. At the third arrow a drop of GAB (G) 10^{-5} M/L is added to the fluid. As this agent diffuses to the cell, the discharge is slowed and then stopped while the resting potential is held below the firing level of the cell. This level was a little above that reached by the inhibitory process during the preceding I stimulation. A renewed train of I impulses (4th and 5th arrows) still causes a small further repolarization. After addition of a drop of 10^{-4} M/L GAB (gap in Fig. 9), I stimuli (last two arrows) did not set up any detectable potential. (Note increased am-

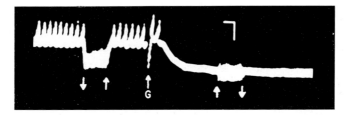

Fig. 10.—Effect of neural and GAB inhibition in K⁺ free solution. Afferent discharges in slowly adapting cell are inhibited by *I* stimuli at 40/sec (first two arrows). The *I* hyperpolarization is much greater than in solution containing K⁺ (see Fig. 9). At third arrow (G) GAB (10^{-5} (*M*/L) added. Artefact is due to drop reaching solution. Within 0.1 sec inhibitory hyperpolarization starts, abruptly stopping discharges. *I* impulses repeated during GAB action, have small hyperpolarizing effect only. Calibration 0.1 mV and 0.1 sec (Kuffler and Edwards, unpublished).

plification in strip after the gap; deflections are artefacts). It is assumed that with the higher GAB concentration both the neural inhibitory process and the artificially applied inhibitor produced the same equilibrium level and therefore no additional effect occurred. After varying periods discharges were resumed again, apparently due to inactivation of GAB in the thin film of fluid surrounding the cell. The recovery from inhibition was not due to adaptation because during continued replacement of the bathing fluid with fluid containing the same concentration of GAB, the inhibition persisted.

The parallel action of neural and GAB inhibition also appears from the experiments done in the absence of K⁺ in the saline surrounding the cell. As soon as K⁺ free solution is applied to the cell, the resting potential rises. This is to be expected if the resting potential is principally determined by the K⁺ distribution. Inhibitory impulses (at 40/sec) now cause a greatly augmented hyperpolarization as compared with their action in normal ringer (first 2 arrows, Fig. 10). Application of 10^{-5} *M*/L GAB in K⁺ free saline at third arrow (G) suppresses the afferent discharges within 0.1 sec and in addition hyperpolarizes the membrane to a similar level as the preceding *I* impulses. Renewed *I* axon stimulation has a small added effect only (last two arrows).

It is tempting to conclude on the basis of analogous actions that the normal inhibitory transmitter and GAB exert effects by activating a similar mechanism. This is also supported by the finding that GAB shortens the time course of the inhibitory potential, probably by increasing the membrane conductance. Further, it reduces or abolishes the afterpositivity (undershoot) of antidromic impulses in slightly stretched cells, just as inhibitory impulses do [36]. GAB acts by driving the cell potential below the firing level thereby preventing excitation. Its advantage in these studies is that its action can be graded, according to concentration, while the transmitter effect of individual impulses cannot be controlled. It is thought that in low effective concentrations the principal action of GAB consists in increasing the conductance of the dendrite membrane to specific ions. At present there is no evidence which establishes GAB as a physiologically occurring transmitter substance. A study of related compounds is in progress.[1]

Inhibition of Conducted Impulses

Inhibition of conducted activity, although not physiologically established in the central nervous system, suggests itself from the existence of synapses on axons. Axo-axonic synapses which occur in medullated portions of axons, as pointed out by Bodian [8], may well be inhibitory. That physiological inhibition of conducted impulses can occur is strongly indicated by Hutter and Trautwein's [33] findings in sinus fibers of the frog heart. Their recordings, however, were mainly done in muscle fibers which possess special properties and a specific generator (pacemaker) system for the setting up of impulses.

A simple example of neural inhibition of conducted activity was seen by Trautwein and Kuffler (unpublished) in the frog's auricle. Frog auricles were cut open and continued to beat, excitation originating at the sinus pacemaker region. A branch of the vagus, innervating a circumscribed area, was cut under transmitted illumination and the peripheral stump was stimulated by trains at different frequencies. The area innervated by the branch could be made to relax completely while the rest of the heart beat at its regular rhythm. Apparently the muscle impulses were blocked as they conducted into the area of vagal stimulation (the nerve branches actually also contained a sympathetic component). With intracellular electrodes one could confirm that impulses did not propagate into the non-contracting region. The heart action potentials reaching the area normally showed the typical plateau which during initial vagal excitation disappeared; this was followed by diminution and eventual total suppression of conducted muscle impulses. No significant resting membrane potential change below the diastolic level was registered in those trials.

This type of inhibition is almost certainly basically similar to the synaptic

[1] Recent preliminary studies by Eliot, Kaji, Seeman, Ubell, Kuffler and Burgen (*Biol. Bull.* **113**, 344 (1957)) have shown that some fractions of nerve tissue extracts which are not GAB can also cause inhibition similar to that described here. Details relating to GAB mechanisms are found in Kuffler and Edwards (*J. Neurophysiol.* (in press)).

processes which have been discussed. The question still remains whether the extent of the known conductance changes can reasonably account for the phenomena.

Inhibition by Depolarization

If the membrane potential of the cell body is reduced by about 35 mV through stretch on dendrites, conducted responses can neither leave nor enter the cell [19]. Block is preceded by very high frequency discharges. This observation resembles the well known cathodal depression of nerve and the underlying mechanism is likely to be different from the specific synaptic inhibition discussed above. The phenomenon of 'overstretch' in the undissected preparation, left normally attached in the tail, was first noted by Wiersma, Furshpan and Florey [45]. In cerebellar cells Granit and Phillips [27] also found a cessation of activity, apparently due to excessive depolarization. The possibility is therefore open that in the nervous system there exists a physiological mechanism by which a cell cuts itself off, or is inhibited, through very intense stimulation (cf. also Buser and Rougeul [11]).

GENERAL DISCUSSION

Comparative Aspects

Studies of the stretch receptor cells have pointed to many broad analogies with other structures. They provide models which may be of use in the study of nervous organization elsewhere. For instance, they have focussed attention on some special properties of certain portions of the cell. Particularly the problem of dendrites has become available to almost direct scrutiny at this relatively simple cellular level. Dendrites show a high degree of specialization in their ability to carry graded activity. They possess a mechanism by which the neuron's threshold can be adjusted to various levels. They present a system which can translate distinct phasic events, such as the relatively brief synaptic potentials set up by neuronal bombardment converging from many sources, into prolonged maintained states in one cell. While in the axon there is little physiological scope for anything but the staccato of all-or-none impulses, in the dendritic system there is added a great measure of flexibility. The dendritic extension of a cell provides an example of 'integration' on a small scale, largely due to the 'plastic' property within the arborization. At the dendritic end of cells then, the input is converted into graded responses. The magnitude and time course of an impressed stimulus, as reflected in the generator potential, determines in the cell body-axon region the frequency of impulses which arise in the neuron. These standard coins of information exchange, serving merely as rapid links over varying distances, are transmitted unaltered to the other end of the neuron. There graded responses are produced once more in the next cell through a transformation into synaptic potentials which then may start a new series of events. Thus dendrites and synapses can carry out activity which has long been known to be a characteristic of the central nervous system with its property of summating excitatory and inhibitory states of varying duration.

As already pointed out, the recent work of Bishop and coworkers [7] indicates transitional types of activity in the cortical dendrites. Purpura and Grundfest [42] regard the dendrites (or presumably a large portion of individual dendrites) as 'electrically' inexcitable. This expression does not seem to indicate, as may be inferred, that the structures do not react at all, or cannot change their potentials, if electric current is passed through them. The term is currently applied to many aspects of cell behavior which differ markedly from the all-or-none self-regenerating impulses of axons. It seems perhaps more suitable for only that type of tissue which normally is activated by chemical transmitters, namely certain subsynaptic tissues.[1] It appears from the studies of Fatt and Katz [21] that the endplate is unable to respond with the self-regenerating axon-type impulse if stimulated through its nerve. The same applies to the slow muscle fibers which are densely invested with junctions and do not give conducted impulses [39], not even when directly stimulated [10]. Also the junctional material in the electric organ of Torpedo has somewhat similar properties [1, 29]. It is possible that the graded response mechanism in dendrites is at least partly due to dense synaptic covering. However, the median receptor of the seventh segment in the lobster which is apparently devoid of synapses [3] also shows similar graded responses. By blocking synaptic activity Purpura and Grundfest [42] abolish

---

[1] It is interesting that 'electrical' synaptic transmission, i.e. excitation of the postsynaptic membrane by the action current of the presynaptic impulse, has been widely accepted for decades without any good specific experimental evidence. Recently the chemical nature of transmission, i.e. release of a transmitter substance by presynaptic impulses, has obtained further convincing support at the neuromuscular junction. It has been demonstrated that action currents do not spread effectively across the nerve-muscle junction (for a review see del Castillo and Katz [12]). In addition, inhibitory events as described in this paper could hardly be explained by action current spread. As a consequence chemical transmission is now almost generally accepted. It is at this stage that the first convincing experiments for 'electrical' transmission have been made by Furshpan and Potter [25a] in a synapse of the crayfish cord. This one-way synapse shows remarkable properties of rectification, allowing depolarizing currents generated by a presynaptic impulse to spread to the postjunctional region. Depolarizing currents of an antidromic impulse in the post-fiber spread to the pre-fiber in negligible amounts only. Synaptic delays are practically absent. In view of such findings generalizations about 'electrically inexcitable' tissues are not justified.

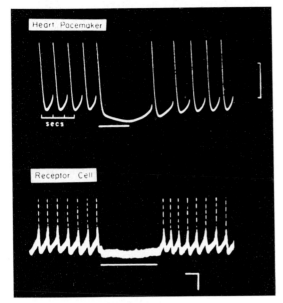

Fig. 11.

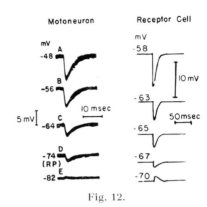

Fig. 12.

Fig. 11.—Intracellular records from a heart pacemaker fiber in the sinus venosus of the frog [33] and from a receptor cell. Inhibitory stimuli (20/sec in heart and 100/sec in receptor cell), marked by white line, suppress the generator potentials in both tissues, thus preventing conducted impulses from arising. Spike peaks not seen at this high amplification; in lower photograph part of impulse rising phase drawn in (dotted). Upper calibration 20 mV, lower 10 mV and 0.1 sec. Note different time scales.

Fig. 12.—Inhibitory potentials at different membrane levels recorded with intracellular leads. *Left*, Motoneuron membrane potential preset to indicated values by passing a steady background current through one barrel of a double microelectrode. Note reversal of *I* potential around 80 mV (after Coombs, Eccles and Fatt [14]). *Right*, Tracings of similar records from receptor cell, the membrane potential preset by different degrees of stretch. Note reversal around 70 mV [36].

or reduce the surface negative potentials in cortical dendrites while leaving the underlying cell body and axon activity. These dendrites therefore do not seem to carry the usual all-or-none impulses. This approach to central nervous system analysis, going beyond axon physiology, is still in its early stages. It is most promising as a tool for the understanding of the complex potentials at present obtained by various methods of recording.

There is the question of the possible similarity of the physiological processes during inhibition in different species. A comparison of some known events in crustacean neuromuscular junctions, in receptor cells, heart muscle of vertebrates and the mammalian motoneuron, makes one confident that similar basic mechanisms are involved. For instance, in all these tissues one sees the phenomena of hyperpolarization or repolarization. More significantly perhaps, this seems to be brought about by ionic fluxes of similar nature. In Fig. 11 a comparison between vagal inhibition at the pacemaker region of the sinus venosus in the frog heart [33] and in a receptor cell is made. The heart's pacemaker cells produce a generator potential (pacemaker potential), just as the receptor cells do, leading to conducted impulses (impulse peaks off screen in both recordings). It is at the generator level in both tissues that inhibition exerts its primary action in controlling the discharge rate. In Fig. 12 the relationship between membrane potential and inhibitory potential is compared in motoneurons and the receptor cells. A reversal of potential occurs in both instances indicating the existence of an equilibrium level near the resting potential of the cells. It should be noted that in the motoneuron the membrane potential was altered by passing current through the cell, while in the receptor neuron the same was brought about by using the physiological mechanism. It is interesting that the compensatory mechanism driving the membrane toward the I equilibrium level is stronger in the receptor cell than in the motoneuron. This presumably indicates conductance changes of greater magnitude in the sensory receptor. An inhibitory equilibrium level at the neuromuscular junction of crustacea during large impressed membrane potential changes has also been shown by Fatt and Katz [22]. The same authors [21] have demonstrated an equilibrium level for the excitatory transmitter process in frog endplates. In contrast to inhibition, the excitatory transmitter brings the membrane towards zero potential (full depolarization), apparently by increasing the permeability to all ions.

Ionic Movement and Other Aspects

If one assumes that the inhibitory transmitter combines with specific spots in the postsynaptic membrane and permits certain ions such as K^+ and Cl^- to move but not others, the conductance changes should be measured in order to find out how far, by themselves, they could account for the observed phenomena. No quantitative measurements are available at present. Specific increase in K^+ and Cl^- flow in an active cell could restore the membrane potential to below the neuron's firing level, as actually observed. So long as the inhibitory equilibrium is below that level, but not necessarily at the resting potential, the cell cannot discharge. Since I impulses can inhibit whether they produce depolarization, hyperpolarization or no potential change, it follows that *the electrically recorded membrane change is not the primary significant factor in inhibition.* The conductance change itself can occur even in the absence of appreciable I potentials (Fig. 8 B, b, c) and as implied elsewhere it can be readily understood how a greatly reduced space constant can prevent spread of current which is essential for excitation and conduction.

It is not certain whether an *I* equilibrium level which is depolarized compared to the resting potential of a completely relaxed cell is quite normal. Depolarizing *I* potentials have been seen not only during intracellular recordings when they can be attributed to Cl⁻ leakage into the cells, but also with extracellular electrodes. In the latter case, however, they are relatively rare, especially when the preparation appears fresh. However, during progressive experimentation over several hours the *I* level has been seen to shift towards greater depolarization without impairing the cell's survival or the effectiveness of inhibition. It is possible that a small increased Na^+ conductance also occurs in such instances. In any event, the inhibitory equilibrium can change independently of other parameters. It is generally different from the impulse restitution process. The positive afterpotential (undershoot), for instance, recorded in the cell body may have a different equilibrium level; it may be either higher or lower than the inhibitory level. It should also be pointed out that the inhibitory action of individual *I* impulses need not reach the *I* equilibrium level. In some preparations, the *I* impulses sum and a relatively high frequency is needed to reach the ceiling effect. Further, the *I* effect also depends on the intensity of the stretch deformation (excitation). The *I* mechanism controls the membrane potential more effectively if it has to counteract a small stretch. The inhibitory process in receptor cells is similar to that of spinal cord motoneurons in these and other aspects [16]. From a comparative view it seems important that also the specific ionic conductance increases appear similar, and this can be extended to the heart. In the latter a K^+ conductance increase was already postulated by Burgen and Terroux [9] and more recently a greatly accelerated radioactive K^+ exchange (two to seven fold increase in rate constant) was actually demonstrated during ACh inhibition by Harris and Hutter [30]. A Cl⁻ ion conductance increase may occur in the receptor cell during inhibition, but specific evidence is lacking.

The duration of the inhibitory transmitter cannot readily be determined with accuracy. It is clear that there is an intensive phase lasting for several msec. which decays during the membrane restitution process when the *I* potential declines. The latter, however, need not be exponential suggesting a purely passive dissipation of an impressed charge. It has already been indicated that the increased conductance change may last for the entire duration of the *I* potential (Fig. 7). Further, it was shown that repetitive *I* excitation may be followed by a prolonged (over 100 msec.) phase of hyper-polarization (Fig. 8, [36]) and in some cells single I potentials lasted for 200 msec. or longer. Occasionally the potentials had a distinct brief and a slow component. How much such membrane changes represent an actual prolonged survival of the transmitter substance or a secondary process can not be determined.

In addition to ionic changes there exists evidence for another type of inhibitory mechanism. *Competitive inhibition* on the model of the curare-acetylcholine antagonism was suggested by Kuffler and Katz [38] for crusta-cean nerve-muscle junctions (these two compounds are not effective in these species). Fatt and Katz [22] have actually obtained supporting evidence for such a view since they believe that the great diminution of e.p.p.'s could not be attributed to conductance changes alone. In the crustacean receptor competitive inhibition is quite unlikely, unless one assumes that stretch-deformation liberates first a transmitter which then leads to depolarization. Similarly in the mammalian motoneuron with its distinct spatially separated synapses it is not likely that an I transmitter substance diffuses and thus blocks excitatory synapses. Rather, the interaction of excitatory and in-hibitory synapses is best explained by assuming that each tends to change the subsynaptic membrane in opposing directions, each setting up ionic current flow. The resulting potential change of the whole cell will determine the outcome. If the inhibitory (hyperpolarizing) currents can prevent a critical depolarization (about 10 mV) no cell discharge results. Also in the heart, competitive mechanisms are not likely to explain suppression of pacemaker or conducted activity since it seems that the accelerator and in-hibitor action activates different patches of the same cell.

SUMMARY

The crustacean stretch receptor 'organs', discovered by Alexandrowicz, are suitable for the study of numerous cell properties. This report focuses (i) on the properties of dendrites and their role in leading to cell excitation and (ii) on mechanisms of synaptic inhibition.

The sensory neuron of the stretch receptor has its cell body in the periphery and inserts dendrites into a fine muscle strand. In crayfish a single inhibitory axon forms synapses with the dendritic region. The following sequence of events leads to excitation: stretch deformation sets up in the dendritic terminals a generator potential which secondarily, by electrotonic spread, reduces the resting potential of the adjoining cell portions until the 'firing level' is reached, leading to conducted impulses. The site of origin of propagated impulses varies, depending on conditions of stretch and presumably on the configuration of cells.

The peripheral portions of the dendrites possess properties which set them apart from the rest of the cell. They are specialized for extensive graded activity and serve to adjust over a considerable range the membrane potential; thereby they can 'set' the threshold of the cell. Once the neuron discharges, the impulse frequency is determined by the intensity of dendritic depolarization. The generator mechanism in the dendrites is analogous to the pacemaker in other tissues. It is concluded that only the dendrite portions near the cell body carry all-or-none impulses, which cannot propagate to the distal regions of the dendrites. Analogies with cortical dendrites are made.

The synaptic inhibitory neuron acts by controlling the membrane potential in the dendrites where the generator is set up. Inhibitory processes hold the membrane potential below the cell's firing level, thereby stopping or preventing afferent discharges.

Following the arrival of an inhibitory impulse, the membrane resistance in the postsynaptic region is decreased. If the resting potential is initially reduced (depolarization), the inhibitory action will repolarize a cell. At the full resting potential, a small inhibitory depolarization may result. The reversal point of the inhibitory potential is called the equilibrium level of the inhibitory process. At that level, no significant membrane potential change is set up by inhibitory impulses, although the membrane resistance is reduced and the inhibitory process itself is fully active. Thus the electrical potential changes are secondary events. Due to the existence of the equilibrium level, the potentials set up by inhibitory impulses increase as the cell membrane is displaced in either direction from the inhibitory equilibrium.

Experiments in receptor cells indicate that the inhibitory transmitter increases specifically the movement of K^+ across the cell membrane leading to the observed potential changes whenever the membrane has been shifted from the equilibrium level of this ion (and perhaps of Cl^-). This mechanism is similar to that in motoneurons and in heart pacemaker or auricle cells.

Some effects caused by gamma aminobutyric acid (GAB) are discussed. GAB action resembles the effects produced by the normally occurring neural transmitter. It inhibits sensory discharges by preventing the dendritic generator potential from reaching the cell's firing level. If extracellular K^+ is reduced, both GAB and inhibitory impulses have an increased hyperpolarizing action. GAB, like the inhibitory transmitter seems to increase the membrane conductance to specific ions.

518   S. W. Kuffler

I wish to thank Dr. Charles Edwards with whom some of the unpublished experiments were performed.

ADDENDUM

Fig. X.—(A) Modified method for accurate cell penetration. Note, grounding of shield important for high voltage membrane work. (From Satoko, Susumu & Kazu; *Proc. Penetr. Soc.; Acta Wilmerica*, im-pressed.) (B) Neuron reaction following intracellular injection of supercritically charged anions. Postinhibitory rebound slightly increased. Note inadequate shielding of right patellar region. (From St. G. & Bishop, St. Louis, *Acta Psycho-Physica* 1984).

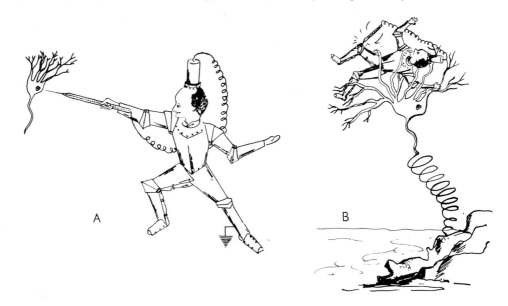

A   B

REFERENCES

1. Albe-Fessard, D., *Arch. Sci. Physiol.* **5**, 45 (1951).
2. Alexandrowicz, J. S., *Quart. J. Microscop. Sci.* **92**, 163 (1951).
3. —— *ibid.* **93**, 315 (1952).
4. Alvarez-Buylla, R. and Ramirez de Arellano, J., *Am. J. Physiol.* **172**, 237 (1953).
5. Bazemore, A., Elliott, K. A. C. and Florey, E., *Nature* **178**, 1052 (1956).
6. Bessman, S. P., Rossen, J. and Layne, E. C., *J. Biol. Chem.* **201**, 385 (1953).
7. Bishop, G. H., *Physiol. Rev.* **36**, 376 (1956).
8. Bodian, D., *Cold Spring Harbor Symposia Quant. Biol.* **17**, 1 (1952).
9. Burgen, A. S. V. and Terroux, K. G., *J. Physiol.* **120**, 449 (1953).
10. Burke, W. and Ginsborg, B. L., *J. Physiol.* **132**, 586 (1955).
11. Buser, P. and Rougeul, A., *J. Physiol. Paris*, **46**, 287 (1954).
12. Castillo, J. del and Katz, B., *Progress in Biophysics and Biophysical Chemistry* **6**, 121 (1956).
13. Clare, M. H. and Bishop, G. H., *EEG. Clin. Neurophysiol.* **7**, 85 (1955).
14. Coombs, J. S., Eccles, J. C. and Fatt, P., *J. Physiol.* **130**, 326 (1955).
15. —— *ibid.* **130**, 396 (1955).
16. Eccles, J. C., The Physiology of Nerve Cells. Baltimore, The Johns Hopkins Press, 1957.
17. Edwards, C. and Kuffler, S. W., *Federation Proc.* **16**, 145 (1957).

18. EYZAGUIRRE, C. and KUFFLER, S. W., *Biol. Bull.* **107**, 310 (1954).
19. —— *J. Gen. Physiol.* **39**, 87 (1955).
20. —— *ibid.* **39**, 121 (1955).
21. FATT, P. and KATZ, B., *J. Physiol.* **115**, 320 (1951).
22. —— *ibid.* **121**, 374 (1953).
23. FLOREY, E. and FLOREY, E., *J. Gen. Physiol.* **39**, 69 (1955).
24. FLOREY, E. and McLENNAN, H., *J. Physiol.* **129**, 384 (1955).
25. FUORTES, M. G. F., FRANK, K. and BECKER, M. C., *J. Gen. Physiol.* **40**, 735 (1957).
25a. FURSHPAN, E. and POTTER, D., *Nature* **180**, 342 (1957).
26. GRANIT, R., Receptors and Sensory Perception. New Haven, Yale University Press, 1955.
27. GRANIT, R. and PHILLIPS, C. G., *J. Physiol.* **133**, 520 (1956).
28. GRAY, J. A. B. and SATO, M., *J. Physiol.* **122**, 610 (1953).
29. GRUNDFEST, H., *Progress in Biophysics* **7**, 1 (1957).
30. HARRIS, E. J. and HUTTER, O. F., *J. Physiol.* **133**, 58 P (1956).
31. HAYASHI, T. and NAGAI, K., *XXth Internatl. Physiol. Congress*, p. 410 (1956).
32. HODGKIN, A. L., *Biol. Rev.* **26**, 339 (1951).
33. HUTTER, O. F. and TRAUTWEIN, W., *J. Gen. Physiol.* **39**, 715 (1956).
34. KATZ, B., *J. Physiol.* **111**, 261 (1950).
35. KUFFLER, S. W., *J. Neurophysiol.* **17**, 558 (1954).
36. KUFFLER, S. W. and EYZAGUIRRE, C., *J. Gen. Physiol.* **39**, 155 (1955).
37. KUFFLER, S. W., HUNT, C. C. and QUILLIAM, J. P., *J. Neurophysiol.* **14**, 29 (1951).
38. KUFFLER, S. W. and KATZ, B., *J. Neurophysiol.* **9**, 337 (1946).
39. KUFFLER, S. W. and VAUGHAN WILLIAMS, E. M. *J. Physiol.* **121**, 289 (1953).
40. LEKSELL, L., *Acta Physiol. Scand.* **10**, *Suppl. 31*, 84 (1945).
41. OTTOSON, D., *Acta Physiol. Scand.* **35**, 7 (1956).
42. PURPURA, D. P. and GRUNDFEST, H., *J. Neurophysiol.* **19**, 573 (1956).
43. ROBERTS, E., *Progr. in Neurobiol.* **1**, 11 (1955).
44. TRAUTWEIN, W., KUFFLER, S. W. and EDWARDS, C., *J. Gen. Physiol.* **40**, 135 (1956).
45. WIERSMA, C. A. G., FURSHPAN, E. and FLOREY, E., *J. Exptl. Biol.* **30**, 136 (1953).

STUDIES IN THE NERVOUS MECHANISM OF TASTE

Y. ZOTTERMAN

Department of Physiology, Veterinärhögskolan, Stockholm, Sweden

THE old conception of four classes of taste, viz. sweet, sour, bitter, and salt, which we have inherited from the psycho-physics of the previous century, appears to most people as simple and comprehensible, and so much in agreement with general experience that very few people have been interested in the basic problems of taste until recent advances in electrophysiological technique created new means of a direct study of the activity within the very taste nerve fibres themselves.

One would be inclined to believe that such a comparatively simple sense as taste would be easy to elucidate, at least in its peripheral mechanism. This, however, has not proved to be so for a diversity of reasons. First, all the taste nerve fibres are relatively small fibres [13] and thus difficult to handle and to record from. At the time I found that the cat possessed taste fibres which responded to salt, bitter and acid solutions but not to sweet-tasting solutions. Pfaffmann [9] confirmed this, but, still more important, he showed that acid solutions of a pH below 2.5 stimulated all kinds of taste nerve endings. Thus a complication was added to our concept of taste in that it became necessary to speak of salt-acid fibres, i.e. fibres that responded to the application of salt as well as acid on the tongue. But besides this he also found fibres that reacted only to acids. The salty taste should thus be discriminated from the acid taste only by the absence of impulses in the specific acid taste fibres.

SPECIFIC FIBRES RESPONDING TO WATER

Seven years ago I observed that the frog possessed taste fibres which responded to the application of pure water on the tongue. I first believed that these water fibres served a particular purpose in the regulation of the water intake in these animals living mostly in fresh water. This finding, however, raised the old question debated by psychologists for half a century, whether mammals, including man, are equipped with specific taste organs for water. In Stockholm David Katz, the professor of psychology, had long keenly maintained that this must be the case. In examinations he often put the question, "What is the taste of water?" The correct answer was: "wet".

The suspicion that even warm-blooded animals might possess specific water receptors was strengthened substantially by a recent series of taste tests made by Liljestrand on himself. Confirming earlier investigations in this field, he found that the threshold value for NaCl solutions lay between 0.009 and 0.002 M, i.e. about 0.05–0.01 per cent NaCl. It was just between the concentrations where I had found that the specific water taste fibres began to respond. But at that concentration the NaCl does not taste salty. Nevertheless, it is possible with 100 per cent certainty to differentiate between distilled water and the tap water of the city of Stockholm when they have both been boiled and cooled down again to the same temperature.

Animal experiments have confirmed, beyond doubt, that mammals can detect water with their taste buds. Leading off the action potentials from the entire chorda tympani nerve in the cat, dog and pig Liljestrand and the present writer [8] were able to demonstrate that these animals possessed taste fibres the endings of which responded to the application of water on the tongue. By splitting up the nerve in fine strands we were able to find preparations which responded to the application of water on the tongue but not to 0.5 M NaCl solutions, and also strands which responded to 0.5 M NaCl but not to water. We could therefore state that these animals obviously possessed specific taste nerve endings which responded to water containing no electrolytes or only very small amounts.

Skramlik [12] reported that, in humans, salt solutions below 0.03 M taste sweet and that "saltiness" appears only with concentrations above 0.03 M. Although it may be dangerous to generalise from cat receptor-threshold to human sensation, it is nevertheless intriguing that a salty taste is evoked in humans only when a saline concentration is reached where the cat's "water" fibres are completely depressed. This may indicate that the salty sensation evoked by relatively low salt concentrations is due to the absence of activity in "water" fibres.

Discrimination within an entire stimulus range by two distinct fibre types with frequency maxima at opposite ends of the range is similar to the way the thermo-reception problem has been solved (see [15]). The warm fibres of the thermoceptive system can be considered analogous to the "salt" taste fibres in that both respond only in the relatively high intensity region of their respective stimulus range. The "water" fibre plays a role similar to the cold fibre by responding in the low-intensity region. Thus, for at least two extero-ceptive systems, adequate discrimination within the entire physiologically significant stimulus range is beyond the capability of a single receptor; the general solution of employing two distinct fibre types which respond in

TABLE I.

Stimulus	Fibre type response				Sensation evoked
	"Water" fibre	"Salt" fibre	"Acid" fibre	"Quinine" fibre	
H_2O (salt $< 0.03 \, M$)	+	0	0	0	→ water
NaCl (0.5 M)	0	+	0	0	→ salt
HCl (pH 2.5)	+	+	+	0	→ sour
Quinine	+	0	0	+	→ bitter

opposite regions of the sensitive range has been evolved as a solution for this problem.

In the previous investigations the fibres responding to water were differentiated from those responding to hypertonic salt solutions though both kinds responded to acids. It is known from Pfaffmann's work [9] that many mammalian taste fibres respond to more than one chemical stimulus, and it was felt that the response spectrum of the mammalian "water" fibres should be more rigidly defined. For that purpose Cohen, Hagiwara and I [4] undertook an investigation in which the response of single fibres from the chorda tympani of the cat was thoroughly analysed. The results of this study are summarised in Table I.

From this table it will be seen that most "water" fibres were found to be stimulated not only by water but also, besides acids, by quinine. In later experiments, however, single-fibre preparations have been obtained which responded to water and acids, but not to quinine. It is apparent from these investigations on single fibres that even so-called primary taste sensations are built up from a composite input pattern of several taste fibre types. In the cat there are only two substances which stimulate one kind of fibre only, i.e. NaCl and water; all other sapid solutions stimulate more than one kind of taste fibre, and this is in full accordance with our subjective experience. NaCl solutions are the only salt solutions which elicit a real pure salty taste.

Even with stimuli which activate only one fibre respectively, such as water and NaCl, the impulse pattern must still be considered important in that lack of response in the other taste fibres is necessary for the arousal of a water or salt sensation. It appears that the activity of the two-fibre types which respond only to one stimulus, i.e. the "quinine" fibre and "acid" fibre, dominates "water " fibre activity centrally during simultaneous stimulation.

Most likely the same holds true for the "sweet" fibres in the dog and pig, etc. Thus a bitter taste or a sweet taste results when "quinine" and "sweet" fibres respectively respond simultaneously with "water" fibres. A water taste is aroused when the "water" fibres alone are stimulated or in animals lacking specific water fibres when no taste fibres are stimulated.

SPECIES DIFFERENCES

In recent years Pfaffmann and Beidler in the U.S.A., using electrophysiological methods, have noticed very great species differences in the response of the taste fibres of the chorda tympani. Thus they have both observed the great difference between the rat and the cat in respect to their response to weak NaCl solutions as well as to quinine.

Due to these great species differences the present writer recently extended the study of water taste to the pig, the rabbit and the white rat as well as to sheep and cattle. The pig produced a response to water very similar to that of the cat, and the rabbit also demonstrated a definite response to water; the response in this latter animal was delayed a few seconds but was of lasting character.

In contrast to the mammals previously tested, the rat, the sheep and the calf did not show any positive response to water. The application of water on the rat's tongue caused only an immediate decrease of the spontaneous activity which could be reduced to nil, to return slowly in ten seconds after the cessation of the water flow. After a water rinse, even as weak a solution as 0.003 M NaCl caused an obvious and persisting response in this animal.

The high level of spontaneous activity observed in the rat's chorda tympani is most likely an expression of the high sensitivity of its taste receptors to NaCl. The chloride ion concentration of the rat's saliva seems to be a constant stimulus to the salt receptors. In the cat, dog, rabbit and pig, on the other hand, the receptors adapt quickly to a NaCl solution of that concentration.

The very high sensitivity of the rat to weak NaCl solutions found in these experiments is in accordance with the result of Pfaffmann's behaviouristic experiments on rats and can in itself explain the high discriminating power of these animals. There is as yet no information in regard to salt-discrimination in the cat, dog or pig. If these animals were entirely dependent upon their salt fibres their discrimination of salty solutions should be rather poor. But these species possess water fibres which may serve very well in the discrimination between water and weak salty solutions.

PRELIMINARY EXPERIMENTS ON THE CHORDA TYMPANI OF MAN

As concerns our own discrimination in this respect, Åhlander and I have recently made several attempts to lead off from the chorda tympani of man during operations on the middle ear when the chorda can be exposed to the electrodes. Once the technical difficulties for recording the weak action potentials of a nerve stem were overcome, only in two out of eight cases did we succeed in getting a fair response from the chorda tympani to touching the tongue, but very faint responses from the application of tasting solutions to the tongue. We obtained thus a weak response to 0.5 M NaCl solution, to 10 per cent sucrose, to 0.02 M quinine HCl as well as to dilute acetic acid and to saccharine but no response to water. The responses were, however, so faint that they were just noticeable in the loud-speaker but could not be recorded or further analysed. Thus we still lack definite proof whether man possesses any specific water fibres. Thus while we still lack direct proof of the existence of any water fibres in man, it would be premature to discuss whether our own discrimination is due to highly sensitive salt receptors alone as in the rat, or to a dual system of salt and water fibres, the activities of which contrast with each other because of their reciprocal mode of stimulation.

THE CORTICAL RECEPTION OF AFFERENT IMPULSES FROM
THE TONGUE

Using microelectrodes, which enables the recording of the activity of single cortical cells, we have recently made an extensive study of the reception of the inflow of impulses in the cat's sensory tongue area [5]. We succeeded in 5 cases in finding cells in the cortex which responded to the application of tasty solutions on the tongue. These cortical taste cells responded to many stimuli—to salt, bitter and acid solutions, and water too, but not to sweet tasting solutions nor to Ringer's solution. These cells were thus specific central receivers only for the modality "taste". They did not respond to touch or temperature. Thus their activity probably means nothing more to our subjective sensation than just "taste" in contrast to touch, warmth or cold. Specific cells in the tongue cortical area have been found for taste, touch, warmth and cold. Thus these modalities possess specific pathways from the periphery to the cerebral cortex. The touch cell is fired with a latency of 5 msec. and the first spike appears on the rising phase of the evoked potential. From this we can conclude that such a cell must be a primary cortical touch cell.

As the conduction velocity of the cold fibres is about one-third of that of the fastest touch fibres, we expected a longer latency of the cold cells in the cortex, and Landgren [6, 7] found a latency of 15 msec. when stimulating specific cold cells which did not respond to any other mode of stimulation than cooling of the tongue. The first spike of such a specific cold cell will thus appear on the falling phase of the evoked potential. Besides these specific cells Landgren [6, 7] has found other cells with much longer latencies, 80–200 msec. or more which respond to various modes of stimulation of the tongue. Most of these cells respond to mechanical stimulation of the tongue as well as to taste or thermal stimulation. The response of these cells to touch is, however, quite different from that of the primary specific touch cells. The latency to touch may be the same (5 msec.) but the spike frequency starts at low value and increases with repeated stimulation. When stimulated mechanically these cells behave as if they had a lot of inertia. It looks as if the spontaneous activity of these cells became facilitated by repeated mechanoceptive stimuli. On the other hand they respond very keenly to cooling of the tongue or to tasty solutions. There is thus a very great difference between the behaviour of these cells and the specific touch cells in their way of responding to touch. Their high frequency response to thermal or gustatory stimulation of the tongue would indicate that they are essentially engaged in thermal or gustatory perception respectively. The fact that they also can to a minor degree be discharged by tactile stimulation of the tongue suggests that the mechanoceptive stimulation facilitates their response to thermal or gustatory stimuli.

It is no doubt true that if we accept the implications of these new findings we must recognise the great difficulties in interpreting directly the results of our introspective analysis of sensations in terms of the physiological analysis of the afferent nervous mechanisms. But new pathways of advance are opening before us: our methods of investigating the nervous system now allow us to record cortical events within the cortical elements themselves. We can now hope that in the future we may be able to elucidate the nervous mechanism of integration of the afferent inflow which underlies our taste experiences.

SUMMARY

1. Specific afferent fibres responding specifically to the application of water upon the tongue have been found in cat, dog and pig as well as in rabbit, but not in rat, calf and lamb.

2. Contrary to the dog and the rat, the cat, the calf and the lamb do not possess any fibres responding to sweet tasting solution.

3. Experiments on the sensory tongue area of the cat's cortex are reported which show the existence of cells which respond only to gustatory stimulation of the tongue. These cells respond to almost all types of gustatory stimulation but do not respond to any other sensory modality. They are thus specific to the modality of taste but not the quality of taste.

REFERENCES

1. BEIDLER, L. M., *J. Neurophysiol.* **16**, 595 (1953).
2. —— *J. Gen. Physiol.* **38**, 133 (1954).
3. BEIDLER, L. M., FISHMAN, Y. and HARDIMAN, C. W., *Am. J. Physiol.* **181**, 235 (1955).
4. COHEN, M. J., HAGIWARA, S. and ZOTTERMAN, Y., *Acta Physiol. Scand.* **33**, 316 (1955).
5. COHEN, M. J., LANDGREN, S., STRÖM, L. and ZOTTERMAN, Y., *Acta Physiol. Scand.* **40**, *Suppl.* 135 (1957).
6. LANDGREN, S., *Acta Physiol. Scand.* **40**, 202 (1957).
7. —— *ibid.* **40**, 210 (1957).
8. LILJESTRAND, G. and ZOTTERMAN, Y., *Acta Physiol. Scand.* **32**, 291 (1954).
9. PFAFFMANN, C., *J. Cellular Comp. Physiol.* **17**, 243 (1941).
10. —— *Science* **117**, 140 (1953).
11. —— *J. Neurophysiol.* **18**, 429 (1955).
12. SKRAMLIK, E. v., Handbuch der niederen Sinne, Bd. **1**. Thiemse, Leipzig, 1926.
13. ZOTTERMAN, Y., *Skand. Arch. Physiol.* **72**, 73 (1935).
14. —— *Acta Physiol. Scand.* **18**, 181 (1949).
15. —— *Ann. Rev. Physiol.* **15**, 357 (1953).
16. —— *Acta Physiol. Scand.* **37**, 60 (1956).

Experimental Cell Research, Suppl. **5**, *527–546 (1958)*   527

AN ANALYSIS OF THE CHANGES ATTENDING
FERTILIZATION OF THE SEA URCHIN EGG

J. RUNNSTRÖM

Wenner-Grens Institute, University of Stockholm, Sweden, and Stazione Zoologica, Naples, Italy

ACCORDING to the belief of some research workers there must be a common denominator in all stimulation processes irrespective of how different they may appear to be at first sight. This belief may no doubt induce an inspiring interaction between very different fields of research. It is perhaps appropriate briefly to recall this when I am trying to analyze changes in the egg cell upon fertilization at this symposium mainly devoted to the nerve cell.

The Surface Layers in the Mature Unfertilized Egg

As an introduction to my analysis I have to mention something about the composition of the surface layers of the non fertilized ripe sea urchin egg, cf. Fig. 1. The outermost layer is the jelly coat. It is rich in water and consists of glycoprotein. The estimations made by Vasseur [33] indicate the presence of about 20 per cent amino acids probably combined to protein and 80 per cent of a polysaccharide esterified with sulphate. Aminosugars seem to be absent in the substance of the jelly coat. In the analytical ultracentrifuge it seemed to separate into one main and one minor component [26]. The relation between these is still obscure. Below the jelly coat the vitelline membrane is found. Its existence which has been doubted is now ascertained both by direct electronmicroscopic and by indirect evidence [1, 29]. Its thickness is 100 Å and it may be inferred from its sensitivity to various proteolytic enzymes that it contains proteins or peptides. Below the vitelline

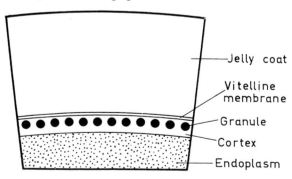

Fig. 1.—Diagram showing the different surface layers of the sea urchin egg.

Jelly coat

Vitelline membrane

Granule

Cortex

Endoplasm

membrane the cortical layer of the cytoplasm is found. It has a thickness of about 1.5–2 microns [21]. It has a higher rigidity than the interior cytoplasm, the endoplasm. In the surface of the cortical layer a stratum may be distinguished which contains acid mucopolysaccharides indicated by staining with the acetic-acid-iron reagent of Hale [30]. From jelly free eggs acid mucopolysaccharides could be isolated which might be identical with the histochemically demonstrated stratum. The chemical study of these compounds is under way. In dark field the surface layer is orange yellow, the surface exhibits a birefringence positive in the radial direction. The cortex contains a number of granules—the cortical granules. Their diameter is somewhat below one micron and the number is about 30,000 in one egg (*Psammechinus miliaris*). Electron micrographs [1] show that the cortical granules have a rather complicated structure with variations according to the species studied.

Changes Attending Fertilization

Fertilization brings about very thorough changes in the egg cell, the most fundamental being that the eggs acquire the capacity to develop. Put into more chemical terms this means that a number of synthetic processes are released after fertilization. But the syntheses are intermingled with splitting processes. Apparently these latter dominate the picture during the first hours after fertilization. A breakdown of proteins and of nucleic acids has been reported [4, 16]. At the same time syntheses occur which in their turn dominate the picture in certain phases, cf. Kavanau [16].

There are certain one-event changes which attract attention. One of these is the change of colour of the surface when viewed with dark field illumination [25, 23]. The most well known is the formation of the membrane which has turned out to be a complicated process, cf. for references [26]. The vitelline membrane is elevated from the surface of the cortex. Moreover, the cortical granules are expelled from the cortex and merge with the vitelline membrane. During this process the granules undergo certain changes which are not understood in all details. The result is the formation of a tough fertilization membrane 500 Å thick [1, 21] which shows a pronounced mainly textural birefringence whereas the vitelline membrane presents no or at the most a very low birefringence [26]. The outermost region of the cortex assumes the character of a thin "hyaline layer".

The type of plasmolysis observed in eggs immersed in a hypertonic solution changes upon fertilization in an obvious way. This indicates changes in the structure of the cortical layer but also that of the endoplasm undergoes obvious changes which are visible in the ordinary light microscope but

particularly in phase contrast or dark field. The endoplasm is less homogenous, more opaque before fertilization than after. This may also be recognized on sections [26]. The difference is reflected in the distribution of
the yolk granules which may be rendered distinguishable by means of the
Hotchkiss reaction which is much more uneven in unfertilized than in
fertilized eggs. Their staining with the Schiff reagent becomes also more
intense after fertilization [14]. Likewise electron microscopy demonstrates
that in unfertilized eggs the mitochondria are aggregated, whereas after
fertilization they exhibit a more even distribution [2]. These differences in
distribution of the formed particles which manifest themselves to a varying
degree reflect probably conditions in the ground substance. According to the
writer's opinion the ground cytoplasm of the fertilized eggs is richer in hydrophilic groups than that of unfertilized ripe eggs. The increase in rate of swelling which is observed after fertilization may correspond to a transition from
a more hydrophobic to a more hydrophilic state, cf. [26]. The following
observation [28] points in the same direction. Eggs were left in sea water
between slide and coverslip. Owing to evaporation the medium gradually
became hypertonic. Numerous birefringent fibre-like structures appeared in
the unfertilized eggs, whereas no such structures became visible in the fertilized
egg. It could be proved in centrifugation experiments that the birefringent
fibres belonged to the ground substance of the cytoplasm. They form part
of what Porter [22] has designated as the "endoplasmic reticulum". An
important change in properties of the ground cytoplasm thus occurs upon
fertilization.

It seems unsatisfactory, however, to make comparisons in a general way
between unfertilized and fertilized eggs. As both kinds of eggs are changing a
time axis is necessary when comparisons are to be made.

Timed Blocking with Lauryl Sulphate

A procedure of timed blocking will allow us to follow the fertilization
process more in detail. Such a procedure was used by Rothschild and
Swann [24] to determine the rate of fertilization in sea urchin material. Their
scope was to study the kinetics of the sperm egg interaction. Further considerations have been presented on this subject by E. Hultin [12], and Hagström and Hagström [8] introduced a more convenient method of interrupting
fertilization. According to his method samples of the eggs are brought into a
10^{-3} per cent solution of lauryl sulphate at different times after insemination.
This method lends itself to routine work. Numerous studies could therefore
be carried out concerning the effect of different substances on the rate of

fertilization in sea urchins. By way of example the reader is referred to Fig. 2. In the control eggs, curve 1, fifty per cent of the eggs were fertilized after 36 seconds. If the eggs had been pretreated with 2×10^{-6} sodium periodate in sea water, the rate of fertilization doubled, curve 3. Evidently the improvement is here due to a change in the properties of the eggs as the sperm had no contact with the periodate which was removed before the insemina-

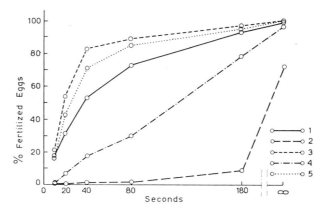

Fig. 2.—Rate of fertilization of eggs of *Psammechinus miliaris* under different conditions. *1*, Control eggs; *2*, eggs fertilized in the presence of 1.8×10^{-2} per cent "fertilization inhibitor" from *Fucus vesiculosus*; *3*, eggs pretreated with 2×10^{-6} *M* sodium periodate, fertilized in sea water; *4*, eggs pretreated with 2×10^{-6} *M* sodium periodate and fertilized in the presence of 1.8×10^{-2} per cent "fertilization inhibitor" (cf. curve 2); *5*, eggs with the jelly coat removed at pH 5.5, fertilized in normal sea water. Unpublished data of B. Hagström and Ulla Esping.

tion. Curve 2, on the other hand, gives an example of the action of an inhibitor which is contained in an extract from *Fucus vesiculosus*. Vasseur and Esping (cf. [5]) have subjected the inhibitor to a certain purification without obtaining, however, a pure substance. The inhibiting extract contains a polysaccharide with ester bound sulphate and a phenolic substance. It is uncertain whether these components are chemically combined or not. The inhibitor does not block fertilization altogether but it slows down the rate very considerably. The 50 per cent fertilization time (curve 2) would in the present case exceed one hour which is in contrast to the value 36 seconds, observed in the control test. If the inhibitor is removed by washing, the eggs become normally fertilizable again. On the other hand, the sperm is not damaged when suspended in a solution of the Fucus inhibitor. They even retain their fertilizing capacity for a longer time than when suspended in normal sea water. The rigidity of the egg cortex was tested with the aid of a centrifuge method according to a procedure similar to that introduced by E. N. Harvey [11], see also E. B. Harvey [9, 10]. According to this method the rigidity of the egg cortex increases under the action of the inhibitor, cf. [29].

The Fucus inhibitor is a representative of a group of fertilization inhibitors to which belong e.g. heparin, chondroitine sulphate, dextran sulphate, human bloodgroup H-substance etc. To a varying extent they decrease the rate of fertilization. These inhibitors have the character of acid muco-polysaccharides and their action is assumed to depend on complexing with the acid mucopolysaccharides which histochemical methods show are present in the surface of the cortical layer [13, 30]. The natural inhibition which this surface offers to the spermatozoa may be increased by complexing with the exogenous inhibitor. The increase in rigidity which as yet has been demonstrated only for the Fucus inhibitor may have the same cause.

Periodate which enhances the rate of fertilization has a depolymerizing effect on the jelly layer. But this is not the only cause of its enhancing effect. It also attacks the surface of the cortical layer. The most probable point of attack is here α-glycol groups within the acid mucopolysaccharides. If the eggs have been pretreated with periodate they become less susceptible to the Fucus inhibitor, cf. curve 4, Fig. 2. There is apparently an additive action of the endogenous and the exogenous inhibitor. When the former has been made weaker the total inhibitory effect is less intense.

Curve 5 shows the rate of fertilization in the same eggs as those represented in curve 1 after removal of the jelly layer by washing with sea water at pH 5.0. It is evident that the rate of fertilization is higher in the eggs deprived of their jelly layer [6, 7]. This has been born out in a wide variety of experiments. In certain combinations also cross fertilization occurred in a higher percentage when eggs deprived of their jelly layer were used in the experiment [7]. From this is inferred that the jelly coat functions as a barrier which exerts a selective action on the spermatozoa, only those of a certain chemical and mechanical potency being able to penetrate to the egg surface. This, on the other hand, constitutes a second barrier where the spermatozoa are again put to a test concerning their potency of overcoming the barrier. These views are at variance with the notion of the substance of the jelly layer as a "fertilizin", i.e. a fertilization promoting factor [32]. Even the addition of jelly layer substance in solution (jelly solution) delays fertilization and brings about formation of an imperfect fertilization membrane [29]. In sufficient concentration the jelly solution may even block fertilization altogether. The jelly is chemically related to heparin and other substances which act as inhibitors of fertilization and of artificial activation as well.

Substances like heparin are known to be enzyme inhibitors. The same holds true for the Fucus inhibitor. It was found to be a potent inhibitor of hyaluronidase, of ribonuclease, of urease [5] and of at least one of the proteolytic enzymes present in the sea urchin egg [20]. These inhibitors are probably not directed against special active groups but they react in a more general way with proteins.

From the results reported the idea has emerged that the mucopolysaccharides of the egg surface act as enzyme inhibitors and that their depolymerization upon fertilization causes a release of an enzyme activity which is instrumental in the starting of the development of the egg [30].

Further Analysis of the Action of Lauryl Sulphate

It seemed of interest to make a more detailed study of the action of lauryl sulphate in the experiments on fertilization rate. When the gametes are brought in contact with the detergent solution all further fusion between male and female cells is stopped, but in all cases where reaction between spermatozoon and surface of the cortex has occurred the further steps in the activation process are completed and even a division and development take place while the eggs remain in the detergent solution. This means that the only process blocked in the experiments with 10^{-3} per cent lauryl sulphate is the attachment of the spermatozoon to the egg surface. As soon as this has occurred the fertilization process will go to completion.

In experiments with eggs of *Paracentrotus lividus* the concentration of the detergent was doubled (2×10^{-3} per cent). This concentration proved to be fatal to the development of the eggs which did not proceed beyond a stage of about 100 cells. The transfer to the detergent occurred after the following number of seconds, respectively: (*a*) 10, (*b*) 20, (*c*) 30, (*d*) 40, (*e*) 50, (*f*) 60, (*g*) 120, (*h*) 300.

There was maximum injury in (*a*); (*b*)–(*d*) showed a gradual improvement whereas in (*e*) and (*f*) the result was similar to that observed in (*d*). In (*g*) and (*h*) cleavage proceeded further than in the case of the preceding transfers. The cytoplasm had also a somewhat more homogeneous appearance. In the following table counts of the different groups of eggs in (*a*) and (*g*) are summarized; *n* means the total number of eggs counted in each test. The other figures mean percentages.

	1- and 2-cells	8–16-cells	64-cells or more	*n*
(*a*)	71.5	22.5	6	293
(*g*)	15.0	8.0	77	209

This tends to show that the eggs are more sensitive to the detergent immediately after having reacted with the spermatozoon. Even if the sensitivity has a maximum in the test (*a*) it remained strong also in (*b*)–(*f*), whereas 2–5 minutes after insemination an increased resistance develops which, however, is not sufficient to bring the eggs beyond an advanced cleavage stage. Despite this rather pronounced inhibitory effect of the detergent on development the cortical changes took place in a normal way. Smooth membranes were elevated and a hyaline layer also appeared. This was even more obvious in the arrested stages than under normal conditions. This seems to be due to a precipitation of the hyaline layer which transforms the relatively inconspicuous structure to a membrane with a pronounced birefringence, reminescent of the fertilization membrane.

Timed Blocking with Potassium Cyanide

Experiments of a similar type as those recorded for the detergent were also carried out with potassium cyanide (Immers). Only some few data will be reported. Suffice it to say that the transfer to 8.5×10^{-4} cyanide according to the same scheme as that adopted in the detergent experiments did not interfere with the cortical changes. Both membrane and hyaline layer appeared.

Moreover the state of the cortex was established which manifests itself in the angular type of plasmolysis in eggs which are transferred to a hypertonic solution (20 ml sea water + 6 ml 2.5 N NaCl), cf. [26]. The development of this state was slower, however, in the presence of cyanide than in pure sea water. The control eggs underwent angular plasmolysis 5 minutes after fertilization, whereas the eggs in cyanide exhibited a smooth plasmolysis at the same time—that is the type of plasmolysis found in the eggs during the first minutes after fertilization. Ten minutes after fertilization, however, the eggs in cyanide also underwent an angular plasmolysis. In eggs showing smooth plasmolysis the hyaline layer appeared as a rim on the egg surface exhibiting a weak birefringence with the same sign as shown by the membrane. In the eggs undergoing angular plasmolysis in the presence of the hypertonic solution the hyaline layer was elevated and showed not only the same sign of birefringence but also the same retardation as the fertilization membrane.

Despite the fact that cyanide must prevent the normal increase in respiration a series of complicated morphogenetic processes occur. Apparently these processes take place spontaneously, but probably the energy transferred from the oxidation processes is replaced by simpler breakdown processes.

One indication of such processes is given in the acid formation which has been demonstrated in some species of sea urchins [26].

The eggs subjected to cyanide were transferred to normal sea water after different intervals of time. It turned out that an exposure to cyanide ($8.5 \times 10^{-4} M$) for e.g. 60 minutes was harmful to the eggs. A delay of the cleavage was observed. This delay was much longer than the duration of the exposure to cyanide. Apparently the delay in cleavage was dependent on the time of transfer to cyanide. There are indications of a maximum susceptibility when the eggs were exposed to cyanide 3–5 minutes after fertilization. When the transfer was made earlier (10–100 seconds after fertilization) or later (10–15 minutes after fertilization) the delay was less pronounced. Considerably more work is required to map out these relations in detail. One thing seems certain, however, viz. that an injury is inflicted to the egg by the exposure to cyanide. Probably the fine structure of the protoplasm is sensitive to the deprivation of the normal supply of energy from the respiration, at least it holds for the conditions of the present experiment.

In addition it may be mentioned that there is a sensitive period to 2,4-dinitrophenol some minutes after insemination, whereas 8–10 minutes later the eggs are much more resistant [17]. In this case the block does not concern respiration but mainly the transfer of energy released in respiration to energy-rich phosphate compounds.

Timed Blocking with Porphyrexid

It was illustrated above how treatment of unfertilized eggs with periodate increases the rate of fertilization. The question was soon raised how other oxiding agents compare with periodate. It was stated that periodate was rather unique in its action [29]. Other oxidizing agents so far tested have proved rather to be inhibitors of fertilization. During the last year the writer has had the opportunity of testing the effect of the two high potential indicators porphyrindin and porphyrexid which proved to be inhibitors of fertilization. It was inferred that the inhibition is due to the stiffening of the surface layers of the egg, whereas the interior of the egg is not directly affected by the indicators, as was proved in centrifuge experiments of the type mentioned above [29, 31]. The indicators lend themselves also for the timed blocking procedure.

An experiment carried out with gametes of *Paracentrotus lividus* and porphyrexid as oxidizing agent will be referred to below.

Preliminary experiments had shown that porphyrexid in the concentration

1.75×10^{-4} M prevents the fertilization of *Paracentrotus* eggs. This was used therefore as the agent in the procedure of timed blocking. Eggs deprived of their jelly layers were inseminated and brought to the porphyrexid after the following number of seconds:

(*a*) 10,   (*b*) 20,   (*c*) 30,   (*d*) 40,   (*e*) 50,   (*f*) 60,   (*g*) 120,   (*h*) 300.

Moreover unfertilized and fertilized eggs were kept as controls.

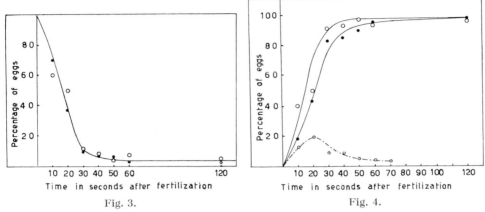

Fig. 3.   Fig. 4.

Fig. 3.—Diagram showing the percentage of unfertilized eggs after immersion of inseminated eggs (*Paracentrotus lividus*) in lauryl sulphate (circles) and porphyrexid (dots) respectively. Each value obtained by counting 700–800 eggs.

Fig. 4.—Diagram showing the percentage of developing eggs after immersion of inseminated egg (*Paracentrotus lividus*) in laurylsulphate (larger circles) or porphyrexid (dots), respectively. In one group of eggs the spermatozoon has been trapped in the membrane (small circles, broken line). The material is the same as that represented in Fig. 3.

Parallel to the transfer to porphyrexid samples of the same material were immersed in 0.001 per cent lauryl sulphate. In the curve Fig. 3 the percentages of unfertilized eggs are plotted as a function of time of transfer to porphyrexid and laurylsulphate, respectively. Practically, the values fall on the same curve. That means that the block to fertilization is instantaneous also in the case of porphyrexid of the appropriate concentration.

The curves, Fig. 4, show the number of fertilized eggs counted after different times of transfer. There is only one class of fertilized eggs in the lauryl sulphate. They all undergo cleavage. Conversely, in the porphyrexid two classes of eggs are found. The majority of these undergo cleavage but as will turn out later their development is dependent to some extent on the time of transfer to porphyrexid. A minority of eggs has reacted with a spermatozoon but no cleavage occurs. There is either a local formation of a membrane or the membrane is present all over the egg. In both cases the spermatozoon has been trapped in the vitelline membrane which becomes toughened following the contact with the indicator. In the eggs with local elevation of the membrane the nucleus remains intact and its position is eccentric. Where the membrane has separated completely from the egg surface the nucleus migrates to the center of the egg and a monaster develops.

Both types of eggs have not been kept separate in the counts. The lower curve 3 in Fig. 4 represents the sum of the two types of eggs with trapped spermatozoa. The maximum of such types was found in the eggs transferred 20 seconds after fertilization and here the eggs with the locally elevated membrane predominated. This was also found to be valid for the eggs transferred 10 seconds after insemination. In the later transfers, however, the eggs with locally elevated membranes were absent or rare whereas the monasters predominated. It must be pointed out that even in the control 2 per cent monaster eggs were found in this experiment.

The studies on the locally activated eggs have given useful information about the first steps of fertilization. Fig. 5 may serve as an illustration of what happens (although Fig. 5 as well as the following Fig. 6 refer to experiments other than that described in this paragraph). A concavity has developed which marks the region of sperm entry. However the spermatozoon is not always found in the centre of the concavity but often nearer to its border. The cortex is not only changed in the region of the conspicuous concavity but the whole surface of the egg seems to have been brought in motion. Numerous small concavities may be found over the whole egg surface outside the main concavity. There are also signs of streaming movements directed toward the main concavity, which are obvious in the egg represented in Fig. 5. The state of movement is fixed by the solidifying effect of the indicator.

Above the concavity a thin membrane is elevated, which might mainly correspond to the vitelline membrane. The sperm seems to be elevated along with the membrane. This points to the conclusion that the spermatozoon has met a resistance in the stiffened vitelline membrane which it could not overcome.

In the monaster eggs, Fig. 6, the spermatozoon is also trapped in the vitelline membrane. The more complete membrane formation and the induction of monaster must be due to a somewhat deeper penetration of the spermatozoon. The direct demonstration of this is difficult, however.

There is one more important feature of the eggs with only partial elevation of the membrane. In the unfertilized eggs phase contrast allows the recognition of a central part which is rich in dark granules embedded in the opaque

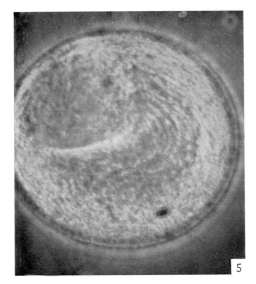
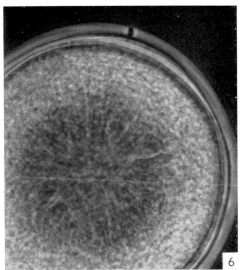

Fig. 5.—Eggs of *Paracentrotus lividus* inseminated in the presence of a solution of porphyrexid which blocked the sperm penetration in a large number of eggs. Nevertheless a strong local reaction occurs in these eggs, which brings about a strong concavity. Tangential arrangement in the cortex indicates streaming of cortical material. This egg had also received a light hypertonic treatment. The porphyrexid solution was aged and its concentration was therefore not exactly defined (around 10^{-5} M).

Fig. 6.—Egg of *Paracentrotus lividus* with trapped spermatozoon. The egg had been pretreated for 17 hours with 7.4×10^{-5} porphyrindin in sea water. Thereafter they were transferred to pure sea water and were inseminated here.

ground substance. In the region of the large concavity the central part moves toward the cortex. These two cytoplasmic regions are thus brought into a more intimate contact, one with the other.

The eggs brought into porphyrexid offer one more opportunity namely to follow different steps in the formation of the fertilization membrane. In this respect one has to resort to the eggs which have undergone complete fertilization. This manifests itself in the cleavage of the eggs. As late as 6–7 hours after fertilization the diameter of the membranes was measured. From the values found the mean diameter of the egg was substracted. In this way a measure was obtained of the degree of elevation of the membrane. The curve in Fig. 7 shows the width of the perivitelline space as a function of the log time of transfer of the eggs to the porphyrexid solution.

Moreover there is an opportunity of studying the stepwise incorporation of the cortical granules into the membrane. From the stage 20–25 seconds after fertilization granules were seen to adhere to a thin membrane. The incorporation of the granules becomes more and more intimate. In the eggs transferred

60 seconds after insemination the membrane has still a granular structure. Only 120 seconds after insemination is the membrane smooth, which means that the incorporation of the granules has been completed. The process of incorporation may also be followed in the polarization microscope. The retardation increases with increasing degree of incorporation of the cortical granules. The increase in retardation may simply reflect the increasing thickness of the membrane.

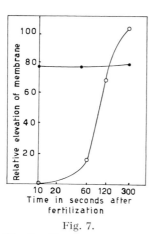

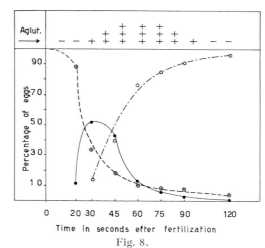

Fig. 7.   Fig. 8.

Fig. 7.—The width of the perivitelline space as a function of the log time of transfer of the eggs to the porphyrexid solution (1.75×10^{-4}). Same experiment as that to which Fig. 3 and 4 refer.

Fig. 8.—Diagram showing the different types of eggs (*Paracentrotus lividus*) present when transferred to 4 per cent formaldehyde different number of seconds after insemination. Circles with inscribed cross, eggs without visible membrane; dots, eggs with local membrane separation; circles, eggs with membranes separated all over the egg surface. Above the curve the degree of agglutination is indicated with + signs.

Immersion of the eggs in 3.2×10^{-5} M Cu^{++} in sea water different times after fertilization gave likewise the opportunity to follow the gradual incorporation of the cortical granules with the fertilization membrane.

As a contrast to the curve in Fig. 7 discussed already, there is also in the same figure three points which lie on almost the same level. These points refer to the average width of the membranes of eggs which in the parallel experiment were immersed in lauryl sulphate, 0.001 per cent. The common level of the points bear out what was stated previously, viz. that lauryl sulphate does not inhibit the formation of a normal fertilization membrane. The incorporation of the granules occurs normally even when the eggs are transferred to lauryl sulphate as early as 10 seconds after insemination. The retardation is the normal one.

As already mentioned cleavage occurred in all the fully fertilized eggs which had been exposed to the indicator but the development was rather different according to the time of transfer to the indicator solution. The blastocoel was extremely narrow in the test (*a*) (transfer 10 seconds after insemination). There was a gradual improvement with increasing interval between insemination and transfer. This improvement took a definite step in (*g*) and (*h*), i.e. when the interval was 120–300 seconds. Here the development approached, but did not fully reach the level of the control. Again the result emerges that the eggs are more susceptible in the stages following closely upon insemination.

Timed Blocking with Formaldehyde

In connection with work on sea urchin development 3.5–4 per cent formaldehyde in sea water (pH 7.6) was used extensively as a fixing agent. Incidentally the observation was made that eggs of *Paracentrotus* immersed in formaldehyde about one minute after insemination were not well fixed but rather presented signs of breakdown. This contrasts with the unfertilized eggs which usually are rather well fixed in 4 per cent formaldehyde. Starting from this observation timed blocking experiments were carried out also with formaldehyde. Fig. 8 gives a general survey of one experiment of this type. Curve 1 gives the number of eggs after different intervals in which no membrane elevation is visible. In some of these eggs a reaction with a spermatozoon has already occurred although the membrane has not started its elevation.[1] Curve 2 indicates the number of eggs with a local membrane formation and with a concavity below the membrane. The degree of elevation is variable. Sometimes the membrane extends over a larger region than that of the concavity. The third curve refers to eggs with the membrane separated all over the egg. This does not exclude the possibility that the egg has an eccentric position within the membrane. On the top of the figure the degree of agglutination between the eggs and between eggs and the bottom of the glass dish is indicated. The eggs were devoid of their jelly layers. The fertilization membrane is sticky during the time of its elevation. The molecular orientation which gives stickiness correlates also to a low resistance against mechanical and chemical disturbances; 100 seconds after insemination stickiness disappears and the membrane gains in mechanical and chemical resistance. Even before the stage 30 seconds after insemination there is a certain degree of stickiness which thus resides in the non elevated membrane material.

---

[1] Cf. a forthcoming paper by R. D. Allen and J. L. Griffin, Exptl. Cell Research, 1958.

The main observation is, however, that during a period which corresponds roughly to the period of agglutination a destruction of the egg occurs. When the membrane has elevated locally hyaline blisters sometimes but not always are seen within the perivitelline space, Fig. 9. When the local membrane has elevated to a larger extent blisters of considerable size may appear below the membrane. They may have a varying degree of density. In general one will find that the cytoplasmic structure in these egg is rather normal in other respects. A displacement of the interior endoplasm in direction of the cortical concavity is readily observed as in the porphyrexid experiments, Fig. 10. Sometimes a brown cytolysis occurred even in the eggs with a local elevation of the membrane. This kind of cytolysis is always found in eggs where the separation of the membrane from the egg surface is complete but the membrane has not yet reached its full degree of elevation. The brown cytolysis means a fine granular precipitation of the cytoplasm which confers a pronounced opacity on the egg. Also in the stages mentioned, e.g. 30–90 seconds after insemination, substances are eliminated from the interior. This is indicated by the higher opacity of the perivitelline space in phase contrast. Moreover numerous small "dark" granules are carrying out Brownian movement in the perivitelline space. Also myeline figures are observed which exhibit varied forms like those found when lecithin is swelling in a salt solution [25]. Particularly fascinating are the tubular forms which with a width hardly exceeding 1 micron may be longer than the diameter of the egg.

The egg is most sensitive toward immersion in formaldehyde during the time of membrane elevation. The state of the membrane during this period which has been discussed above is probably analogous to the state of the cytoplasm. The agglutination (cf. Fig. 8) may indicate that certain complexes

Fig. 9.—Egg of *Paracentrotus lividus*, immersed 30 seconds after insemination in 4 per cent formaldehyde. Concavity below a local membrane. Blisters.

Fig. 10.—Egg of *Paracentrotus lividus*, immersed 40 seconds after insemination in 4 per cent formaldehyde. One looks directly into a broad concavity. A ring of darker endoplasmic material adjacent to the region of the concavity.

Fig. 11.—An egg of *Paracentrotus lividus* immersed 40 seconds after insemination in 4 per cent formaldehyde. On the upper side is seen the concavity which marks the region of sperm entry (sperm only partially engulfed). Above this region there is a smooth and refractile membrane. On the opposite side (that most remote from the site of sperm entry) rather dense blisters have appeared.

Fig. 12.—Egg of *Paracentrotus lividus* centrifuged for five minutes so as to stratify its endoplasm. The egg was inseminated and 60 seconds later immersed in 4 per cent formaldehyde. Blisters appear in the region of the hyaline cytoplasm and the yolk granules. The closer to the centripetal pole the larger the blisters.

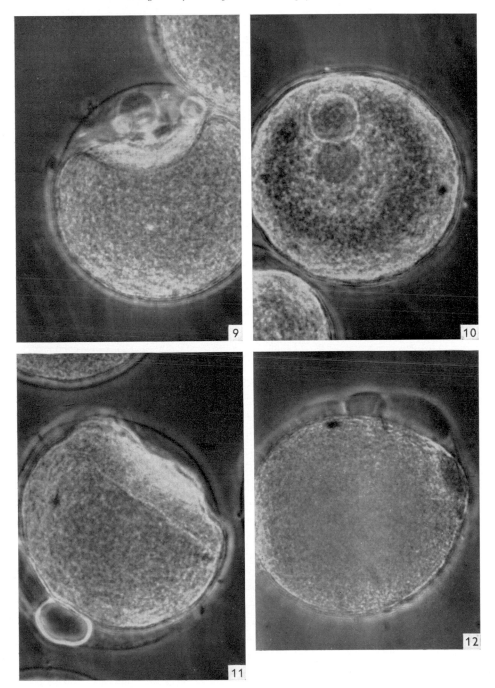

in the membrane are opened up. The same would occur in the cytoplasm with the consequence that certain components are split off and eliminated to the perivitelline space. A similar lability of the cytoplasm obtains in the normal development but there it is reversed at the expense of energy supplied by respiration or other energy-yielding degradation processes. Formaldehyde favors probably processes in which certain complexes are split up. In particular it may inhibit such processes which lead to a restoring of more stable structural conditions in the protoplasm.

The dispersed substances present in the perivitelline space in eggs exposed to formaldehyde in the period of elevation of the separated membrane seem to be identical with the constituents of the blisters. In the phase of blister formation these substances are in a less liquefied, paracristalline state. As briefly indicated above the blisters may show a higher or lower density—corresponding to different degrees of liquefaction. It has been directly observed in phase contrast how a separation of phases may occur in blisters probably owing to the degradation and dissolution of one of its components. Under such conditions the exterior limitation of the blister may remain but in the interior a number of myeline figures become visible. Besides these also some regions are observed which eventually are dispersed as granules which are dark in phase contrast. They are of the same size and optical properties as those dancing in the perivetelline space in eggs which have been immersed in formaldehyde in the stage of elevation of the separated membrane. Certain observations indicate that porphyrexid has a precipitating effect on some components of the blisters.

The site of sperm penetration may be recognized by the more rapid elevation of the membrane to one side and by greater phase contrast effect of the membrane in that region. Owing to this it was possible to recognize that blisters might eventually appear at the pole of the egg opposite to that of sperm entry, Fig. 11. The state which was initially confined to the entry site has propagated to the egg region most remote from this site.

Origin of the Blisters

From which component of the egg cell is the content of blisters derived? This would also answer the question about the origin of the substances dispersed in the perivitelline space which were mentioned above. To approach this question unfertilized eggs were centrifuged so as to bring out a stratification of their contents. As well known the centrifugal pole of centrifuged *Paracentrotus* eggs is occupied by the mitochondria [11]. The next layer in centripetal direction contains the yolk granules. Thereafter follows a hyaline zone and in the most centripetal position the so called oil cap, probably correspond-ing to certain lipoprotein complexes. The centrifuged eggs were inseminated and as in the experiments described above, the eggs were transferred to formaldehyde after different time intervals. The result was that the blisters appear in the regions of the hyaline and the yolk layer which under the con-ditions of the present experiments did not separate sharply, Fig. 12. Further experiments are necessary but it seems probable that the blisters originate at least basically from submicroscopic cytoplasmic components, in particular the microsome fraction. This is rich in lipids and ribonucleic acid, which give rise respectively to the myelin figures and the dark granules of the blister material.

Concluding Remarks

It is a well-known fact that calcium plays a special role in the activation of the sea urchin egg, cf. for references [26]. Magnesium on the other hand, antagonizes the calcium effect [15]. We may conceive of the presence of magnesium stabilized complexes of proteins, lipids and polysaccharides in the cortex of the mature unfertilized egg. These complexes presumably form flat parallel micelles within the cortical layer. This arrangement gives rise to the birefringence of the layer. The activation of the sea urchin egg involves primarily a breakup of these Mg-stabilized complexes. In this process cal-cium plays a part. The breakup process renders streaming movements possible which bring about an *increase in the surface of the cortical layer* which is reflected in the formation of the concavity at the site of sperm entry and of the wavy outline of the egg surface, often made visible in eggs subjected to porphyrexid. The streaming movements in the cortex brings about an interaction with the endoplasm in which also displacement of material occurs. The breakup processes referred to present many analogies to the behavior of coacervates and the views presented by Booij and Bungeberg de Jong [3] concerning the conditions of their stability may be pertinent to the complexes in the egg cytoplasm. Breaking up of complexes must expose groups pre-viously bound or occluded and consequently an enhanced enzymatic activity is to be expected. The insemination is followed by an activation of certain proteolytic enzymes as was demonstrated in our laboratory by Lundblad [19, 20]. Possibly also other hydrolytic enzymes may be activated. The acid formation mentioned above correlates probably to degradation processes. The circumstances referred to create labile conditions in the cytoplasm of the egg after attachment of the spermatozoon to the egg cortex.

The oxidation-reduction state in the egg is a factor which should be considered in this connection. It has been shown how a high potential oxidation-reduction indicator is able to block the progress of the fertilization process.

Of special importance are probably the interactions which occur at the boundary between cortical layer and endoplasm. One should probably not conceive of only one impulse wave spreading from the place of sperm entry but of several. After the period of lability more stable conditions are built up again but on a new basis, cf. [27]. Agents like formaldehyde prevent completely their attainment whereas other agents may act more specifically on partial processes. The procedure of timed blocking gives promise of lending itself to a more detailed analysis of the activation impulse, cf. [34, 35].

SUMMARY

A survey is given of the different layers in the cytoplasm of the sea urchin egg, their chemical nature, as far as known, and their changes upon fertilization.

A method of determining the rate of fertilization [8] has been used to study the effect of certain inhibitors. To these belong certain acid mucopolysaccharides, among those the jelly layer substance in solution.

Pretreatment with sodium periodate in concentration of 2×10^{-6} enhances the fertilization rate. Removal of the jelly layer has a similar effect.

The blocking of the fertilization with lauryl sulphate, which is used in the method of determining the fertilization rate [8] has been studied. In this method 10^{-3} per cent lauryl sulphate was used. This concentration prevents fertilization but does not impede activation and cleavage of eggs in which an effective attachment has occurred at the moment of immersion in lauryl sulphate. If the concentration of the detergent was 2×10^{-3} per cent the fertilized eggs were mostly blocked in early cleavage if immersed 10–60 seconds after insemination. If the immersion occurred 120–300 seconds after insemination the eggs were more resistent.

Eggs were transferred at different intervals after insemination in 8.5×10^{-4} potassium cyanide. This does not inhibit the cortical changes. Even the angular plasmolysis is exhibited when the cyanide treated eggs are subjected to hypertonic medium although the change in type of plasmolysis is somewhat delayed in the presence of cyanide.

Timed transfer of eggs to 1.75×10^{-4} M porphyrexid interrupts fertilization like lauryl sulphate but porphyrexid also blocks momentarily the cortical changes, the membrane elevation and the incorporation of the cortical granules. In this way the time course of these phenomena can be studied.

Timed transfer to 3.2×10^{-5} Cu^{++} gave a similar opportunity of following the cortical changes.

Eggs were also transferred after different intervals to 4 per cent formaldehyde in sea water, pH 7.6. During the first 60–90 seconds after insemination there is a tendency for breakdown of the eggs transferred to formaldehyde. This tendency is particularly strong from about 30 seconds after insemination. The egg cytoplasm becomes brown and substances are exuded from the interior. These may appear in the form of blisters or fill the perivitelline space more homogenously. The exuded substance is rich in lipids and originates from the submicroscopic components of the cytoplasm.

The lability of the cytoplasm toward formaldehyde is due to the breakup of certain complexes which occurs during the cortical changes. Increased stability against formaldehyde is regained when the membrane approaches its final degree of elevation.

The results presented indicate that studies on timed exposure to various agents of inseminated eggs will promote the analysis of the activation impulse.

REFERENCES[1]

1. AFZELIUS, B. A., *Exptl. Cell Research* **10**, 257 (1956).
2. —— personal communication.
3. BOOIJ, H. L. and BUNGEBERG DE JONG, H. C., *Protoplasmologia* **I**, 2 (1956).
4. ELSON, D., GUSTAFSON, T. and CHARGAFF, E., *J. Biol. Chem.* **209**, 285 (1954).
5. ESPING, U., *Arkiv Kemi* **11**, 107, 117 (1957).
6. HAGSTRÖM, B. E., *Exptl. Cell Research* **10**, 24 (1956).
7. —— The Role of the Jelly Coat and the Block to Polyspermy in the Fertilization of Sea Urchins. Dissertation. Almqvist and Wiksell, Uppsala, 1956.
8. HAGSTRÖM, B. E. and HAGSTRÖM, B., *Exptl. Cell Research* **6**, 479 (1954).
9. HARVEY, E. B., *Biol. Bull.* **62**, 155 (1932).
10. —— *ibid.* **64**, 125 (1933).
11. HARVEY, E. N., *ibid.* **61**, 273 (1931).
12. HULTIN, E., *Exptl. Cell Research* **10**, 286 (1956).
13. IMMERS, J., *Arkiv Zool.* (2), **9**, 367 (1956).
14. —— *Exptl. Cell Research* **12**, 145 (1957).
15. KALTENBACH, J., *Arkiv Zool.* (2), **11**, 77 (1957).
16. KAVANAU, J. L., *Exptl. Cell Research* **7**, 530 (1954).
17. KRISZAT, G. and RUNNSTRÖM, J., *Arkiv Zool.* (2), **10**, 595 (1957).
18. LILLIE, R. S., *Am. J. Physiol.* **26**, 106 (1910).
19. LUNDBLAD, G., *Arkiv Kemi* **7 B**, 127 (1954).
20. LUNDBLAD, G., Proteolytic Activity in Sea Urchin Gametes. Dissertation. Almqvist and Wiksell, Uppsala, 1954.
21. MITCHISON, J. M., *Exptl. Cell Research* **10**, 309, 316 (1956).
22. PORTER, K. R., *J. Exptl. Med.* **97**, 727 (1953).
23. ROTSCHILD, LORD and SWANN, M. M., *J. Exptl. Biol.* **26**, 164 (1949).
24. —— *ibid.* **28**, 403 (1951).

[1] When possible reference has been made to review articles where a more detailed survey is given of the pertinent field.

25. RUNNSTRÖM, J., *Protoplasma* **4**, 388 (1928).
26. —— *Advances in Enzymol.* **9**, 241 (1949).
27. —— *Symposia Soc. Exptl. Biol.* **6**, 39 (1952).
28. —— *Exptl. Cell Research* **8**, 49 (1955).
29. —— Festschrift Arthur Stoll. Basel, 1957.
30. RUNNSTRÖM, J. and IMMERS, J., *Exptl. Cell Research* **10**, 354 (1956).
31. RUNNSTRÖM, J. and KRISZAT, G., *Exptl. Cell Research* **12**, 526 (1957).
32. TYLER. A., *Physiol. Rev.* **28**, 180 (1948).
33. VASSEUR, E., The Chemistry and Physiology of the Jelly Coat of the Sea Urchin Egg. Dissertation. Stockholm, 1952.
34. YAMAMOTO, T., *Cytologia* **14**, 219 (1948).
35. —— *Exptl. Cell Research* **6**, 56 (1954).

Experimental Cell Research, Suppl. **5**, *547–559 (1958)*

STUDIES ON MEMBRANE RESTING POTENTIALS
OF MUSCLE

EFFECTS OF K-LACK, X-IRRADIATION AND DNP[1]

J. W. WOODBURY

Department of Physiology and Biophysics, University of Washington School of Medicine, Seattle,
Wash., U.S.A.

O$_N$ a short-term, non-steady-state basis, the transmembrane resting potential (RP) of the striated muscle fibers of frogs depends directly on the internal and external concentrations of K$^+$ ion ([1], see also for other references), and is little affected by other ions. RP is defined as the potential of the inside minus the potential of the outside. However, in experiments where external ion concentrations are varied, the internal concentrations are also changing, and the resulting net fluxes will determine the RP. *In vivo*, on the other hand, the ion concentrations remain relatively constant, and the RP is maintained at about -90 mV (inside negative), a value somewhat smaller than the potassium equilibrium voltage, $V_K = (RT/F) \log K_0/K_i = 59 \log 2.5/140 = -103$ mV [1] where K_0 and K_i are, respectively, the external and internal potassium concentrations. Hence, although the electrical and concentration gradients acting on K ions are oppositely directed and the membrane permeability to K is relatively large, it appears that the K concentration gradient is not the ultimate energy source that maintains the RP, since in the steady state the gradients are not quite equal. Rather, the K gradient acts as a potential energy store that tends to prevent large or sudden variations in RP in adverse circumstances.

For Na ions, on the other hand, both the voltage and the concentration gradient (the electrochemical gradient) act to drive Na into the fiber. Although the sodium permeability (P_{Na}) is small in comparison to P_K, the large electrochemical gradient produces an appreciable Na influx [11]. There is considerable evidence to document the logical necessity for an active extrusion of Na from the cell interior [2, 7, 12, 13, 14, 16]. In this context, "active" means that work must be done on a Na ion to carry it out of the cell against the electrochemical gradient. This "Na pump" appears to be the energy source

[1] Supported in part by research grants (B 462 and B 823) from the National Institute of Neurological Diseases and Blindness of the National Institutes of Health, U.S. Public Health Service and the State of Washington Research for Biology and Medicine.

which maintains the resting potential and the concentration differences across the cell membrane [18].

Since the maintenance of the resting potential appears to depend ultimately on active Na extrusion, then something of the nature of this process may be learned from the manner in which the RP declines with time in an excised muscle subjected to various untoward conditions. Experimental variables of interest are those which would be expected to slow the rate of Na pumping or to increase membrane permeability to ions. This paper describes and discusses experiments in which the effects of X-irradiation, the metabolic inhibitor 2,4 dinitrophenol (DNP), and low external K concentrations on the time course of the RP decline were studied.

METHODS

Pairs of sartorius muscles from the green frog (*Rana pipiens*) were excised and pinned inward, face up, at normal length in wax bottom chambers. Solutions of the desired composition were perfused through the chambers. One muscle was used as a control and the other was subjected to the experimental procedure. Membrane resting potentials were measured with 3 M KCl-filled, Ling–Gerard microelectrodes, impaled transversely across the cell membrane. At appropriate time intervals, a set of 10 surface cells at random distances across the muscle were impaled to obtain an estimate of the mean RP of the muscle fibers. In the experiments with X-irradiation, both muscles of a pair were mounted in radiation chambers. The experimental muscle was then exposed to 10,000–80,000 r with 50 kv X-rays. Thereafter the muscles were handled as described above.

Normal Ringer's solution of the following composition (in mM/l) was used: NaCl, 110; KCl, 2.5; CaCl$_2$, 1.07; NaHCO$_3$, 2.38; K$_2$HPO$_4$, 0.08. The pH was about 7.5. Initially, normal Ringer's solution was perfused through both chambers, and one or two sets of readings were obtained. In most experiments, the perfusion fluid to one or both chambers was then changed to a K-free Ringer's solution. Either the experimental muscle had been irradiated, or DNP (10^{-4} M) was added to the perfusion fluid. All experiments were carried out at room temperature (21–26°C) during June to September.

RESULTS

To establish a basis for comparison, the time course for the decline of the mean RP of excised muscles kept in flowing Ringer's solutions was determined. The survival time (t_s) at which the mean potential had fallen to one-half its initial value varied greatly from muscle to muscle. The curves in Fig. 1 are plots of mean RP's as a percentage of initial values for control, radiated, and DNP-treated muscles kept in normal Ringer's solutions. Most of the points are means of about 100 readings, calculated by combining all values obtained in successive 3-hour intervals and plotting the point in the middle of the interval. The vertical lines subtend ± 2 S.E. The average t_s of control muscles was 12 hr. The RP was well-maintained for 7.5 hr, and then fell off more rapidly. The t_s of individual muscles varied considerably, but

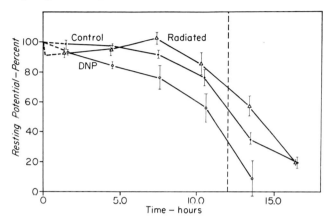

Fig. 1.—Time course of RP decline in excised frog muscles soaked in normal Ringer's solution. *Abscissa*, time in hours since excision; *ordinate*, RP in per cent of initial control values. Each point is the mean of about 100 readings. Readings from all muscles used were lumped into 3-hour intervals and averaged. Vertical bars subtend ± 2 S.E. Radiated: muscles were given 50,000 r at zero time. DNP: 5×10^{-5} *M* DNP added to both at zero time.

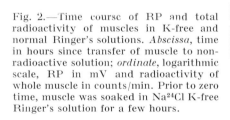

Fig. 2.—Time course of RP and total radioactivity of muscles in K-free and normal Ringer's solutions. *Abscissa*, time in hours since transfer of muscle to non-radioactive solution; *ordinate*, logarithmic scale, RP in mV and radioactivity of whole muscle in counts/min. Prior to zero time, muscle was soaked in Na²⁴Cl K-free Ringer's solution for a few hours.

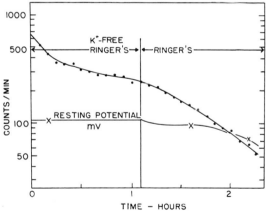

the shape of the individual curves was generally similar to the mean curve. The mean initial RP was about 90 mV, as can be seen from Figs. 3, 4, and 5.

The effects of massive X-irradiation (50,000 r) on muscles kept in Ringer's solution (Radiated curve, Fig. 1) were not striking. The most dramatic and consistent effect of radiation was a 5–10 mV fall in RP. This change was

found in the first readings taken after the radiation. The consequent rise of
the RP to initial control values at 7.5 hr after the initial, radiation-induced
drop, although statistically significant, was obscured by variation in individual
experiments. The mean survival time was 13.5 hr. Radiation dosages of

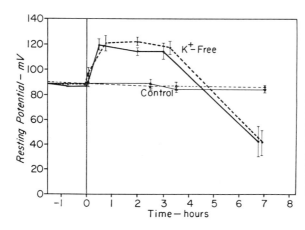

Fig. 3.—Effects of K-free solutions on
RP. *Abscissa*, time in hours; *ordinate*,
RP in mV. Solid lines RP's of sartorius muscles from frog *A*; dashed
lines, frog *B*. All muscles kept in
flowing normal Ringer's solution prior
to zero time. At zero time one muscle
of each pair was transferred to flowing
K-free Ringer's solution.

this size are sufficient to cause gross structural changes and extensive microscopic damage [3]. Although the late rise in RP might result from the metabolic
alterations, the initial, immediate fall must be attributed to membrane
changes. The simplest hypothesis is that the X-ray photons "punch" holes
in the membrane and thereby increase membrane permeability to all ions.

Originally the effects of DNP on RP were studied on the supposition that
DNP inhibits active Na extrusion in muscle as it does in the squid giant axon
[7]. However, Keynes and Maisel [12] have shown that DNP does not affect
Na efflux in frog muscle. This finding has been confirmed by the author
(unpublished observations). Nevertheless, it is evident from the DNP curve
in Fig. 1 that DNP in moderate concentrations (ca. 5×10^{-5}) definitely increases the rate of RP decline, and decreases mean survival time by nearly
2 hr. The cause of this effect has not been definitely established, but it may
result from an increase in P_{Na}. This possibility will be discussed later.

Effects of K-free Ringer's on RP.—Hodgkin and Keynes [7], using cephalopod giant axons, and Keynes [11], using frog muscle, have demonstrated
direct dependence of Na outflux upon *external* K concentration. This suggests
that a Na–K exchange reaction is involved. In cephalopod axon this exchange
has been definitely established, and it accounts for about two-thirds of the
Na efflux, i.e., efflux falls to one-third if all external K is removed. Keynes
[11] found an average rate constant of 1.12 hr^{-1} for Na efflux in 2.5 mM

K/1 Ringer's solutions and 0.64 hr^{-1} in K-free. Fig. 2 illustrates an experiment in which Na efflux and RP were measured simultaneously. Originally, the muscle had been soaked in a K-free, Na^{22}, Ringer's solution for several hours; muscle radioactivity was then determined, as a function of time, while first K-free and then K-containing, non-radioactive Ringer's solution were perfused past the muscle. The rate constant in the K-free solution was about 0.4 hr^{-1}, and in 2.5 mM K/1 (normal) Ringer's solution, about 1.3 hr^{-1}. These values fall well within the range of Keynes' measurements. However, the values may be erroneous since the surface fibers were in rather poor condition when the transmembrane potentials were measured. In the K-free solution, the RP was only slightly above 100 mV, which is low for this solution, and when the muscle was transferred to normal Ringer's solution, the RP dropped immediately to the normal value of 90 mV. Thereafter the RP fell rapidly, and was 70 mV at 2 hr. Of course, surface fibers are in the minority, and the majority of fibers may have been in better condition. Measuring the RP's of surface fibers gives a biased sample of the whole muscle, and one which is likely to be low since these are the fibers most likely to be damaged and directly exposed to changes in the bathing medium.

If it is assumed that the decline of RP in an excised muscle results from a gradual failure of the Na pump and from the concomitant intracellular gain of Na and Cl and loss of K, a reduction in survival time would be expected to follow any change increasing Na influx and/or decreasing Na outflux. Removal of K from the bathing medium not only decreases Na outflux to 0.3 of normal, but also increases influx because the higher RP augments the inward driving force of Na ions. Fig. 3 shows the effects of K-free Ringer's solution on the RP. The solid lines are data obtained on the sartorius muscles from frog *A*, and the dashed lines, from frog *B*. At time zero, the perfusion solution for one muscle of each pair was changed to K-free. The control muscles maintained a constant RP of 90 mV during the 7 hr of the experiment. The RP's of the K-free treated muscles rapidly increased to 120 mV. In these muscles, the RP was well-maintained for 3 hr, but thereafter fell rapidly towards zero. The t_s of the K-free treated muscles was only 6 hr; whereas the t_s for the control muscles must have been at least twice as much. This pattern of potential change as a function of time was always observed in muscles in good condition placed in K-free solutions, but the value of t_s varied considerably.

The reduced t_s in K-free solutions and the probable reasons for it suggest that the K-free conditions render the muscle more sensitive to untoward environmental changes, such as X-iradiation and DNP, which possibly act by increasing P_{Na}. This expectation is borne out by experiments of the types illustrated in Figs. 4 and 5. As in Fig. 3, solid lines are RP's of muscles from frog A, and dashed lines, from frog B. In the experiment of Fig. 4, one muscle from each frog was kept in normal Ringer's solution for the duration of the

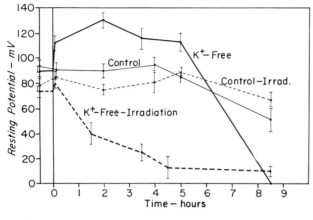

Fig. 4.—Effects of X-irradiation on RP of muscles. Same type of experiment as in Fig. 3, except muscle pair B was given 50,000 r of X-irradiation. See text for further explanation.

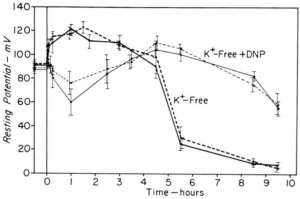

Fig. 5. Effects of DNP on RP. Same experimental design as in Fig. 3, except at time zero all four muscles were transferred to flowing K-free Ringer's solution. The solution perfusing one muscle of each pair contained 5×10^{-5} M DNP.

experiment, and the other was transferred to a K-free solution at zero time. Pair A was not irradiated; pair B was given 50,000 r. The muscles in the normal solution showed the general behavior illustrated in Fig. 1, the irradiated muscle outlasting the non-irradiated. The RP's of the non-irradiated K-free muscle followed a time course like that in Fig. 3. However, when the irradiated test muscle was transferred to K-free Ringer's solution, the RP showed only a slight initial rise, which was followed by a rapid decline to near zero values. The survival time was only 1.5 hr. In irradiated muscles, the initial rate at which the potentials declined after transfer to K-free solutions depended directly on the X-ray dosage. The dose could be adjusted so that the RP did not change on transfer to K-free solutions. The curve of RP as a function of external potassium concentration, K_0, was peculiarly shaped in X-irradiated muscles: The RP at low K_0's may well be lower than in normal K_0's, but attempts to establish the detailed RP versus K_0 curves for irradiated muscles did not yield consistent results because the muscles in low K solutions survived such a short time.

Fig. 5 shows the results of an experiment in which DNP (5×10^{-5} M) was added to the K-free Ringers perfusing one muscle of each pair, the other muscle of each pair being perfused with K-free Ringer's solution. The K-free solutions were started at zero time. The control muscles showed a time course of potential changes like that in Fig. 3, while the potentials of the DNP-treated muscles rapidly fell 20–30 mV within an hour. Thereafter, however, the potential recovered to the near-normal, K-free RP of about 110 mV, and was still well-maintained at 9 hr, 4 hr after the controls in K-free solutions alone were dead. DNP-treated and irradiated muscles behaved quite similarly immediately after transfer to K-free solutions, but after an hour, DNP-treated muscles showed marked recovery while the X-rayed muscles showed none. Muscles irradiated in smaller amounts, however, did tend to show recovery after the initial fall, but the effect was not as distinct as that in DNP-treated fibers.

DISCUSSION

If an adequate quantitative theory of RP decline as a function of time after excision could be developed, the interpretation of the results given above would be easier and more meaningful. Attempts to construct such a theory have been only moderately successful, even though there is a considerable body of evidence on which to base a theory. Before the results are discussed in detail, a review of the factors which affect the net ionic fluxes through a membrane may be helpful. The net flux of an ion through the membrane (ΔM), defined as the outflux minus the influx, determines the rate at which the internal concentration of that ion changes:

$$dC_i/dt = - \Delta M \cdot A/v \qquad (1)$$

Where C_i is the internal concentration of the ion, t is the time, and A/v is the surface to volume ratio of the cell. The factors determining the in- and outfluxes of an ion are not well-defined experimentally. Also, the theory of ionic movements through diffusion barriers is not yet any great help because the equations are mathematically complex and detailed knowledge of membrane structure is not yet available. For lack of a better model, the equations describing ion movements in the simplest case, that of an infinitesimal membrane, will be used. If V, the potential, is assumed to be zero in the middle of the membrane, then the passive membrane fluxes M_0 and M_i of an ion of permeability P are:

$$M_0 = PC_i \exp(\beta V Z), \tag{2}$$

$$M_i = PC_0 \exp(-\beta V Z), \tag{3}$$

and

$$\Delta M = M_0 - M_i = P[C_i \exp(\beta V Z) - C_0 \exp(-\beta V Z)]$$
$$= PE = 2P\sqrt{C_i C_0} \sinh \beta Z(V - V_i), \tag{4}$$

$$V_i = \frac{1}{2\beta Z} \ln C_0/C_i, \tag{5}$$

where β is $F/2RT$, Z is the valence, and E is defined as the electrochemical potential.

In words, the flux (current) equals permeability (conductance) multiplied by the electrochemical gradient (driving voltage). The final condition necessary to specify the system is that the sum of all (ionic fluxes × valence) must equal zero; otherwise, there would be charge accumulation. This condition determines the membrane voltage, i.e., a temporary net flux imbalance charges the membrane capacity until the voltage has changed sufficiently to nullify this net flux. If it is assumed that Na, K and Cl are the only ions contributing importantly to membrane flux, then the equations describing the system are:

$$\left.\begin{aligned} d\mathrm{K}_i/dt &= -\Delta M_\mathrm{K} \cdot A/v, \\ d\mathrm{Na}_i/dt &= -\Delta M_\mathrm{Na} \cdot A/v, \\ d\mathrm{Cl}_i/dt &= -\Delta M_\mathrm{Cl} \cdot A/v, \end{aligned}\right\} \tag{6}$$

$$\Delta M_\mathrm{K} + \Delta M_\mathrm{Na} - \Delta M_\mathrm{Cl} = 0. \tag{7}$$

Cl ions are probably not actively transported in muscle, so equation (4) describes all Cl fluxes. Na and K movements are, of course, complicated by active transport. At least three components comprise Na outflux: passive movement (negligible at normal membrane potentials) and two types of active extrusion, one independent of external K and the other a Na–K exchange reaction [7, 8]. In addition, there may well be exchange diffusion, as postulated by Ussing [17], in which there is a one-to-one exchange of internal and external Na ions via a Na-specific carrier. Potassium outflux is apparently passive [8], and its influx is partly active and partly passive. The net fluxes for each ion are:

$$\Delta M_{Cl} = - P_{Cl} E_{Cl}, \tag{8}$$

$$\Delta M_K = P_K E_K - M_{NK}, \tag{9}$$

$$\Delta M_{Na} = P_K E_K + M_{NK} + M_a, \tag{10}$$

where M_{NK} and M_a are the fluxes of the Na–K exchange and straight Na extrusion, respectively. Substituting equations (8), (9) and (10) in equation (7) gives

$$P_K E_K + P_{Na} + P_{Cl} E_{Cl} + M_a = 0. \tag{11}$$

Since the E's are functions of concentrations and voltage only, equation (11) specifies membrane voltage if the concentrations are given. Equations (6), combined with (8), (9) and (10), give the concentrations as functions of time and initial values. Equations (6) to (11) form a set of four, simultaneous, first-order, non-linear, differential equations which can be solved for any set of parameters and initial conditions.

Equation (11) has some interesting aspects. Firstly, if it is solved explicitly for V with M_a equal to 0, the result is identical with that obtained from a constant field assumption, as first developed by Goldman [6], namely

$$V_r = \frac{RT}{F} \ln \frac{P_K K_0 + P_{Na} Na_0 + P_{Cl} Cl_i}{P_K K_i + P_{Na} Na_i + P_{Cl} Cl_0}, \tag{12}$$

where the V_r, resting potential, is defined as the potential of the inside minus the potential of outside. It is evident that with a Na–K exchange pump, equation (12) can represent the voltage of a steady-state system since the exchange reaction does not contribute to membrane current. If M_a is not zero and does not depend upon membrane voltage, equation (11) is quadratic in exp βV. Equations (11) and (12) differ somewhat in form. As a check on the validity of (11), an attempt was made to fit Adrian's [1] K_0 versus V_r data, which cannot be described by the Goldman equation. Neither can they be described by equation (11), but the fit is better with (11). However, it must be remembered that equation (11) contains one more parameter and a better fit is expected on this basis alone.

As a first approximation, ionic permeabilities were assumed to be independent of V. Permeability constants for Na and K were calculated from known membrane potentials, internal concentrations [1, 2], and fluxes [4, 11]. P_{Cl} was taken as 0.25 of P_K [10]. The product of permeability multiplied by the surface to volume ratio gives a rate constant (hr^{-1}) which, when multiplied by E, the electrochemical gradient (mM/l), gives the rate of change of internal concentration $(mM/l/hr)$. The ratio of $P_{Na}/P_K = 0.023$, calculated in this way, agrees well with the ratio which Jenerick [10] obtained from the V versus K_0 curve. Na outflux was taken as one-third M_a and two-thirds M_{NK}. M_a was assumed to be proportional to Na_i [9] and M_{NK}, proportional to $\sqrt{K_O}$ [11]; 10^{-11} $M/cm^2/sec$, the total Na outflux measured with tracer Na [11], was used for $M_{Na} + M_{NK}$.

These values for the parameters and the initial conditions were used to compute approximate solutions of the differential equation on an IBM type 650, magnetic-drum, data-analyzing machine. Programming difficulties have thus far prevented complete calculations. However, even with a "dead" Na pump, the predicted rates of fall of RP are far smaller than the rates observed in muscles perfused with either normal or K-free Ringer's solutions.

Jenerick [10] found that if the muscle membrane is depolarized with KCl, the membrane resistance increases exponentially with membrane voltage. His data are well described by $G = G_r \exp 2\beta(V - V_r)$; where G is total membrane conductance, and G_r is the conductance at the resting potential, V_r. There is no evidence on whether the relationship in muscle is between conductance and voltage or between conductance and K_0, but in squid giant axon, conductance is highly voltage-dependent [5]. When the above relationship between G and V was inserted in the differential equations (assuming P's proportional to G's), the simple scheme used for approximating the solutions became unstable since, eventually, successive values showed oscillations of increasing amplitude. The portions of the curve obtained before instability occurred, indicate that the assumption of voltage-dependent permeabilities and of an inactive Na pump will give rates of fall of RP greater than those observed experimentally. The assumption, mentioned above, that active Na extrusion depends on internal Na [9] and external K [7, 8, 11] concentrations appears to be necessary for the prediction of the phase of maintained, high RP's seen in K-free solutions.

One interesting finding from these computations is that only a few minutes after a sudden change in voltage, V_{Cl} is nearly equal to V. This near equality occurs because P_{Cl} is relatively high, 0.25 of P_K, and Cl_i is small, of the order of K_0, so that any net Cl flux quickly produces large relative changes in Cl_i. Adrian [1] has speculated on this point. As predicted from the equations, the curves of the internal Na and K concentrations with the Na pump inactive are roughly exponential and quite similar to those measured by Shaw and Simon [13] in excised toad muscle soaked in normal Ringer's solution but in which there must have been active Na transport. The differential equations so far have not been modified to include Hodgkin and Keynes' [8] finding that K ions move through the membrane "in file", i.e., outflux depends not only on K_i, as assumed by equation (3), but also on K_0. A decrease in K_0 increases the outflux of K.

Radiation effects.—In view of the nature of this conference it would be interesting to know what changes in cell and membrane ultrastructure are produced by heavy X-irradiation. Gerstner *et al.* [3] have studied acute radiation effects on the histological structure and contractile ability of skeletal muscle. The effects of X-rays on RP are most readily explicable in terms of a rather large increase in P_{Na}. The exact mechanism bringing about this increase in P_{Na} is not known. It may be the indirect chemical effects of the hydrogen peroxide produced by the interaction between X-ray photons and water, a direct interaction between the photons and the highly specialized membrane structure, or both. In any case, the integrity of the membrane is presumably breached, so that there are more pores through which all small molecules can pass. How low concentrations of H_2O_2 affect RP's has not been tested. The crucial test of the hypothesis that X-irradiation increases P_{Na} is, of course, to study Na influx in irradiated muscles either with tracer Na or by altering Na_0, experiments which have not been performed. From equation (11) it can be calculated that doubling P_{Na} will prevent a significant rise in RP on transfer to K-free solutions, and that a quadrupling of P_{Na} will cause a distinct fall in RP in both normal and K-free solutions.

The slow rise of RP to normal values following the irradiation-induced drop is perhaps attributable to a stimulation of the Na pump by the slowly rising internal Na, or perhaps, to an increase in metabolism produced directly by the irradiation. The Na–K exchange pump must play an important role in this recovery since removal of external K causes such a rapid fall in RP (Fig. 4). However, the increased survival time of irradiated muscles in normal solution is difficult to explain.

DNP effects.—The actions which DNP exerts on the RP of muscles in normal and K-free solutions are difficult to explain. Simon [15] has reviewed the biochemical evidence on the nature of DNP toxicity. At the concentrations used in these experiments, DNP stimulates respiration and inhibits oxidative phosphorylation. Initially, at least, DNP does not inhibit Na outflux, so the accelerated fall of RP found in DNP-treated muscles in normal solutions must be attributed to some other cause. Another possibility is that DNP has the direct effect on the membrane of increasing P_{Na}. Such an increase in P_{Na} could also explain the initial rapid fall in RP observed when the muscle is transferred to K-free Ringer's solution containing DNP. If P_{Na} were increased, then the reduction of the external Na concentration should likewise reduce the observed DNP effects. Preliminary experiments on the RP's of muscles placed in K-free, 20 per cent NaCl, 80 per cent sucrose, Ringer's solutions indicate that the reduction in RP produced by DNP in K-free solutions still occurs even when most of the Na is removed from the bathing solution. Thus the initial effects of DNP on the RP seemingly cannot be attributed to either an inhibition of the Na pump or an increase in P_{Na}. Further experiments with low Na solutions and with radioactive Na uptake are clearly needed. DNP is only slightly ionized at pH 7.5, and has a negative charge in the ionic form. Clearly, then, the initial depolarization seen in K-free, DNP solutions is not attributable to direct ionic penetration by DNP. For the moment, DNP's effects must go unexplained, since no simple hypothesis capable of explaining the data at hand is apparent.

Another puzzling phenomenon of DNP's action is the decreased t_s in normal Ringer's solution, compared with untreated controls, and the recovery of the RP and increased t_s of DNP-treated muscles in K-free solutions. It might be supposed that DNP is less toxic if in K-free rather than normal solutions. Kirschner (personal communication) found that DNP induced similar increases in the O_2 uptake of frog muscles kept in K-free and in normal solutions. The mean increase in muscles kept in normal solutions was 2.50 times, and for muscles in K-free solutions, it was 2.1 times. Perhaps, this slightly lower increase in O_2 uptake in K-free solutions is a difference in the right direction: the increase in O_2 uptake in K-free-treated muscles is less than in controls; therefore, the muscles may be less affected by the DNP, and over long terms, may be more capable of handling the increased demands for Na extrusion produced by the K lack. Further experiments are necessary to elucidate the mechanisms of DNP's actions on membrane resting potentials.

SUMMARY

1. The effects of massive (10,000–80,000 r) X-irradiation and of 2,4 dinitrophenol (DNP) on the resting membrane potentials (RP) of excised frog sartorius muscles have been studied.

2. In normal Ringer's solution, the RP of an excised muscle is well-maintained for about 10 hr and then falls off quite rapidly. DNP ($5 \times 10^{-5} M$) causes the RP to decline at a faster rate. X-irradiation causes an immediate drop in RP, but thereafter there is a slow recovery to initial control values. The survival time of irradiated muscle is greater than that of controls.

3. The actions of DNP and X-irradiation on RP are accentuated by removal of K from the Ringer's solution. In control muscles, the removal of K from the bathing solution causes a rapid increase of RP from 90 to 120 mV. Survival time is shortened; the RP is maintained for 5–8 hr.

4. In X-irradiated muscles in K-free solutions the RP falls rapidly towards zero (in about 2 hr).

5. DNP added to K-free solutions causes an initial rapid fall in RP followed by a recovery to near control values. Survival time is greater than that in muscles in K-free solutions without DNP.

6. The actions of X-irradiation are explicable on the assumption that membrane permeability to sodium ions is increased. The actions of DNP are difficult to explain; the simpler possibilities appear to be excluded.

I am indebted to Dr. Leonard B. Kirschner of Washington State College, Pullman, for testing the effects of K lack on O_2 uptake. Drs. John Lee, Vern N. Walker and Joseph W. Voegtlin rendered valuable assistance in carrying out most of the routine resting potential measurements.

REFERENCES

1. ADRIAN, R. H., *J. Physiol.* **133**, 631 (1956).
2. DESMEDT, J. W., *J. Physiol.* **121**, 191 (1953).
3. GERSTNER, H. B., LEWIS, R. B. and RICHEY, E. O., *J. Gen. Physiol.* **37**, 445 (1954).
4. HARRIS, E. J., *J. Physiol.* **120**, 246 (1953).
5. HODGKIN, A. L., HUXLEY, A. F. and KATZ, K., *J. Physiol.* **116**, 424 (1952).
6. HODGKIN, A. L. and KATZ, B., *J. Physiol.* **108**, 37 (1949).
7. HODGKIN, A. L. and KEYNES, R. D., *J. Physiol.* **128**, 28 (1955).
8. —— ibid. **128**, 61 (1955).
9. —— ibid. **131**, 592 (1956).
10. JENERICK, H. P., *J. Cellular Comp. Physiol.* **42**, 427 (1953).
11. KEYNES, R. D., *Proc. Roy. Soc.* **B142**, 359 (1954).
12. KEYNES, R. D. and MAISEL, G. W., *Proc. Roy. Soc.* **B142**, 383 (1954).
13. SHAW, F. H. and SIMON, S. E., *Australian J. Exptl. Biol. Med. Sci.* **33**, 153 (1955).
14. —— *Nature Lond.* **176**, 1031 (1955).
15. SIMON, E. W., *Biol. Rev.* **28**, 453 (1953).
16. STEINBACH, H. B., *Am. J. Physiol.* **167**, 284 (1951).
17. USSING, H. H., *Cold Spring Harbor Symposia Quant. Biol.* **13**, 193 (1948).
18. —— *Symposia Soc. Exptl. Biol.* **8**, 407 (1954).

560   *Experimental Cell Research, Suppl.* **5**, *560–567 (1958)*

THE MORPHOLOGY OF MUSCLE FIBERS AND MUSCLE CELLS WITH DIFFERENT PROPERTIES OF CONDUCTION OF EXCITATION [1]

H. RUSKA

Division of Laboratories and Research, New York State Department of Health, Albany, N.Y., U.S.A.

CONDUCTION of excitation has been associated with the occurrence and properties of membranes since Nernst's [12, 13] physical theory of electric excitation. Concerning the nature of these membranes, Lloyd [9] states that they are not, and "should not be in present state of our knowledge, identified with any definite structure visible in any form of microscope". Electron microscopists, however, can hardly avoid seeing membranes, consequently they must describe their course and eventually speculate on their meanings. They have added to the long recognized surface membrane of the cell the knowledge of an internal membrane system designated as endoplasmic reticulum by Porter and Thompson [16]. The endoplasmic reticulum actually forms a communicating system of tubules, vesicles, and cysternae containing a separate fluid phase different from the cytoplasmic matrix and enclosing the cell nucleus within the perinuclear cysterna. Thus far, these internal membranes can be considered as carriers of membrane potentials in a manner similar to the outer plasma membrane and the membranes of vacuoles in plant cells where potentials have actually been measured. Furthermore, the endoplasmic reticulum could have the necessary properties for conduction since morphogenetically its membranes originate from the cell surface membrane [14] and therefore might be closely related to the outer plasma membrane in their chemical composition and functional properties [18, 10].

Unfortunately we cannot measure potentials and propagation of potential alterations in the dimensions of the endoplasmic reticulum. But what we can do, is to compare skeletal muscles with different properties of conduction, and also heart muscle and smooth muscle, with respect to plasma membranes and endoplasmic reticulum and see how morphological observations support and widen present concepts of membrane potentials and their propagation.

[1] The presentation is based on observations and interpretations advanced together with G. A. Edwards and R. Caesar from the Division of Laboratories and Research and with D. H. Moore, working with the author in the College of Physicians and Surgeons, Columbia University, New York.

SKELETAL MUSCLE FIBERS

In the last few years so many electron micrographs of striated muscle fibers have been demonstrated (e.g., [5, 4, 19, 15]) that one might believe the morphology of these fibers is sufficiently known. A muscle fiber reconstruction by Bennett [1] summarizes the present knowledge. The contractile material is arranged in fibrils which are separated by a fine three dimensional network of endoplasmic reticulum. The main directions of this network are longitudinal between the fibrils, and transversal on both sides of the Z band and around the M band. At these levels, the reticulum is attached to the sarcolemma. Mitochondria lie either longitudinally between the fibrils (birds) or preferably transversally on both sides of Z (mammals). However, there exists some doubt whether this fibrillar arrangement is true for all striated fibers in vertebrates. Krüger [7], who started his studies almost 30 years ago, claims that muscles with tonic function are composed of, or contain, fibers which show no fibrillation. In cross sections their contractile material appears to be arranged in irregular, large fields (see also Krüger and Günther [8]). Naturally, the fields were considered by others as an artifact but thus far we have been able to confirm Krüger's important observation in muscles of frogs, birds and mammals [4, 17]. The *mm. latissimus dorsi anterior* and *posterior* of certain birds, where, according to Krüger [6], the *anterior* contains only fibers with field structure whilst the *posterior* contains only fibrillar fibers, proved to be an especially valuable object for electron microscopic studies. As every electron microscopist knows, there is, in general, no lack of artifacts in osmium fixed and methacrylate embedded specimens but they look quite different from what could be an artifactual transformation of a fibrillar fiber to an afibrillar fiber. Fig. 1 shows the conventional fibrillar fiber of a crow. The afibrillar fiber, or fiber with cross sectional field structure, taken from the same bird is demonstrated in Fig. 2. It is obvious that a fibrillar separation of the contractile material is missing over wide areas in tonic fibers. This means that coincidentally there is considerably less endoplasmic reticulum in these fibers. We are, however, not yet able to give a full reconstruction of its three dimensional distribution.

The sarcolemmas of fibrillar and afibrillar skeletal muscle fibers appear the same. An inner dense layer, the plasma membrane, covers the content of the fiber and a less dense layer separated by a narrow interspace forms the limitation against the interstitial space. This outer layer is equivalent to the basement membrane of epithelia and capillaries. Since excitation of skeletal fibers remains restricted to the individually excited fiber, even though contact between sarcolemmas may be very close, one might consider the plasma membrane as the selective ion barrier and the basement membrane as a restrictive barrier [18] protecting the fiber against ion loss into the more aqueous interstitial space and insulating the fibers one from another.

HEART MUSCLE CELLS AND CONDUCTING SYSTEM

In the cellular mammalian heart muscle the endoplasmic reticulum is essentially arranged as in the fibrillar skeletal muscle plasmodium [10] and is particularly abundant close to the sarcolemma. The plasma membrane of the heart sarcolemma shows indentations which cannot be distinguished from indentations found on many other cells (macrophages, capillary endothelia, peritoneal endothelia, smooth muscle cells) and is considered as the appearance of pinocytosis [14, 11]. The indentations may form vesicles which then unite with the endoplasmic reticulum to feed extracellular fluid into the inner phase and the plasma membrane substance into the membranes of the endoplasmic reticulum. The morphological and physiological bases for intracellular transmission of excitation are thus provided by the endoplasmic reticulum.

The conduction along the cell surfaces must involve two different structures in the heart muscle; the sarcolemma and the intercalated discs. Both are cell borders. The sarcolemma consists of two different layers apposed to the interstitial space. The disc consists of two equal plasma membranes between adjacent heart muscle cells. With the plasma membrane of both, the endoplasmic reticulum has an intimate contact. It seems likely that excitation spreads from cell to cell not only along the sarcolemma but also across the intercalated discs. The basement membrane, that is, the sheath considered to restrict free movement of ions and to insulate muscle fiber from muscle fiber, is missing between the plasma membranes of the disc. Since the heart muscle is cellular and not syncytial, contraction must start almost simultaneously in all cells. It does not proceed as a single contraction wave over the whole heart.

The conducting system of the heart (Fig. 3) is again cellular. The cell

Fig. 1.—*M. latissimus dorsi posterior* of a crow. Longitudinal section of contracted phasic fiber showing three myomeres with two Z bands (Z) of twelve fibrils, separated by endoplasmic reticulum (er). Mitochondria (m) at the lower left (Moore and Ruska, unpublished). ×9800.

Fig. 2.—*M. latissimus dorsi anterior* of a crow. Longitudinal section of contracted tonic fiber showing three myomeres with two Z bands (Z) but no fibrillation. Mitochondrion (m) at the lower left (Moore and Ruska, unpublished). ×13,600.

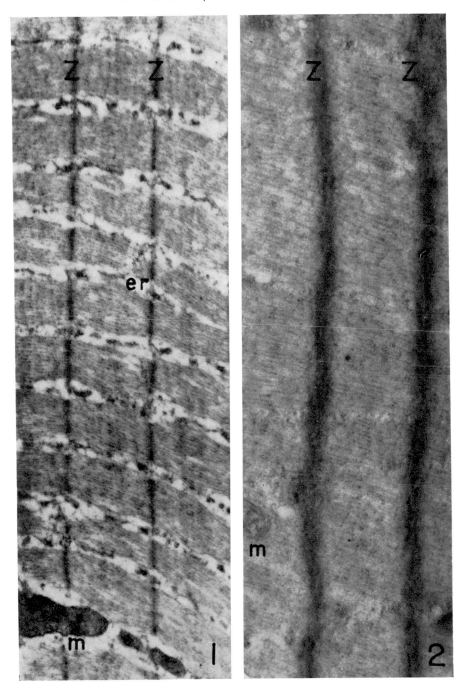

borders appear adjacent to connective tissue as sarcolemmas and apposed to neighboring cells of the conducting system as plasma membranes only [2].

SMOOTH MUSCLE CELLS

In smooth muscles it was very doubtful whether there exist membranes to serve in conduction. Most smooth muscles were considered to form a syncytium, in which the contractile material passed from one nuclear area to another and where the exoplasm between nuclear areas contained the collagen fibrils of the tissue without being separated from it by cell borders. Through the muscular syncytium there passed a network of communicating unmyelinated axons of the autonomic nerve system, accompanied only by naked Schwann nuclei and ending in some places close to the smooth muscle nuclei or in the contractile material. Electron microscopy had to discard this concept [3]. Smooth muscles of urinary bladder, gall bladder and uterus were found to be cellular. Each cell is bordered by its cytolemma consisting of a plasma membrane, a basement membrane and their interspace. The plasma membrane frequently shows pinocytosis. The endoplasmic reticulum preferentially appears at the periphery and at the extremities of the nucleus. The cytolemmas may contact each other or be separated by interstitial tissue containing collagenous fibrils, a few interstitial cells and capillaries. Nerve axons are very abundant in the interstitium and they are always enclosed or accompanied by sheath cell cytoplasm (Fig. 4). They also occur between adjacent cytolemmas of smooth muscle cells. Free axons and naked neurofibrils were not observed, but it seems likely that axons or axon ends contact surfaces of smooth muscle cells on the one side and are covered by sheath cell cytoplasm on the other thus forming an equivalent to neuromuscular junctions of striated fibers.

The electron microscope gives definite evidence for the existence of distinct cell membranes which can serve in the conduction of excitation for each cell. From a pure morphological point of view, spread of conduction from cell to cell seems unlikely, since, in contrast to the heart muscle, apposing

Fig. 3.—Two adjacent cells of the conducting system of sheep heart. Myofibrils cut longitudinally. Some mitochondria (*m*) close to the myofibrils. Tubules of the endoplasmic reticulum (*er*) in the cytoplasm of the upper cell. Two apposing plasma membranes run from (*p*) to (*p*) as indicated by arrows. They cross fibrils, forming intercalated discs or take their course parallel with the fibrils [2]. ×27,000.

Fig. 4.—Smooth muscle tissue of mouse urinary bladder. Myofilaments and nerve cut longitudinally. Apposed cytolemmas run horizontally from (*c*) to (*c*). Others are separated by an interstitial space. Nerve axon (*a*) surrounded by thin cytoplasmic layer and membranes of sheath cell (*s*) [3]. ×13,500.

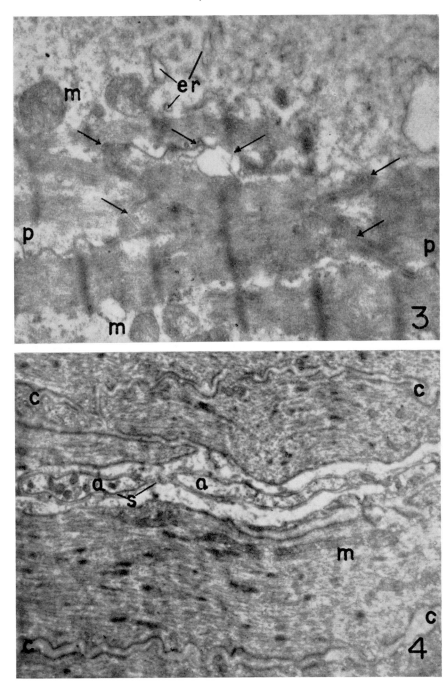

plasma membranes have not been found. There are always basement membranes between adjacent cells. Furthermore, contacts between nerve axons and muscle cells in the urinary bladder are so frequent that possibly more than one exists for each cell.

MEMBRANE SYSTEMS AND CONDUCTION

The limiting membrane common to all muscle fibers and enclosing all muscle cells completely is the plasma membrane. It is also this layer of the sarcolemma or cytolemma which shows indentations, and forms vesicles; furnishing membrane substance for the endoplasmic reticulum. We consider therefore the plasma membranes, together with the endoplasmic reticulum, as the carriers of membrane potentials and the structures propagating potential alterations. If this concept is justified, reactions of contractile cells depend not only on the modus of innervation or stimulation and on the striated or smooth nature of the contractile material, but also on the relation of the endoplasmic reticulum to the contractile material. This seems to be most obvious in the different morphological forms taken by the endoplasmic reticulum in phasic and tonic skeletal muscle fibers.

The endoplasmic reticulum might influence the contractile process by the same means as has been stated for the excited cell surface membrane, that is, by ion exchange across the membrane. Through both membranes ions can enter or leave the cytoplasmic matrix, but the endoplasmic reticulum in the fast reacting phasic fiber and in the heart muscle brings potential alterations and ion exchange into the immediate vicinity of the Z and M bands of each fibril segment, resulting in the fiber twitch. It is obvious that these principles would also apply to any other innervated cell containing endoplasmic reticulum, ergastoplasm or Nissl substance. The crucial question which remains is whether the interpretation of the endoplasmic reticulum as the intracellular conducting system, in addition to conduction along different types of cell membranes, results in a better understanding of electrophysiological data obtained from different types of muscle fibers, muscle cells, other innervated cells and innervating cells.

SUMMARY

The membranes of the endoplasmic reticulum in muscle fibers and muscle cells are considered to carry potentials and propagate excitation in a manner similar to the outer plasma membranes of cells. The concept of inner membrane potentials might contribute to the understanding of physiologic differences in muscles, where the endoplasmic reticulum varies in morphology and quantity. The concept should be taken into consideration in the interpretation of glandular innervation and of the origin of nerve impulses in the neuron in that the endoplasmic reticulum constitutes part of the ergastoplasm and the Nissl substance.

REFERENCES

1. BENNETT, H. ST., *J. Biophys. Biochem. Cytol.* **2**, *Suppl.*, 171 (1956).
2. CAESAR, R., *Ann. Rep. Div. Labs. and Research*, N.Y., p. 26 (1956).
3. CAESAR, R., EDWARDS, G. A. and RUSKA H., *J. Biophys. Biochem. Cytology* **3**, 867 (1957).
4. EDWARDS, G. A., RUSKA, H., DE SOUZA SANTOS, P. and VALLEJO-FREIRE, A., *J. Biophys. Biochem. Cytol.* **2**, *Suppl.*, 143 (1956).
5. HODGE, A. J., *J. Biophys. Biochem. Cytology* **2**, *Suppl.*, 131 (1956).
6. KRÜGER, P., *Zool. Anz.* **145**, *Suppl.*, 445 (1950).
7. —— Tetanus und Tonus der quergestreiften Skelettmuskeln der Wirbeltiere und des Menschen. Leipzig, Akad. Verlagsges., 1952.
8. KRÜGER, P. and GÜNTHER, P. G., *Acta Anat.* **28**, 135 (1956).
9. LLOYD, D. P. C., *in* A Textbook of Physiology. Ed. by J. F. FULTON. Seventh Edition, W. B. Saunders Co., Philadelphia and London, 1956.
10. MOORE, D. H. and RUSKA, H., *J. Biophys. Biochem. Cytol.* **3**, 261 (1957).
11. —— *ibid.* **3**, 457 (1957).
12. NERNST, W., *Nachr. Ges. Wiss. Göttingen, Math.phys. Kl.*, p. 104 (1899).
13. —— *Arch. ges. Physiol.* **122**, 275 (1908).
14. PALADE, G. E., *J. Biophys. Biochem. Cytol.* **2**, *Suppl.*, 85 (1956).
15. PORTER, K. R., *ibid.* **2**, *Suppl.*, 163 (1956).
16. PORTER, K. R. and THOMPSON, H. P., *J. Exptl. Med.* **88**, 15 (1948).
17. RUSKA, H., *Ann. Rep. Div. Labs. and Research*, N.Y., pp. 24 and 27 (1954 and 1955).
18. RUSKA, H., EDWARDS, G. A. and CAESAR, R., *Experientia* **14**, 117 (1958).
19. SPIRO, D., *J. Biophys. Biochem. Cytol.* **2**, *Suppl.*, 157 (1956).

QUANTITATIVE AND CYTOCHEMICAL STUDIES ON THE INTESTINAL PLEXUSES OF THE GUINEA PIG

L. C. U. JUNQUEIRA, W. L. TAFURI and C. P. TAFURI

Laboratory for Cell Physiology, Faculdade de Medicina, Universidade de São Paulo, Brasil

THE authors developed an improved method for dissecting the nervous plexus of the digestive tract of laboratory animals. Thus permanent preparations were obtained that permitted cytological, cytochemical and quantitative study of tissue spreads avoiding paraffin embbeding and sectioning.

Previous quantitative data on this subject are scarce and most authors do not refer to the segment of intestine used in their counts. None so far have treated their results by statistical methods assaying the variability of their samples.

In the guinea pigs Auerbach's plexus counts have been performed by Irwin [1], Matsuo [2] and Okubo [4]; this last author presenting observations also on Meissner's plexus.

Quantitative results on other animals are still scarcer and subject to the criticism above mentioned.

Systematic cytochemical studies on these structures are not available, reference should be made, however, to the report of Nachlas and Seligman [3] who observed α-naphtholesterase activity in the intestinal plexus of the guinea pig.

Guinea pigs were selected for this study, since previous morphological observations exist for this material and its ileum is frequently used in pharmacology and physiology.

MATERIAL AND METHODS

Segments of the ileum, colon and caecum of 10 adult male guinea pigs were dissected, washed in running water, spread out on a cardboard and fixed with Zenker-formalin for 3 hours. These fragments were washed overnight and dissected isolating the submucosa with the Meissner's plexus and the external muscular layer with the Auerbach's plexus. These tissue spreads were washed and stained in 1 per cent toluidine blue at pH 4.5.

A correction for changes in area due to shrinkage was performed as described in detail by W. L. Tafuri [5].

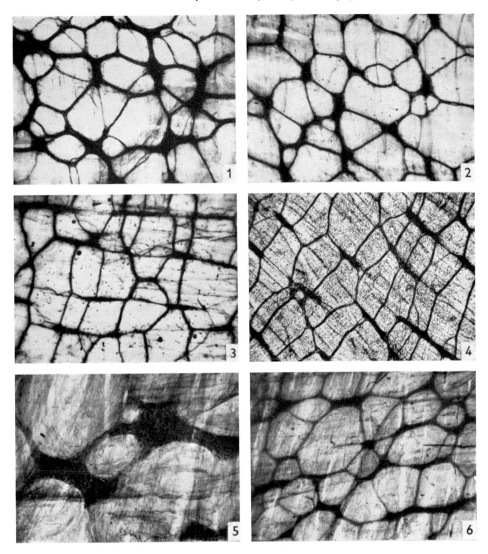

Fig. 1–5.—Nucleotidase activity in the guinea pig. ×36.
Fig. 2.—"Alkaline" phosphatase activity, same material. ×36.
Fig. 3.—"Alkaline" phosphatase in ileum. ×36.
Fig. 4.—"Acid" phosphatase in ileum. ×36.
Fig. 5.—α-Naphtol esterase activity in the colon. ×128.
Fig. 6.—Baker's acid hematin technique in the colon. ×36.

In these preparations counts of the number of ganglia, number of nervous cells per ganglia and nervous cells per area were performed and treated statistically as described in W. L. Tafuri [5].

For cytochemical studies the intestinal fragments were fixed in Baker's formalin-calcium, alcohol-acetone, Zenker-formalin, 10 per cent iced formalin and subsequently the plexuses were dissected.

Several cytochemical tests were performed on this material as detailed in Table II.

RESULTS AND DISCUSSION

The quantitative results are summarized in Table I. It is evident that from a general point of view the Auerbach's plexus is far richer in ganglia, nervous cells per ganglion and nervous cells per area than the Meissner's plexus. Referring to cells per area this difference is very big and suggests functional implications.

As to the distribution of these results in the different portions of the digestive tract studied one may see that the ileum and colon are for both plexuses always richer in cells per area than the caecum. It is true that the caecum has more ganglia per area in the Auerbach's plexus than in the ileum and colon. This increase is however due to the fact that the ganglia are smaller in this region, and consequently the number of cells per ganglion smaller.

The results obtained from the statistical analysis are expressed in Table I.

TABLE I. *Quantitative results concerning Auerbach's and Meissner's plexus of the guinea pig.*

Plexus	Ileum	Caecum	Colon
Number of ganglia per sq.mm			
Meissner	1.87	0.29	1.41
Auerbach	1.20	2.21^{a}	2.06^{a}
Number of nervous cells per ganglion			
Meissner	8.6	20.0^{a}	20.9^{a}
Auerbach	81.0^{a}	20.5	76.5^{u}
Number of nervous cells per sq.mm			
Meissner	193.61^{a}	39.0	228.7^{a}
Auerbach	1421.1^{a}	929.2^{a}	3557.1

[a] These groups have no statistically significant difference between them.

TABLE II. *Cytochemical results in Auerbach's plexus in the guinea pig.*

Test	Substance	Results
Brachet Ribonuclease abolishable basophilia	Ribose polynucleotide	Positive in the Nissl substance and nucleoli
Periodic acid Schiff	1–2 glycol	Positive in nerve fibers. No influence of saliva
Sudan Black B and piridine extraction	Lipids	Positive in lipochondria and lipofuchsin. Lipochondria negative after pyridine extraction
Baker's acid hematein	Phospholipids	Same as above
Nile blue sulphate	Lipids	Blue colour in cells and fibers
Plasmal	Acetal-phosphatides	Nerve cell cytoplasm and nerve fibers stained
Ninhidrin-Schiff	Protein-amino-groups	Positive in nerve cells and fibers
α-Naphtol esterase AS acetate esterase Tween 60-esterase	—	Positive in cells and fibers. Strongest reaction with α-naphtol and Tween 60
Gomori's test	Alkaline phosphatase	Nerve cell cytoplasm and its expansions
Gomori's test	5 nucleotidase	Same as above
Gomori's test	Acid phosphatase	Positive in nerve cells and fibers. Picks up selectively some cells and fibers

The cytochemical results obtained only for the Auerbach's plexus so far are presented in Table II. Although several cytochemical procedures must still be used in this material its relative richness in chemical components is striking. Further studies conducted under different physiological and pathological conditions will probably contribute towards clarifying the function of these structures.

SUMMARY

Quantitative statistical and cytochemical studies have been made on the Auerbach and Meissner plexuses of the ileum, caecum and colon of the guinea pig. The number of ganglia per mm² and the number of nervous cells per ganglion and per mm² were counted in these segments of the digestive tract.

The results obtained are discussed.

This research was supported in part by a grant of the Conselho Nacional de Pesquisas.

REFERENCES

1. IRWIN, D. A., *Am. J. Anat.* **49**, 141 (1931).
2. MATSUO, H., *Jap. J. Med. Sci. Anat.* **4**, 417 (1933).
3. NACHLAS, M. A. and SELIGMAN, A. M., *Anat. Rec.* **105**, 677 (1949).
4. OKUBO, K., *Jap. J. Med. Sci. Anat.* **6**, 21 (1937).
5. TAFURI, W. L., *Acta Anat.* (in press).

Experimental Cell Research, Suppl. **5**, *573–585 (1958)*

CILIARY COORDINATION IN THE PROTOZOA

L. E. ROTH

Division of Biological and Medical Research, Argonne National Laboratory, Lemont, Ill., U.S.A.

THE ubiquitous cilium has been studied both intensively and extensively for many decades, but the last few years have undoubtedly been the most important in adding to our knowledge of structure and function. In a large measure, the electron microscope has been responsible for this recent progress, since it has allowed a careful study of the morphological aspects of cilia and their associated structures. Many studies have been made of a great variety of ciliated cells by several electron microscope techniques so that a rather large amount of data has now been collected. It is the purpose of this presentation to summarize briefly this material and other data in the particular area of ciliary coordination. For technical details of the preparation of the material presented in the accompanying illustrations, the reader is referred to other presentations by the author [13, 14, 15].

CILIARY STRUCTURE

It has now been established by many studies that a basic fibrillar organization is present in all kinocilia including those in protozoan cilia, in cilia from ciliated epithelia, in protozoan flagella, and in sperm flagella. The four features that characterize this basic pattern can be listed as follows.

(1) Eleven fibrils are present of which two are arranged in a central position and nine in a peripheral ring.

(2) The central pair is composed of simple, single fibrils oriented so that a line drawn through their centers is perpendicular to the direction of beat.

(3) The peripheral fibrils have a figure-eight cross-section, are regularly spaced around the central pair, and are radially oriented.

(4) A membrane surrounds the complete fibril complex.

These characteristics are illustrated by cross-sections through sperm tails from the snail, *Helix aspersa* (Fig. 1).

While this is the basic pattern, variations may appear in the shaft membrane, the tip or the base. The membrane may be single-layered (Fig. 1) or double-layered as in *Euplotes* [13] and may have adsorbed material on the membrane as in *Melanoplus* sperm [15] and the *Peranema* flagella (Fig. 4, *TF*). The tip is usually tapered with the central fibrils ending before the peripheral ones which in rat tracheal epithelium fuse at the tip according to Rhodin and Dalhamn [12]; on the other hand, the peripheral ones may end before the central ones as in *Euplotes* [13].

From a functional viewpoint, however, the more important variations are found in the basal region. The peripheral fibrils usually extent into the base where they may have a structure similar to the shaft as shown in *Euplotes patella* (Figs. 2, 8, and 9), *Paramecium aurelia* (Fig. 3), *Peranema trichophorum* (Fig. 4), and *Stentor coeruleus* (Fig. 5) or they may show elaborations or modification in their basal ends as pointed out by Fawcett and Porter in the mouse oviduct [5] and by Rhodin and Dalhamn in the rat tracheal cilia [12]. The central fibrils usually end at the level of the cell surface [5, 12] (Figs. 3, 5). However, in *Euplotes* they are found in the base (Figs. 2, 6, 8, 9, 10) while in *Peranema* (Fig. 4) and in *Euglena gracilis* [16] they are not present either in the base or the near-basal region of the shaft.

The present concepts of the method by which the eleven-fibril complex produces ciliary beat have been discussed in detail by Bradfield [1] and also by Manton [10] and briefly by Roth [13]. To summarize, the peripheral fibrils are said to be capable of producing a shortening of one side of the cilium to create a beat, and the later shortening of the opposite side is responsible for the back stroke. Preferential shortening is probably produced by fibril contraction, perhaps of the type discussed by Szent-Györgyi [20], starting in one peripheral fibril, spreading through adjacent fibrils on either side, and terminating at the two fibrils opposite the first one. The central fibrils probably do not contract actively, but may passively determine the direction of beat. In spite of minor variations in basal structures, a definite relationship is maintained, in that the peripheral fibrils are almost always present in the base while the central fibrils usually are not.

Fig. 1.—The eleven ciliary fibrils are shown here in cross-sections of sperm tails from *Helix aspersa*, the snail. Notice the regularity and radial placement of the nine peripheral fibrils (*P*), the single-layered membrane (*ME*), and the central pair of fibrils (*C*) which in this case appear to be connected. × 85,000.

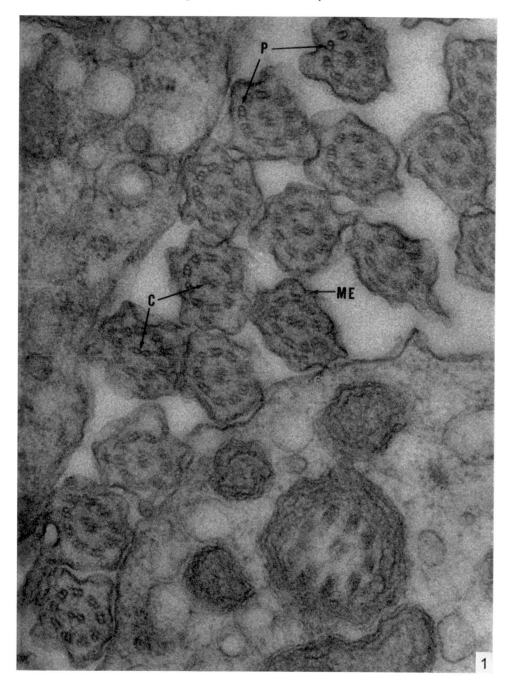

ROOTLET FIBRIL STRUCTURE

Considerable attention has also been given to the ciliary rootlets. In the fresh water mussel *Elliptio*, Fawcett and Porter [5] have shown that the rootlets are branching and striated and that they may be almost as large in diameter as the "basal granule". In *Paramecium*, Metz, Pitelka, and Westfall [11] and Sedar and Porter [19] describe the rootlets (kinetodesmal fibrils) as striated tapering fibrils which overlap so that five rootlet fibrils closely parallel each other (see also Fig. 3). A similar situation exists in *Stentor* except that each rootlet is longer so that larger numbers of fibrils parallel each other (Fig. 5).

The protozoan hypotrich, *Euplotes patella*, is of special interest because of its rootlet system which has been studied by the author [13, 14]. Taylor [21] in a careful study of the types of movement which can be executed by *Euplotes eurystomus*, described three creeping and six swimming movements. Such a complexity of movements indicates that the organism is capable of precise coordination of ciliary structures. In this connection, it is also interesting to note the complexity of the rootlet fibrils which interconnect the bases of the ciliary groupings in this organism.

Euplotes is characterized by three types of ciliary groupings: the cirrus consisting of four to six rows with six or less cilia per row (Figs. 6, 7, and 9), the membranelle with two or three rows of twenty to thirty cilia per row (Fig. 7), and single or paired cilia (Fig. 7). With the light microscope, Yocom [25] described fiber interconnections from cirrus to cirrus and also from both cirri and membranelles to a small, darkly-staining, anterior granule called a motorium. With the electron microscope, additional interconnections have been demonstrated. Membranelles may be directly interconnected (Fig. 8), a cirrus and membranelle may be directly connected, and cilia may also be directly interconnected [14]. In each of these cases the interconnection is by filaments measuring 21 mμ in diameter. (Yocom had observed fibers com-

Fig. 2.—A longitudinal section through ciliary bases in a membranelle from the protozoan *Euplotes patella*. The central ciliary fibrils (C) are present in the basal region and the peripheral fibrils (P) extend directly from the shaft into the base. At two different levels, small granules (G) are associated with the ciliary bases. × 52,000.

Fig. 3.—An oblique section through the pellicle of *Paramecium aurelia*. The basal regions of several cilia in cross-section (B) show the absence of central fibrils and the close association of the rootlets (kinetodesmal fibrils) with the peripheral fibrils. Slightly more distally the central fibrils (C) are present. Rootlets (R) are seen after they have extended farther from the bases; they are now located immediately below the pellicular membranes. This section is from a region of the pellicle which characteristically has two cilia in each pellicular depression. A mitochondrion (M) is also shown. × 26,000.

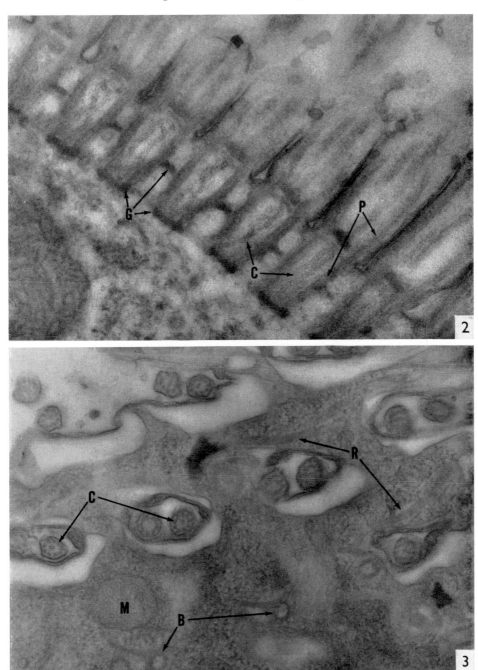

posed of numerous filaments.) Similar filaments are found in a sub-pellicular system composed of anterior-posterior and transverse filaments just below the pellicular membranes (Figs. 6, 8 and 9). This sub-pellicular system may be connected by similar filaments to cirri so that the ciliary rootlet system and the sub-pellicular system are interconnected. The micronucleus may also be included in the system since numerous filaments have been observed very close to its membrane [14]. The single or paired cilia previously mentioned are singularly distinguished by a lack of rootlet filaments.

In this connection, a consideration of the sensory structures present in *Euplotes* is appropriate. In the past literature, Yocom [25] suggested that the single cilia not included in cirri and membranelles were sensory structures and Turner [22] suggested an external fibrillar system also as a sensory structure. However, since the "external fibrillar system" cannot be demonstrated by electron microscopy, and since these cilia are not included in the rootlet system, it no longer seems appropriate to ascribe such a function to them. It is possible that the sub-pellicular filament system or that cilia acting in addition to their motor function could serve a sensory function although evidence is lacking for both concepts.

From this summary of ciliary morphology let us proceed to additional studies dealing with ciliary function and coordination; such evidence can be divided into five major categories, each of which is briefly presented below.

Studies of protozoan rootlet systems have emphasized the role of direct or indirect fibrillar connection of cilia. In *Euplotes* especially, both light and electron microscope studies have shown fibrils directly connecting cilia and ciliary groups. Taylor [21] using microdissection techniques convincingly demonstrated that when the larger rootlet fibrils in *Euplotes* were cut, there was an interference with normal movements and a lack of coordination but no change in body shape. Similar microdissection experiments performed by Worley [23] and Worley, Fischbein, and Shapiro [24] on the gill cilia of the clam *Mytilis*, also demonstrated an interference with the coordination of beat.

Fig. 4.—A section through the basal region (*B*) of one of the two flagella in the protozoan *Peranema trichophorum*. Notice the absence of the central fibrils which are also absent from the near-basal region of the other flagellum (*F*). The central fibrils are present slightly more distal; they are seen in the trailing flagellum outside of the flagellar reservoir (*C*). A mitochondrion (*M*) is also shown. ×18,000.

Fig. 5.—Ciliary rootlets (*R*) in a section through the pellicle of the protozoan, *Stentor coeruleus*. The individual rootlets are seen in close association with the basal portions of the peripheral fibrils (*P*); the central fibrils again are lacking in the basal region but are present (*C*) distally from the level of the pellicle. ×16,000.

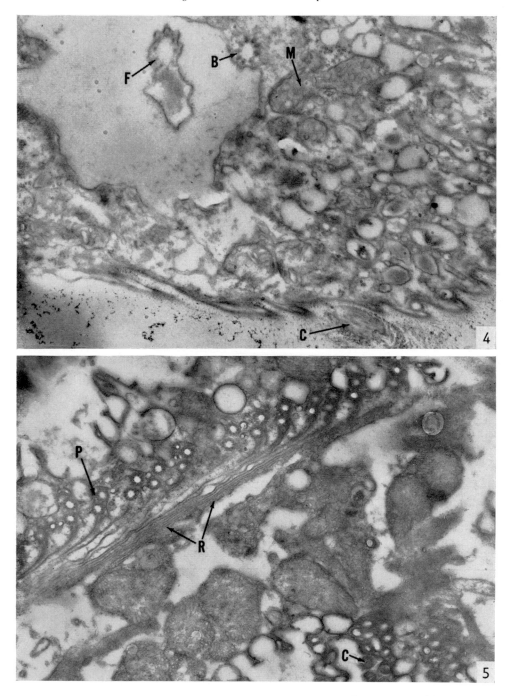

Secondly, in certain protozoa where the ciliary beat can be stopped completely and reactivated upon proper stimulation, e.g., *Tetradimorpha radiata* (see Kudo [9]) and in numerous other cases, e.g., *Paramecium, Stentor, Euplotes*, it has been shown that a disturbing stimulus causes an avoiding reaction involving a change in ciliary movement. In addition, Copeland [3] has shown in two snails of the genus *Alectrion* that the pedal cilia cease to beat when the organisms are at rest; stimulation of the receptors on the tentacles with food causes the cilia to resume motion and beat. (An interesting discussion of older studies and concepts of ciliary control is given by Gray [7].) This evidence shows that in several cases, it has been established that the organism has precise control of its cilia and that in some cases, control may be through nerve pathways.

In the third case, there is a generalized correlation between the complexity of the rootlet systems in the protozoa and the capability of the organism to perform a variety of movements. The individual cilia of *Euplotes* not included in cirri and membranelles, which have no rootlets, were described by Hammond [8] as neither rigid nor vibratile but showing slight movements which are probably passive; the lack of rootlets is associated with a rather passive state. In most flagellates, rootlets exist only as one or a few rhizoplast fibrils and thus little or no coordination of movement is associated with an almost insignificant rootlet system; for example, in the flagellate *Peranema*, the leading flagellum serves only for propulsion, and changes of direction are effected by the body of the organism. In ciliates such as *Paramecium* and *Stentor*, in which a limited number of movements are possible, there is a coordinated beat involving many more cilia, and a rootlet system which is considerably more complex. In *Euplotes* where a still more complex rootlet system exists, a series of nine different swimming or creeping movements are known. It would be possible to elaborate on this group of examples of correlation in complexity of rootlet systems with complexity of ciliary coordination.

Furthermore, Gray [6] has shown that there is an effect on ciliary beat by varying the concentrations of the inorganic ions Na^+, K^+, Mg^{++}, and Ca^{++};

Fig. 6.—A section through the pellicle of *Euplotes patella* showing one cirrus and the rootlets (*R*) attaching to the peripheral fibrils (*P*) at dense granules (*G*). Protrusions of the membrane (*ME*), seen around ciliary shafts, are the only structures present which can contribute to the functional unity of this bundle of cilia. The pellicle is composed of an outer membrane, the pellicular membrane (*PM*), which is continuous with the ciliary membrane, and an inner cytoplasmic membrane (*CM*). The filaments of the sub-pellicular system (*S*) are seen just under the two pellicular membranes. Mitochondria (*M*), a portion of the macronucleus (*MA*), and numerous cytoplasmic granules (*GG*) are also visible. These latter structures are described by Roth [14]. × 24,000.

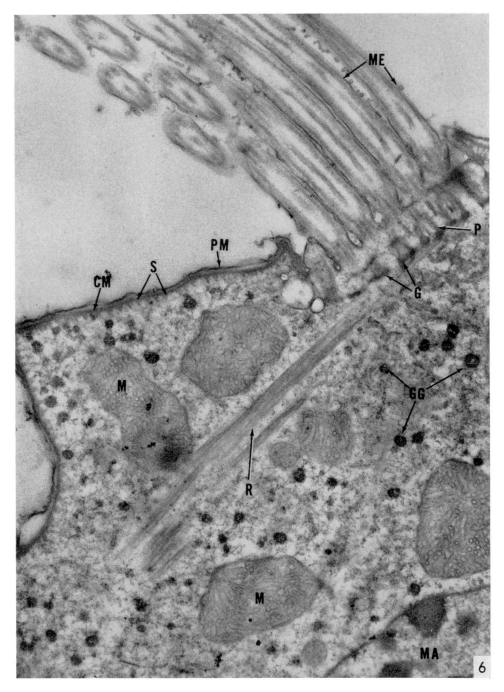

the effects of the latter two are most specific in that magnesium and calcium are mutually antagonistic, i.e., excess magnesium behaves like calcium lack in that either will slow or stop ciliary beat in the gill cilia of *Mytilis*. A similar action of these ions on the end plate is reported by del Castillo and Katz [4] in their review of neuromuscular transmission. They suggest that in pre-synaptic events, calcium and magnesium display a direct competitive antagonism, although this is not the case in the axon or muscle fiber where the effects of the two ions are qualitatively the same.

Finally, Seaman [17] has demonstrated that acetylcholine is not only present in the protozoan *Tetrahymena* but that it is localized in the pellicular fraction of fragmented organisms. It has been shown by Seaman and Houlihan [18] and by Roth [16] that the rate of ciliary beat is affected by treating living organisms with acetylcholinesterase inhibitors, e.g. eserine. Similar experimentation was reported by Bulbring, Burn, and Shelley [2] on gill cilia of the clam, *Mytilis*, in a study worthy of consideration by all readers interested in this subject; they concluded that "acetylcholine cannot be acting as a humoral transmitter of nerve impulses but rather as a local hormone, maintaining the rhythmic movement".

In view of this evidence it seems warranted to suggest that rootlet fibrils play a major role in ciliary coordination by functioning as electrical conductors. Such a concept does not imply that this is the sole function of ciliary rootlets, but that it is one of perhaps several functions. Conduction and contraction of intracellular fibrils are implicit in these considerations; although the functional mode of action is not known, the bioenergetic phenomenon suggested by Szent-Györgyi [20] for triplet excitation of protomyosin, which offers a mechanism for muscle fiber function, may be applicable in understanding both rootlet filament and ciliary fibril function.

If significant new evidence is to be found in this area, studies should be directed toward the elucidation of methods of ciliary function and coordination rather than descriptions of normal structures. If the ciliary rootlets could be attacked in such a way that the surrounding cytoplasm were not so drasti-

Fig. 7.—Survey micrograph illustrating the three types of ciliary groupings in *Euplotes patella*: Four cirri (two are incomplete) in the upper portion, four membranelles (one incomplete) at the lowere left, and two bristle cilia (*BC*) at the right. Notice the ciliary vesicles located around the bristle cilia. × 6500.

Fig. 8.—A section through the pellicle of *Euplotes* including portions of three membranelles. Rootlet filaments (*R*) both separately and in bundles are shown interconnecting the membranelles. Between the bases of a few cilia, rootlet filaments (*F*) are shown interconnecting adjacent cilia. Filaments of the sub-pellicular system (*S*) are cross-sectioned just below the pellicular membranes; mitochondria (*M*) and ciliary vesicles (*V*) are also included. × 23,000.

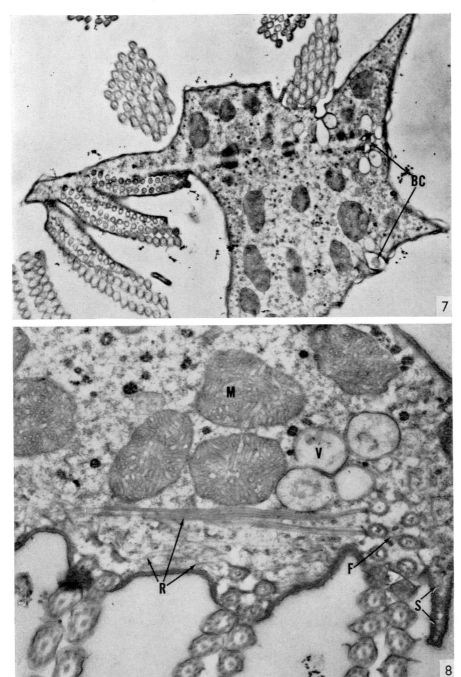

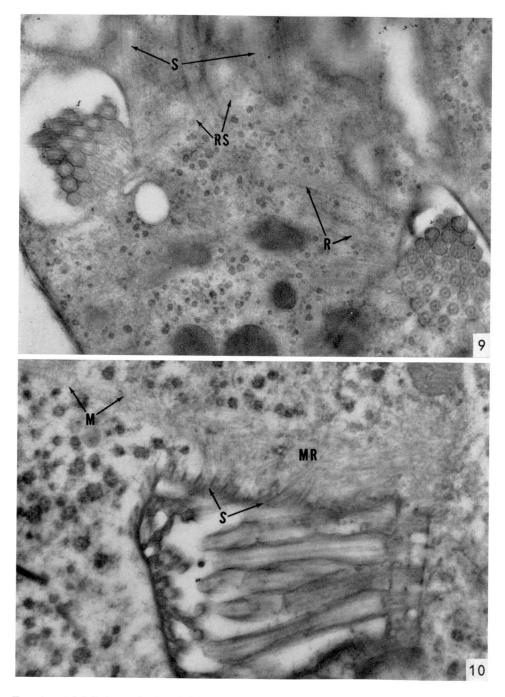

cally changed as in microdissection techniques, then the effect on ciliary function could be studied more carefully. Methods of study on the possible sensory role of cilia will also be significant. Formation and regeneration of cilia and ciliary rootlets is also an important problem which may give new evidence.

SUMMARY

Evidence has been presented to suggest that rootlets play a major role in ciliary coordination by functioning as electrical conductors. In considerations of ciliary function, both conduction and contraction of intracellular fibrils seem to be implicit; a possible mode of action is the triplet excitation which has been suggested by Szent-Györgyi as a mechanism for muscle function.

REFERENCES

1. BRADFIELD, J. R. G., *Symposia Soc. Exptl. Biol.* **9**, 306 (1955).
2. BULBRING, E., BURN, J. H. and SHELLEY, H., *Proc. Roy. Soc. (London) Ser. B* **141**, 445 (1953).
3. COPELAND, M., *Biol. Bull.* **37**, 126 (1919).
4. DEL CASTILLO, J. and KATZ, B., *in* Progress in Biophysics and Biophysical Chemistry **VI**, p. 121. BUTLER, J. A. V. and RANDALL, T., eds. Academic Press, New York, 1956.
5. FAWCETT, D. W. and PORTER, K. R., *J. Morphol.* **94**, 221 (1954).
6. GRAY, J., *Proc. Roy. Soc. (London) Series B* **96**, 95 (1924).
7. GRAY, J., Ciliary Movement, p. 117. University Press, Cambridge, 1928.
8. HAMMOND, D. M., *Quart. J. Microscop. Sci.* **79**, 507 (1937).
9. KUDO, R. R., Protozoology. C. Thomas, Springfield, Illinois, 1954.
10. MANTON, I., *in* Cellular Mechanisms in Differentiation and Growth, p. 61. REIDNICK, D., ed. University Press, Princeton, 1956.
11. METZ, C., PITELKA, D. R. and WESTFALL, J. A., *Biol. Bull.* **104**, 408 (1953).
12. RHODIN, J. and DALHAMN, T., *Z. Zellforsch. u. mikroskop. Anat.* **44**, 345 (1956).
13. ROTH, L. E., *J. Biophys. Biochem. Cytol.* **2** (Supplement), 235 (1956).
14. —— *J. Biophys. Biochem. Cytol.* (in press).
15. —— *J. Biophys. Biochem. Cytol.* **3**, 816 (1957).
16. —— unpublished data.
17. SEAMAN, G. R., *Proc. Soc. Exptl. Biol. Med.* **76**, 169 (1951).
18. SEAMAN, G. R. and HOULIHAN, R. K., *J. Cellular Comp. Physiol.* **37**, 309 (1951).
19. SEDAR, A. W. and PORTER, K. R., *J. Biophys. Biochem. Cytol.* **1**, 583 (1955).
20. SZENT-GYÖRGYI, A., *Science* **124**, 873 (1956).
21. TAYLOR, C. A., *Univ. Calif. (Berkeley) Publs. Zoöl.* **19**, 403 (1920).
22. TURNER, J. P., *Biol. Bull.* **64**, 53 (1933).
23. WORLEY, L. G., *J. Cellular Comp. Physiol.* **18**, 187 (1941).
24. WORLEY, L. G., FISCHBEIN, E. and SHAPIRO, J. E., *J. Morphol.* **92**, 545 (1953).
25. YOCOM, H. B., *Univ. Calif. (Berkeley) Publs. Zoöl.* **18**, 337 (1918).

Fig. 9.—A section in the basal region of two cirri in *Euplotes patella*. Three filament groupings are shown: the sub-pellicular system (*S*), rootlets interconnecting the two cirri (*R*) and rootlets (*RS*) interconnecting the left cirrus with the sub-pellicular system. × 13,000.

Fig. 10.—The motorium region (*MR*) in *Euplotes patella*. There is a close intertwining of filaments from the sub-pellicular system (*S*), from the membranelles (*M*), and from the cirri (not included in this section) to form the motorium. × 32,000.

Experimental Cell Research, Suppl. **5**, *586–644 (1958)*

FINE STRUCTURE OF THE LIGHT RECEPTORS IN THE COMPOUND EYES OF INSECTS[1]

H. FERNÁNDEZ-MORÁN[2]

Nerve Ultrastructure Department, Venezuelan Institute for Neurology and Brain Research (IVNIC), Caracas, Venezuela

THE structural pattern of organization of the compound eye of insects and other arthropods is characterized by the aggregation of numerous separate visual elements known as ommatidia, each of which consists of seven or eight sensory "retinula" cells with its own dioptric system [19, 36]. The lower resolving power and other salient optical features of this composite array of apparently simple units had been generally regarded as elementary, in comparison with the performance of the more highly developed vertebrate eye. However, with succeeding advances in our analytical techniques, these deceptively stereotyped visual organs have proven to be endowed with remarkable functional capacities. Thus, true color vision has been demonstrated in many insects [3, 15, 19], and their visible spectrum which extends far into the ultra-violet [36] is actually broader than that of man. Also, for many insects [3] the maximum critical flicker frequency (60–300/ sec.) is higher than the corresponding figure for man (45 to 53/sec.). This enhanced temporal resolution is probably of considerable importance in form discrimination and movement perception [3, 36] by flying insects. Moreover, an unforeseen capacity of the compound eye to analyze polarized light was revealed by the investigations of von Frisch [14, 15, 16], Autrum and Stumpf [2] and others on the direction-finding ability of honey bees.

An indication of the complex morphological substrate underlying these

---

[1] The substance of this paper was presented together with an electron micrograph exhibit on March 22, 1957 at the Symposium on the "Submicroscopic Organization and Function of Nerve Cells" held by the Venezuelan Institute of Neurology and Brain Research in Caracas. The original report has been expanded to take into account the interesting studies on the fine structure of the compound eyes of insects and other arthropoda published since then by W. H. Miller [21], T. H. Goldsmith and D. E. Philpott [17], and J. J. Wolken, J. Capenos and A. Turano [38].

[2] Present address: Biology Department, Massachusetts Institute of Technology, Cambridge, Mass., and Mixter Laboratories for Electron Microscopy, Department of Neurosurgery, Massachusetts General Hospital, Boston, Mass., U.S.A.

highly differentiated functions was already obtained when Cajal and San-chez [25] demonstrated the perplexing maze of neural pathways in the optic centers of insects. However, in view of the minute size and extremely compact arrangement of its components, an adequate analysis of the fine texture of the compound eye was precluded by the limitations of light micro-scopy.

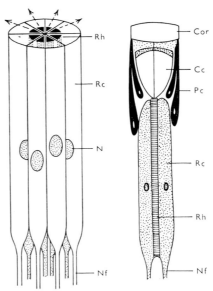

Text-fig. 1.—Schematic diagram of a longitudinal section through an ommatidium with apposition type of image formation showing the rhabdomeres (arrows) attached to the medial borders of the re-tinula cells (*Rc*). *Cor*, corneal lens; *Cc*, crystalline cone; *Pc*, pigment cells; *Rh*, rhabdom; *N*, nucleus of the retinula cells; *Nf*, Nerve fibers. (According to Grenacher and Hesse.)

Recent electron microscope studies [11, 17, 21, 39] of the ommatidia show that certain differentiated elements of the retinula cells called rhabdomeres exhibit a lamellar fine structure, and are symmetrically arranged within the optic rod or rhabdom of each ommatidium. With improved preparation techniques it is now possible to examine serial thin sections through ex-tensive areas of a compound eye, disclosing hereby an integrated pattern which is manifest at all levels of organization: from the ordered array of the rhabdom groups to the macromolecular architecture of the receptors. An attempt has therefore been made to survey the main submicroscopic features of the light receptors and associated structures in representative specimens of compound eyes with apposition, superposition and intermediate types of image formation [8, 36]. In the apposition type of image formation found among most diurnal insects, only rays of light which are parallel to the long axes of the ommatidia will reach the short retinulae placed immediately be-hind the crystalline cones (Text-fig. 1). However, in the elongated ommatidia of the nocturnal insects with a superposition type of image formation the retinulae are separated from the cones by a wide intervening space filled with a non-refractile medium, and devoid of pigment. Since each retinula then receives additional light rays from the adjacent cones, a greater proportion of the light coming from an external source is thus concentrated on a single rhabdom [19, 36]. In the intermediate types of eyes found in Mantids the image formation in the anterior parts of the eye is of the apposition type, while the lateral parts are of the superposition type, certain functional transitions being effected by pigment migration in the iris cells [36].

The present study deals primarily with the fine structure of the rhabdoms and retinula cells of selected tropical Diptera, Lepidoptera, Orthoptera and Odonata.

It is hoped that this preliminary survey will serve as a basis for systematic investigation of the submicroscopic organization of the compound eyes, and of the associated neural pathways within the optic lobes.

MATERIALS AND METHODS

Materials.—As representatives of eyes with an apposition type of image formation the following specimens were studied:

   (a) the compound eyes of the house-fly (*Musca domestica*) found locally in the IVNIC region near Caracas;
   (b) the compound eyes of *Drosophila melanogaster*;
   (c) the compound eyes of the honey bee (*Apis mellifera*).

The following representatives of eyes with a predominant superposition type of image formation were also examined:

   (a) the compound eyes of the giant tropical moth *Erebus odora* and related varieties found in the high jungle areas near Caracas;
   (b) compound eyes of tropical "Skipper" butterflies (*Epargyreus* and related specimens of the *Hesperiidae* family), found mainly in Caracas and adjacent areas.

Fig. 1.—Oblique cross section through the retinula portion of several ommatidia of the house-fly eye showing the regular pattern formed by the rhabdoms and their associated retinula cell and tracheal system structures. The seven dense rhabdomeres with their characteristic internal structure are symmetrically grouped around the central matrix of each rhabdom. The rhabdomeres are attached to the medial borders of the retinula cells, which contain abundant mitochondria and small pigment granules. Magnification × 5000.

Fig. 2.—Oblique cross section through the rhabdom of a house-fly retinula showing the six external rhabdomeres symmetrically arranged around the smaller central rhabdomere (*D*). The external rhabdomeres can be grouped into three pairs of matched elements (*A1, A2; B1, B2; C1, C2*) located on opposite sides of the central matrix, and with their transverse dense bands oriented approximately parallel to an ommatidial radius. Notice the serrated line of attachment of the rhabdomeres to the retinula cell borders, and the concentration of small pigment granules in these areas. Magnification × 25,000.

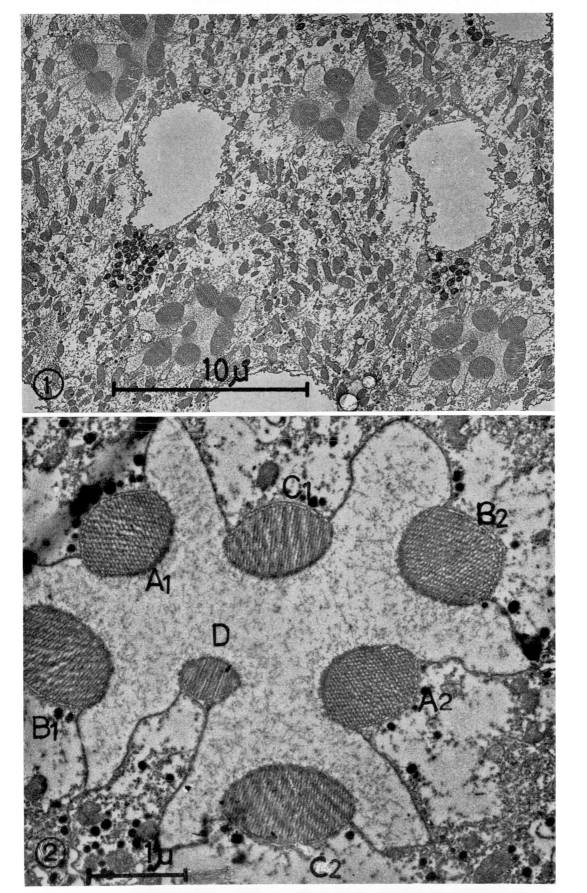

A limited number of specimens taken from the compound eyes of the grasshopper (*Dissosteira*), and of tropical dragonflies (*Odonata*) were also investigated.

Preparation of the insect eyes.—The eyes were removed from the living insect by swift decapitation, and transferred immediately to the cold fixation fluid, where further dissection and subdivision of the compound eyes into smaller segments was usually carried out. The use of sharp microscissors to produce clean incisions through the tough chitin components of the insect eye, without introducing undue pressure, was found to be essential in obtaining well preserved preparations. The apparently tough compound eye is in reality a remarkably delicate organ, in which even slight mechanical deformation, poor penetration of the fixative or inadequate embedding can obliterate important features of its submicroscopic organization.

The large superposition eyes of nocturnal tropical moths like *Erebus*, where the whole receptor layer is separated from the corneal surfaces and can therefore be exposed with a minimum of trauma, afford a unique opportunity to study the fresh retinula in the living insect. By suitable cooling the living insect can be immobilized, and after lateral puncture of the compound eye with a sharp needle point to reduce the internal pressure resulting from subsequent manipulations, the thin corneal shell is cut away with microscissors under the binocular microscope. After carefully removing the corneal shell and the subjacent semi-liquid material, the hemispherical surface containing the retinula cell layer is fully exposed, exhibiting characteristic color phenomena (Figs. 13–16). This type of preparation is not only ideal for investigations of the electrical activity, optical behavior, biochemical properties and other studies of insect light receptors under essentially physiological conditions, but also for electron microscopy. Direct application of the cold fixation fluid to the exposed retinulae gave the best degree of preservation in these cases.

Fixation.—The following fixation agents were used for application *in situ* to the exposed fresh receptors, or for immersion of small segments of the compound eye:

(*a*) Fresh solutions of 1 or 2 per cent osmium tetroxide in isotonic veronal-acetate buffer (pH 7.2) according to Palade [24], at a temperature of 1–4°C for periods ranging from 1 to 18 hours.

(*b*) Phosphomolybdic and phosphotungstic acids in 1 to 2 per cent solutions applied for 15 minutes to 6 hours at 0°C. In several cases greater contrast was observed when the standard osmium fixation was followed by complementary staining in alcoholic 1 per cent solutions of phosphotungstic or phosphomolybdic acid, and uranyl acetate.

Embedding.—After dehydration by passage through a graded series of ethanol or methanol (50 per cent to absolute alcohol by increments of 10 per cent), the specimens were impregnated for longer periods (24 to 96 hours) in the methacrylate monomer before being embedded in prepolymerized *n*-butyl methacrylate. This precaution

---

Fig. 3.—Oblique cross section through the retinula portion of adjacent ommatidia showing the general pattern of organization. The equivalent rhabdomeres (*A*1) of contiguous ommatidia are oriented with their main axes in the same direction, thus introducing a degree of "structural polarization" in the overall pattern which must bear relation to the analysis of polarized light in the insect eye. Notice the large tracheae (*T*) and the associated network of fine tracheoles. Magnification × 10,000.

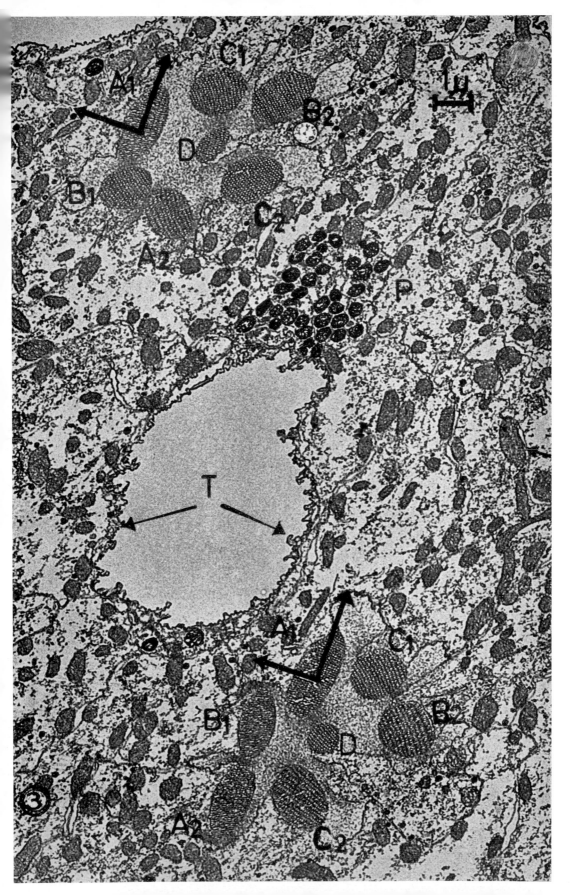

was found necessary in order to permeate and preserve the integrity and relationships of fine structural detail in these tissues with a chitinous framework of tracheoles
and a maze of minute interstices. Alternatively, gelatin embedding [12] was tried,
in order to avoid the possible extraction effects of ethanol treatment.

Microtomy.—As pointed out previously [11], it is difficult to prepare satisfactory
ultrathin sections of the insect eye because of the tough and resilient character of its
chitin framework. The irregular compression ridges and distortions commonly encountered when this material is sectioned with glass or steel knives frequently obscure significant details of the highly regular receptor fine structure. Improved thin
sectioning techniques based on the use of a diamond cutting edge [12, 13] proved
therefore to be of particular value in this type of study requiring the examination of
uniformly thin serial sections from large areas without introducing distortion, or
impairing the definition of minute structural detail. The ultrathin serial sections of
100 to 300 Å were prepared with a Morán ultramicrotome equipped with a diamond
knife [9]. The sharpness of the diamond cutting edge, its exceptional durability, and
the high degree of stability of the Morán ultramicrotome were important technical
factors in obtaining the required large number of satisfactory ultrathin serial sections from large block faces. Only in satisfactory thin sections through a whole
retinula group (Figs. 8, 9, 17, 18) can the extraordinary regularity of the general
pattern, and the unique degree of compact structural differentiation at the various
levels of organization be fully appreciated.

The sections were mounted on thin carbon films, or on fenestrated Formvar
films with uniformly distributed pores of 200 to 2000 Å [12]. These films are particularly suitable for high resolution studies because the edges of the minute holes facilitate rapid focusing, and the areas of the section lying over the openings can be
examined free from the supporting substrate.

Phase contrast microscopy of thin sections proved very useful for control purposes,
and in many cases revealed the general configuration of structural details of the
retinula (Fig. 7) in good agreement with the corresponding electron micrographs.

Light microscopy of the living retinula using perpendicular or oblique incident illumination, preferably combined with polarized light studies, or with fluorescence
microscopy, opens up a fascinating field of investigation. Observations of the receptors in living insects over extended periods of time not only permit an analysis of
those modifications in their ultrastructural pattern which are literally "reflected"
in characteristic optical effects like the polychromatic iridescence described in the
eye of Skipper butterflies (Figs. 14, 15, 16). Of greater importance is the inherent
possibility of recording ultrarapid changes in these living receptors during various
phases of activity (by using electronic flash or stroboscopic techniques), and to

---

Fig. 4.—Oblique longitudinal section through 3 adjacent rhabdomeres of a housefly retinula
showing the lamellar and reticular type of internal structure, depending on the orientation of the
sectioning plane. The highly regular submicroscopic organization is illustrated by the nearly
perfect parallel array of about 150 transverse dense bands occupying the entire rhabdomere on
the left side. These parallel bands correspond to the dense "walls" of the tubular compartments
sectioned longitudinally, while the polygonal framework of the adjacent rhabdomere represents
oblique cross sections of these tightly packed tubular units of the rhabdomere. Magnification
× 39,000.

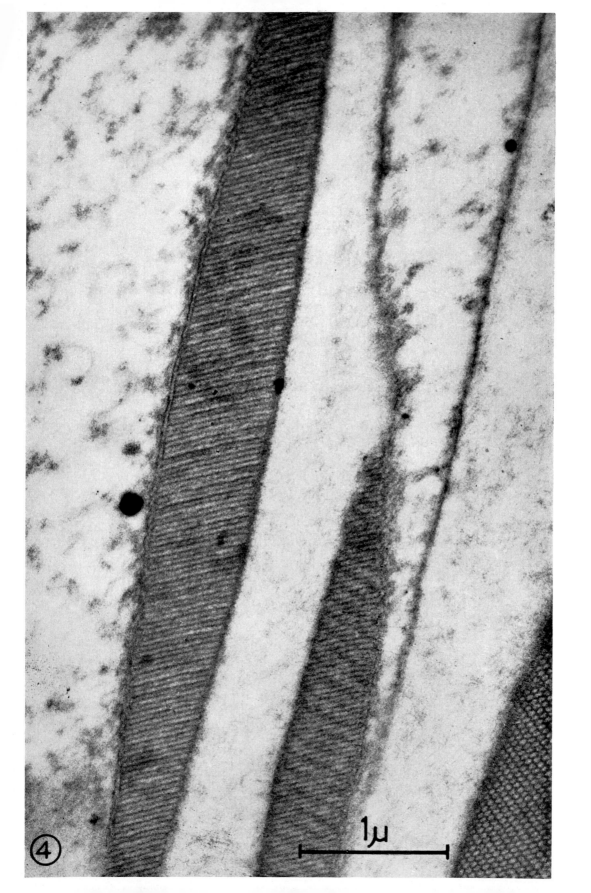

④   1μ

establish a correlation with sequentially arrested modifications in the receptor ultra-structure, by means of high resolution electron microscopy.

Electron microscopy.—A Siemens Elmiskop 1 and an RCA EMU 3 electron microscope connected to a specially regulated power supply were used in this study. The micrographs were taken at electron optical magnifications ranging from 1000 × to 42,000 ×. The observations described here are based on the evaluation of 4000 plates, in which an average resolution of 20 to 30 Å was regularly achieved.

OBSERVATIONS

Compound Eye of the House-Fly (Musca domestica)

Depending on the size of the compound eyes in the specimens examined, the 3000–4000 constituent cylindrical ommatidia [19] of the house-fly vary in diameter from 12 to 20 microns, and from 80 to about 160 microns in length. A sheath of pigment cells surrounds the individual ommatidia, and extends from their distal end containing the crystalline cone to the proximal segment resting on a fenestrated basement membrane with numerous nerve fibers and tracheae running through [29, 36].

As shown in the schematic diagram of Text-fig. 1, the percipient portion or *retinula* at the base of each ommatidium consists generally of eight elongate visual cells which are radially arranged around the central *rhabdom*. In the house-fly ommatidia one of the retinula cells is rudimentary, and the rhabdom is composed of seven rod-shaped *rhabdomeres*, which are differentiated structures derived from the medial borders of the seven visual cells. The single rhabdomeres measure only 1 to 1.5 microns in diameter and 60 to 70 microns in length, and are closely packed together around the axial cavity or central matrix of the rhabdom. Although the rhabdomeres have long been regarded as the photoreceptor elements, an analysis of the fine structure of these minute components has only recently been possible by means of electron microscopy [11, 17, 21, 39].

In ultrathin transverse sections through the basal portion of the ommatidia the general pattern of organization is clearly shown (Fig. 1). The in-

---

Fig. 5.—High resolution electron micrograph of longitudinal ultrathin section through a rhabdomere of the house-fly retinula, demonstrating the fine structure of the tubular compartments. The regular array of sharply outlined polygonal annular profiles (400 to 500 Å in diameter) bounded by a dense osmiophilic substance is interpreted as representing cross sections of the closely packed tubular compartments. This differentiation of the electron-dense "walls" of the compartments into a thin osmiophilic boundary line, 20 to 30 Å wide, associated with a dense layer of approximately 60 Å, may be of interest in relation to the postulated models of the macromolecular photoreceptor complexes. The variation in the diameter of the annular profiles (arrows) is due to oblique orientation of the sectioning plane. Magnification × 93,000.

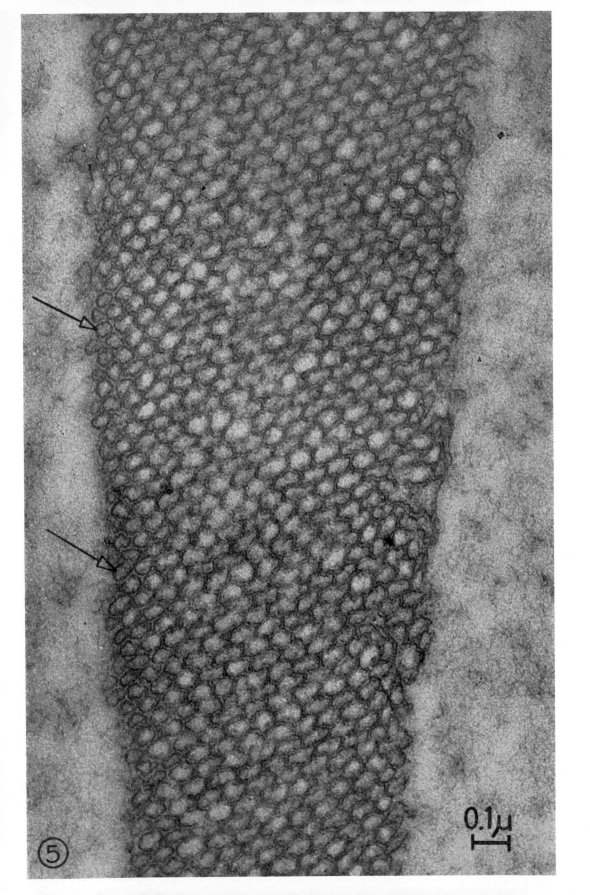

⑤

0.1μ

dividual ommatidia are surrounded by compact aggregates of pigment granules, and alternate at periodic intervals with tracheae or tracheoles to form a mosaic of striking regularity.

The rhabdoms, 6 to 8 microns in diameter, constitute the most conspicuous components with their seven dense rhabdomeres, which are symmetrically grouped around the light central matrix. This *central matrix* (Fig. 2) consists of a loose network of extremely fine filaments, 50 to 100 Å wide, associated with a granular component of approximately the same dimensions. The appearance of this precipitated material in osmium fixed preparations suggests the possibility that the central cavity is filled with a fluid [11, 39].

The individual rhabdomeres exhibit a highly ordered internal structure, and are found attached to the medial borders of the corresponding retinula cells (Figs. 1, 2, 3). The large number of mitochondria clustered around the rhabdoms and the tracheoles frequently obscure the retinula cell boundaries.

Fine Structure of the Rhabdomeres

Confirming our previous observations [11], and the electron microscope studies of Goldsmith and Philpott [17] on *Sarcophaga bullata*, and of Wolken, Capenos and Turano [38] on *Drosophila melanogaster*, the seven rhabdomeres appear in transverse sections as round or oval bodies of about 1 to 2 microns in diameter, with a periodic lamellar structure. Each rhabdomere is traversed by a series of 20 to 35 parallel dense bands, about 100 to 120 Å wide, which alternate with less dense interspaces of approximately 280 to 380 Å to give a regular period of 400 to 500 Å. In cross sections the borders of each rhabdomere show a peculiar scalloped outline, and at the zone of attachment to the retinula cell membrane, a double contoured, serrated demarcation band of approximately 200 Å is discernible (Fig. 2). As Wolken, Capenos and Turano [39] have pointed out, the parallel dense bands extend across the rhabdomere in a direction approximately normal to the line of attachment between the rhabdomere and the retinula cell. This transverse lamellar pattern is observed in all of the seven rhabdomeres only in true

---

Figs. 6*a*, *b*.—High resolution electron micrographs of cross-sectioned tubular compartments in rhabdomeres of the house-fly retinula. The individual hexagonal or polygonal compartments appear in these slightly oblique cross sections as annular profiles of variable diameter (400 to 500 Å), bounded by uniform, thin osmiophilic layers of 20 to 30 Å, apparently cemented together by the associated dense, intermediate substance. In certain areas the dense compartment "walls" show a tendency towards granular dissociation. In the marginal areas many of the tubular compartments appear to be "open", and collateral observations indicate that these compartments of the rhabdomeres may be considered as differentiated tubular microvilli arising from the retinula cell border. Magnifications × 93,000.

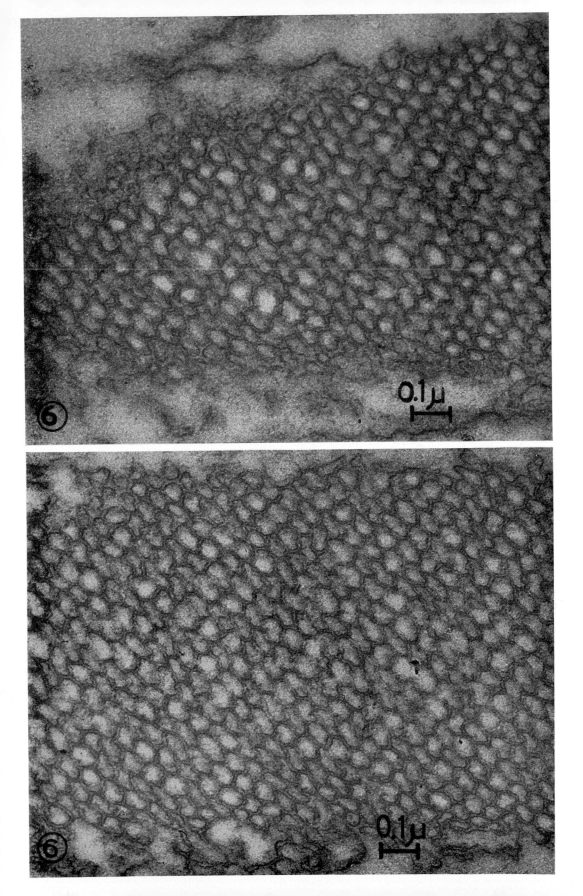

cross sections, since even in slightly oblique sections some of the rhabdomeres show a characteristic reticular structure (Figs. 2, 3). This uniform
structure consists of a roughly hexagonal framework of dense bands about
100 Å thick, separated by less dense interspaces approximately 300 to 400 Å
in diameter. In longitudinal sections through a rhabdom, the lamellar and the
reticular type of structural pattern are regularly encountered in contiguous
rhabdomeres.

The remarkable degree of structural regularity embodied in the submicroscopic organization of these slender light receptors can be directly
visualized in Fig. 4, which demonstrates the precise arrangement of about
150 transverse dense bands occupying the entire longitudinal section of a
rhabdomere.

In our first report [11] the transverse lamellar pattern was interpreted as
corresponding to corrugated membranes oriented parallel to the long axis
of the rhabdomere, while the reticular pattern was ascribed to fenestrated
disks arranged perpendicular to the longitudinal axis. However, as Goldsmith and Philpott [17] have correctly pointed out, this interpretation is not
consistent with the available findings, and must therefore be discarded in
favor of a single structural unit packed in such a way that the two different
general patterns observed will depend only on the plane of sectioning.

Examination of a more extensive material with improved preparation
techniques has led us in the meantime to an interpretation which is essentially in agreement with the transverse rod or tubular structure of the rhabdomeres proposed by Goldsmith and Philpott [17], and by Wolken, Capenos
and Turano [39].

The available evidence indicates therefore that the rhabdomeres are built
up of tightly packed rod-shaped or tubular units, approximately 400 Å in
diameter and 1000 to 15,000 Å long, which are oriented in parallel array
with their long axes at right angles to the longitudinal axis of the rhabdomeres, and in a direction approximately normal to the point of attachment
with the retinula cell. The tubular or hexagonal appearance of these compartments is due to the greater electron density of the "walls" compared
with the less dense interior in osmium fixed and methacrylate embedded

---

Fig. 7.—Phase contrast micrograph of thin transverse section through a group of retinulae from
the eye of the tropical moth *Erebus odora*, showing the characteristic "stellate" or "pinwheel"
patterns formed by the 7 radially arranged rhabdomeres of each retinula. The interspaces are
packed with fine longitudinally oriented tracheoles, which form part of the tracheal tapetum
structure in this superposition type of compound eye common to nocturnal insects. Magnification
× 1250.

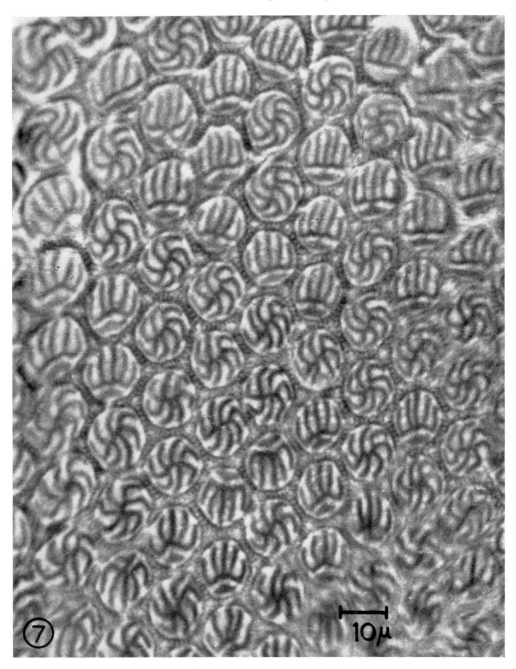

preparations. These electron-dense bands have generally been regarded as uniformly dense bands with no discernible fine structure [11, 17, 39]. However, upon examining high resolution micrographs of suitably thin and well-preserved specimens, additional details of the fine structure of the rod-shaped compartments can be detected.

Each of the dense bands can be resolved into two thin marginal lines of approximately 20 to 30 Å, which stain intensely with osmium and enclose a uniformly dense, particulate intermediate material.

Moreover, in oblique and longitudinal rhabdomere sections (Figs. 5, 6 *a*, *b*) the cross-sectioned hexagonal or polygonal compartments are now directly visible as annular profiles bounded by these thin lines of 20 to 30 Å, and apparently cemented together by the dense intermediate substance. In certain preparations (Figs. 6 *a*, *b*) the normally "empty" interior of the compartments contains a fine granular material condensed around the "walls", which in turn shows a tendency towards granular dissociation. Although interpretation of structural detail of these dimensions is uncertain due to the numerous artefact sources, there are definite indications that the outer part or "wall" of the compartments consists of a dense osmiophilic boundary line or "membrane" of 20 to 30 Å in thickness, associated with a dense layer of about 60 Å.

When viewed in suitably oriented longitudinal sections, the "walls" of the tubular compartments appear closed and rounded off at the ends adjoining the central matrix of the rhabdom. The other ends of the compartments which are oriented at right angles to the corresponding retinula cell membrane generally appear "open". These features of the tubular compartments are probably responsible for the "scalloped" borders [39] of the rhabdomeres in contact with the central matrix, and for the clear serrated fringe regularly observed along the zone of attachment of the rhabdomere to the retinula cell.

Particularly in the basal portion of the ommatidia there seems to be a closer relationship between the tubular compartments of the rhabdomeres and certain multiple-membrane or microvesicular structures regularly found in the cytoplasm of retinula cells. In these areas there is an interesting simi-

Fig. 8.—Electron micrograph of thin transverse section through a group of retinulae from the eye of *Erebus odora*, showing the symmetrical arrangement of the 7 rhabdomeres surrounded by numerous cross-sectioned fine tracheoles. As indicated by the arrows, the main axes of the equivalent rhabdomeres of each retinula are oriented in the same direction, contributing thus to an overall "structural polarization" and spatial integration of the corresponding ommatidial components which must be of particular functional significance in these eyes with a superposition type of image formation. Magnification × 5000.

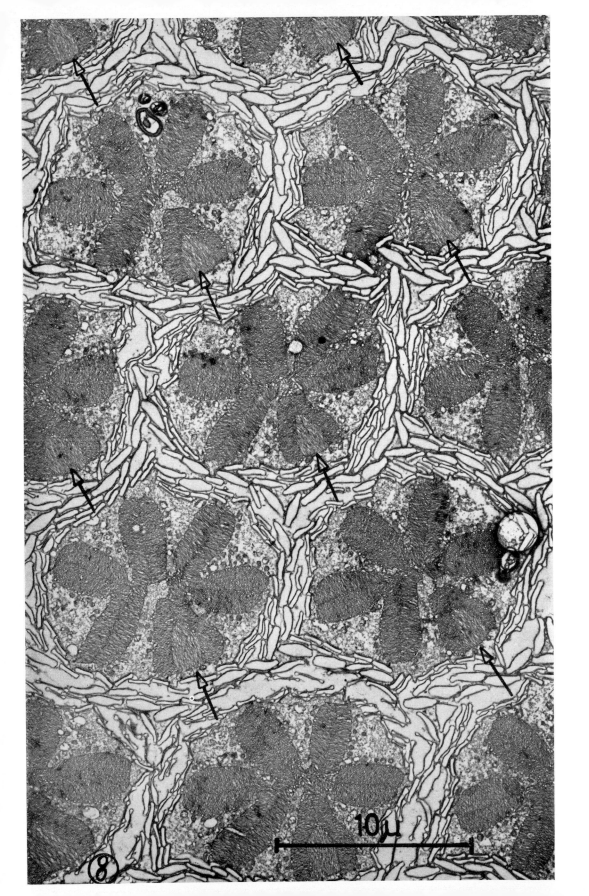

10μ

8

larity with the tube-like structures described by Miller [21] in the rhabdomeres
of *Limulus*, the spider, and the centipede *Scutigera*, which are interpreted
as specialized microvilli of the receptor cell's border. Pursuing this analogy
further, and bearing in mind their characteristic relationship with the retinula cells, the tubular compartments of the rhabdomeres could be considered
as differentiated tubular microvilli arising from the medial borders of the
retinula cells.

The described pattern of fine structure is observed throughout the entire
length of the rhabdomeres, except at their distal end bordering on the crystalline cone. In these distal areas the rhabdomeres exhibit a characteristic
pointed shape, and contain a homogeneous osmiophilic substance which
fuses into the differentiated tubular structure.

Pattern of Organization of the Rhabdomeres

The characteristic symmetrical arrangement of the seven rhabdomeres
in the single rhabdoms which was described earlier [11] has also been observed by Goldsmith and Philpott [17] and Wolken, Capenos and Turano
[39]. As demonstrated in transverse or slightly oblique sections (Figs. 1, 2, 3)
the six external rhabdomeres grouped around the central rhabdomere can
be divided into three pairs of elements, in which the size and configuration
of the rhabdomeres, and particularly the orientation of their transverse
bands are approximately matched. These paired rhabdomeres are usually
located opposite or diagonally opposite to each other, depending on the
plane of sectioning and on the location of the ommatidia. The most suitable
reference point is the central rhabdomere which can be recognized by its
small size (0.3 to 0.8 microns in diameter), and the narrow duplicature of
the corresponding retinula cell process which permits it to extend far into
the center of the rhabdom matrix. Large numbers of mitochondria within
these cell processes and a preferential distribution of the small pigment
granules (0.15 to 0.16 microns in diameter) along the attachment zone of the
rhabdomeres, which was first pointed out by Goldsmith and Philpott [17],
are further distinguishing topistical features.

Fig. 9.—Electron micrograph of an oblique cross section through a group of retinulae from the
eye of *Erebus* showing the organization of the rhabdomeres and their relationship with the retinula
cells. The large, paddle-shaped rhabdomere segments fuse together in the central region of each
retinula, and occupy most of the available space, leaving only marginal zones of retinula cell
cytoplasm. In addition to the characteristic wedge-shaped and eccentrically located rhabdomeres
(arrows) there are six other components which despite their composite structure might be grouped
in 3 matched pairs. However, an alternative grouping based on matching of the V-shaped rhabdomere segments contained within each retinula cell territory appears more suitable. Magnification
× 6000.

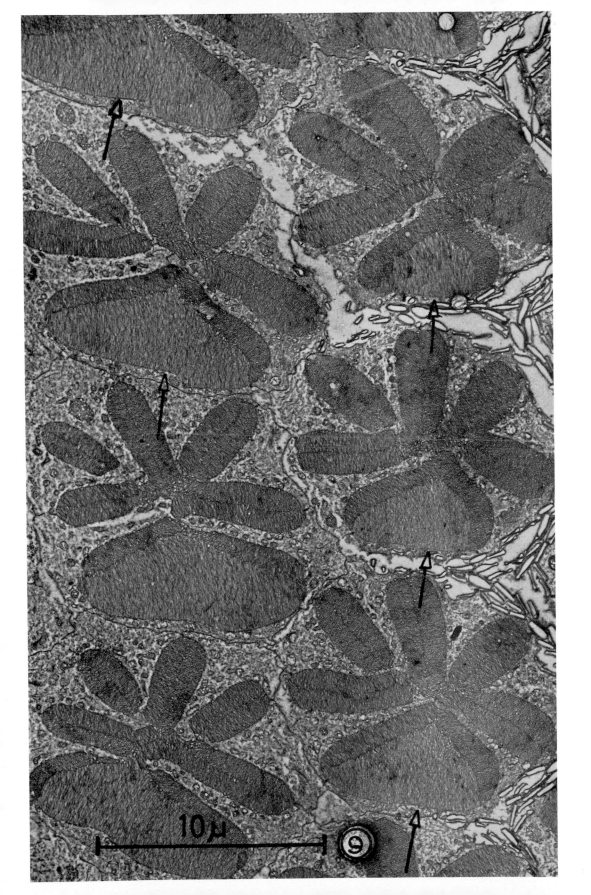

10μ

Beyond this local symmetry an overall three-dimensional regular pattern of organization of all the rhabdomeres in a given area becomes apparent upon examining undistorted ultrathin serial sections of large specimen blocks prepared with the diamond knife. It is then seen (Figs. 1, 3) that the highly regular mosaic pattern of the compound eye results not only from the orderly arrangement and interrelationship of the ommatidia, associated tracheae and pigment cells, but mainly from the periodic spatial polarization of the corresponding elements in adjacent rhabdoms. Thus, the equivalent rhabdomeres in the cross-sectioned ommatidia of a given region are oriented with their main axes in the same direction (Fig. 3). Imaginary lines connecting the two principal axes of the equivalent rhabdomeres would therefore form a series of periodically intersecting arcs, the configuration of which will be determined by the regional curvature of the compound eye [13]. The relationship of this superimposed regional pattern formed by structural coupling of groups of ommatidia, with the corresponding ommatidial angle [7, 36] in different parts of the eye is now being investigated. Likewise, the possible functional significance of this coordinated orientation of equivalent receptor elements in a group of ommatidia merits further study; particularly in connection with the postulated ability of the bee to determine not only the plane of polarized light, but to recognize also the regional patterns of polarization of the sky depending on the position of the sun [15, 16, 2].

Retinula Cell Structure

The characteristic abundance of mitochondria of varying size and shape (0.2 to 3 microns) in the retinula cells has already been pointed out by Goldsmith and Philpott [17]. The largest mitochondria (2 to 3 microns long) are usually found adjacent to the rhabdomeres, with their long axes, and frequently also the plane of their internal double membranes, oriented

---

Fig. 10.—Oblique cross section through a single retinula from the eye of *Erebus* showing the fine structure of the fused rhabdomeres. At this level the paddle-shaped rhabdomere segments stand out as separate components, and exhibit the characteristic transverse membrane structure corresponding to closely packed tubular compartments with an average diameter of 700 Å. A fine boundary line runs down the center of each rhabdomere sector or "ray", indicating the plane along which the tubular compartments terminate. The other ends of the tubular compartments project freely into the adjacent retinula cell cytoplasm, and are frequently found attached to multiple membrane profiles or invaginations of the retinula cell membrane. This is particularly marked in serial sections through the basal portions of the retinula, where the broader compartments of the eccentric rhabdomere appear clearly as villous projections of the corresponding retinula cell. In close analogy with the rhabdomeres of *Limulus* and of the spider described by Miller [21], the tubular compartments arise here as specialized microvilli from the retinula cell border. Magnification × 13,000.

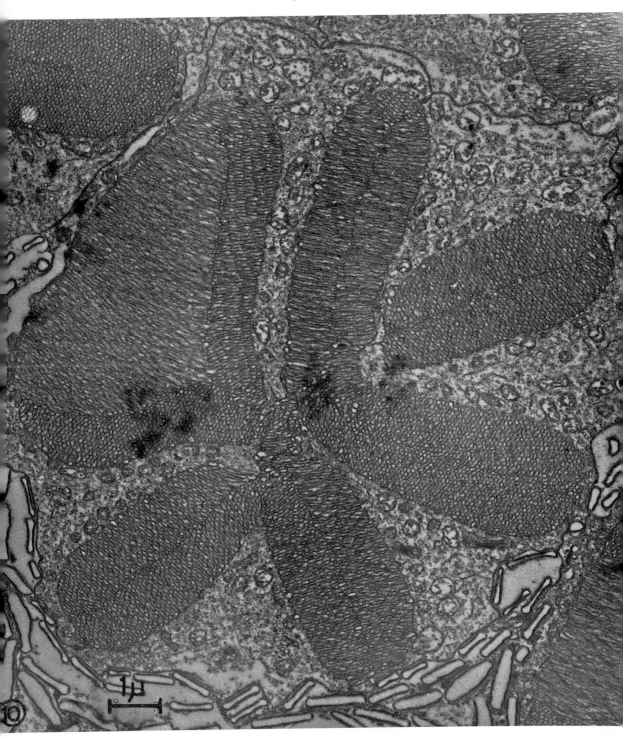

parallel to the rhabdomere axis. In addition to the mitochondria and fine pigment granules (0.15 to 0.16 micron in diameter) the cytoplasm of the retinula cells contains dense particles of 50 to 100 Å, associated with multiple membrane profiles, resembling the endoplasmic reticulum. Around the medial borders of the retinula cell, and particularly towards the region of the basement membrane, a characteristic microvesicular component, about 300 to 500 Å in diameter, is regularly encountered. Frequently, the microvesicles appear more like short segments of tubules, and surround large multiple membrane convolutes or whorls (0.2 to 0.4 micron in diameter) adjoining the retinula cell membrane. The polygonal nuclei of the retinula cells are located at the periphery, close to the pigment cells, and feature numerous conglomerates of granular chromatin attached to the double-contoured nuclear membrane. The cytoplasm of the pigment cells can be clearly distinguished from the retinula cytoplasm by its large pigment granules (0.25 to 0.35 micron in diameter), and the dense conglomerates of small (150 to 200 Å) osmiophilic granules.

Distribution of the Tracheae

Numerous tracheae (2 to 10 microns in diameter) penetrate through the basement membrane, and run in regular longitudinal array between the retinulae, branching out at periodic intervals to form a dense network of fine tracheoles (0.2 to 0.4 micron in diameter) closely associated with the rhabdoms. In suitably oriented sections it can be seen that these tracheoles establish direct contact with fine gaps of about 500 to 1000 Å diameter, which run between the retinula cells straight into the central matrix of the rhabdom. These patent submicroscopic channels therefore establish a direct communication between the tracheoles and the central region containing the rhabdomeres, thus facilitating respiration and disposal of metabolic products in these particularly active receptor areas. The tracheoles of the house-fly retinula have a typical "coiled spring" appearance when isolated intact from dissociation preparations; and in thin sections the sub-

Fig. 11.—Oblique cross section through a single retinula from the eye of *Erebus* showing the pattern of the rhabdomeres as determined by the retinula cell boundaries. Considering the tubular compartments as microvilli derived from the retinula cell, it is then seen that the central dividing line of the rhabdomere sectors is in reality the retinula cell boundary. The true rhabdomere units would therefore be the V-shaped segments arising from both internal borders of each retinula cell. The cytoplasm contains numerous large mitochondria, a dense particulate component, and characteristic "fenestrated bodies" (arrows) associated with an abundant microvesicular component and with multiple membranes. Magnification × 14,000.

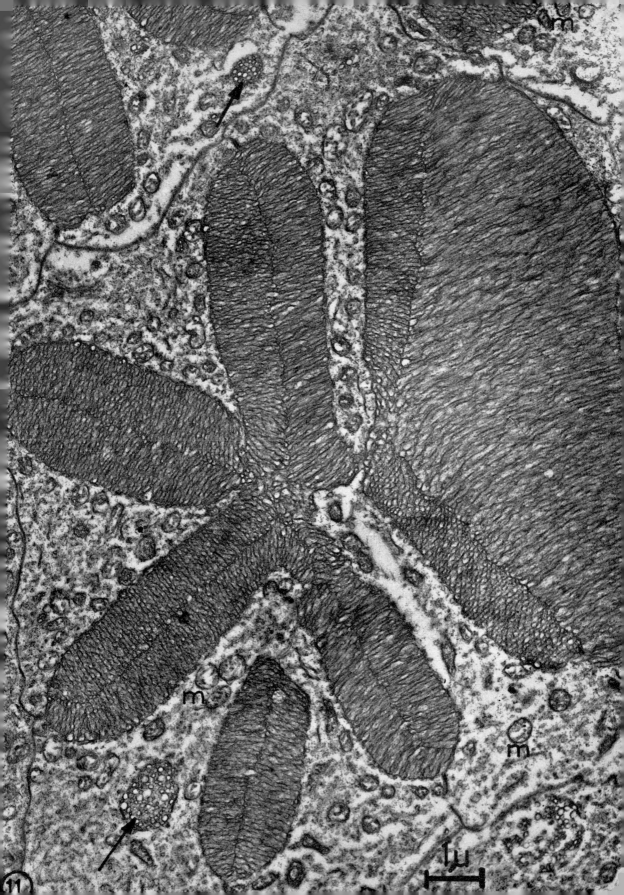

11

microscopic spiral folds or taenidia exhibit a delicate double-membrane fine structure.

There are certain indications that each retinula cell is associated with a single nerve fiber at the level of the basement membrane, but this relationship has not been satisfactorily investigated, as in the case of the *Erebus* retinulae to be described later on.

Structure of the Retinula in Drosophila melanogaster and Apis mellifera

All of the structural features described in the rhabdomeres, rhabdoms, retinula cells and associated structures of the house-fly eye are essentially similar to those encountered in the corresponding components of *Drosophila*, and of the honey bee, *Apis mellifera*. In view of the excellent descriptions already given by Wolken, Capenos and Turano [39], and by Goldsmith and Philpott [17], the details of individual variations observed in various Diptera with an apposition type of ommatidia will not be included here.

Compound Eye of the Tropical Moth Erebus odora

In the large (10 to 15 mm diameter) compound eyes of the giant tropical moth *Erebus odora*, with a superposition type of image formation, the entire receptor layer is separated from the crystalline cones by a transparent medium, and can therefore be exposed intact and under ideal conditions for observation in the living insect. It is then seen (Fig. 13) that the facets of the retinulae are closely packed together to form a regular hexagonal lattice on the surface of a hemispherical body located deep within the eye. This regular mosaic of photoreceptors, which superficially resembles the surface patterns of the receptor layer in the vertebrate retina, displays a vivid yellow or orange color. This color, which gradually fades away under illumination, has been attributed to an impregnation of the retinulae with a special coloring substance [4, 19]. The silvery sheen produced by light reflected from the underlying tracheal structure known as the *tapetum* becomes more marked

---

Fig. 12.—Oblique cross section through a few retinulae from the eye of *Erebus* demonstrating the symmetrical arrangement of the fused rhabdomeres. In this more distally located plane a widespread fusion of the individual rhabdomeres has taken place, and only small peripheral areas of retinula cell cytoplasm are still visible. Considering the V-shaped segments delimited by the central boundary lines of each paddle-shaped sector as the true rhabdomere units, it is possible to discern 3 groups of paired rhabdomeres in addition to the wedge-shaped eccentric rhabdomere. The general configuration and orientation of the tubular compartments in any one of these pairs is matched by the corresponding rhabdomere pattern directly or diagonally opposite to it. The few remaining areas of cytoplasm contain large "fenestrated bodies" formed by closely packed annular profiles. Magnification × 6000.

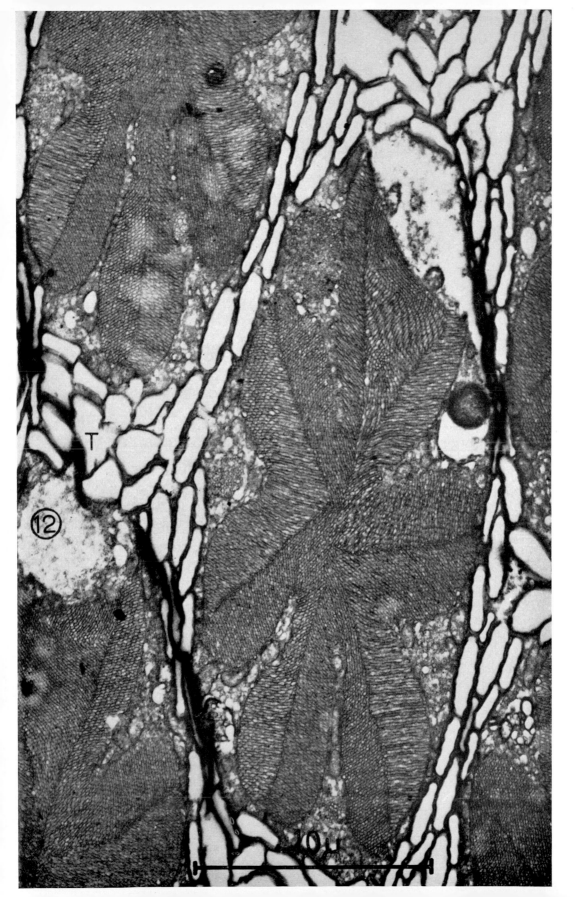

as the natural yellow color is bleached. The air-filled tracheal branches of the tapetum reflect incoming light back through the retinulae a second time, thus enabling these night-flying insects to make optimum use of faint illumination [19, 36]. As Bugnion and Popoff [4] have shown in a comprehensive study of the compound eye of nocturnal insects, the tracheae forming the tapetum in the region of the basement membrane divide into longitudinally oriented fine tracheoles that envelop the individual retinulae.

In phase contrast micrographs of thin transverse sections through the hemispherical receptor layer (Fig. 7) the distribution of the tightly packed tracheoles lodged between the retinulae can be observed. The large round or polygonal retinulae, with diameters of about 12 to 20 microns, display characteristic "stellate" or "pinwheel" patterns formed by the seven radially arranged rhabdomeres. The shape of the retinulae is approximately cylindrical with a tapering configuration at the distal end, as determined by phase contrast examination of serial sections through the whole eye.

Organization of the Rhabdoms

Electron microscope examination of a transverse thin section through a group of retinulae (Figs. 8, 9) discloses a strikingly regular and symmetric pattern of organization. The rhabdom is constituted by seven fused rhab-

---

Fig. 13.—Low power color micrograph of a "living" compound eye of *Erebus odora*, with the cornea and the adjacent structures partially cut away to expose the hemispheric surface of the retinula cell layer. In this superposition type of eye the retinulae are separated from the crystalline cones by a transparent medium, and appear closely packed together to form a regular mosaic reminiscent of the receptor layer in the vertebrate retina. The characteristic yellow or orange color, which gradually fades away, may be due to impregnation of the retinulae with a special coloring substance, and stands out against the silvery glistening tracheae of the associated tapetum. Magnification × 8.

Fig. 14.—Color micrograph of a segment of the fresh retinula cell layer from a tropical "Skipper" butterfly (Fam. Hesperiidae), showing the regular honeycomb structure of the exposed retinulae surfaces. When great care is exercised in preparing these fresh specimens, the entire surface layer of retinulae in the still active, light adapted eye exhibits characteristic iridescent reflections upon being observed with incident light. The whole hemispherical retinula surface shows a metallic sheen, which varies in color from predominantly blue to green or orange, depending on the angle of light incidence, and is mainly localized to the retinulae facets. Even in undamaged specimens this striking effect gradually disappears as the iridescence of each facet extinguishes, leaving finally a dark hexagonal framework dotted with the red glow originating in the tracheoles of the interspaces. Magnification × 100.

Fig. 15.—Color micrograph of a segment of the fresh retinula cell layer from a tropical "Skipper" butterfly, showing the iridescent color patterns observed in the retinulae. Closer examination of the iridescent reflections discloses a differentiated pattern within each retinula, consisting of an orange or green border enclosing the metallic blue core. This beautiful optical effect is exceedingly sensitive to mechanical trauma or anoxia, and even slight pressure exerted on the retinulae in the process of cutting away the cornea may abolish it. Micrograph taken with direct illumination (Ultropak) using polarized light. Magnification × 300.

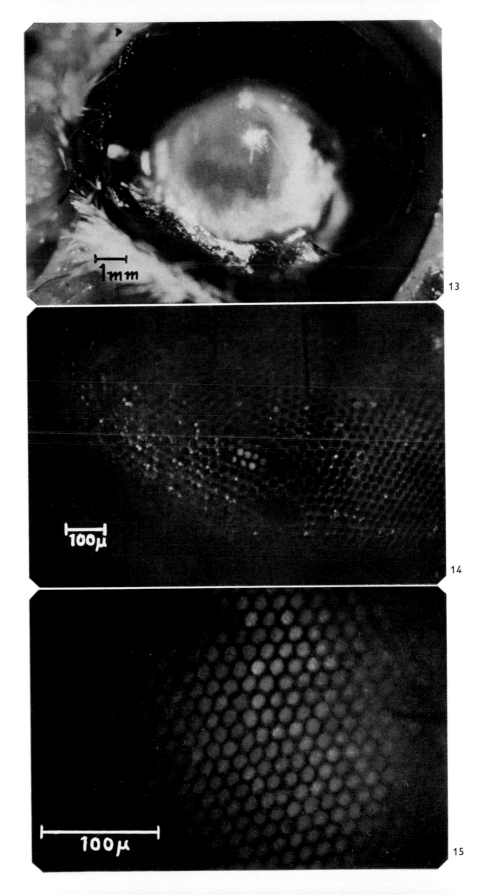

13

14

15

domeres, and occupies the bulk of each retinula with only scant marginal areas of retinula cell cytoplasm wedged in between the paddle-shaped sectors. Numerous rows of fine tracheoles, with diameters ranging from 0.2 to 1 micron, completely surround each retinula and fill the interspaces in tightly packed array. Pigment granules are conspicuously absent in most of the sections examined, and were only occasionally seen in the basal portions of the retinulae. The seven spatular rhabdomere segments, which fuse together in the central region of each retinula, exhibit an ordered lamellar fine structure, with a fine boundary line running down the middle of the sectors. An eccentrically located rhabdomere with a characteristic wedge-shaped configuration stands out clearly among the symmetrically arranged rhabdomere segments. Using this eccentric rhabdomere as a reference point, it can be seen that the main axes of the equivalent rhabdomeres in each retinula are oriented in the same direction within a given region.

The resulting regional pattern superimposed on the structural pattern of the individual retinulae is even more pronounced and regular in this super-position type of eye with its uniform spherical receptor surfaces, than in the apposition eye of the fly described earlier. Here again it would appear that the structural coupling of groups of ommatidia underlying this regional pattern must have an important functional significance.

Fine Structure of the Rhabdomeres

In cross sections or oblique sections (Figs. 10, 11, 12) the paddle-shaped rhabdomere segments (6 to 8 microns long, and about 2 to 3 microns wide) show essentially the same type of transverse lamellar or reticular structure described in the house-fly eye. However, the parallel arrangement of the

---

Fig. 16.—Color micrograph of the same specimen from the compound eye of a tropical "Skipper" examined at higher magnification. The individual retinulae with notched contours are symmetrically arranged within the dark hexagonal framework formed by the tightly packed tracheoles and pigment granules in the interspaces. Each retinula displays a differentiated iridescent color pattern, with a predominance of blue or violet in the center and orange or green at the periphery. Comparison of these images of fresh retinulae with the electron micrographs of the corresponding thin sections (Figs. 17–21) suggests a correlation between the color patterns and the retinula fine structure, which features a core of fused rhabdomeres surrounded by a highly differentiated cytoplasmic border. Moreover, the demonstration of a network of extremely fine intracellular tubules regarded as "ultratracheoles" (*ut* in Figs. 20–24) in this marginal zone indicates that we may be dealing with a physical coloration due to complex diffraction and scattering effects, like in the case of butterfly wing-scales. Although structural colors are commonly associated with the tracheal structures of the insect eye, this striking effect has so-far only been observed in the retinulae of "Skipper" butterflies with their uniquely differentiated submicroscopic organization, which literally "reflects itself" in the polychromatic iridescent sheen as a delicate indicator of physiological activity. Magnification × 1700.

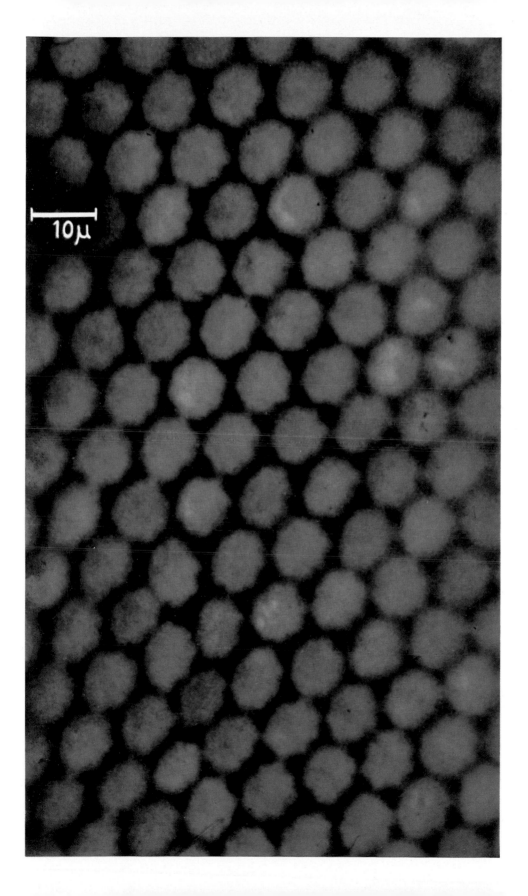

double-contoured, transverse dense bands is less regular, and their average separation ranges from 600 to 800 Å. The sinuous profiles of the radially oriented bands in the "eccentric" rhabdomere show an even greater separation of about 1000 to 1200 Å. A further distinguishing feature is the presence of a fine granular material within the less dense interspaces, in contrast to the interspaces of the fly rhabdomeres which generally appear "empty". Longitudinal or oblique sections reveal the characteristic mosaic of reticular and lamellar zones separated by the fine boundary lines already noted by Goldsmith and Philpott [17] in the rhabdom of the dragonfly.

According to the available evidence, the rhabdomeres of this superposition ommatidium are built up of rod-shaped or tubular units, 600 to 1200 Å in diameter, which are oriented with their long axes obliquely or at right angles to the longitudinal rhabdomere axes. These slightly irregular compartments appear to contain a particulate material (20 to 30 Å) associated with a less dense homogeneous material, and the outer part or "wall" exhibits a dense boundary line of 20 to 30 Å combined with a layer of about 60 Å. Although the presence of granular components within the compartments favors the simile of a rod-shaped unit in this case, most of the findings indicate that we are probably dealing with tubular compartments which can fill up with a presumably liquid substance giving the granular precipitates upon fixation. The tubular compartments are apparently sealed off all along the fine boundary line running down the center of each rhabdomere sector. At their other ends, however, the tubular compartments appear "open", and extend into the adjacent retinula cell cytoplasm. In these areas the compartment walls are often found attached to multiple membrane profiles or invaginations of the cell membrane. In serial sections through the basal portions of the retinulae, where this relationship is most manifest, it can be seen that the tubular compartments are actually "microvilli" arising from the retinula cell border. This concept of the tubular compartments as specialized microvilli which was first applied by Miller [21] in the structural analysis of *Limulus*, spider, and centipede rhabdomeres, also furnishes the basis for elucidation of the fused rhabdomere patterns. At first glance each of the seven finger-like sectors of the stellate rhabdoms might be considered as a separate rhabdomere, and despite their fusion in the central region 3 matched

Fig. 17.—Electron micrograph of oblique cross section through a group of retinulae from a tropical "Skipper" butterfly, showing the characteristic symmetrical arrangement of the retinulae structures. The individual retinulae have lobulated contours derived from 8 segments, and are completely bounded by patent tracheal compartments associated with tightly packed pigment granules. Compare with the corresponding color micrograph (Fig. 16). Magnification × 4000.

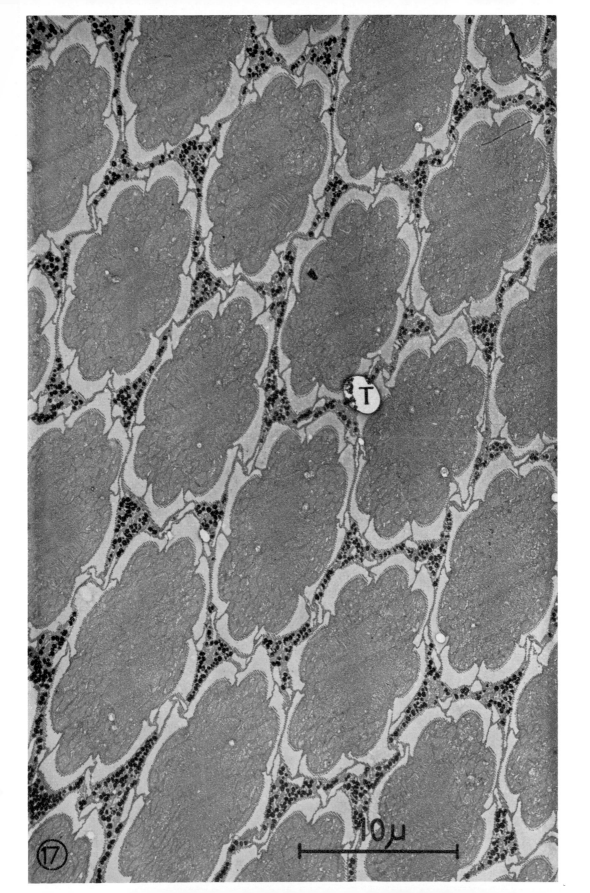

pairs (excluding the eccentric rhabdomere) could be recognized. Widespread fusion of the rhabdomeres occurring in the distal regions of the retinulae (Fig. 12) soon effaces this pattern, although diagonally opposed radial sectors of a rhabdom can still be associated with each other. However, only a delimitation of the rhabdomeres based on the individual retinula cell territories leads to a satisfactory pattern definition. Bearing in mind that the tubular compartments are microvilli derived from the medial borders of the retinula cell, it is then seen that the central dividing lines of each pair of adjacent rhabdomere sectors represent in reality the boundaries of the corresponding wedge-shaped retinula cell (Figs. 10, 11). The V-shaped segments arising from both internal borders of each retinula cell would therefore be the true rhabdomere units. The V-shaped rhabdomeres can be more readily arranged in matched pairs located opposite each other, as T. H. Goldsmith pointed out to the author. The close apposition of adjacent rhabdomeres along such a sharply defined boundary zone must nevertheless be of some significance, and the possibility that the paddle-shaped sectors might act as functional units should not be discounted.

Retinula Cell Structure

The wedge-shaped retinula cell is bounded at the periphery by a double-contoured cell membrane, which is attached by means of short prolongations to the tips of adjacent pairs of rhabdomere sectors (Fig. 10). Its cytoplasmic tendrils extend deep into the central areas of the rhabdom, where the confluence of cell expansions may give rise to a light zone reminiscent of the central matrix of the rhabdom.

Numerous large mitochondria and rosette-shaped conglomerates of dense particles (50 to 100 Å in diameter), which are regularly associated with multiple membrane profiles, can be seen in the cytoplasm. In the basal portions of the retinulae numerous multiple membrane profiles associated with a microvesicular or microtubular component (400 to 600 Å in diameter), and frequently connected with extensions of the tubular compartments, can be readily discerned. However, the most prominent structures

---

Fig. 18.—Oblique cross section through a group of retinulae from a tropical "Skipper" butterfly demonstrating the general pattern of submicroscopic organization. The highly regular filigree character of the overall pattern derives from the wealth of minute structures, which preserve a symmetrical arrangement throughout the various levels of organization. There are 8 tracheal compartments directly applied to the retinula segments, with their sectioned taenidiae forming the delicately serrated contours of each retinula. Within the extremely compact retinulae it is difficult to differentiate clearly the fused rhabdomeres from the associated cytoplasmic components. Magnification × 6000.

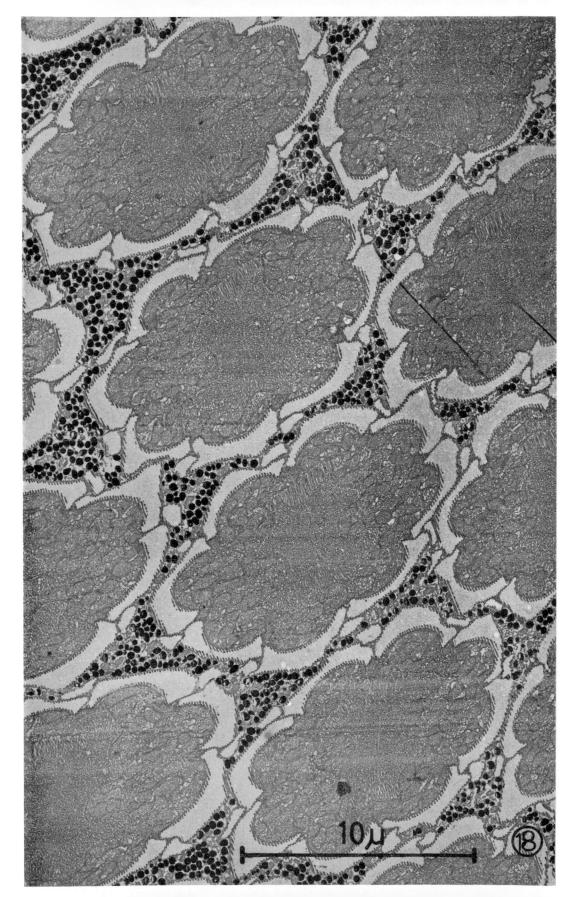

10μ

⑱

regularly found in only one or a few cells of each retinula are the "fenestrated bodies". These large bodies, 1 to 1.5 microns in diameter (Fig. 11), are formed by compact aggregation of several score of annular profiles (500 to 1000 Å diameter) which appear to be bounded by a fine membrane. From their appearance in serial sections, these profiles might correspond to cross-sectioned tubular elements with their long axes oriented parallel to the long axes of the rhabdomeres. The fenestrated bodies are usually located in the marginal zones of the retinula cell cytoplasm, not very far from the fine tracheoles, and occasionally in the vicinity of compactly packed multiple membranes resembling the concentric lamination of the myelin sheath. Further studies are now in progress in order to identify the fenestrated bodies, and establish their relationship with the rhabdomeres.

The Tracheoles

The fine tracheoles (0.2 to 1 micron diameter) surrounding each retinula have a comparatively smooth lumen with few taenidia, in contrast to the prominent series of taenidial ridges encountered in the larger tracheoles of the tapetum. In cross sections the tracheolar walls exhibit certain areas which are bridged only by a diffuse, light membrane. A fine granular material associated with a delicate system of delimiting membranes is regularly observed between the tracheolar walls in junctional regions.

Retinula-Nerve Fiber Relationships

Based on observations with the light microscope, it has been assumed that each retinula cell is associated with a single nerve fiber, which passes through the basement membrane and enters the outermost tract of the optic lobe designated the periopticon [29, 36]. The uncertainties still prevailing in connection with this relationship are not only due to the limited resolving power of light microscopy, but also in large measure to the exceedingly compact and intricate structural organization of this region. Thus, although accurate visualization of the entire fine structure is now possible by means of electron microscopy, interpretation of the bewildering textural complexity revealed in ultrathin sections still presents serious difficulties. Therefore,

---

Fig. 19.—Oblique cross section through a single retinula from a tropical "Skipper" butterfly showing the fine structure of the fused rhabdomeres and the associated elements. The central region is occupied by a complex array of transverse membranes and reticular structures corresponding to the tubular compartments of the 8 fused rhabdomeres in oblique section. The rhabdom is surrounded by an even more compact cytoplasmic marginal zone, which is filled with rows of large mitochondria, grouped together in radial columns by a network of fine tubular structures. Magnification × 18,000.

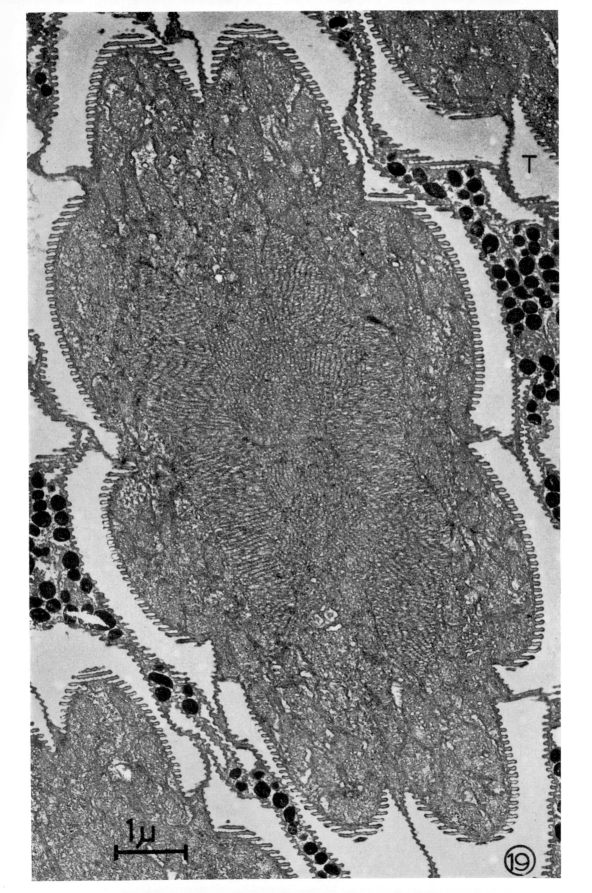

T

1μ

⑲

the preliminary observations recorded here can merely be regarded as a first approximation to the question of the nerve fiber–retinula cell relationship.

In transverse serial sections through the basal portion of the retinulae in the region of the basement membrane, a transitional zone is found (below the basement membrane) where the outlines of the individual retinulae are gradually replaced by large round or polygonal bodies, of approximately the same diameter as the retinulae, which contain cross-sectioned nerve fibers (Figs. 28a, b). Each of these primary bundles formed by 7 to 9 nerve fibers is surrounded by a dense granular and fibrous material, closely associated with large pigment granules and with numerous tracheoles. Despite the close packing, the continuous sheath of each nerve fiber consisting of a dense double-contoured membrane can be clearly discerned (Fig. 28b). The axons contain numerous cross-sectioned axon filaments (100 to 200 Å diameter), a dense granular material, and intra-axonal mitochondria which are usually closely attached to the sheath.

Although the structures mediating the connection between the base of the retinula cells and these nerve fibers have not been adequately studied yet, the available data indicates that each retinula cell is associated with a single nerve fiber. Likewise, the complex synaptic apparatus of the periopticon through which the nerve fibers establish contact with the ganglion cells remains to be investigated. It is nevertheless of interest that each retinula cell with the corresponding rhabdom appears to have its individual nerve fiber connection with the periopticon, and that there is at least transitional preservation of the basic spatial arrangement in these bundles before projecting into the optic lobes.

Compound Eye of the Tropical Skipper Butterflies (Hesperiidae)

The compound eyes undoubtedly play an important role in steering the "Skipper" type of butterflies throughout their characteristic darting, bounding excursions. These predominantly tropical insects belong to the large family of the Hesperiidae [19], and are most active during the day. Their medium-

---

Fig. 20.—Transverse section through two retinulae from the tropical "Skipper" butterfly showing the arrangement of the fused rhabdomeres, and the marginal network of fine tubular structures. In these slightly extracted preparations the pattern formed by the 8 fused rhabdomeres can be clearly distinguished. The 8 V-shaped rhabdomeres formed by transverse tubular compartments can be grouped into 4 matched pairs, usually facing each other. The central matrix of the rhabdom (R) is occupied by a cross-sectioned filamentous material. A sharply outlined network of dense tubular elements (ut) extends radially from the tracheal (T) boundary zone towards the rhabdom, enclosing large mitochondria and other cytoplasmic components. Magnification × 14,000.

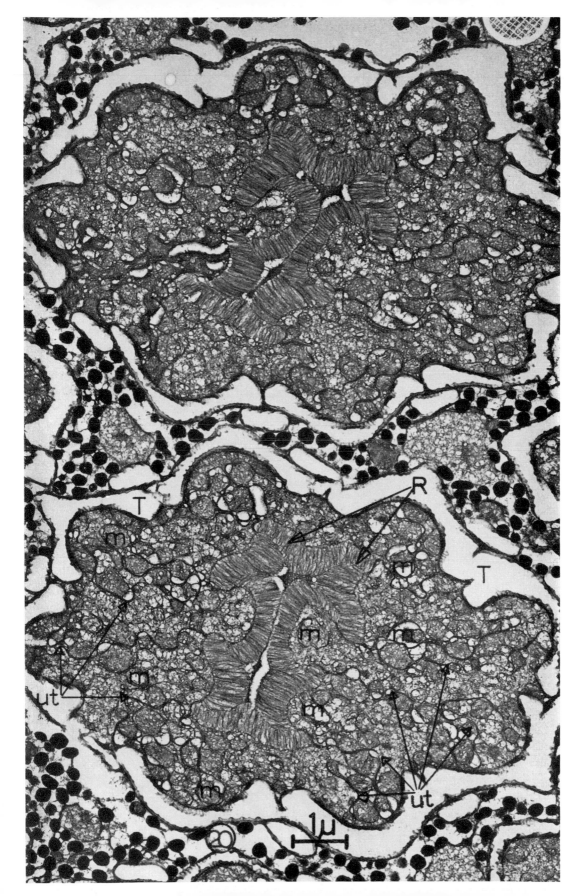

sized eyes are mainly of the superposition type, and would hardly have been singled out for study were it not for the striking optical effects displayed by the fresh receptor layers.

If the corneal shell is carefully removed, the exposed hemispherical receptor surface lodged within the living eye exhibits refulgent iridescent reflections imbued with an intense metallic sheen upon being illuminated (Figs. 14, 15). This unique iridescence is present over the entire retinula layer, and, depending on the angle of light incidence, the predominantly metallic blue color can shift over to green or orange. In this respect there is a close resemblance with the properties of a curved optical grating. Beyond this general effect visible with the naked eye, microscopic examination with direct illumination reveals that the iridescence derives from the individual retinulae facets, which are distributed in regular array within a dark hexagonal framework (Figs. 14, 15, 16). Moreover, within each retinula a differentiated color pattern can be discerned, with a predominance of blue or violet in the center and orange or green at the margins (Figs. 15, 16). The described beautiful optical phenomena are extremely sensitive to mechanical trauma or anoxia, and can only be observed in the intact retinulae. Even in well preserved specimens the intensity of the effect soon diminishes, and it gradually disappears as the iridescence of each facet is extinguished, finally leaving a mosaic of dark patches outlined by the hexagonal framework which now emits a red glow coming from transmitted light in the tracheoles of the interspaces (Fig. 14).

The coloration effects found in the receptor layer of the Skipper's eye are quite different from the pigmentary coloration commonly observed in other types of superposition eyes, and obviously correspond to the class of "structural colors". Structural colors depend primarily on the physical properties of the object, and are caused by rather complex interaction of the incident light (reflection, refraction, diffraction, scattering) with its structural components [1, 19]. Although certain structural colors can be related to the fine tracheal formations of the insect eye, we are dealing here with an effect mainly local-

---

Fig. 21.—Oblique cross section through a single retinula from the tropical "Skipper" butterfly showing the fine structure of the cytoplasmic marginal zone, and the distribution of the tubular structure network. Only part of the rhabdom (R) is visible in this section, while a retinula cell nucleus and the adjoining cytoplasmic territories occupy most of the retinula. A distinct network of double contoured, striated filaments, about 250–300 Å in diameter, which are tentatively designated "ultratracheoles" (ut), branches out from the tracheal compartments (T) towards the rhabdom. Within the regularly spaced (0.4 to 0.5 microns) meshes of this network numerous large mitochondria (m) are to be found which appear to be longitudinally oriented forming regular columns. The arrows indicate certain areas where the "ultratracheoles" (ut) establish direct contact with the tracheal compartments. Magnification × 29,000.

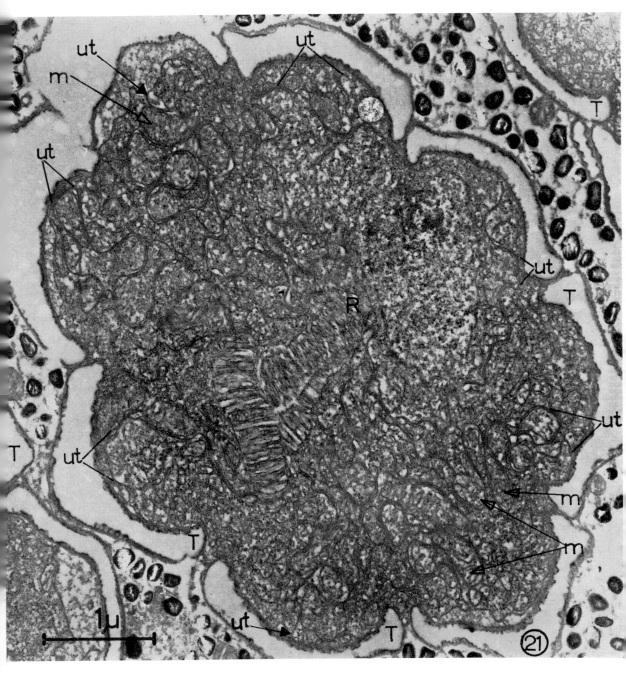

ized to the retinulae, and uniquely dependent on the preservation of their submicroscopic organization. It appeared therefore of interest to establish a correlation between these coloration effects observed in the living eye, and the ultrastructure of the light receptors as revealed by electron microscopy.

Organization of the Retinulae

Comparison of color micrographs of the fresh retinula (Fig. 16) with electron micrographs of the corresponding thin sections (Figs. 17 to 21) reveals the adequate preservation of the structural relationships down to the submicroscopic level. Among all the light receptors examined up till now, the Skipper retinulae show the highest degree of compact structural differentiation. The individual retinulae with lobulated contours formed by 8 segments are symmetrically arranged within an octagonal framework composed of patent tracheal compartments associated with dense rows of pigment granules. The delicately serrated taenidial ridges attached to the retinulae borders emphasize the filigree character of the symmetrical textural pattern. Within each retinula a central region occupied by the rhabdom (Fig. 20) can be distinguished from a more compact cytoplasmic marginal zone. The rhabdom is formed by 8 fused rhabdomeres symmetrically arranged around a central matrix which is filled with a fine filamentous-granular material. The marginal cytoplasmic zone of the retinula cells completely envelops the rhabdom, and contains numerous large mitochondria which are closely packed in radial columns delimited by a network of fine filamentous or tubular structures. The diameter of the individual retinulae ranges from 10 to 15 microns.

Fine Structure of the Rhabdomeres

In transverse and longitudinal sections the open V-shaped rhabdomeres exhibit the same type of transverse lamellar and reticular structures corresponding to rod-shaped or tubular compartments, 700 to 900 Å in dia-

---

Figs. 22 a, b.—High resolution electron micrograph of a retinula segment from the tropical "Skipper" butterfly, showing the fine structure of the intracellular tubular structures, and their relationship with the tracheoles. These "ultratracheoles" (*ut*) appear in osmium-fixed preparations as long, double-contoured filaments, about 200–300 Å in diameter, with characteristic cross striations which are regularly distributed to give an axial period of approximately 150–200 Å. They are invariably found in direct contact, and as if arising from the lumen of the tracheal compartments (*T*) (arrows in Fig. 22 a). The "ultratracheoles" form an interconnected network within the cytoplasm of the retinula cells, enclosing columnar rows of large mitochondria (*m*), and usually terminate around the rhabdomeres (*R*). Magnifications: 22 a, ×57,000; 22 b, ×85,000.

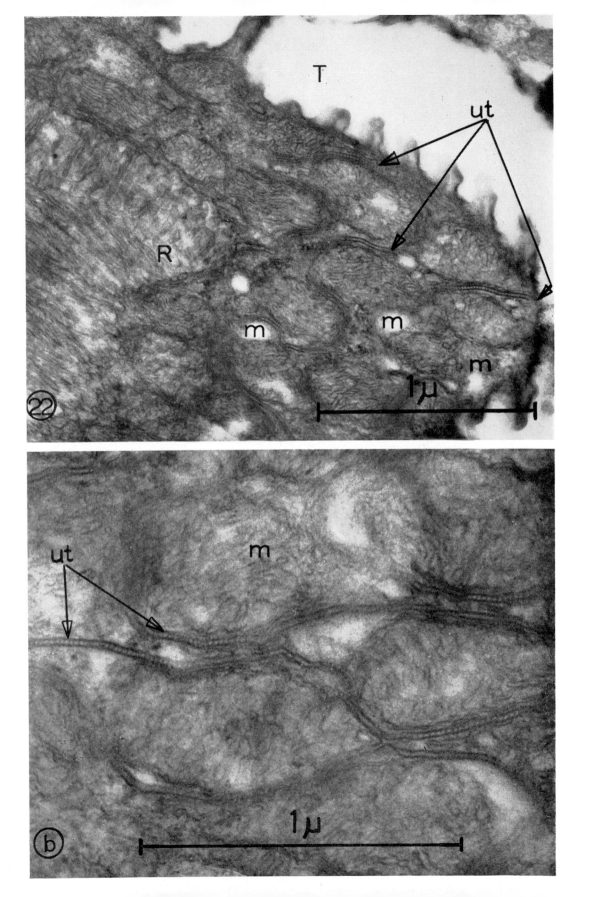

meter, oriented obliquely or perpendicular to the longitudinal rhabdomere axes. The compartments are similar to the tubular rhabdomere units in *Erebus* with double-contoured "walls", an internal particulate material, and a slightly irregular, sinuous configuration. The rhabdomere loops are fused together to give the rhabdom a characteristic elongated shape with a long, narrow space occupied by the filamentous or granular material of the central matrix (Figs. 19, 20). The 8 rhabdoms can be grouped together into 4 matched pairs with corresponding orientations of their tubular compartments.

Fine Structure of the Marginal Zone of the Retinulae

The marginal zone appears nearly completely filled with large (1 to 2 microns long) mitochondria which are longitudinally oriented and closely packed into radially arranged columns (Figs. 19, 20, 21). These radial columns, usually formed by a single row of mitochondria, have an average width of 0.4 to 0.5 micron, and are delimited by a sharply defined network of double-contoured, striated filaments about 250 to 300 Å in diameter. As seen particularly in oblique cross-sections (Figs. 19, 22) the entire marginal zone of the retinulae appears partitioned into these clearly delimited, long wedge-shaped "mitochondrial compartments" with a fairly periodic spacing of 0.4 to 0.5 micron.

In addition to the mitochondria, the usual dense particulate component and the multiple membrane profiles characteristic of the retinula cell body can be distinguished. In the basal portions of the retinulae the cell nuclei (Fig. 21) are more frequently encountered. However, the most conspicuous elements of the marginal zone are the double-contoured, striated filaments which have been tentatively designated "ultratracheoles".

Fig. 23.—High resolution electron micrograph of a retinula segment from the tropical "Skipper" butterfly, showing the fine structure of the longitudinally sectioned ultratracheoles. These double-contoured filaments with their distinctly outlined borders and the characteristic cross striations do not resemble any of the known connective tissue fibers, and appear to be closely related with the tracheoles. They seem to arise directly from the walls of the tracheal compartments, or from specialized intracellular tracheolar cisternae. Although ultratracheoles of these dimensions have not been encountered before, the available evidence is consistent with the assumption of this air or liquid filled intracellular network of tracheolar branches establishing intimate contact with the mitochondria (*m*) and the rhabdomeres. By virtue of their periodic arrangement in longitudinally oriented laminar compartments with spacings of about the same size as the wavelengths of light, these ultratracheolar nets could also contribute to the complex diffraction and scattering effects operative in the insect retina. Magnification × 126,000.

Fig. 24.—Transverse section through the wall of the tracheal compartment associated with a retinula segment of a tropical "Skipper" butterfly, showing the taenidiae of a tracheole (*T*), a group of pigment granules (*P*) and several mitochondria (*m*). Notice the microvesicular component clustered around the cell membrane. Magnification × 40,000.

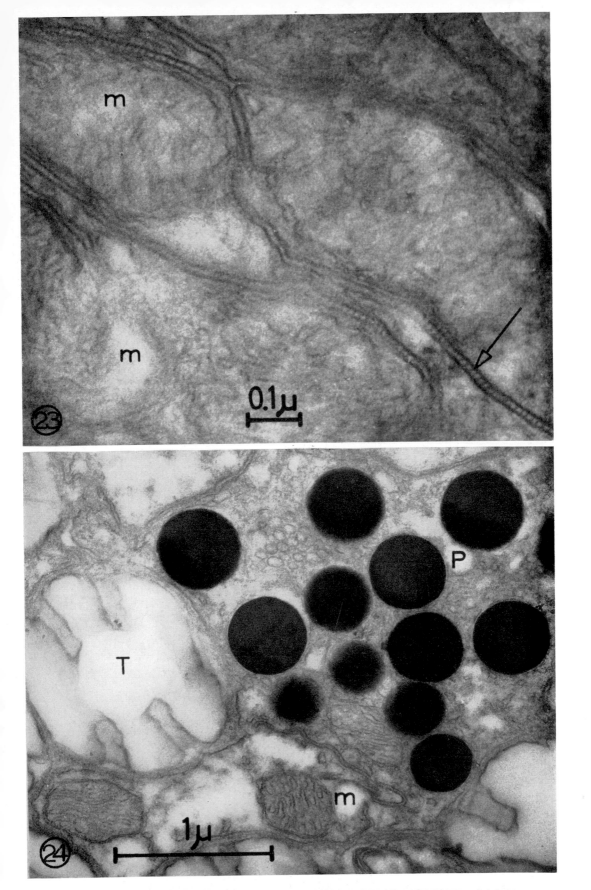

The Tracheolar Structures

   The ultratracheoles are invariably found extending from the lumen of the tracheal compartments, through the marginal zone where they form a wide-meshed network, into the central rhabdom region where they usually terminate (Figs. 21, 22, 23). In longitudinal sections (preferably 300 Å thick) the ultratracheoles (*ut*) appear as relatively long (2 to 6 microns) and straight double-contoured structures formed by two dense lines (20 to 30 Å wide) which are separated by a clear space, with an overall average diameter of 250 to 300 Å. Each of the double-contoured structures exhibits well-defined *cross-striations*, formed by dense lines, 30 to 40 Å wide, which are regularly spaced at right angles to its long axis with an average periodicity of 150 Å. Carrying the interpretations of the "ultratracheoles" to their logical conclusion, these cross-striations would be considered "microtaenidia". Actually, in oblique thin sections (Figs. 21, 22 *a*) certain areas can be detected which exhibit numerous delicate parallel striations of exactly the same dimensions (150 Å), and would correspond to the "microtaenidia" of tangentially sectioned ultratracheoles. From these findings and numerous double-contoured, striated annular profiles completely surrounding cross-sectioned mitochondria, it appears that we are not dealing exclusively with tubular structures but rather with differentiated intracellular extensions of the fine tracheoles, which penetrate into the submicroscopic interstices of the retinula, and thus establish direct communication with the tracheolar system. These submicroscopic tracheolar expansions can assume a variety of forms: from ultratracheolar tubules to ultratracheolar cisternae, but even at this level of macromolecular structure they appear to be invested with characteristic reinforcements patterned after the taenidia. Even in areas of closest apposition to the mitochondria membranes (Figs. 22 *a*, *b*, 23) the walls of the ultratracheolar elements can always be clearly distinguished because of their characteristic association with the cross-striations. As pointed out earlier, the ultratracheoles arise either directly from a gap in the wall of the large tracheolar compartments (Fig. 22 *a*), or from a series of ultratracheolar spaces located immediately below the zones of attachment of the tracheoles to the borders of the retinulae. The images observed in these cases are very

---

Fig. 25.—Oblique cross section through the basal portion of two ommatidia from the grasshopper eye, showing the general organization of the retinula. The retinula cells with their eccentrically located nuclei are grouped around the fused rhabdomeres constituting the rhabdom. A large number of mitochondria and pigment granules of various sizes are regularly found clustered around the rhabdom. A zone of confluent intracellular spaces surrounding the rhabdom probably represents cross-sectioned tracheolar compartments. Magnification × 6000.

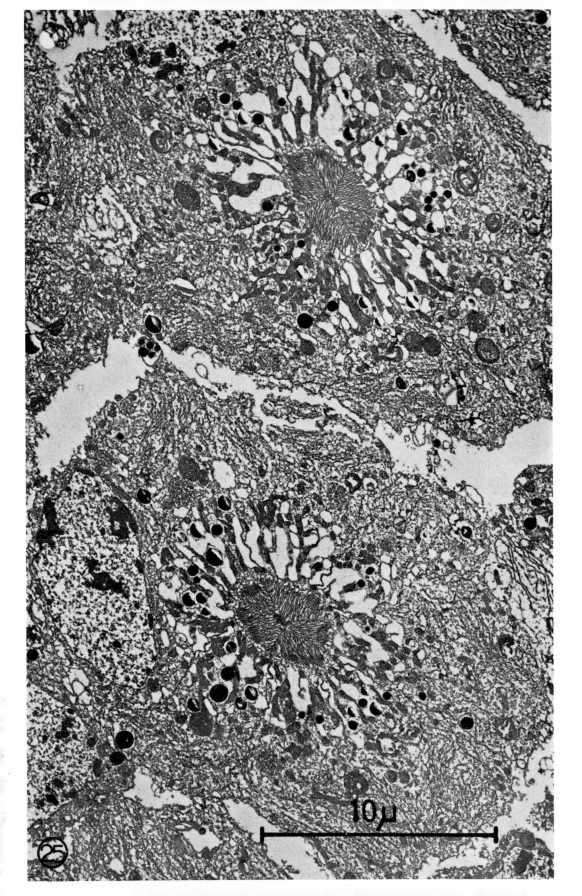

25

10μ

similar to the submicroscopic gaps between the retinula cells of the house-fly ommatidia, which also serve to establish direct communication between the tracheoles and the rhabdoms. In this connection it is interesting to recall that taenidia only 250 Å broad have been observed with the electron microscope in tracheoles 2000 Å in diameter by Richards and Anderson [26, 27].

Compared with the adduced evidence in favor of the ultratracheolar nature of the double-contoured intracellular network, a possible alternative interpretation regarding it as a connective tissue structure appears unlikely. Nevertheless, convincing proof has yet to be furnished that we are really dealing with patent "tubular" structures.

As shown in Fig. 24, the areas between the tracheolar compartments are filled with large pigment granules, numerous mitochondria, and granular or microvesicular components.

Correlation of the Iridescence Phenomena Observed in the Fresh Retinulae with Their Submicroscopic Structure

It is noteworthy that despite the marked similarity in the submicroscopic organization of the retinulae of the moth *Erebus* and the "Skipper" butterfly, there should be such a striking difference between the characteristic coloration effects observed in the eyes of these two insects. Since the distinctive iridescence phenomena are localized in the retinulae of the "Skipper" butterflies, any correlation attempt must naturally stem from the only significant structural difference encountered so far, which is the presence of an intracellular ultratracheolar network within the Skipper retinulae. Moreover, comparison of the color micrographs of the fresh retinulae (Fig. 16) with the corresponding electron micrographs (Figs. 17–21) suggests an obvious correlation between the color patterns and the retinula fine structure. Thus, the core of each retinula which is occupied by the regular tubular or lamellar structure of the rhabdomeres with a 700 to 900 Å spacing, might furnish the basis for the deep blue or violet color observed in this region under favorable conditions. In analogy with the structural color known as Tyndall blue [1, 19], which is due to scattering of the shorter wavelengths

Fig. 26.—Oblique cross section through a single rhabdom from the grasshopper eye, showing the fine structure of the fused rhabdomeres. The rhabdomeres are formed by closely packed tubular compartments, 700 to 900 Å in diameter, bounded by double-contoured membranes, and containing an internal diffuse granular material. The predominantly radially oriented compartments seem to arise as differentiated microvilli from the membranous structures lining the medial border of the retinula cells. At these boundary regions the membranes of the tubular compartments show a more dense, imbricated structure. The central matrix of the rhabdom is formed by tightly packed filaments which appear as circular, dense profiles in cross section, about 100 to 150 Å in diameter. Magnification × 38,000.

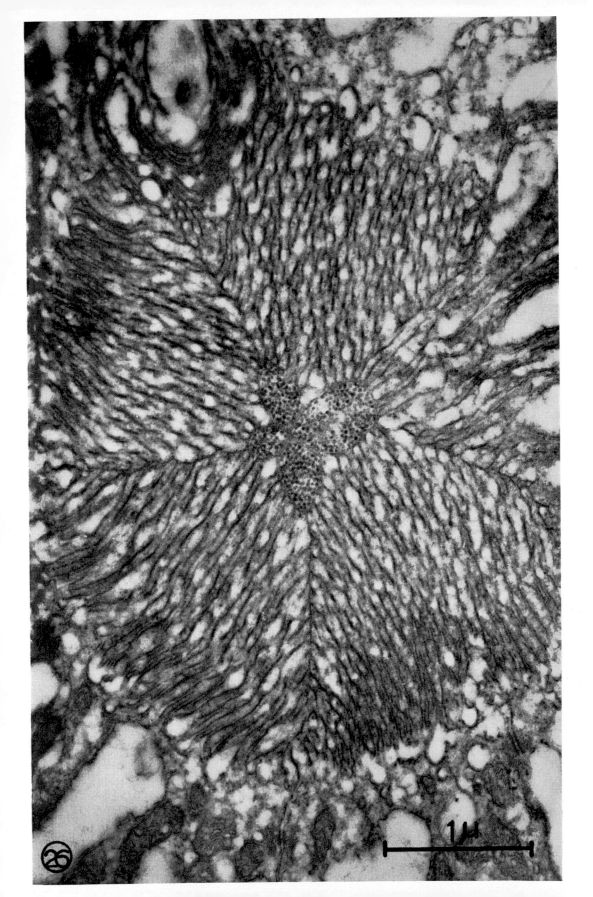

1μ

of incident light by particles of about the same size as the wavelengths, we might be dealing here with combined scattering and diffraction of the reflected light along selected planes of the highly regular lamellar structure of the rhabdomeres. Similarly, the assumption of an air- or liquid-filled intracellular network of tracheolar branches delimiting the laminar compartments of the marginal zone to give a regular spacing of the order of the wavelength of light (about 0.5 micron) could account for the complex diffraction effects predominantly responsible for the orange and green colors observed in this region. However, both phenomena must also be dependent on the special structural relationship between the retinulae and the adjacent tracheolar and pigment systems which characterizes the receptor layer of the Skipper's eye. From a functional point of view, this tracheolar-pigment system intimately associated with the retinulae must contribute to the formation of sharp images in bright sunlight.

Compound Eye of the Grasshoppers

The compound eyes of various specimens of grasshoppers (*Dissosteira*) and of the locust (*Schistocerca*) were examined, because pigment migration enables them to function both as apposition and superposition types. In the eye of *Schistocerca*, for example, the striped appearance observed during the day-time is due to expansion of the pigment in the iris cells, while the banding disappears at night when the pigment retracts [36]. All of the eyes were light-adapted prior to fixation.

Organization of the Retinulae

The general structural pattern of each retinula is seen in oblique cross sections through the basal portion of the ommatidia (Fig. 25). The relatively large retinulae (15 to 20 microns in diameter) are formed by groups of retinula cells surrounding the distinctly smaller rhabdom (5 to 8 microns in diameter). The retinula cells feature prominent, eccentrically located nuclei, and contain a large number of mitochondria and pigment granules of various

---

Fig. 27.—High resolution electron micrograph of a cytoplasmic segment near the medial border of a retinula cell from the grasshopper eye showing characteristic microtubular and multiple membrane complexes. These contorted microtubular formations or multiple membrane aggregates are frequently found in direct contact or otherwise structurally associated with the extensions of the tubular rhabdomere compartments. It is therefore assumed that they represent intermediate stages in the process of differentiation of microvilli from the medial border of the retinula cells to form the tubular compartments of the rhabdomeres. Notice the abundant dense particles commonly found associated with the membranous structures of the cytoplasm. Magnification × 58,000.

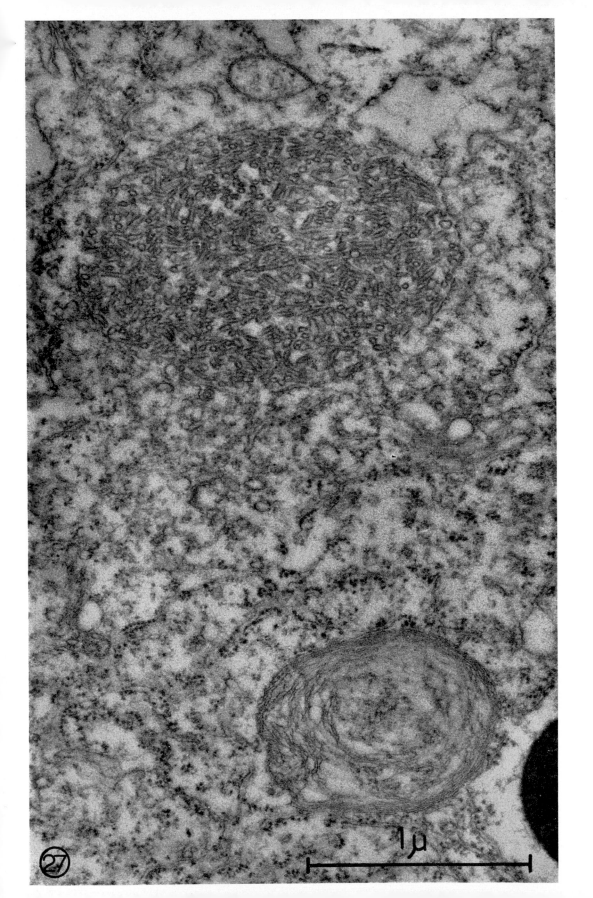

27

1μ

sizes (0.2 to 0.6 micron diameter). Around the rhabdom series of radially arranged, confluent patent spaces (1 to 2 microns long) are found, and probably correspond to cross-sectioned tracheolar compartments. The rhabdom is formed by the fusion of wedge-shaped rhabdomeres which are built up of tubular compartments, 700 to 900 Å in diameter, with double-contoured "walls" and a particulate internal component. At the marginal regions of the rhabdom the membranes of the tubular compartments exhibit a more compact, imbricated structure (Figs. 26, 25). A distinguishing feature is the presence of tightly packed filaments, about 100 to 150 Å in diameter, in the central matrix of the rhabdom. Characteristic microvesicular and microtubular complexes, and multiple membrane formations (Fig. 27) are regularly found in the cytoplasm of the retinula cells.

Although there is a superficial resemblance with the "fenestrated bodies" of the *Erebus* retinulae, these microvesicular complexes are usually separated from the rhabdoms by a palisade of radially arranged mitochondria and tracheolar spaces. Despite the structural preponderance of the retinula cell bodies, the rhabdoms of the grasshopper ommatidia have certain features in common with those of typical superposition eyes, such as fused rhabdomeres composed of tubular compartments filled with particulate elements. However, it is the localization and characteristic movements of the pigment components which make the grasshopper eye eminently suited for an investigation of the pigment migrations occurring during light adaptation. Depending on the intensity of illumination the pigment granules cluster together or become dispersed, while no perceptible changes have been detected in the shape and position of the corresponding iris or retinula cells [36]. By using these intracellular pigment granules of various sizes as cytoplasmic "markers", it appears therefore possible to study the mechanisms of pigment migration, and to trace the concomitant rearrangements occurring in the submicroscopic pattern of the retinulae during the transition from the dark-adapted to the light-adapted state. Preliminary studies along these lines, which will be reported elsewhere, indicate that there are characteristic dis-

---

Figs. 28 a, b.—Cross sections through nerve fiber bundles in the region of the basement membrane from the compound eye of *Erebus*. These primary nerve fiber bundles, which appear to connect the individual ommatidia with the periopticon, usually contain 8 to 9 nerve fibers enveloped by a dense granular material associated with numerous pigment granules and tracheoles. As shown in Fig. 28 b, each nerve fiber has a continuous sheath formed by a dense, double-contoured membrane. Intra-axonal mitochondria are often found closely attached to the sheath membrane, together with a dense granular material and cross-sectioned axon filaments. The available evidence indicates that each retinula cell is associated with a single nerve fiber. Magnifications: 28 a, × 9000; 28 b, × 12,000.

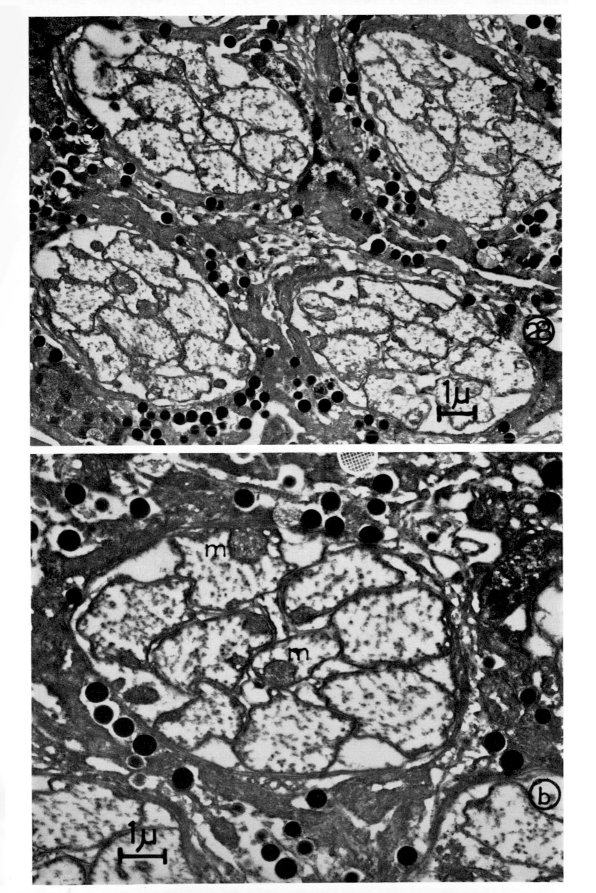

placements of the pigment granules within the loose radial network of clear spaces surrounding the rhabdoms, and associated changes in the mitochondria and microvesicular complexes during adaptation to bright illumination.

Fine Structure of the Rhabdoms of the Dragonflies

In the large compound eyes of the *Odonata* (tropical dragonflies belonging to the family of the *Aeshnidae*) the long, cylindrical rhabdoms are formed by the fusion of wedge-shaped rhabdomeres. Confirming the observations of the rhabdom fine structure in the dragonfly *Anax junius* first reported by Goldsmith and Philpott [17], the rhabdomeres are built up of radially oriented polygonal compartments, 400 to 600 Å in diameter, with double-contoured walls. It is difficult to determine the exact number of constituent rhabdomeres, because the boundary lines do not always coincide with the corresponding retinula cell territories. The organization of the retinula cells and other features of these highly developed compound eyes will be described in a later publication.

DISCUSSION

Upon reviewing the organization of the insect retinula in the principal types of compound eyes, it is possible to recognize certain salient features underlying the fine structure of the rhabdoms, the retinula cells, and the associated tracheolar components. All types of rhabdomeres examined are built up of closely packed submicroscopic tubular compartments, which are radially oriented in parallel array, and appear to be differentiated microvilli of the retinula cell border. There is thus a certain resemblance to the piles of unit discs constituting the external segments of the rods and cones of the vertebrate retina [28, 10], which are generally regarded as the sites where the visual process is initiated. The fact that in the insect eyes the regularly repeated structural unit is tubular or rod-shaped instead of platelike, may be closely related to the incidence of light from all directions, as largely determined by the surrounding tracheal branches which reflect the light back into the rhabdom. Under these conditions a greater effective receptor area is presented to incoming light by the more numerous tubular compartments in each rhabdomere (an estimated 20,000 to 30,000 in each rhabdomere of the house-fly), than in the case of the several hundred discs forming the rod outer segments. A visual pigment corresponding to the rhodopsin of the vertebrate rod outer segments has not as yet been demonstrated in the insect receptors. However, Wolken, Mellon, and Contis [40] have recently found that the action spectrum in three eye color mutants of *Droso-phila melanogaster* "is indicative of a pigment absorbing at 508 millimicrons, similar in absorption spectra to the visual complexes found in the vertebrate photoreceptors" [39]. Successful isolation and satisfactory localization of the visual pigment postulated within the rhabdomeres on the basis of these findings would furnish conclusive proof that the rhabdom is the actual site of photoreception. Wolken and co-workers [39, 40, 38] have also proposed a general geometrical representation of a photoreceptor in which the pigment molecules are oriented as monolayers at the aqueous protein and lipoprotein interfaces. It is interesting to compare this model with the fine structure of the osmium-fixed compartment "walls", by assuming that the pigment molecules could lie within the dense bands of 30 Å, while the associated less dense outer lining of 60 Å would correspond to the lipoprotein layer. However, since little more is known about the constitution of the rhabdomere frame-work beyond the early experimental evidence indicating that the rhabdom resembles a rod of cuticle [20, 22], further cytochemical studies are neces-sary before a detailed correlation between chemical composition and fine structure can be attempted.

The observed variations of density and internal structure in the various types of "tubular" compartments, and their intimate association with intra-cellular cisternae and other retinula cell components, suggest the hypo-thetical possibility of a regulating mechanism based on periodic rearrange-ments of internal contents taking place within the tubular compartments during different physiological states. Thus, reversible "filling" and "empty-ing" of the tubular compartments in a given region would furnish the basis for an exceedingly delicate and differentiated control of the optical proper-ties of the rhabdomeres, without otherwise modifying the highly regular sub-microscopic organization of these receptors. In this connection it is tempting to reflect that the central matrix of the rhabdom, which appears to be filled with a liquid, might act as a local "pool" for the fluid components of the adjacent rhabdomeres.

As pointed out earlier [11], and repeatedly noted by other workers [17, 39] the differentiated submicroscopic organization of the rhabdoms strongly suggests a correlation with the insect's capacity for analyzing polarized light. It was assumed that the radially arranged rhabdomeres with their periodic fine structure would be functionally equivalent to the polarized light analyzer postulated within the insect eye by Autrum and Stumpf [2]. Such an analyzer must be capable of resolving light into ordinary and extraordinary rays polarized at right angles to one another (birefringence), and to selectively reduce the intensity of one of these components, by absorption for example (dichroism) [27, 17]. Stockhammer [31] has recently demonstrated the bi-refringence of the individual rhabdomeres in thin sections of the fly's eye. Moreover, when viewed between crossed Nichols, pairs of rhabdomeres lying opposite each other appear similar, which is in agreement with the electron microscope observations [11] indicating that the orientation of the layered fine structure is similar in opposite rhabdomeres. By analogy, Goldsmith and Philpott [17] suggest that the molecules of the postulated dichroic visual pigment [32, 31] are perhaps similarly oriented in the matched pairs of rhabdomeres located on opposite sides of the central matrix.

It is thus seen that the periodic compartment structure of the rhabdo-meres, containing oriented dichroic visual pigment, can fulfill the main optical requirements of a sensitive polarized light analyzer, such as aniso-tropic absorption (dichroism) and anisotropic refraction (birefringence). The additional possibility of anisotropic diffraction should also be taken into consideration, particularly in view of the greater sensitivity of the bee [16] and other insects [30] to polarized light in the near ultraviolet and violet. Diffraction phenomena of this type might occur along selected planes of the lamellar or reticular "grating" structure of the rhabdomeres with a spacing (500 to 1000 Å) of about a quarter or half the wavelength of ultraviolet light.

However, the rhabdoms are merely the functional units, and the ability of the insect eye to analyze polarized light must necessarily involve a co-ordinated activity at the higher level of the ommatidial groups. The super-imposed local patterns formed by the co-ordinated orientation of equivalent receptor elements in groups of ommatidia, undoubtedly play a role in the recognition of the regional patterns of polarization of the sky, as a basis for true "compass orientation" in insects. The demonstration of individual nerve fiber connections for each retinula cell is of interest in this respect, since a corresponding "nervous coupling" of equivalent ommatidial regions would then be possible.

The highly ordered submicroscopic organization of the insect retinula, and its intimate association with a three-dimensional network of air-filled tracheoles, provide an ideal substrate for the production of structural colors. In contrast to the more ornamental character of the physical coloration ob-served in the cuticle, the striking iridescence described in the Skipper eyes suggests the possibility that the periodic layers of the retinula, alternating at regular intervals with fine tracheolar compartments, might act as color filters or in a similar function related to color vision. The regularly arranged tracheolar extensions would contribute to the formation of the required multiple thin films separated by a material of slightly different refractive index, as in an interference filter. This effect would be particularly marked if the "ultratracheolar" compartments were filled with air, carbon dioxide or oxygen (i.e. produced locally by enzymatic processes in the adjacent mito-chondria). Whatever the detailed mechanisms of their origin may be, the described structural colors of the retinulae could become valuable analytical tools as extremely sensitive and differentiated "optical indicators" of the changes occurring in the submicroscopic organization of the living retinula cells.

The rich tracheal supply of the insect retinula would appear to be of particular significance, because in addition to its main function of mediating respiration, the tracheal system also serves as an important structural com-ponent of the optical apparatus. Thus, the occurrence of movements of fluids in the tracheoles similar to those described by Wigglesworth [34–37] in other insect tissues during different states of activity, would tend to modify the optical properties of the receptors by shifting the gas-liquid interfaces permeating their functional elements. Indeed, a more refined mechanism of optical modulation can hardly be imagined, than this reproducible variation of the optical properties of the receptor elements by controllable shifting of gas or liquid columns within a preformed network of compartments, without altering hereby the overall textural pattern.

In addition to the numerous mitochondria clustered around the rhabdo-meres, there are other structural features of the retinula cells reminiscent of the groups of mitochondria and adjacent components of the endoplasmic reticulum found in the inner limb of vertebrate receptors [17, 13]. These structural similarities emphasize the potential value of the insect retinula in the study of the basic processes associated with energy transfer and storage mechanisms in photoreceptors.

Upon recapitulating the present findings, it becomes evident that the insect retinula is admirably endowed by virtue of the repetitive features of its highly differentiated fine structure, providing a periodic array of gas-liquid-solid interfaces, to make full use of all the possibilities of selective inter-action (absorption, reflection, refraction, diffraction, scattering) with in-coming light signals, thus enabling the compound eye to extract maximum information from its environment. Moreover, in contrast to the vertebrate retina, the receptor sites where this selective interaction can take place are defined with great precision within the three-dimensional submicroscopic framework of the insect retinula. Therefore, instead of the simple juxta-position of luminous areas postulated by the classical mosaic theory of vision, we are dealing here more likely with a "co-ordinate system" type of vision, in which the various modalities of information (intensity, wavelength, polarization of incoming light) are registered in far more differentiated form within the groups of ommatidia, and hereby spatially indexed for subsequent reconstruction and analysis within the insect's optical centers. It must be assumed, of course, that this highly differentiated submicroscopic organization of the receptors has a correspondingly differentiated representation or equivalent "conformal mapping" in the nerve centers of the insect. In fact, the structural patterns of the receptors may eventually furnish essential clues for unravelling the intricate maze of textural detail disclosed in the nerve centers of insects [25, 29].

Having attained this unique degree of miniaturization, the insect retinula seems to be "geared" functionally as well as structurally to the submicroscopic domain [13]. Successful correlation of ultrastructure and function will therefore largely depend on further improvements in electron microscopy, which would permit us to visualize, during sequentially arrested states of activity, the integral structural pattern throughout various hierarchies of organization down to the molecular level.

SUMMARY

1. The fine structure of the light receptors and associated components of the insect retinula has been studied with the electron microscope in representative specimens of compound eyes with apposition, superposition and intermediate types of image formation. The observations were made on thin sections of large segments from osmium-fixed compound eyes of *Musca domestica, Drosophila melanogaster, Apis mellifera*, the tropical moth *Erebus odora*, "Skipper" butterflies (*Hesperiidae*), *Dissosteira*, and tropical dragonflies (*Odonata*).

2. In all types of rhabdoms examined the constituent rhabdomeres are built up of numerous closely packed rod-shaped or tubular units, which vary from 400 to 1200 Å in diameter, and are oriented in regular array with their long axes obliquely or at right angles to the longitudinal rhabdomere axes. In agreement with other workers, these tubular rhabdomere compartments are regarded as differentiated microvilli of the retinula cell borders which are connected with cytoplasmic membranes and cisternae of the retinula cells. The "walls" of the compartments exhibit a dense boundary line of 20 to 30 Å combined with a less dense layer of about 60 Å in osmium-fixed preparations. The interior of the unit compartments in many types of rhabdomeres appears to contain a fine particulate component combined with a less dense homogeneous substance. This ordered compartment structure is found throughout the entire length of the rhabdomeres, except at the distal tip of the house-fly rhabdomeres bordering on the crystalline cone which contains a uniform granular material.

3. The rhabdomeres are grouped around an axial cavity or central matrix of the rhabdom which is filled with a loose filamentous network, resembling the precipitates commonly found in liquid-filled tissue interstices. The central rhabdom cavity in the retinula of *Dissosteira* contains compact bundles of uniform filaments about 150 Å in diameter.

4. Within each rhabdom the rhabdomeres are radially arranged in a symmetrical pattern formed by matched pairs of rhabdomeres which exhibit similar orientation of internal structure, and are usually located opposite to each other. In addition to this local pattern there is a co-ordinated orientation of the equivalent rhabdomeres of adjacent rhabdoms within a larger group of ommatidia, giving rise to a superimposed regional pattern of receptor organization.

5. The differentiated submicroscopic organization of the rhabdoms and their structural coupling in regional patterns suggests a detailed correlation with the insect's capacity for analyzing polarized light. Significant data supports the assumption that the individual rhabdoms, which are composed of radially arranged rhabdomere pairs with molecular layers of the dichroic visual pigment similarly oriented in their periodic compartment structures, may correspond to the functional units of the analyzer for polarized light postulated in the compound eye. The remarkable ability of the insect to recognize the regional patterns of polarization of the sky as a basis for light-compass orientation, would then involve a co-ordinated activity of these functional units at the level of the ommatidial groups.

6. In the large compound eyes of the giant nocturnal tropical moth *Erebus odora* with a superposition type of image formation, the entire receptor layer is separated from the dioptric elements, and can therefore be exposed while still active in the living insect. It is then seen that the large retinulae are closely packed in hexagonal array, and display a vivid yellow or orange color which is bleached by illumination, indicating the presence of a special light sensitive pigment. The rhabdom occupies the main part of each retinula, and is constituted by seven wedge-shaped rhabdomeres fused together in the central region. The long tubular compartments, 600 to 1200 Å in diameter, appear to be filled with a displaceable granular component, and extend with their "open" ends into the retinula cell body. The characteristic rhab-

dom and regional group patterns are more regular in this superposition eye
with its uniform spherical receptor surfaces.

7. In the region of the basement membrane of *Erebus* eyes there are
regularly distributed structures containing bundles of 7 to 9 single nerve
fibers which appear to connect the individual ommatidia with the periopticon, or outermost tract of the optic lobe. The available evidence indicates
that each retinula cell is associated with a single nerve fiber.

8. The exposed receptor layer in the still active, and light adapted superposition eyes of the diurnal "Skipper" butterflies (*Fam. Hesperiidae*) exhibits characteristic iridescent reflections upon being observed with direct
illumination. The whole hemispherical receptor surface displays a metallic
blue color with transitions to green or orange depending on the angle of
light incidence, and is mainly localized to the retinulae facets. Within each
retinula a transient, differentiated color pattern can be discerned, featuring a
predominance of blue or violet in the center, and orange or green at the
margins. This physical coloration, which is extremely sensitive to trauma or
anoxia, can be correlated with the fine structure of the retinula, and the
associated tracheolar and pigment components. It is assumed that the described structural colors are due to complex scattering and diffraction phenomena occurring mainly within the air or liquid-filled network of fine tracheolar branches permeating the retinulae in a regular, three-dimensional array.

9. The rhabdom of the "Skipper" retinula is formed by 8 fused rhabdomeres symmetrically arranged in matched pairs around the filaments of the
central matrix. The marginal cytoplasmic retinula zone contains large mitochondria closely packed in radial columns which are delimited by a network of double-contoured structures, about 250 to 300 Å in diameter, with
characteristic cross-striations exhibiting an axial period of 150 Å. These
structures have been tentatively designated "ultratracheoles", since the
present findings indicate that we are probably dealing with intracellular
extensions of the fine tracheoles surrounding each retinula.

10. The close relationship of the profuse tracheolar network with the
general organization of the sensory portion of the ommatidia suggests that in
addition to mediating respiration, the tracheal system may play an important role as a functional component of the optical apparatus in the compound eye.

11. The retinula cells in the various types of eyes contain a large number
of mitochondria, which are regularly concentrated around the rhabdomeres.
There is also a well-developed endoplasmic reticulum represented by
conglomerates of dense particles associated with multiple membranes, or

with a microtubular component 400 to 500 Å in diameter. Large elements resembling over-sized mitochondria, and referred to as "fenestrated bodies", are regularly found in the marginal zone of the retinula cells containing fused rhabdomeres.

12. The different types of pigment granules and their distribution within the retinulae are described. Characteristic displacements of the pigment granules occurring during adaptation to bright illumination have been observed in the clear areas surrounding the rhabdoms of the grasshopper (*Dissosteira*) retinulae.

13. Salient features underlying the submicroscopic organization of the retinulae and associated structures are discussed in relation to the highly differentiated functional capacities of the insect compound eyes.

The author wishes to express his sincere thanks to Engs. H. Kabe, W. Rawyler, J. Weibel, O. Geisler, J. Suter, A. Trommer, R. Hauser, and S. Liendo for their essential technical collaboration in the preparation and reproduction of the electron micrographs. The generous assistance of Dr. G. Ochsner in the preparation of the manuscript is gratefully acknowledged.

REFERENCES

1. ANDERSON, T. F. and RICHARDS, A. G., *J. Appl. Phys.* **13**, 748 (1942).
2. AUTRUM, H. and STUMPF, M., *Z. Naturforsch.* **5 b**, 116 (1950).
3. BUDDENBROCK VON, M., Vergleichende Physiologie, Band I: Sinnesphysiologie. E. Birkhauser, Basel, Switzerland, 1952.
4. BUGNION, E. and POPOFF, N., *Arch. Anat. Microscop.* **16**, 261 (1914).
5. CHAPMAN, G. B., *J. Morphol. Physiol.* **95**, 237 (1954).
6. DE ROBERTIS, E., *J. Biophys. Biochem. Cytol.* **2**, 319 (1956).
7. DEL PORTILLO, J., *Z. vergl. Physiol.* **23**, 100 (1936).
8. EXNER, S., Die Physiologie der fazettierten Augen von Krebsen und Insekten. Franz Deuticke, Vienna, 1891.
9. FERNÁNDEZ-MORÁN, H., *J. Biophys. Biochem. Cytol.* **2**, No. 4, suppl., 29 (1956).
10. —— *Progr. Biophys. and Biophys. Chem.* **4**, 112 (1954).
11. —— *Nature* **177**, 742 (1956).
12. —— *J. Biophys. Biochem. Cytol.* **3**, 725 (1957).
13. —— Electron Microscopy of Nervous Tissue. Metabolism of the Nervous System. Pergamon Press, London, 1957.
14. FRISCH VON, K., *Experientia* **5**, 142 (1949).
15. —— Bees: Their Vision, Chemical Senses, and Language. Cornell University Press, New York, 1950.
16. —— *Sitz.ber. math. naturw. Kl. bayer. Akad. Wiss. München* No. 17 (1954).
17. GOLDSMITH, T. H. and PHILPOTT, D. E., *J. Biophys. Biochem. Cytol.* **3**, 429 (1957).
18. HARTLINE, H. K., WAGNER, H. G. and MACNICHOL, E. F., *Cold Spring Harbor Symposia Quant. Biol.* **17**, 125 (1952).
19. IMMS, A. D., RICHARDS, O. W. and DAVIES, R. G., A General Textbook of Entomology. Methuen and Co., London, 1957.
20. MACHATSCHKE, J. W., *Vestnik Československ. Zool. Spol.* **4**, 90 (1936).
21. MILLER, W. H., *J. Biophys. Biochem. Cytol.* **3**, 421 (1957).

22. NOVIKOFF, M., *Z. wiss. Zool.* **138**, 1 (1931).
23. PALADE, G. E., *Anat. Record* **114**, 427 (1952).
24. —— *J. Exptl. Med.* **95**, 285 (1952).
25. RAMON Y CAJAL, S. and SANCHEZ, D., *Trabajos inst. Cajal invest. biol. (Madrid)* **13**, 1 (1915).
26. RICHARDS, A. G. and ANDERSON, T. F., *J. N.Y. Entomol. Soc.* **50**, 147 (1942).
27. RICHARDS, A. G. and KORDA, F. H., *Ann. Entomol. Soc. Amer.* **43**, 49 (1950).
28. SJÖSTRAND, F. S., *J. Cellular Comp. Physiol.* **42**, 15 (1953).
29. SNODGRASS, R. E., Principles of Insect Morphology. New York, McGraw Hill Book Company, 1935.
30. STEPHENS, G. C., FINGERMAN, M. and BROWN, F. A., *Ann. Entomol. Soc. Amer.* **46**, 75 (1953).
31. STOCKHAMMER, K., *Z. vergleich. Physiol.* **38**, 30 (1956).
32. VRIES DE, H. L., SPOOR, A. and JIELOF, R., *Physica* **19**, 419 (1953).
33. WATERMAN, T. H., *Proc. Natl. Acad. Sci.* **40**, 258 (1954).
34. WIGGLESWORTH, V. B., *J. Exptl. Biol.* **15**, 235 (1938).
35. —— *ibid.* **15**, 248 (1938).
36. —— The Principles of Insect Physiology. Methuen and Co., London, 1950.
37. —— *Quart. J. Microscop. Sci.* **94**, 507 (1953).
38. WOLKEN, J. J., *Trans. N.Y. Acad. Sci.* **19**, 315 (1957).
39. WOLKEN, J. J., CAPENOS, J. and TURANO, A., *J. Biophys. Biochem. Cytol.* **3**, 441 (1957).
40. WOLKEN, J. J., MELLON, A. D. and CONTIS, G., *J. Exptl. Zool.* **134**, No. 2 (1957).